THE

INTERNATIONAL SERIES

OF

MONOGRAPHS ON PHYSICS

GENERAL EDITORS

W. MARSHALL D. H. WILKINSON

THE THEORY OF NEUTRON RESONANCE REACTIONS

BY

J. E. LYNN

CLARENDON PRESS . OXFORD
1968

Oxford University Press, Ely House, London W.1

GLASGOW NEW YORK TORONTO MELBOURNE WELLINGTON
CAPE TOWN SALISBURY IBADAN NAIROBI LUSAKA ADDIS ABABA
BOMBAY CALCUTTA MADRAS KARACHI LAHORE DACCA
KUALA LUMPUR HONG KONG TOKYO

PRINTED IN GREAT BRITAIN AT THE PITMAN PRESS, BATH

PREFACE

THE original intention governing the scope of this monograph was to provide a coherent theoretical background for experimental physicists working in the field of slow neutron spectroscopy. There is more justification in regarding the theory of this subject as an entity, however, than that provided by the bounds of an experimental technique. Research in nuclear physics can be divided very roughly into two activities, the investigation of nuclear structure on the one hand and the study of nuclear reactions on the other. For the latter, the technique of neutron spectroscopy provides a 'microscope' that is almost unique; only charged-particle reactions with light nuclei provide the same kind of highly detailed information that is really basic for understanding nuclear reactions, and these are generally much more difficult to interpret because of the large range of angular momenta involved.

From the theoretical standpoint, then, the scope of this book can be defined as the study of neutron cross-section phenomena exhibiting or involving resonances. Experimentally, resonances are usually not measurable above a few thousands or tens of thousands of electron-volts in neutron energy. Nevertheless, the basic underlying structure of the average cross-sections measured up to, say, one hundred thousand electron-volts is a resonance one involving, like the observed low-energy resonances a very restricted range of angular momenta and parity, and it is only sensible to interpret them as resonance reactions. The same thing is true of certain neutron-induced fission cross-sections at much higher energy. For this reason such reactions, although outside the experimental field of slow neutron spectroscopy, are included in this book.

Although this book contains many tabulations of data, particularly of average resonance parameters, it does not include exhaustive lists of detailed resonance parameters, except in one or two important cases as examples. This is partly because of the vast amount of space that such data would require, and partly because these things can be found in the recent excellent compilation *Neutron Cross-sections*, 2nd. edn., Supplement 2, by J. R. Stehn, M. D. Goldberg, R. Wiener-Chasman, S. F. Mughabghab, B. A. Magurno, and V. M. May. I am greatly indebted to these volumes for their usefulness both in research and in writing the present book.

Acknowledgements are due to many people: first, to Dr. E. Bretscher, until May 1966 Head of the Nuclear Physics Division at Harwell, who greatly encouraged me through many years in this field of research and was responsible for the initial suggestion that I should write such a review; second, to Dr. A. M. Lane, who introduced me to theoretical nuclear physics and has always been a source of guidance in the subject. He also read the first draft of the manuscript and made useful suggestions concerning the organization of material. Third, many of my experimental colleagues, both at Harwell and other laboratories, have participated over the years in discussions which have led, directly or indirectly, to many of the ideas formulated here. Special thanks are due to Dr. E. R. Rae for support and encouragement, to M. C. Moxon, for supplying the experimental data for preparing Figs. 1.1 and 1.14, to Dr. N. W. Dalton for his critical proof-reading, and to other colleagues at Harwell for pointing out various errors in the first draft. Mention must also be made of the auspices of the United Kingdom Atomic Energy Authority, both in a general sense, for it has been a privilege to work within the intellectual climate at the Harwell laboratory, and in a special sense, because of their attitude of encouraging the publication of a work such as this.

I wish to acknowledge the permission of the following individuals and publishers to use material in tabular or graphical form: Dr. M. D. Goldberg of Brookhaven National Laboratory for permission to use material from *Neutron Cross-sections*, mentioned above, for the preparation of Figs. 1.2, 1.4, 1.5, 1.6, 1.8, 1.9, 1.10, 8.16, and Table 1.1; Prof. T. D. Newton of University of Guelph and the National Research Council of Canada for permission to use the material of Table 4.1, taken from the *Canadian Journal of Physics;* Prof. H. W. Newson, of Duke University, and the North-Holland Publishing Company for permission to use Fig. 4.5, taken from *Nuclear Structure Study with Neutrons*, and Fig. 6.22, taken from *Physics Letters;* Prof. S. G. Nilsson of the University of Lund for permission to use Fig. 4.6; Dr. G. Kluge, of the Technischen Hochechule, Darmstadt, and the North Holland Publishing Company for permission to use Figs. 4.13, 4.14, and 4.15, taken from *Nuclear Physics;* Dr. T. Kammuri, of Osaka University, Japan, and the publishers of *Progress of Theoretical Physics*, Kyoto University, for permission to use Figs. 4.16, 4.17, and 4.18. Dr. N. Rosenzweig of Argonne National Laboratory for permission to use Fig. 5.1; Dr. M. Gaudin, of Saclay, and the North-Holland Publishing Company for permission to use Table 5.1, taken from *Nuclear Physics;* Prof. W. W. Havens, of Columbia University, and the American

Institute of Physics for permission to use Figs. 5.3, 5.4, 5.14, and 5.15 taken from *The Physical Review;* Prof. F. J. Dyson, of the Institute of Advanced Study, Princeton, and the American Institute of Physics for permission to use Table 5.5, taken from the *Journal of Mathematical Physics;* Dr. P. B. Kahn, of New York University, and North-Holland Publishing Company for permission to use Tables 5.6 and 5.7. taken from *Nuclear Physics;* Dr. J. D. Garrison, of General Atomics, and Academic Press, Inc. for permission to use Fig. 6.2, taken from *Annals of Physics;* Prof. B. Margolis of McGill University for permission to use Fig. 6.14; to Academic Press, Inc. for permission to use Fig. 6.21, taken from *Annals Of Physics;* Dr. L. M. Bollinger, of Argonne National Laboratory, and the North-Holland Publishing Company for permission to use Fig. 7.2 taken from *Nuclear Physics;* Dr. N. Starfelt, until recently of AB Atomenergi, Studsvik, and the North-Holland Publishing Company for permission to use Figs. 7.4, 7.10, and 7.11 taken from *Nuclear Physics;* Dr. L. Groshev, of the I. V. Kurchatov Institute, Moscow, and the North-Holland Publishing Company for permission to use Figs. 7.5, 7.6, and 7.7 taken from *Nuclear Physics;* Dr. A. G. W. Cameron, of NASA, and National Research Council of Canada for permission to use Fig. 7.9 taken from the *Canadian Journal of Physics;* Dr. O. A. Wasson of Brookhaven National Laboratory, and the American Institute of Physics for permission to use Fig. 7.14, taken from *Physical Review Letters;* Dr. S. A. Moszkowski, of the University of California, and Springer-Verlag for permission to use Fig. 8.2, taken from *Handbuch der Physik;* Prof. S. Johansson, of the University of Lund, and the North-Holland Publishing Company for permission to use Fig. 8.5, taken from *Nuclear Physics;* Dr. R. H. Stokes, of Los Alamos National Laboratory, and the American Institute of Physics for permission to use Fig. 8.14, taken from *The Physical Review;* Dr. A. Michaudon, of Saclay, for permission to use Figs. 8.19 and 8.20; Dr. J. S. Fraser, of Chalk River Laboratory, and the International Atomic Energy Agency for permission to use Fig. 8.23; Dr. T. D. Thomas, of Princeton University, and the I.A.E.A. for permission to use Fig. 8.24; and Dr. M. S. Moore, of Phillips Petroleum, Idaho Falls, and the I.A.E.A. for permission to use Fig. 8.24, the last three being taken from *Physics and Chemistry of Fission;* Dr. C. D. Bowman, of Livermore, for permission to use Fig. 8.29 (and for supplying his latest data for it); Dr. G. A. Jones, of Oxford University for permission to use the data of Fig. 8.31.

J.E.L.

Harwell
March 1967

CONTENTS

I

INTRODUCTION

A. HISTORICAL BACKGROUND

SINCE slow neutron reactions were discovered in 1935 their study has been an important part of nuclear physics, having led to many of the principal concepts of nuclear reaction theory. The survey of slow neutron cross-sections made by Fermi's group (Amaldi *et al.* 1935) promoted the single-particle model of nuclear reactions (Bethe 1935, Amaldi *et al.* 1935), which did not survive long at that time under the increasing weight of experimental evidence. The Bethe theory was based on a statistical analysis of slow neutron total cross-sections and gave estimates of the thermal neutron capture cross-sections that approached the order of magnitude of the scattering cross-sections when both were large, i.e. when the single-particle *s*-wave state of the nuclear potential well was close to the neutron separation energy. Later measurements showed that the ratio of capture to scattering of moderated neutrons was very high for some nuclei (Dunning *et al.* 1935). At about the same time the earliest measurements in the field of slow neutron spectroscopy were made and revealed rapid variations in neutron cross-sections over narrow energy intervals—the neutron resonance phenomenon (Moon and Tillman 1936, Rasetti *et al.* 1936).

Neutron resonance was impossible to explain as a feature of the single-particle model. Size resonances in neutron cross-sections were expected indeed as part of that model but energy variations were also expected to be very gentle. The crisis induced in nuclear physics by the discovery of slow neutron resonance was resolved by Bohr (1936). His compound nucleus theory contrasted with the potential well of the earlier model by recognizing that the target nucleus is composed of nucleons interacting with strong short-range forces. While this many-body problem could not be solved quantitatively, Bohr was able to show that very long-lived states would occur in the region where the energy was sufficient for particle emission. This is due to rapid sharing of the ingoing nucleon energy among the other nucleons. Once this has occurred in a system of many nucleons it is very unlikely that a large amount of energy will be concentrated on one particle: thus the system will last a long time, executing a large number of collisions and energy exchanges before decaying by particle emission or electromagnetic radiation.

Wigner and Breit (1936) independently introduced the idea that a bombarding nucleon was very likely to excite a two-particle long-lived state (analogous to the Auger states of atoms). From this model they derived the well-known formula for the energy dependence of the cross-section close to such a virtual state. Much important later work was devoted to obtaining a more formal and rigorous derivation of the cross-section formula based on the observed fact of the long life of the resonant states rather than on a very doubtful assumption such as weakness of perturbing forces. In particular, Kapur and Peierls (1939), Wigner and Eisenbud (1947), and Humblet and Rosenfeld (1961) produced formalisms that are soundly based and have been much used either in the analysis of experimental data or in the study of theoretical models. One of the main conclusions of these investigations, that close to a narrow, well-isolated resonance level the Breit–Wigner formula is a good approximation, was verified by detailed investigations of the prominent resonance in the cadmium cross-section (Goldsmith 1947).

The Breit–Wigner formula embodies the principal result of the compound nucleus theory, that the decay of the compound nucleus is independent of its formation. It is this principle, which stems from the long life of the compound nucleus virtual states, that is nowadays taken to be the content of the theory. This is more general than the original position of Bohr (1936) who introduced the idea of the nucleus being analogous to a liquid drop. The latter view seemed confirmed after the discovery of neutron-induced fission (Hahn and Strassmann 1939, Meitner and Frisch 1939), for which the theoretical treatment by Bohr and Wheeler (1939) using the liquid-drop picture seemed most successful.

Thus, in a few years, the two extreme models of nuclear reactions had been expounded; on the one hand stood the single-particle model with elastic scattering, dominated by a few extremely broad resonances, as virtually the only particle reaction; and on the other hand was the liquid-drop model with strong short-range forces between the rapidly interacting nucleons leading to the extremely fruitful principle of independence of formation and decay of the compound nucleus. Of the two, the latter was obviously far closer to the truth, and the compound-nucleus principle was explored very fully in the following decade, particularly by Weisskopf and Ewing (1940) and Feshbach *et al.* (1947).

In the calculations of the cross-section for formation of the compound nucleus, statistical considerations were applied both in the well-defined resonance region of low-energy nuclear reactions and in the continuum region of higher energies. Thus, in the resonance region, the average over many resonances of the formation cross-section was inferred to be monotonically dependent on the radius and average potential depth of the nucleus and almost monotonically decreasing with energy.

In the period since 1950 the subject of low-energy neutron spectroscopy has had, as its tools, the powerful reactors and accelerators that were built in the post-war period. The flood of data that has emerged since then has revealed that, for relatively low-energy reactions, the strong-coupling models stemming from Bohr's original treatment are not valid (Feshbach *et al.* 1954). In the s-wave resonance region the average compound nucleus formation cross-section was found to exhibit gross size resonances when displayed as a function of target mass number (Carter *et al.* 1954), and at higher energies the giant resonances discovered by Barschall (1952) and Miller *et al.* (1952) revealed that the formation cross-section was not a monotonically decreasing function of energy. The explanation of these phenomena was that the mean free path of a nucleon in nuclear matter was not very short (compared with the nuclear radius) as in the liquid-drop or statistical models nor extremely long as in the single-particle model. It was now recognized to be comparable with nuclear dimensions as expressed phenomenologically by a complex potential well with relatively small imaginary component. A physical basis for the longer mean free path was found in the role of the Pauli principle which, in nuclear matter, would prohibit many of the allowed collisions between free nucleons (Lane and Wandel 1955).

The new view of nuclear reactions was in accord with the recently developed shell model of nuclear structure. The analyses that have been stimulated by more and better spectroscopic data have also been influenced by developments in nuclear structure theory. The shell model, though valuable for nuclei with only a few nucleons or holes extra to the closed shells, was found inadequate for large numbers of intermediate nuclei whose low-lying level structure showed strong vibrational or rotational features. The collective-motion models that attempt to explain these phenomena have also been used to explain some of the average features of resonance data, the complex potential well not being considered as rigidly spherical, but as a deformed or deformable potential coupled to its rotational or vibrational motions. At higher neutron energies this is the mechanism for a form of semi-direct inelastic scattering in which the residual nucleus is left in a state of collective excitation (Chase *et al.* 1958).

A great deal of work has been done to establish the theoretical basis of the complex-potential model. Much of this indicates how the model can be improved in such respects as the spatial dependence of the imaginary part while other work indicates in more detail how the resonances are related to the model (Lane *et al.* 1955). The latter gives a basis for understanding more detailed statistical aspects of the resonances, such as the distribution laws of the partial widths (Porter and Thomas 1956) and qualitative selection rules in the radiation spectra (Lane and Lynn 1960).

Thus, we now appear to have a framework within which it will be possible to gain a good quantitative understanding of the details of low-energy neutron reactions, and in this book the present progress towards this understanding is described. Chapter II deals with the formal reaction theory background required for the subsequent discussions. In Chapter III the success and limitations of the single-particle model are mentioned briefly and the information about the positions of single-particle states is summarized. This is needed for discussions of level densities in Chapter IV, and of neutron strength functions and potential scattering, which are analysed in the light of the complex-potential model, in Chapter VI. It is also required for a discussion of the radiative capture process in Chapter VII. Distribution laws for level spacings are introduced in Chapter V, for neutron widths in Chapter VI, and for partial radiation widths in Chapter VII. Finally, in Chapter VIII, several features of neutron-induced fission are discussed within the framework of the collective model of nuclear structure. In the first place, however, it appears desirable to summarize very briefly the experimental methods yielding the data that are discussed in this book, and this is done in the remainder of this chapter.

B. EXPERIMENTAL BACKGROUND AND RESONANCE DATA ANALYSIS

1. Time-of-flight measurements

(a) *Principle*

Indirect use of the kinematics of well-known charged particle reactions to determine neutron energies (such as the ^{7}Li(p, n) reaction) is of limited value in slow neutron work because adequate resolution can seldom be attained. The time-of-flight method is almost universally used in this branch of nuclear physics, the only considerable exception being the use of crystal spectrometers on reactor neutron beams to obtain monochromatic neutrons from the thermal region up to a few electronvolts. The time-of-flight method requires a pulsed source of neutrons of very short duration and an evacuated flight tube of known length, along which a well-collimated neutron beam may pass. At the end of the flight tube events due to neutrons are detected and timed, and provided that the event and its detection are practically simultaneous with the arrival of the neutron the velocity of the neutron and hence its kinetic energy in the laboratory coordinate system are determined.

If the duration of the neutron pulse is Δt_1 and the uncertainty in the time of detection is Δt_2, the overall uncertainty in the time-of-flight of a neutron over the flight path length, L, is, very roughly,

$$\Delta t \approx (\Delta t_1^2 + \Delta t_2^2)^{\frac{1}{2}}.$$

The consequent uncertainty in velocity, v, is $v(\Delta t/t)$ and in energy, E, is $2E(\Delta t/t)$. Since t is proportional to $E^{-\frac{1}{2}}$ the uncertainty in the energy measurement by time-of-flight, the resolution, is proportional to $E^{3/2}$. This assumes of course that the component time uncertainties Δt_1 and Δt_2 do not depend on neutron energy; this is asymptotically true for higher neutron energies for many pulsed sources. This energy dependence of the resolution indicates that the time-of-flight method is best suited for low neutron energies. With it, resolutions of better than one electronvolt have been obtained for neutron energies up to a few keV.

(*b*) *Pulsed sources*

Various pulsed-source methods are used in modern time-of-flight systems. One of the commonest is the 'fast chopper', a rapidly rotating shutter that interrupts a continuous neutron beam from a high intensity neutron chain reactor (Selove 1952, Bollinger 1958). Such a system is capable of giving a neutron pulse of less than one microsecond in duration. With flight tubes of about 100 m in length energy resolutions are typically around 0·02 μs/m, corresponding to 0·3 eV at 100 eV, say. A unique neutron source is the pulsed reactor at the Joint Institute for Nuclear Research, Dubna (Blokhin *et al.* 1961). Sub-critical masses of ^{235}U are swung through an assembly of ^{239}Pu, the set together forming a critical assembly. The pulse of neutrons thus formed is 40 μs long, and a flight path of 1 km is required to achieve resolutions comparable with those of fast chopper systems.

Particle accelerators are often used to provide pulsed neutron sources. The commonest accelerator for this purpose is the travelling-wave linear electron accelerator. The principle of this method, which was developed at Harwell (see the review of Wiblin 1956), is to bombard a heavy target with the electron beam to produce a source of Bremsstrahlen. These, in turn, fall on uranium, liberating neutrons by photofission and photoneutron reactions. A very brief pulse (ranging from a few nanoseconds to a few microseconds) is characteristic of these accelerators; so the neutron pulse is correspondingly short. For efficient neutron production the Bremsstrahlung spectrum must traverse the giant resonance in the photonuclear cross-section. For heavy nuclei this is at about 13 MeV; so the electron energy must be at least as high as this. There are several accelerators with energies in the range 50 to 100 MeV and at least 1 A of instantaneous current. These give neutron outputs in the region of 10^{18} neutrons per second in the pulse. The output of the present linac at Harwell is further amplified by a sub-critical assembly of ^{235}U surrounding the neutron target (Poole and Wiblin 1958).

The proton synchrocyclotron is another very suitable machine for pulsed neutron production. This method was developed at Columbia University (Rainwater *et al.* 1964). The present accelerator at the Nevis laboratories of Columbia produces 400-MeV protons which bombard a tungsten target, liberating neutrons by spallation. Very high neutron intensities (about 5×10^{18} per second in the pulse) are thereby achieved. The pulse length of such machines is of the order of 20 ns.

Although the pulse length of such particle accelerators is basically so short its advantage cannot be fully reaped. This is because the neutron spectrum peaks in the MeV region and there are relatively very few neutrons in the 1 eV to 100 keV band that is most interesting in the spectroscopy studies. The difficulty is overcome by partially moderating the spectrum with about 2 cm of hydrogeneous material (such as water or nylon) placed around or near the neutron target. The price paid for this is an increase in the effective duration of the pulse owing to the variation in slowing-down time of the moderated neutrons (Groenwald and Groendijk 1947). This increases with decreasing neutron energy and is typically 300 ns at 10 eV, 30 ns at 1 keV. With flight path lengths of 200 or 300 m linear accelerators and synchrocyclotrons are capable of giving resolutions of less than 1 ns/m at energies greater than a few hundred eV.

One other accelerator system ought to be mentioned here. It is the pulsed Van der Graaf proton accelerator (Good *et al.* 1958). Neutrons are produced in pulses of 5 ns by the $^{7}Li(p, n)$ reaction. With such short unmoderated pulses flight paths of only a few metres are required. However, the system cannot be used reliably below a few keV neutron energy.

All the systems mentioned above produce at least several hundred neutron pulses per second. Neutrons that are so slow as to take longer than the interval between pulses to travel the length of the flight path are removed by ^{10}B filters. Neutron intensities are usually sufficient for a cross-section to be adequately measured in a few hours or days of machine running time. There is yet another type of neutron source, however, where the intensity is so high that a single pulse is adequate for a cross-section measurement; this is the nuclear explosion, which is being exploited to an increasing extent by the Los Alamos National Laboratory (Diven 1966).

Polarized neutron sources together with polarized nuclear samples are useful for angular momentum selection. One source for energies up to a few eV is obtained by reflecting reactor neutrons at glancing angles from a magnetized cobalt single-crystal mirror. The interaction of the neutron magnetic moment with the magnetic field of the cobalt crystal interferes with the nuclear scattering to give critical angles of reflection that differ for the two orientations of the neutron spin. The critical angles decrease with increasing neutron energy, and this limits the effective energy range of the method.

More recently, hydrogen filters have been employed for polarizing low-energy neutron beams (Shapiro 1966). The neutron cross-section of hydrogen to well above 10 keV comprises 19·3 barns of the singlet ($J = 0$) component and 1·06 barns of the triplet ($J = 1$) component. Thus 19·65 barns of the cross-section is in the $M = 0$ magnetic substate and 0·7 barn is in the $M = \pm 1$ magnetic substates. Consequently, if the protons of a sample of hydrogeneous material are polarized, neutrons with spins parallel to the proton spins are transmitted preferentially to those with anti-parallel spins. A suitable method of polarizing hydrogen is the dynamical method (see Jeffries 1963) applied to a crystal of lanthanum magnesium nitrate ($La_2Mg_3(NO_3)_{13}.24H_2O$) about 2 cm thick, cooled to 1·2°K. Such a system yields filtered neutrons with a degree of polarization of the order of 50 per cent.

(*c*) *Detection*

(i) *Requirements*. It is evident that the primary requirement of a detector is that its response time between the occurrence of an event and the production of a signal for that event is less than the duration of the neutron pulse. That is, the universally employed detectors ought to have a response time of better than a few nanoseconds. It is also important that the detector should have high efficiency so that long flight paths, and therefore better resolution, can be used.

(ii) *Neutron transmission*. For the measurement of transmission a neutron detector without rapid energy variations in efficiency is placed in the neutron beam. An example of such a detector is a slab of ^{10}B (in the beam) surrounded by sodium iodide scintillation crystals (Rae and Bowey 1953). The $^{10}B(n, \alpha)$ cross-section is inversely proportional to the square root of the neutron energy to at least 100 keV and has the high value of 3837 barns at thermal energy (0·0253 eV). Two groups of α-particles are emitted in the $^{10}B(n, \alpha)$ reaction; the lower-energy group leads to the first excited state of ^{7}Li at 478 keV with a branching ratio of about 90 per cent, and the prompt γ-ray emitted in the decay of this state is detected by the scintillators. (For a review of the scintillation process see Birks (1964).)

The time interval between the pulses from the photomultipliers of the scintillation counters and the neutron pulse at the source is measured electronically and registered. In a typical system the time interval is coded digitally and recorded on a magnetic tape. At the end of the measurement the record is analysed by a digital computer, the time intervals being sorted into a histogram form. The result is the neutron spectrum of the pulsed source over the energy interval of interest. If the measurement is now repeated with a sample of material of nuclear interest in the beam in good geometry (so that a negligible fraction of the neutrons scattered by the sample may reach the detector) the ratio of the two spectra, after making corrections for backgrounds, is the neutron transmission of the sample as a function of neutron energy.

Other detectors suitable for this purpose are liquid and glass scintillators (placed in the neutron beam) loaded with either ^{6}Li or ^{10}B (Brooks 1959; Bollinger *et al.* 1959). The scintillation is thus produced directly in the absorbing medium by the energetic particles emitted in the (n, α) reactions of these two nuclei.

(iii) *Elastic scattering*. This last class of detector may be used for scattering measurements. The scattering sample is placed in the beam and the scintillation counters are placed around it outside the beam, preferably subtending as large a solid angle as possible to the sample. To differentiate against the capture γ-rays also produced by the sample, which can be observed by the same scintillation process, the measurement is repeated with an identical detector loaded with the corresponding *non*-absorbing isotope ^{7}Li or ^{11}B (Asghar and Brooks 1966).

(iv) *Neutron capture.* Detectors for neutron-capture events are designed to signal the cascade of prompt gamma radiation associated with this process. One type of detector is a tank of liquid scintillator, a metre or more in diameter, with several large photomultiplier tubes optically connected to its surface (Diven *et al.* 1960; Gibbons *et al.* 1961). In this tank nearly all of the several MeV of gamma radiation energy is absorbed and converted into a light flash. Thus the efficiency of the detector is practically independent of the exact energy emitted in capture and of the details of the cascade (whether the neutron separation energy of the compound nucleus is emitted as one single high-energy γ-ray or several low-energy γ-rays). The nuclear sample is placed in a tube (part of the neutron flight path) that passes through the centre of the tank.

A detector on a much smaller scale but with the same independence of efficiency to the detailed nature of the cascade consists of a cylindrical annulus of graphite (or other light element) surrounding the sample in the neutron flight path (Moxon and Rae 1961). The graphite is approximately 6 cm thick. Surrounding the graphite is an annular layer of plastic scintillator 0·03 cm thick, optically connected to photomultiplier tubes. Gamma rays are scattered in the graphite producing Compton electrons, which produce scintillation flashes in the plastic. The graphite radiator thickness is chosen so that the efficiency is proportional to the total energy of gamma radiation, but since this is very nearly equal to the neutron separation energy corrections are easily made for measurements on different nuclei. From measurements of the efficiency, the neutron spectrum of the source and the background the neutron capture yield is obtained.

(v) *Neutron capture spectra.* At thermal neutron energies detectors for measuring the energy of individual γ-rays emitted in the capture process can be based on magnetic analysis of Compton electrons. Such detectors are of very low efficiency and consequently other methods have had to be used at higher energies where the available neutron fluxes are much weaker. Originally these were based on large NaI scintillation counters (Bollinger *et al.* 1963). A γ-ray of several MeV energy has a reasonably high pair production cross-section and it is this process that permits the energy measurement. The electric pulse from the scintillation flash in finite crystals is triple-peaked, the two lower peaks corresponding to the escape from the crystal of one or both of the annihilation γ-rays from the positron of the pair. The line shape is improved by surrounding the crystal by an annulus of more sodium iodide and using anti-coincidence electronic devices to select only the pulse which corresponds to absorption of both annihilation gamma-rays within the central crystal. The resolution of such devices is of the order of 0·3 MeV for high-energy γ-rays, but the use of digital computers to carry out least squares analyses of the spectra allows a number of γ-rays to be separated.

A very recent technique, however, is the use of lithium ion drifted germanium semiconductors (see e.g. Rae *et al.* 1967 and, for a general reference, Dearnaley and Northrop 1966). These are proving to be excellent devices for the measurement of γ-ray energies. Efficiencies for high energy γ-rays are at present in the region of 1 per cent and energy resolution is better than 20 keV (better than the Compton spectrometers).

(vi) *Fission.* The richness of phenomena exhibited in fission allows the use of a number of different types of detector. If the sample of target material is very thin the highly energetic charged fission products may be used to trigger the detector action. This is the basis of the gas scintillator. The sample of fissile material is placed in a chamber, with windows for the neutron beam, filled with a noble gas, usually helium, argon, or xenon (see e.g. Bollinger *et al.* 1959). The passage of a heavy charged particle through this material produces a light flash, which is recorded electronically, through photomultiplier tubes, in the usual way. Another useful detector is provided by the fission product falling on a silicon–gold surface barrier counter, a very fast electric pulse thus being produced (see e.g. James 1961).

Such detectors, based on the production of heavy charged particles, are subject to background trouble from the natural α-activity of the fissile sample. In principle the pulse heights from fission products are very much greater than those from α-particles, but build-up of pulses from a heavy flux of the latter can occur. The samples used with these detectors must therefore be very thin to keep such background manageable. This limitation does not apply to devices based on the detection of the fast neutrons emitted in fission. Such a system is a liquid organic scintillator, in which a recoil proton causes the light flash (Brooks 1959).

Pulse shape discrimination is used to distinguish fission events from neutron capture γ-rays.

(vii) *Mass distribution in fission.* Only one method has been used to any extent to measure features of the fission mass distribution as a function of neutron energy in the slow neutron region. This is the wheel method of Cowan *et al.* (1966), used in conjunction with nuclear explosion sources. The fissile material is placed on the rim of a wheel that revolves rapidly after the explosion has been detonated. A narrow aperture allows neutrons to fall on a narrow strip of the rim; as a result of this arrangement different points along the rim correspond to different energies of the incident neutrons. Samples of the fissile material from different points are analysed radiochemically for specific fission products.

2. Neutron cross-section data

(*a*) *Definition of cross-section*

The cross-section for a particular process induced by a beam of incident particles is defined by the ratio

$$\frac{\text{number of events of the given kind per unit time per nucleus}}{\begin{array}{c}\text{number of incident particles passing through unit area}\\ \text{perpendicular to the beam direction per unit time}\end{array}}$$

The total cross-section σ_T is the sum of the partial cross-sections for all processes. The concept of cross-section is useful only if a nucleus can be regarded as interacting independently with the beam.

The transmission of particles through a sample of material with only one nuclear species is easily deduced to be

$$T = \exp(-n\sigma_T) \tag{1.1}$$

where n is the number of nuclei per unit area of the target perpendicular to the beam direction. The yield of a particular reaction r due to the passage of the beam through a sample can be expressed simply only if primary events are considered, i.e. if events due to particles that are initially scattered and then undergo a subsequent history of collisions within the sample are ignored. The yield of primary events is

$$Y_r = (1-e^{-n\sigma_T})\sigma_r/\sigma_T. \tag{1.2}$$

(*b*) *Examples of neutron cross-sections*

The most striking feature of the transmission or yield curves measured as described above is the presence of resonances. In Fig. 1.1(a),

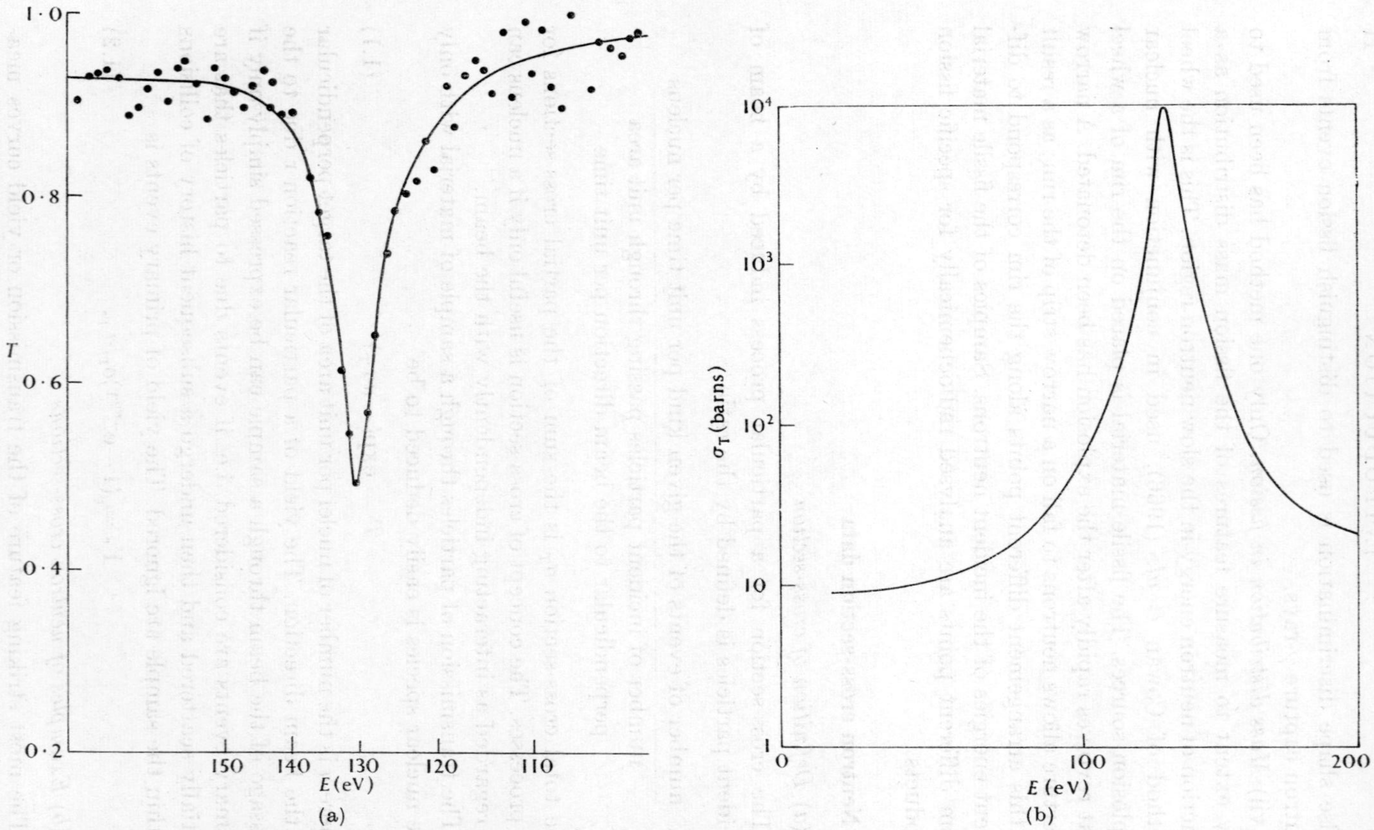

FIG. 1.1. Cross-section of ^{59}Co. (a) Transmission curve for sample thickness $n = 6{\cdot}7\times10^{-5}$ atom barns^{-1}; (b) Total cross-section; (c) Total capture γ-ray yield curve for sample thickness $n = 6{\cdot}7\times10^{-5}$ atom barns^{-1}.

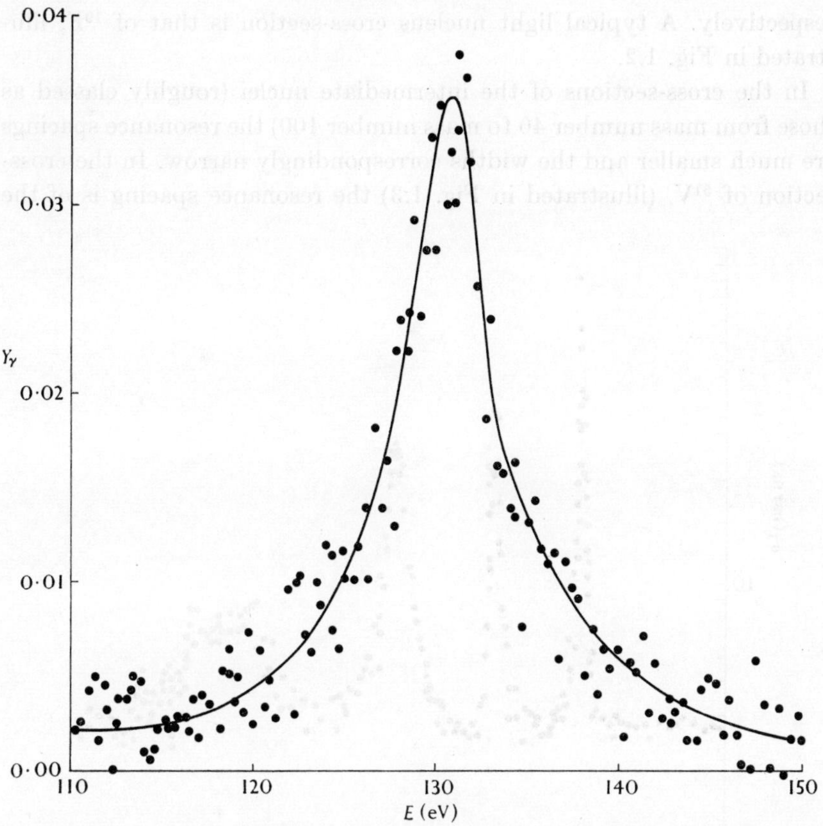

(c)

FIG. 1.1.—*Continued.*

a transmission curve of natural cobalt (100 per cent ^{59}Co) in the region of 150-eV neutron energy is illustrated as an example. The corresponding cross-section curve with its strong peak or resonance around 130 eV is shown in Fig. 1.1(b). A typical yield curve, for neutron radiative capture by ^{59}Co, is shown in Fig. 1.1(c). In this case the target is so thin ($n\sigma_T$ everywhere much smaller than unity) that the yield curve is directly proportional to the cross-section.

The frequency and sharpness of resonances vary widely over the full range of nuclei. In very light nuclei they are spaced at intervals of several hundred keV and are usually tens or even hundreds of keV in width. For example, the lowest resonances in the cross-sections of ^{6}Li and ^{7}Li occur at about 250 keV and are 125 and 35 keV wide, respectively. A typical light nucleus cross-section is that of ^{19}F, illustrated in Fig. 1.2.

In the cross-sections of the intermediate nuclei (roughly classed as those from mass number 40 to mass number 100) the resonance spacings are much smaller and the widths correspondingly narrow. In the cross-section of ^{51}V, (illustrated in Fig. 1.3) the resonance spacing is of the

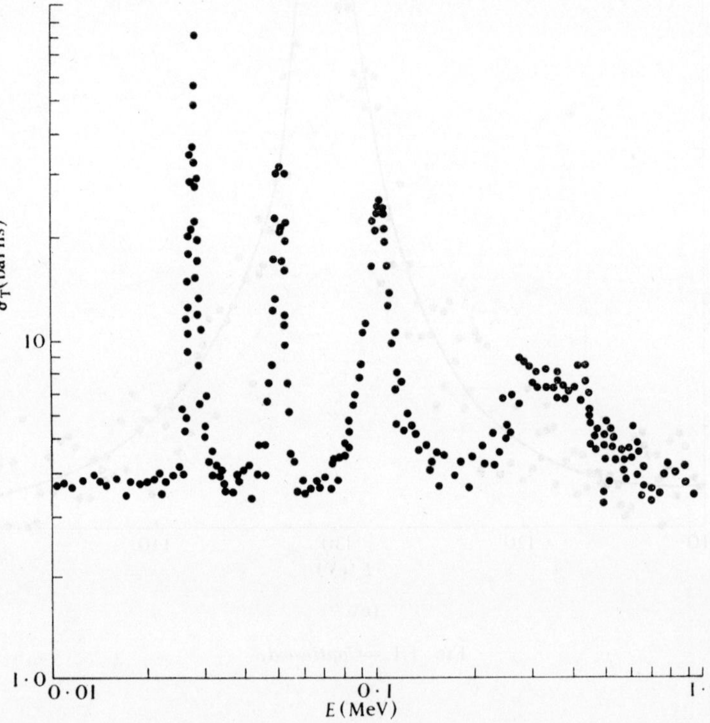

FIG. 1.2. Total cross-section of ^{19}F.

order of 4 keV. Higher in this intermediate range the spacing drops to nearer 100 eV and the resonance widths to less than 1 eV. Part of the cross-section of natural Br (50·5 per cent ^{79}Br and 49·5 per cent ^{81}Br) is shown in Fig. 1.4 as typical of these nuclei.

As the mass number increases the spacings and widths of the resonances become smaller still. Cross-section curves for ^{232}Th are shown in Fig. 1.5; here the resonance spacing is 17 eV. Still smaller spacings are observed among the rare earth nuclei (e.g. the Eu isotopes), and the smallest of all are amongst some of the fissile nuclei; in the cross-section of ^{235}U it is less than 1 eV (see Fig. 1.6). There are exceptions to the general trend of decreasing resonance spacing with increasing mass number; these occur at magic numbers. In the cross-section of ^{209}Bi (illustrated in Fig. 1.7) the spacing is of the order of keV and it is much greater than this in some of the lead isotopes.

At this point it ought to be mentioned that the disappearance of structure usually observed at the high-energy end of published cross-section curves is not due to termination of the resonance behaviour but to resolution (which, it will be recalled, is proportional to $E^{3/2}$ where E is

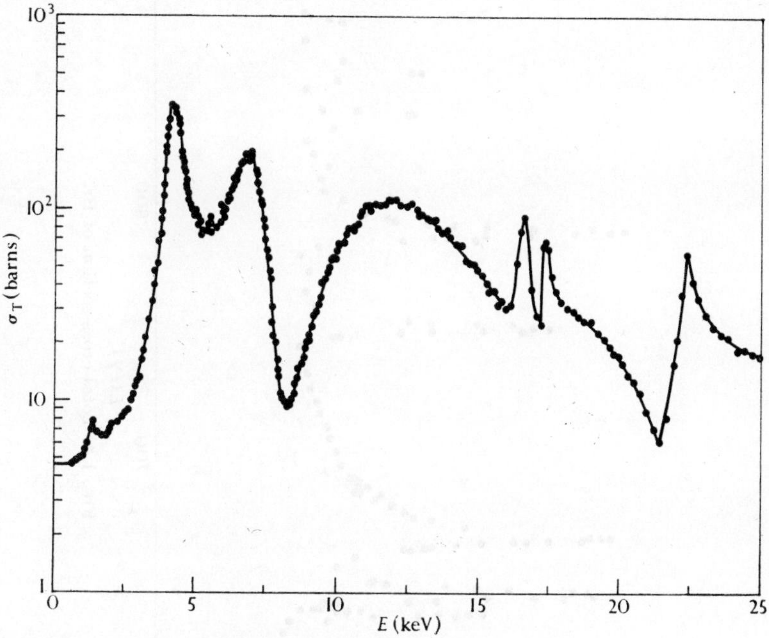

FIG. 1.3. Total cross-section of ^{51}V.

the neutron energy) becoming coarser than resonance spacing. Resonance structure is expected to persist into the MeV region; it must eventually disappear because of increased probability of reaction and higher angular momentum components of the neutron wave impinging on the nucleus. Thus, the total cross-section will gradually become smooth although the individual partial cross-sections will still show structure (Ericson fluctuations; see Ericson 1960) that is not due to individual resonances.

Now let us look at features of low-energy resonance cross-sections in a little more detail. First, there is the question of the division of the total cross-section into its components for different reactions. In all

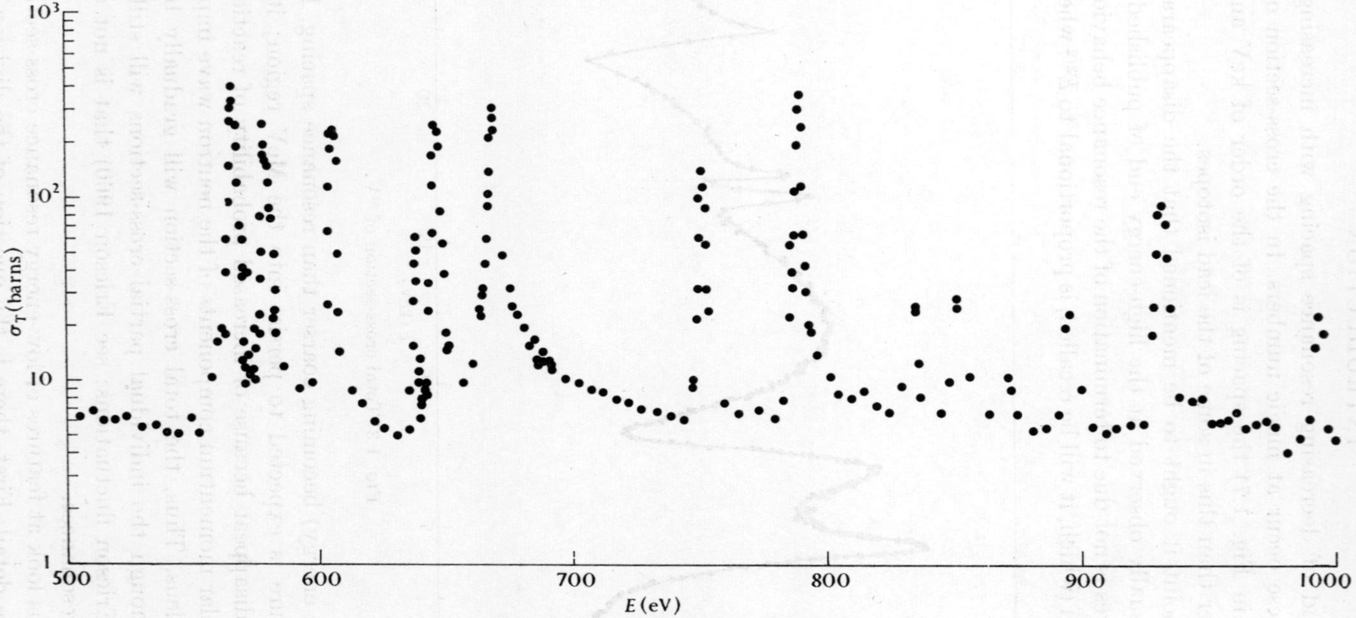

FIG. 1.4. Total cross-section of Br.

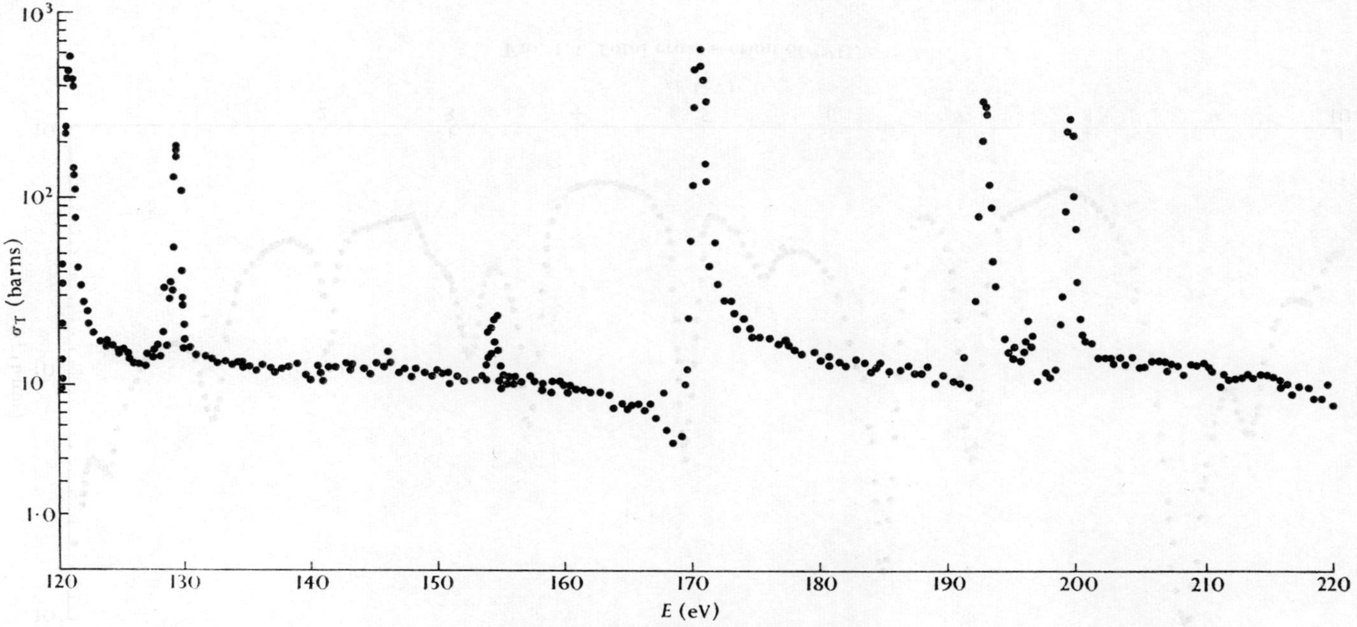

FIG. 1.5. Total cross-section of ^{232}Th.

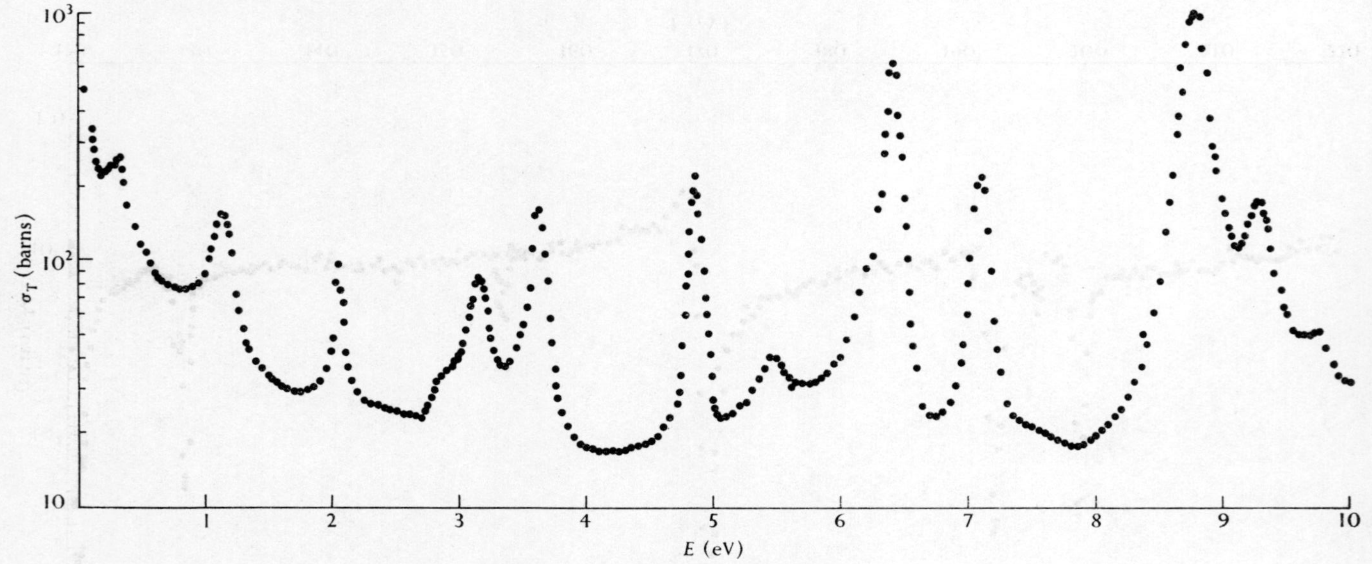

FIG. 1.6. Total cross-section of ^{235}U.

cross-sections there is, of course, (in fact, must be) a component of elastic scattering. The commonest reaction apart from this is radiative capture, observed to be present in greater or smaller degree for all nuclei from the very lightest to the very heaviest. The simpler charged particle reactions, proton or alpha-particle emission following slow neutron absorption, are only found to any appreciable extent in some

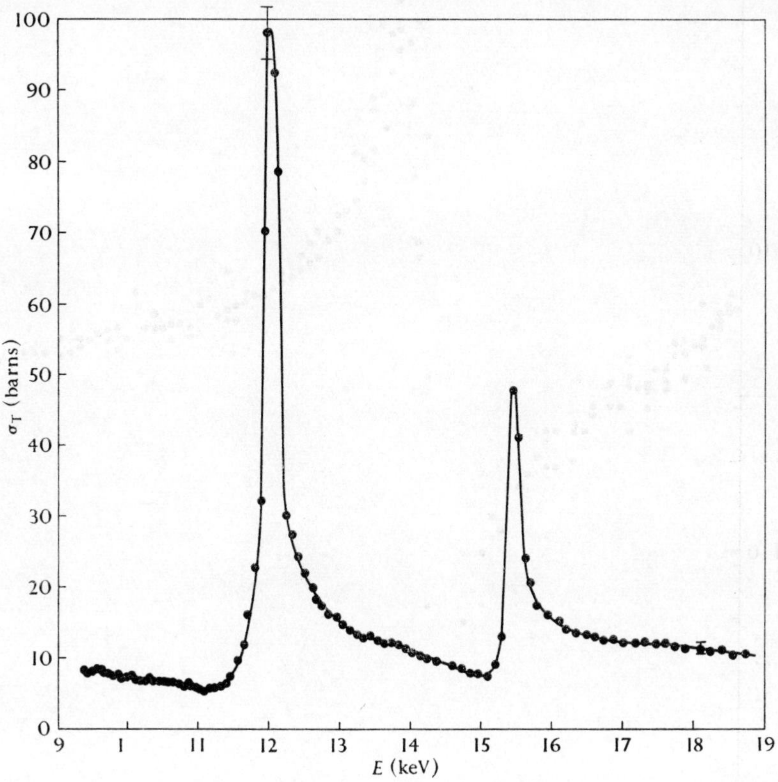

Fig. 1.7. Total cross-section of ^{209}Bi.

of the lighter nuclei, notably ^{3}He(n, p), ^{6}Li(n, α), ^{10}B(n, α). At the other end of the mass-number scale, however, some of the very heavy nuclei exhibit slow neutron-induced fission (e.g. ^{233}U, ^{235}U, ^{239}Pu, ^{241}Pu). In the partial cross-sections of a given nucleus resonances occur at the same energies but their ratios differ from resonance to resonance.

The detailed shape of the elastic scattering cross-section differs qualitatively from that of the reaction cross-sections. In a narrow resonance the latter are almost symmetric in shape and, if the resonance is sufficiently isolated, tail off to indefinitely low values in the wings. A narrow resonance in the elastic scattering cross-section, on the other hand, often shows a marked minimum on its low-energy side (see Fig. 1.8), and the cross-section tails off rather gradually on both sides to a

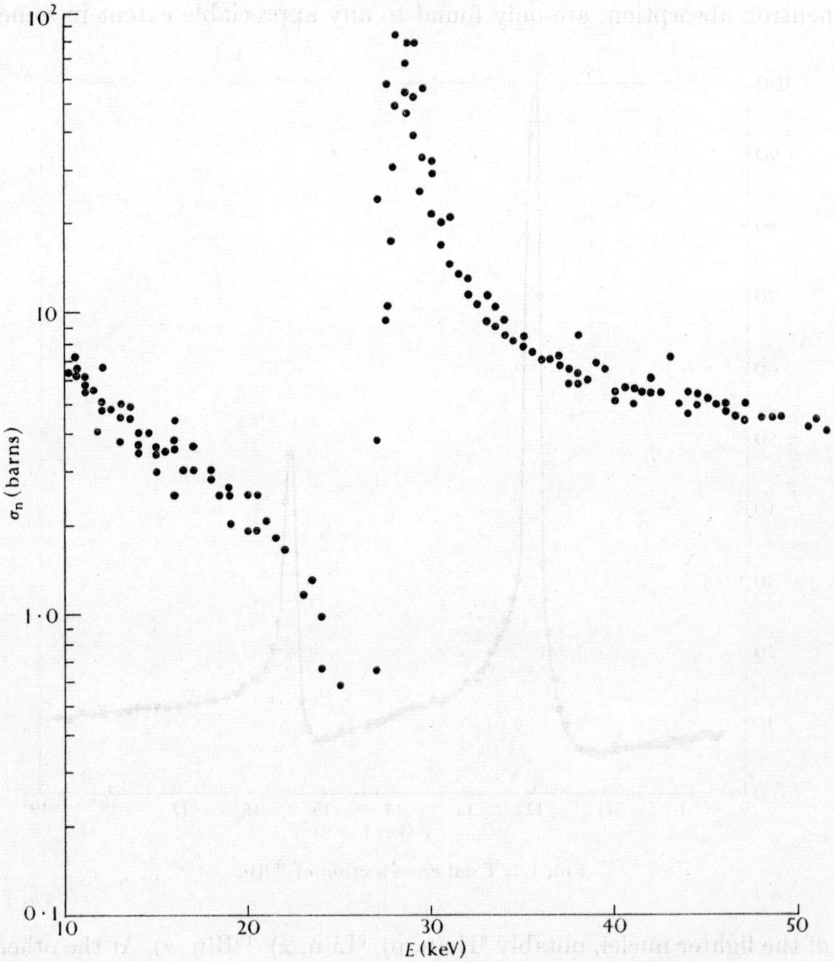

FIG. 1.8. Scattering cross-section of ^{56}Fe showing the strong interference below the 29-keV resonance.

constant value of a few barns, which is usually known as the potential scattering cross-section. Further differences appear in the limiting behaviours of the cross-sections at very low neutron energies. Despite the fading away of the reaction cross-sections on either side of a resonance, at very low energies they are found to increase again in a manner inversely proportional to the square root of the neutron energy (the well-known '$1/v$ law'). An example of this behaviour is shown in Fig. 1.9 (the capture cross-section of ^{103}Rh). Occasionally this feature dominates the resonance that is principally responsible for it (as in the ^{10}B(n, α) reaction). The elastic scattering cross-section, however, tends

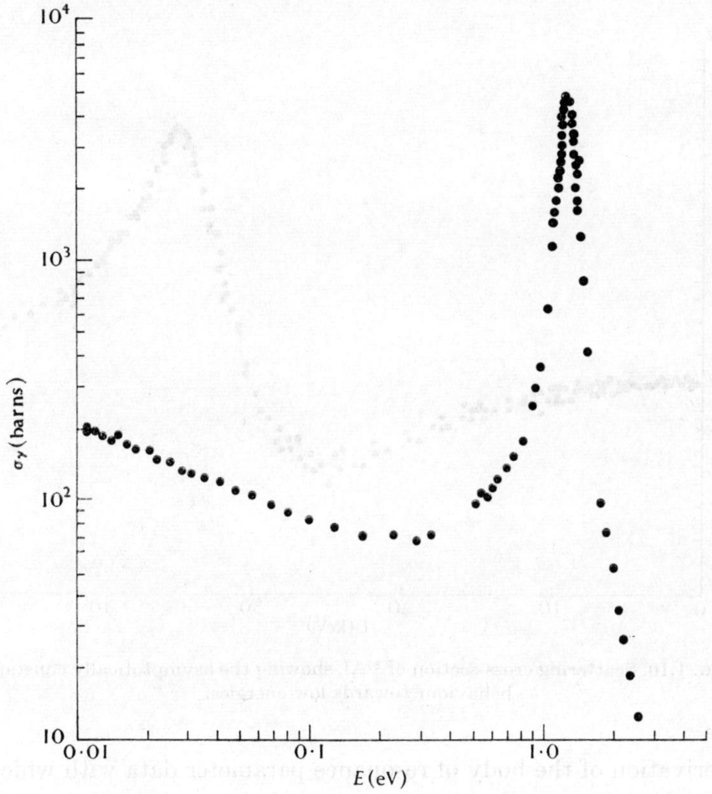

FIG. 1.9. Capture cross-section of ^{103}Rh showing the '$1/v$' rise due to the resonance towards low energies.

to a limiting constant value at very low neutron energies† (this limit need not be the potential scattering cross-section); an example of such behaviour is shown in Fig. 1.10 (the scattering cross-section of ^{27}Al).

† Sharp breaks and rises which are observed at thermal energies and below are not nuclear properties but are consequences of Bragg diffraction in the crystalline samples employed in the measurements.

All these features find their explanation in the formal reaction theory presented in Chapter II.

(c) *Analysis of the data*

(i) *The single-level Breit–Wigner formula.* Most analyses of data of the kind shown in the last section are based on the one-level formula. This is derived in Chapter II but here we quote it in order to describe

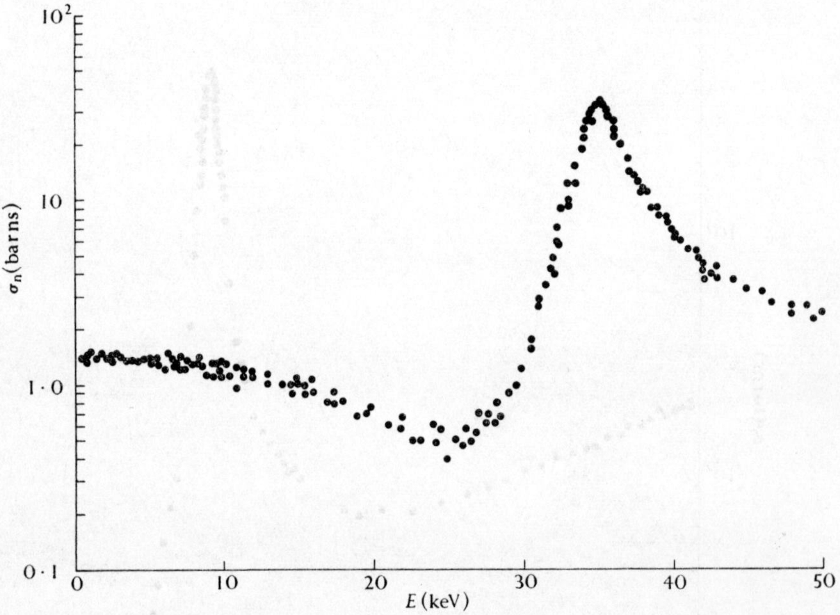

FIG. 1.10. Scattering cross-section of ^{27}Al, showing the asymptotically constant behaviour towards low energies.

the derivation of the body of resonance parameter data with which the theory of subsequent chapters is compared. Up to neutron energies of several keV the elastic scattering cross-section (of s-wave neutrons) is, to a very good approximation,

$$\sigma_{\mathrm{n}}(E) = \pi\bar{\lambda}^2 g_J \frac{\Gamma_{(\mathrm{n})}\Gamma_{(\mathrm{n})}}{(E-E_{\mathrm{R}})^2+(\frac{1}{2}\Gamma)^2} + \frac{4\pi\bar{\lambda} g_J \Gamma_{(\mathrm{n})}(\sigma_{\mathrm{p}}/4\pi)^{\frac{1}{2}}(E-E_{\mathrm{R}})}{(E-E_{\mathrm{R}})^2+(\frac{1}{2}\Gamma)^2} + \sigma_{\mathrm{p}}, \tag{1.3}$$

where $\lambda\!\!\!^{-}$ is the de Broglie wavelength of the relative motion of neutron and target divided by 2π, $\Gamma_{(n)}$ is the neutron width, Γ the total width of the resonance centred at E_R, σ_p is the (constant) potential scattering cross-section and g_J is a statistical spin factor depending on the total angular momentum J of the compound state associated with the resonance. The first term on the right-hand side of eqn. (1.3) is the resonance term, and the second term describes interference between resonance and potential scattering. Scattering due to neutrons of higher orbital angular momentum is described by an analogous formula, but at low neutron energies the corresponding potential scattering and interference terms are too small to be significant. The single-level formula for reaction cross-sections only has the resonance term

$$\sigma_r = \pi\lambda\!\!\!^{-2} g_J \frac{\Gamma_{(n)}\Gamma_{(r)}}{(E-E_R)^2+(\frac{1}{2}\Gamma)^2} \tag{1.4}$$

where $\Gamma_{(r)}$ is the partial width for the reaction r. For a narrow resonance the relation

$$\Gamma = \Gamma_{(n)}+\sum_r \Gamma_{(r)} \tag{1.5}$$

holds to a very good approximation. The partial reaction widths $\Gamma_{(r)}$ are nearly always practically constant over the neutron energy ranges of interest, while for *s*-wave resonances the neutron width is proportional to the square root of the energy. With these relationships analyses of the total cross-section and/or partial cross-sections establish E_R and one or more of the quantities $\Gamma_{(n)}$, $\Gamma_{(r)}$, and g_J. In its simplest form the analysis requires fitting of eqns. (1.3) or (1.4) to the observed partial cross-section, or the sum of these equations to the observed total cross-section. Usually, however, the complications of Doppler broadening and resolution broadening of the resonance profiles have to be considered.

Occasionally, the behaviour of the cross-section at very low energies indicates that the anomaly is due to a bound level, i.e. E_R is negative. In this case the parameters of the level can be extracted by detailed fitting of the cross-sections, particularly if the coherent 'scattering cross-section' governing the intensity of Bragg diffraction effects (see Chapter III, Section B) is known. Examples of this procedure have been described by Romanov and Shapiro (1965).

(ii) *Doppler broadening*. Strictly, the energy E occurring in eqns. (1.3), (1.4) is the energy of relative motion of the neutron and target nucleus in the centre-of-mass system. This is related to the laboratory energy of a neutron (mass m) with the target nucleus (mass M) at rest by

$$E = \{mM/(m+M)\}E_{\text{lab}} = \{1\cdot00898A/(1\cdot00898+A)\}E_{\text{lab}}. \quad (1.6)$$

Conventionally, all energies, including resonance parameters, in slow neutron spectroscopy are quoted in the laboratory system, and eqns. (1.3), (1.4) are still correct in form. However, it is not the case that the target nuclei are at rest; they always have some form of thermal motion, which seldom can be neglected.

In a simple classical treatment the collision of a neutron of velocity v with a free nucleus having velocity component w_x in the direction of the neutron beam is considered. The difference between the neutron laboratory energy and the energy of relative motion is simply

$$E_{\text{t}} = E_{\text{lab}} - E \approx R + mvw_x \quad (1.7)$$

(valid for energies greater than thermal), where the conventional recoil energy R is $mE_{\text{lab}}/(M+m)$. In a sample, the target nuclei will have a distribution of velocities described by a frequency function $p(w_x)$, and the effective cross-section of the nuclei is then

$$\sigma_{\text{eff}}(E_{\text{lab}}) = \int_{-\infty}^{\infty} \mathrm{d}w_x p(w_x)\sigma(E) \Big/ \int_{-\infty}^{\infty} \mathrm{d}w_x p(w_x). \quad (1.8)$$

From eqn. (1.7) this may be rewritten

$$\sigma_{\text{eff}}(E_{\text{lab}}) = \frac{1}{mv}\int_{-\infty}^{\infty} \mathrm{d}E_t p\left(\frac{E_t - R}{mv}\right)\sigma(E_{\text{lab}} - E_t) \Big/ \frac{1}{mv}\int_{-\infty}^{\infty} \mathrm{d}E_t p\left(\frac{E_t - R}{mv}\right). \quad (1.9)$$

Bethe (1937) first applied these considerations to the case of nuclei in a perfect gas, in which case the function $p(w_x)$ is the Maxwell–Boltzmann formula

$$p(w_x)\mathrm{d}w_x = \frac{M}{\sqrt{(2MkT)}}\exp\left(-\frac{Mw_x^2}{2kT}\right)\mathrm{d}w_x \quad (1.10)$$

where T is the temperature of the gas and k is Boltzmann's constant. On application to eqn. (9) this gives

$$\sigma_{\text{eff}}(E_{\text{lab}}) = \frac{1}{\Delta\sqrt{\pi}}\int_{-\infty}^{\infty} \mathrm{d}E_t \exp\left\{-\frac{(E_t - R)^2}{\Delta^2}\right\}\sigma(E_{\text{lab}} - E_t) \quad (1.11)$$

where $\Delta = \sqrt{\{4RkTM/(M+m)\}}$.

In a classical solid, which is considered as a system of harmonic oscillators with energies distributed according to the Boltzmann law, it turns out that the distribution of velocity components w_x is also given by eqn. (1.10), and the formula for the effective cross-section is unchanged.

If the cross-section σ simply has the resonance form of eqn. (1.4) then the effective cross-section can be written in the form

$$\sigma_{\mathrm{eff,r}}(x) = \sigma_{\mathrm{or}}\Psi(\beta, x) \tag{1.12}$$

where the new variable x is

$$x = (E - E_{\mathrm{R}})/(\tfrac{1}{2}\Gamma), \tag{1.12a}$$

the resonance peak cross-section is

$$\sigma_{\mathrm{or}} = 4\pi\bar{\lambda}^2 g_J \frac{\Gamma_{(\mathrm{n})}\Gamma_{(\mathrm{r})}}{\Gamma^2}, \tag{1.12b}$$

the parameter β is

$$\beta = 2\Delta/\Gamma, \tag{1.12c}$$

and the function Ψ is

$$\Psi(\beta, x) = \frac{1}{\beta\sqrt{\pi}} \int_{-\infty}^{\infty} \mathrm{d}y \frac{1}{1+y^2} \exp\left\{-\frac{(x-y)^2}{\beta^2}\right\}. \tag{1.12d}$$

Similarly, the interference term of equation (1.3) gives a contribution to the effective cross-section of

$$\sigma_{\mathrm{eff,int}}(x) = \sigma_{\mathrm{oT}} \frac{2}{\bar{\lambda}} \left(\frac{\sigma_{\mathrm{p}}}{4\pi}\right)^{\frac{1}{2}} \Phi(\beta, x) \tag{1.13}$$

where $\sigma_{\mathrm{oT}} = \sigma_{\mathrm{on}} + \sum_{\mathrm{r}} \sigma_{\mathrm{or}}$ and

$$\Phi(\beta, x) = \frac{1}{\beta\sqrt{\pi}} \int_{-\infty}^{\infty} \mathrm{d}y \frac{y}{1+y^2} \exp\left\{-\frac{(x-y)^2}{\beta^2}\right\}. \tag{1.13a}$$

These new forms are more suitable for computation (see e.g. Lynn 1960) and tabulation (Melkonian *et al.* 1953, Rose *et al.* 1953).

These Doppler-broadening expressions for a classical system suggest that the effect could be removed altogether by cooling the sample to very low temperatures (e.g. liquid helium temperatures). However, at such temperatures quantal effects in the sample become important and there is even some residue of these at normal room temperature. For a simple qualitative discussion, consider the case of an assembly of independent target nuclei each bound in a harmonic oscillator well. At zero temperature in the classical assembly each nucleus is at rest; a coalescing neutron will give it a recoil energy R and the compound system will oscillate in the well with this energy. The effective resonance cross-section then has the Breit–Wigner shape. In the quantal model, on the other hand, each target nucleus is oscillating with zero-point energy initially, and after absorption of a neutron the energy of oscillation will be one of the eigenvalues of the harmonic oscillator well, any given eigenvalue appearing with a certain, non-zero probability; the only relation to the classical picture is that the *expectation* value of the oscillation energy is equal to the recoil energy R. In particular, there will be a finite probability of the oscillator remaining in its initial (ground) state; this is the analogue of the Mössbauer effect (Mössbauer 1958) of recoilless absorption of nuclear gamma rays. In addition to this sharp Breit–Wigner shape at neutron energy E_{R} there will be fine structure (or general broadening if Γ is greater than the spacing of eigenvalues in the oscillator well) at near-by neutron energies so that the 'Mössbauer line' may be obscured.

The modes of oscillation in a crystal are to be considered as a property of the lattice as a whole rather than as residing on individual atoms, but the main qualitative conclusions are similar to those stated above. Lamb (1939) derived expressions for the probability of creation or annihilation of phonons in the various modes and used these in an explicit calculation of the resonance shape to be expected if the target nuclei were bound in a monatomic Debye crystal. For a crystal that is cold relative to the Debye temperature Θ_{D} and for resonance width and recoil energy small or moderate compared with $k\Theta_{\mathrm{D}}$, he showed that a 'recoilless' Breit–Wigner peak could be expected, as well as some crude structure at higher energies. At higher crystal temperatures the usual result is the classical resonance broadening, except that the classical mean energy per degree of freedom, kT, in the Doppler constant Δ of eqn. (1.11), must be replaced by the quantal mean energy,

$$\bar{\varepsilon} = \tfrac{1}{2}\int_0^{\nu_{\mathrm{m}}} \mathrm{d}\nu h\nu \coth(h\nu/2kT) g(\nu), \tag{1.14}$$

where $g(\nu)$ is the spectrum of oscillation modes in the lattice and ν_{m} is the maximum frequency of this spectrum. The mean energy $\bar{\varepsilon}$ is greater than kT; at low temperatures it is equal to $\frac{3}{8}k\Theta_D$, but at high temperatures it approaches kT asymptotically. At room temperature, where $\bar{\varepsilon}$ is only a few per cent greater than kT, it is usually accurate enough to use a simple Einstein model, $g(\nu) = \delta(\nu - \nu_E)$, in its calculation, i.e.

$$\bar{\varepsilon} \approx \tfrac{1}{2}h\nu_E \coth(h\nu_E/2kT). \tag{1.15}$$

The Einstein frequency ν_E is obtained from the Debye temperature of the material by the relation $h\nu_E = \frac{3}{4}k\Theta_D$. If the material is not monatomic then the Debye temperature is not a good guide to the mean quantal energy of the target nuclei (Jackson and Lynn 1962). In this case the amplitude of individual modes of oscillation is different for the different atomic species of the crystal. For instance, the heavy nuclear species of a diatomic crystal tends to carry the low-frequency phonons and the light atoms the high-frequency ones. If the resonance occurs in the cross-section of the heavy nucleus the high Debye temperature of such a material will give an over-estimate of $\bar{\varepsilon}$ for the purpose of effective cross-section calculation. In these circumstances it seems to be better to use the Debye temperature of a monatomic specimen of the target nucleus rather than that of the compound actually used as a sample.

(iii) *Resolution broadening.* Instrumental resolution does not operate on the cross-sections directly but on the transmission or yield curves of specific samples. If the measurement is made at a nominal energy E the effect of resolution may be described by a normalized efficiency function $g(E, E')$ for actually detecting neutrons at the energies E' in the neighbourhood of E. The observed neutron transmission (or yield) at nominal energy E is given by the convolution

$$T_{\text{obs}}(E) = \int dE' g(E, E')T(E'). \tag{1.16}$$

Usually the resolution function g is not known in much detail. It is generally a function peaked about the energy E, somewhat Gaussian in shape, and its width is usually known reasonably well. This information is good enough to allow shape fitting, using eqns. (1.3) or (1.4), only when the resolution width is considerably less than the resonance width.

Resonance widths, however, are usually so narrow compared with resonance spacings that the available resolution will separate resonances over large regions in which it is actually coarser than the widths. To obtain the maximum information about resonance parameters some technique of analysis other than simple shape fitting must be used. Such a method is 'area' analysis (Havens and Rainwater 1951), which may be used if the measurements of transmission or yield are made at a sequence of energies E_i such that

$$\sum_{i=1}^{n} g(E_i, E') = 1 \tag{1.17}$$

for all E' between specified limits E_1 and E_n (Lynn and Rae 1957). This condition is very nearly met by most time-of-flight spectrometers by virtue of the system of measuring the time of an event and then sorting into time bins in a histogram fashion. Condition (1.17) allows the area under a transmission or yield curve to be estimated, independently of resolution, by summing the observations at the energy E_i:

$$\int\limits_{E_1-(E_1-E_0)/2}^{E_n+(E_{n+1}-E_n)/2} \mathrm{d}E'T(E') = \sum_{i=1}^{n} T_{\mathrm{obs}}(E_i)$$
$$= \sum_{i=1}^{n} \int \mathrm{d}E' g(E_i, E')T(E'). \tag{1.18}$$

We give below some of the important area-function relations for transmission: those for yield curves readily follow. The area function is defined, for an isolated resonance, as the integral *above* the transmission curve that is due to the resonance and interference terms alone of the total cross-section, the integral extending from indefinitely far below the resonance to indefinitely far above it:

$$A = \int\limits_{\text{``}-\infty\text{''}}^{\text{``}+\infty\text{''}} \mathrm{d}E'\{1-T(E')/\exp(-n\sigma_p)\}, \tag{1.19}$$

the inverted commas on the limits indicating that these limits cannot be physically realized.

If there are only resonance terms in the total cross-section and if Doppler broadening can be neglected

$$A = \tfrac{1}{2}\pi n\sigma_0\Gamma\exp(-n\sigma_0/2)\{I_0(n\sigma_0/2)+I_1(n\sigma_0/2)\} \tag{1.20}$$

(Ladenburg and Reiche 1913), where I_m is the Bessel function of imaginary argument and order m (Watson 1944) and σ_0 is the peak total cross-section of the resonance

$$\sigma_0 \equiv \sigma_{0\mathrm{T}} = 4\pi\lambda\!\!\!^{-2} g_J \frac{\Gamma_{(\mathrm{n})}}{\Gamma}. \tag{1.21}$$

This function has asymptotic forms (known as the thin and thick sample forms)

$$\lim_{n\sigma_0 \to 0} A = \pi n\sigma_0 \Gamma/2, \tag{1.22a}$$

$$\lim_{n\sigma_0 \to \infty} A = \sqrt{(\pi n\sigma_0)}\Gamma. \tag{1.22b}$$

The thin sample relation is valid in practice when $n\sigma_0$ is less than

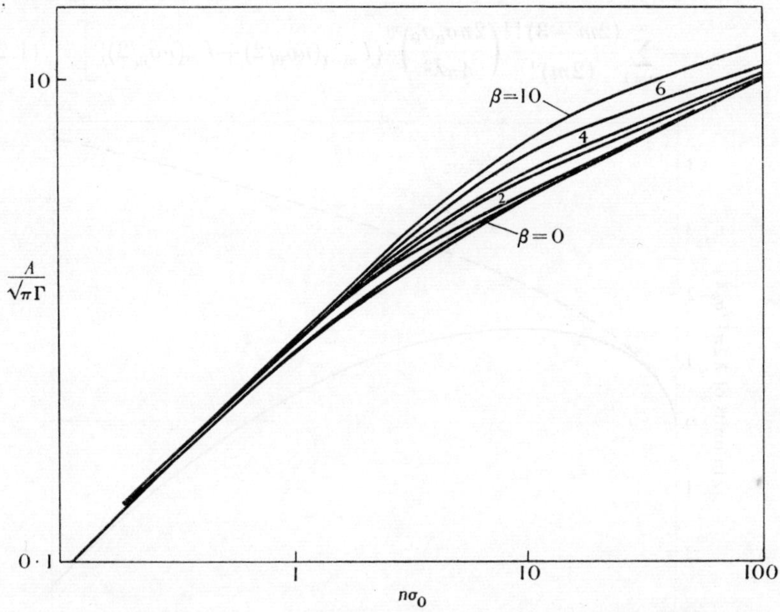

FIG. 1.11. Behaviour of the resonance area function with sample thickness n and Doppler broadening β.

about 0·2 and the thick-sample relation holds for $n\sigma_0$ greater than about 10.

An analytic relation like eqn. (1.20) cannot be written down if Doppler broadening is appreciable, but several numerical computations of the area function have been made in this case. Since Doppler broadening lowers the effective peak cross-section of a resonance, the self-shielding that causes the area function to depart from the thin-sample relation (eqn. (1.22a)), becomes less important, and thus the range of validity of the thin-sample relation increases with increasing β, and the point of onset of the thick-sample relation also rises. Typical curves of area functions for various Doppler-broadening parameters are shown in Fig. 1.11. From such computations, or relations like them, it is possible to extract σ_0 and Γ, and hence $g_J\Gamma_{(n)}$ (and perhaps even $\Gamma_{(\gamma)}, \Gamma_{(n)}$ and g in favourable circumstances), from transmission measurements with different sample thicknesses.

The resonance-potential scattering term can also have a very important effect on the area function (Lynn 1958). When it is included, and there is no Doppler broadening, the area function becomes

$$A = \tfrac{1}{2}\pi n\sigma_0\Gamma\exp(-n\sigma_0/2)\Big[I_0(n\sigma_0/2)+I_1(n\sigma_0/2) - \sum_{m=1}^{\infty}\frac{(2m-3)!!}{(2m)!}\left(\frac{2n\sigma_0\sigma_p}{4\pi\lambda\!\!\!^{-2}}\right)^m\{I_{m-1}(n\sigma_0/2)+I_m(n\sigma_0/2)\}\Big]. \quad (1.23)$$

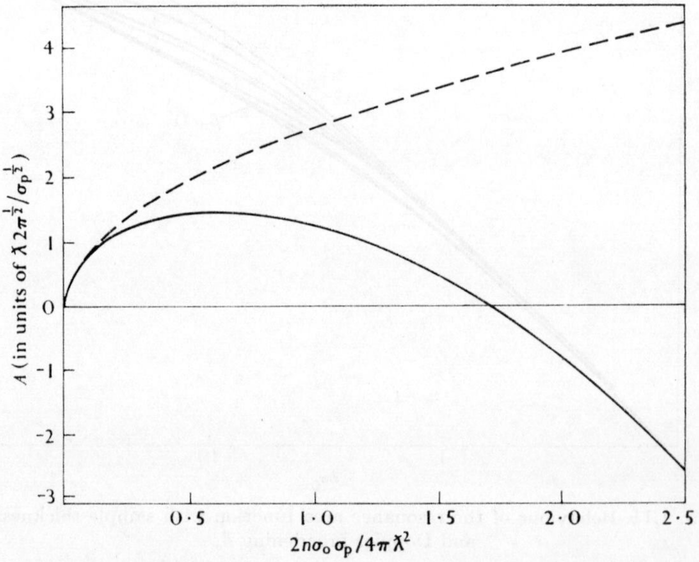

FIG. 1.12. Effect of resonance-potential scattering term on area function.

When $n\sigma_0$ is large this expression has the asymptotic form

$$\lim_{n\sigma_0\to\infty} A = \Gamma\sqrt{(\pi n\sigma_0)}\left\{1-\sum_{m=1}^{\infty}\frac{(2m-3)!!}{(2m)!}\left(\frac{2n\sigma_0\sigma_p}{4\pi\lambda\!\!\!^{-2}}\right)^m\right\}, \quad (1.24)$$

which is shown in Fig. 1.12.

Numerical computations and tabulations are available for the Doppler-broadened case (Lynn 1960). It is apparent that a sequence of thick-sample transmission measurements will yield the quantities $\sigma_0\sigma_p/\lambda\!\!\!^{-2}$ and $\Gamma\lambda\!\!\!^{-}/\sqrt{(\sigma_p)}$ with this kind of analysis. At higher neutron energies (above a few keV) the area function is related to the potential scattering cross-section in a slightly more complicated way (Lynn 1960) but the quantities $g_J\Gamma_{(n)}$ and Γ may still be determined.

The determination of other parameters of a resonance depend on the measurement of partial cross-sections. These are usually made with thin samples ($n\sigma_0 \ll 1$) and the area under a resonance in the yield curve is

$$Y_r = \tfrac{1}{2}\pi n\sigma_0\Gamma(\Gamma_{(r)}/\Gamma). \tag{1.25}$$

With sufficient partial cross-section and transmission measurements the basic parameters of the resonance may be over-determined and a least squares type of analysis is possible, giving statistical errors

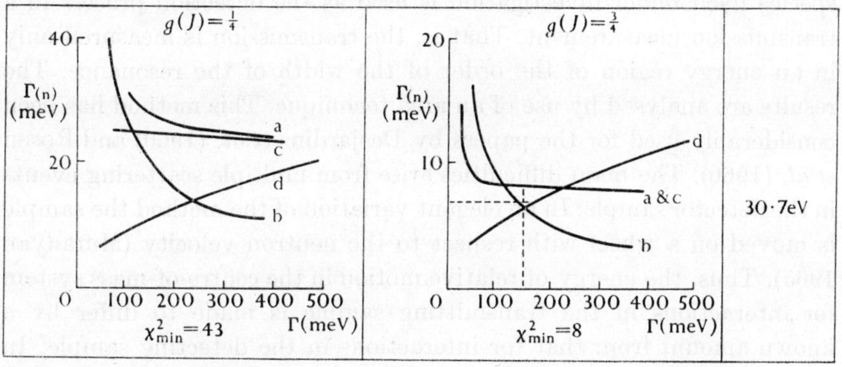

FIG. 1.13. Determination of resonance parameters from areas of transmission and yield curves; *a* indicates radiative capture yield, *b* indicates 'thick sample' transmission, *c* indicates 'thin sample' transmission, *d* indicates elastic scattering yield. These results are for the 30·7-eV resonance in the cross-section of ^{109}Ag. The analysis clearly indicates $g_J = \frac{3}{4}$ ($J = 1$), $\Gamma_{(n)} = 6{\cdot}7 \pm 0{\cdot}4$ meV, $\Gamma = 149 \pm 13$ meV.

as well as best values of the parameters. For example, if only two reactions are significant for slow neutron interaction with an odd-mass nucleus, elastic scattering, and radiative capture (this is the usual case), measurements of the thin-sample yield curves of scattering and capture together with thin-and-thick-sample transmission areas give the four relations:

$$A(\text{thin}) \propto g_J\Gamma_{(n)}, \tag{1.26a}$$

$$A(\text{thick}) \propto g_J\Gamma_{(n)}(\Gamma_{(n)}+\Gamma_{(\gamma)}), \tag{1.26b}$$

$$Y_n \propto g_J\Gamma^2_{(n)}/(\Gamma_{(n)}+\Gamma_{(\gamma)}), \tag{1.26c}$$

$$Y_\gamma \propto g_J\Gamma_{(n)}\Gamma_{(\gamma)}/(\Gamma_{(n)}+\Gamma_{(\gamma)}), \tag{1.26d}$$

for the three parameters g_J (hence J), $\Gamma_{(n)}$, and $\Gamma_{(\gamma)}$. In practice, least squares analysis (see Fig. 1.13) is carried out for the two parameters $\Gamma_{(n)}$ and $\Gamma_{(\gamma)}$ assuming the two possible values of J in turn (Rae *et al.* 1958). The quantity χ^2 is defined as the sum of the squares of the residuals of the functions (1.26) from a point in the $(\Gamma_{(n)}, \Gamma_{(\gamma)})$plane. The best solution of $\Gamma_{(n)}$ and $\Gamma_{(\gamma)}$ is that point for which χ^2 is a minimum, and the most likely value of J is that for which $\chi^2{}_{\min}$ is lower. Standard deviations of $\Gamma_{(n)}$ and $\Gamma_{(\gamma)}$ are obtained from the curvature of the χ^2 function.

The effect of resolution can be partially overcome by use of self-indication measurements. In this method, capture in the nuclear species itself under investigation is used as the detection process in a transmission measurement. That is, the transmission is measured only in an energy region of the order of the width of the resonance. The results are analysed by use of an area technique. This method has been considerably used for the papers by Desjardins *et al.* (1960) and Rosen *et al.* (1960). The main difficulties arise from multiple scattering events in the detector sample. In an elegant variation of the method the sample is moved on a wheel with respect to the neutron velocity (Muradyan 1965). Thus, the energy of relative motion in the centre-of-mass system for interactions in the transmitting sample is made to differ by a known amount from that for interactions in the detecting sample. In this way weak asymmetries (such as those due to resonance potential interference) in the resonance shape can be observed even when masked by resolution.

(iv) *Multiple events*. The interpretation of yield curves obtained with all but the very thinnest sample is complicated by the occurrence of collisions within the sample of a neutron that has already undergone scattering. This problem is very complicated because, first, the energy loss of the neutron on scattering varies with angle of scattering and the thermal motion of the scattering nucleus; second, the neutron cross-section is varying rapidly through the resonance; third, for rather thick samples a neutron may undergo a considerable number of collisions before final absorption or escape. Analytical solutions to this problem have been only approximate, and in practice the best way to deal with it is by Monte Carlo calculations on a digital computer. Here we only draw attention to the problem and indicate its importance by illustrating Monte Carlo calculations and comparison with experiment for the 130-eV resonance of the neutron capture cross-section of ^{59}Co (Fig. 1.14).

(v) *Methods of spin determination.* Resonances in the neutron cross-sections are associated with excited states of the compound nucleus formed by adding the neutron to the target nucleus. It is an important problem to establish the quantum numbers of these excited states and in particular their total angular momentum (spin) and parity. Usually the observed low-energy resonances are caused by the *s*-wave component of the bombarding neutron beam, and the parity of the resonant state is just that of the target nucleus. In this case the spin J of the resonant state can normally have one of two values, $J = I+\frac{1}{2}$ or $|I-\frac{1}{2}|$ where I is the spin quantum number of the target. The usual

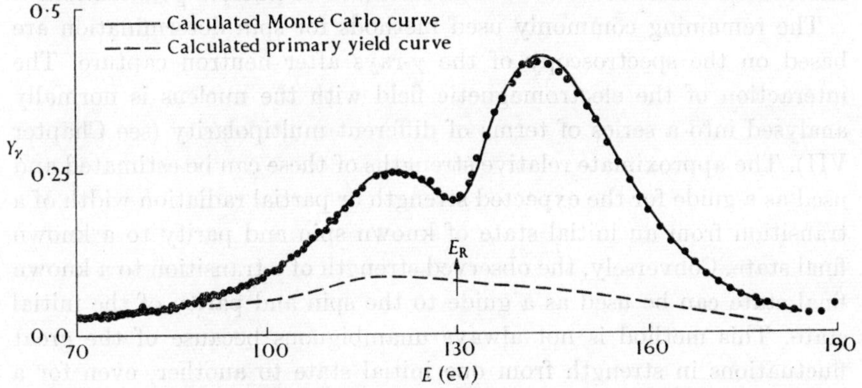

FIG. 1.14. Capture yield curve for thick sample ($n = 9{\cdot}05\times10^{-3}$ atom barns^{-1}) of ^{59}Co, illustrating the effect of multiple events. The fit to the data indicates parameters $\Gamma_{(n)} = 5{\cdot}55$ eV, $\Gamma\gamma = 0{\cdot}405$ eV, $E_R = 130{\cdot}1$ eV.

method for determining J is the parameter analysis of resonance data as described in Sections c(i) and c(iii). In favourable circumstances the spin weighting factor g_J, which is equal to $(2J+1)/2(2I+1)$ (see Chapter II), can be extracted and hence the spin.

The most direct method for the determination of the spin is the use of polarized neutron beams and nuclear samples. To describe the principle involved we consider here only the case when both beam and sample are fully polarized in the direction of the neutron beam. If the polarizations are parallel (rather than anti-parallel) the projection of the neutron spin on the neutron beam direction is $\frac{1}{2}\hbar$ while the projection of the nuclear spin is $I\hbar$. Thus the projection of the total spin of the compound system is $(I+\frac{1}{2})\hbar$. This can be projected only by the angular momentum state $J = I+\frac{1}{2}$, so if the transmission curve shows a resonance in this state of polarization its angular momentum quantum number has this higher value. If the polarizations are anti-parallel, on the other hand, the projection of the total spin is $\pm(I-\frac{1}{2})\hbar$, which can be projected by either value of the total spin quantum number. It can be shown by the algebra of angular momentum coupling (see e.g. Edmonds 1957) that the relative weighting of these two spins in the beam and target system is now $2I/1$ in favour of the lower spin. Thus, a measurement of the transmission in this state of polarization together with a measurement on the unpolarized system can reveal the angular momenta associated with the resonances. In practice, of course, this ideal degree of polarization can never be achieved; so careful measurements have to be made of the rather fine differences in transmission after reversal of either neutron or nucleus polarization.

The remaining commonly used methods for spin determination are based on the spectroscopy of the γ-rays after neutron capture. The interaction of the electromagnetic field with the nucleus is normally analysed into a series of terms of different multipolarity (see Chapter VII). The approximate relative strengths of these can be estimated and used as a guide for the expected strength or partial radiation width of a transition from an initial state of known spin and parity to a known final state. Conversely, the observed strength of a transition to a known final state can be used as a guide to the spin and parity of the initial state. This method is not always unambiguous because of the great fluctuations in strength from one initial state to another, even for a transition of known multipolarity (see Chapter VII, Section B), but where the parity is known (e.g. s-wave resonances) the method can in some cases be used to give a positive identification of one spin. For example, consider a target nucleus of spin and parity $\frac{1}{2}^-$; the s-wave resonances in its neutron cross-section will be associated with spin and parity 0^- and 1^-. If the compound nucleus has a suitable low-lying state of spin and parity 0^+, transitions to this state from the 0^- resonances are forbidden. Thus the observation of a direct γ-ray transition allows the resonance to be classified as a 1^- state. If the transition is not observed nothing can be said, for the resonance may be of spin and parity 1^- but with a very weak partial radiation width. Another example is a $5/2^-$ target nucleus with 2^- and 3^- s-wave resonances. Transitions from the 2^- resonances to a 1^+ final state are electric dipole transitions, which are normally very much stronger than the electric octupole transitions from the 3^- resonances to the same final state. Observation of a reasonably strong transition from a resonance to this final state thus provides fairly certain evidence that the spin of the resonance is 2.

A method that overcomes the difficulty of fluctuations in partial radiation widths is the observation of the coincidence rate between primary γ-rays to many intermediate states within a rather wide energy band and secondary γ-rays from the intermediate states to a low-lying final state of known spin and parity (Bollinger *et al.* 1965). The application of the multipolarity rules for the transition strengths leads to estimates of the ratios of the coincidence rates from resonances of different spin. An example is shown in Fig. 1.15. A resonance of spin and parity 1^+ can make electric dipole transitions to intermediate states of spin and parity 0^-, 1^- and 2^-. Of these, only the second can make

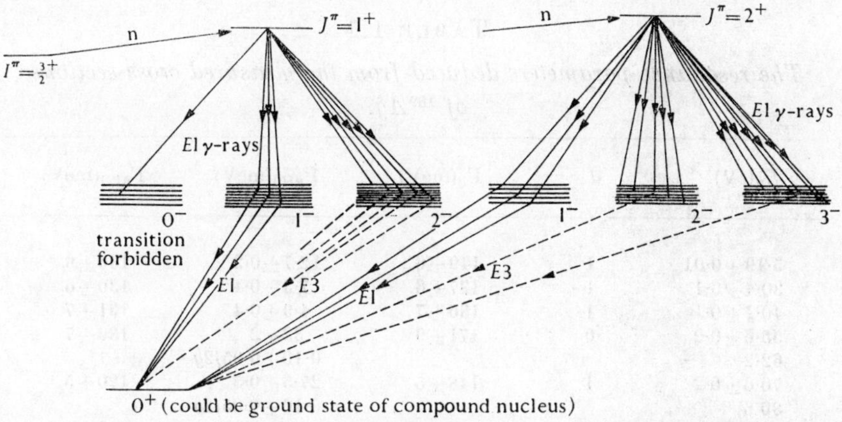

FIG. 1.15. γ-ray transition diagrams for 1^+ and 2^+ resonances in an even-compound nucleus.

secondary electric dipole transitions to a final 0^+ state. The 2^+ resonances can make electric dipole transitions to 1^-, 2^-, and 3^- intermediate states, of which only the first can make strong secondary transitions to the 0^+ state. After allowing for the expected dependence of the intermediate-state density on spin (see Chapter IV, Section B), the coincidence rate in the former case is expected to be 5/3 times that in the second.

(vi) *Other techniques.* The above discussions broadly cover the main methods, as well as some less common ones, for extracting the data of theoretical significance from measurements in the field of neutron resonance spectroscopy. It is clear that more sophisticated methods will employ more and more of the theory to be discussed in subsequent chapters, and to attempt to describe them here is to put them out of logical context. For this reason they are not included in this chapter and are mentioned, where it is felt necessary, only in conjunction with the theory to which they are relevant.

(vii) *Resonance parameters.* There now exists a very large body of information on the resonance parameters of neutron cross-sections; the bulk of this has been extracted by the methods outlined in this chapter. No attempt will be made in this book to reproduce all these data, for besides being much too extensive they can in any case be found in the recent excellent compilations of Stehn *et al.* (1965–66). However it is clearly desirable to show one or two examples of such data. The first is that of the target nucleus ^{109}Ag. This is 48·7 per cent abundant in natural silver, and the range of results in Table 1.1 already

TABLE 1.1

The resonance parameters deduced from the measured cross-sections of ^{109}Ag.

E_R(eV)	J	Γ_R(meV)	$\Gamma_{R(n)}$(meV)	$\Gamma_{R(\gamma)}$(meV)
5·19±0·01	1	149±6	12·7±0·2	136±6
30·4±0·1	1	137±6	7·3±0·4	130±6
40·1±0·1	1	136±7	4·9±0·4	131±7
55·6±0·2	0	171±9	32±2	139±7
62·2			0·10±0·05/2g	
70·6±0·2	1	148±5	27·5±0·5	120±5
80·6			0·16±0·05/2g	
83·5±0·2			0·04±0·02/2g	
87·4±0·2	1	136±15	6·3±0·3	130±15
106·3±0·2			0·2±0·03/2g	
110·9±0·2			0·12±0·08/2g	
133·9±0·2	1	200±7	80±4	120±5
139·7±0·2		135±46	2·2±0·3/2g	133±46
169·8±0·2			0·39±0·13/2g	
173·1±0·2	1	188±20	48±4	140±15
183·6±0·2			0·27±0·07/2g	
209·6±0·2	1	156±20	23±2	133±20
251·3±0·3	1	133±20	13±2	120±20
264·7±0·3		154±40	3·6±0·7/2g	150±40
272·4±0·4			2·0±0·3/2g	
290·9±0·3	0	176±25	36±5	140±20
316·4±0·3	1		169±13	

The spin weighting factor g can in this case have either the value $\frac{1}{4}$ (for resonances with spin $J = 0$) or $\frac{3}{4}$ (for resonances with spin $J = 1$). The results shown here are the recommended values given in the compilation of Stehn *et al.* (1966) and include work by Seidl *et al.* (1954), Draper and Baker (1954), Sheer and Moore (1955), Wood (1956), Grimm (1956), Fluharty *et al.* (1956), Rae *et al.* (1958), Moxon and Rae (1961), Desjardins *et al.* (1960), Singh (1964), Asghar *et al.* (1965), Chrien (1966), Garg *et al.* (1965), and Pattenden (1965).

indicates the precision of present methods in neutron spectroscopy, because the measurements have often had to be made with rather small samples of the separated isotopes. The target nucleus ^{109}Ag has ground-state spin and parity $\frac{1}{2}^-$. The interaction of s-wave neutrons (having intrinsic spin and parity $\frac{1}{2}^+$ and no orbital angular momentum) with this target therefore leads to the excitation of resonant or compound nucleus states of total angular momentum and parity 0^- or 1^- in ^{110}Ag. The properties of these resonant states up to 316-eV neutron energy are shown in Table 1.1. The only reactions that take place with measureable yield on bombardment of silver with slow neutrons are elastic scattering and radiative capture. Only the total radiative capture yields have been measured so only two partial widths are shown in the table, the neutron width and total radiative capture width. The main qualitative features to be observed in Table 1.1 are the following. First, the resonances, even those of the same total angular momentum, are irregularly spaced. Second, there are considerably more resonances with angular momentum 1 than 0. Third, the neutron widths show violent fluctuations in magnitude from resonance to resonance, while, fourth, the total radiation widths are almost constant from one resonance to another, even for those of different angular momentum.

The resonance parameters of silver are quite typical of those of a heavy non-fissile nucleus. The cross-sections of fissile nuclei are very special cases and tables of their parameters will be found in Chapter VIII. Resonance data for a much lighter nucleus than ^{109}Ag are shown in Table 1.2. The target nucleus in this instance is ^{59}Co which has ground-state spin and parity $7/2^-$, so the resonance states excited by s-wave neutrons have total angular momentum and parity 3^- and 4^-. In this table it will be noticed that the resonance spacings and neutron widths are orders of magnitude greater than those of silver, but the radiation widths are only slightly larger. The fluctuations in spacings and neutron widths are again very obvious, but a new feature is that the total radiation widths also fluctuate somewhat from resonance to resonance. Another difference in the two tables is the presence of 'negative energy resonances' in Table 1.2. These occur because it is found impossible to fit all the features of the ^{59}Co cross-sections with the positive energy resonances shown in Table 1.2 alone, and it is inferred that the discrepancies are partly due to bound states of ^{60}Co. These, of course, cannot have positive neutron widths at their actual level energies; so the actual dependence of the neutron width on energy in the positive neutron-energy domain is shown in the table. The reason for the particular choice of the energy function will become apparent in Chapter II. In actual fact, even these bound levels are insufficient to explain all the cross-section data to, say, 20 keV; so extra terms, which give the

TABLE 1.2

The resonance parameters of the measured cross-section of ^{59}Co.

E_R(keV)	J	$\Gamma_{R(n)}$(eV)	$\Gamma_{R(\gamma)}$(eV)
≈ -1	4	$\approx 0{\cdot}045\sqrt{E}$ (in eV)	
$\approx -0{\cdot}08$	3	$\approx 0{\cdot}30\sqrt{E}$ (in eV)	
0·1301	4	5·41	0·440
1·38±·02			
2·26±·03			
3·98±·01		0·12±·08	
4·33±·01	4	95±9	0·7
5·02±·02	3	688±10	1·0
5·80±·01			
6·39±·01		1·9±0·6	(0·22±·03)/2g
8·05±·01	3	39±3	0·31±·04
8·74±·01		0·7±0·4	(0·32±·05)/2g
9·70±·01		2·1±0·6	(0·56±·06)/2g
10·69±·01	4	68±3	0·63±·07
11·85±·02		2·2±0·6	(0·25±·06)/2g
13·26±·01	3	22±2	0·8±0·1
15·62±·01	3	83±4	0·5±0·1
16·89±·01	4	168±8	0·5±0·1
19·75±·04		2·3±0·8	
21·94±·04	3	740±70	
22·50±·03	4	218±40	
24·46±·05	3	390±40	
25·16±·06	4	172±16	
27·35±·06	4	170±17	

The spin weighting factor g can be either 7/16 (for $J = 3$) or 9/16 (for $J = 4$). The results shown here are compiled from the work of Rae (1954), Moxon (1965) and Garg (1966). In the R-matrix fitting a neutron channel radius of 5·4 fm was used and the boundary condition was $B = 0$. To fit the cross-section in detail between 0 and 20 keV residual R-functions in the neutron channel of R_{res} ($J = 3$) $= -0{\cdot}17$ ($\pm{\cdot}05$) $+0{\cdot}26$ ($\pm{\cdot}09$)$\times 10^{-4}$ ($E-10$keV) and R_{res} ($J = 4$) $= -0{\cdot}24$ ($\pm{\cdot}04$)$+0{\cdot}075$ ($\pm{\cdot}003$)$\times 10^{-4}\times$ ($E-10$ keV) were required to provide the effect of levels outside the range quoted here.

gross effect of other states both bound and unbound over this energy range, have to be introduced into the cross-section formulae. The required formula is a many-level formula of the kind discussed in Chapter II, Section E.2.

II

FORMAL NUCLEAR REACTION THEORIES

A. INTRODUCTORY REMARKS

IN ORDER to understand theoretically the features of nuclear reactions, we need to be able to relate the cross-sections to the internal properties of the nucleus. The latter may be calculated in detail (although at present only in a few favourable cases), or estimated in a more qualitative way; or the statistics of these properties may be calculated. The most useful formal treatment of this connexion seems to be the R-matrix theory of nuclear reactions, and this will be used throughout this book to aid our understanding of slow neutron cross-section data. The basic idea of the R-matrix theory is to describe the cross-sections in terms of the eigenvalues and eigenfunction values (for particular configurations) close to the surface of the nucleus, the eigenstates being discrete states formed by solving the nuclear Schrödinger equation with boundary conditions imposed at the surface. This idea is common to some other reaction theories (notably that of Kapur and Peierls 1938) but the R-matrix theory has the distinction of using real, energy-independent boundary conditions with the attendant advantages of real eigenfunctions and eigenvalues and energy-independent parameters. There is a great deal of literature on the R-matrix theory, including some detailed reviews; in this chapter we shall therefore give only the barest outline necessary for the understanding of the remainder of the book. More detailed information can be obtained from the original papers of Wigner and Eisenbud (1947), Teichmann and Wigner (1952), Teichmann (1950), and Thomas (1955). The fullest and most detailed review is by Lane and Thomas (1958); a shorter one has been given by Vogt (1959). Breit (1959) has also written a very extensive review on the theory of nuclear reactions, which includes a large amount of R-matrix theory.

The account of R-matrix theory is developed in sections B to E. In section F some of the conceptual difficulties in applying the boundary condition method are encountered, and this leads, in section G, to the discussion of an alternative formal scheme based on the structure of the wave functions of nuclear scattering; this is known as the S-matrix theory and is at present being extensively developed by Humblet and

Rosenfeld and their collaborators. This theory also is required for discussion of various phenomena in subsequent chapters of this book. Its relationship to R-matrix theory is clearly of great importance, and this is discussed to some extent in section H.

B. CONFIGURATION SPACE

1. The internal region

If a total of A nucleons (the sum of those of the target nucleus and of the projectile) are involved in a nuclear reaction the configuration space of the system has $3A$ dimensions. This is formally divided into an internal region and a set of channels. Physically, the internal region corresponds to all A nucleons being in close proximity. It is bounded by a set of channel radii a_c; if the system is subdivided into two sets of nucleons forming composite particles, the pair being labelled by c, then the system is in the internal region if the separations of the composite particles of all such pairs are less than the radii a_c. These radii must be so chosen that the forces between each pair can be described as a simple central force, there being no 'polarizing' action, causing excitations, on the nucleons within the composite particles. Usually the channel radii are chosen to have their minimum values consistent with the above condition. Ideally, this condition is difficult to realize. For example, the Coulomb force between two charged particles has sufficient variation over the extent of the particles, even at distances considerably greater than conventional nuclear radii, to cause appreciable internal excitation of the particles; this is the well-known Coulomb excitation. In practice, however, such long-range polarizing forces can be treated as minor perturbations, and the channel radii are usually regarded as being only a little greater than conventional nuclear force radii.

2. The channels

At low and moderate excitation energies, for which three- (and more) body break-up is not energetically allowed, only certain regions of configuration space outside of the internal region are physically accessible. These are the channels. The channel radii defining the boundaries between the internal and external regions have already been considered above. Here it remains to specify more closely the definition of the pair of particles whose coordinates constitute the channel. The quantities that are specified are:

(*a*) *Type*

The numbers of neutrons and protons in each particle of the pair obviously must be defined. For example, a channel may be that of a neutron and a nucleus containing the remaining $A-1$ nucleons.

(*b*) *State of excitation of each particle*

In the above example, if the nucleus is in its first state of excitation above ground, the channel corresponds physically to the neutron inelastic scattering with smallest energy loss. The neutron, being an elementary particle (from the point of view of low-energy phenomena), does not have higher states of excitation to be specified. The type and excitations of the pair of particles are usually denoted by the subscript α.

(*c*) *Channel spin*

The total angular momentum, I† and i, of each particle is defined by the state of excitation. These are combined vectorially into the channel spin s; schematically,

$$\mathbf{s} = \mathbf{I}+\mathbf{i} \tag{2.1}$$

according to the usual quantal rules; each value of s corresponds to a different channel.

(*d*) *Relative orbital angular momentum of the two particles, l*

(*e*) *Total angular momentum of the system, J*

This is formed from the combination of s and l.

(*f*) *Projections of the above angular momenta on a spatial axis*

That for the channel spin is denoted by ν, that for orbital angular momentum by m and the projection of the total angular momentum is denoted by M.

The complete set of quantities labelling a channel is usually denoted collectively by a lower-case roman alphabetical character such as c.

C. BASIS WAVE-FUNCTIONS

1. Radial wave-functions in the channels

(*a*) *Ingoing and outgoing waves*

Let us consider a particular channel with positive kinetic energy at infinity, E, in the centre of mass system, and let us denote the coordinate

† We use the common abbreviation of the quantum number, i.e. I, to denote the angular momentum which is really $\hbar\sqrt{\{I(I+1)\}}$.

for radial separation of the two particles by r. The Schrödinger equation for the motion of the particles may be separated in the usual way, the solution of the angular part being the spherical harmonics (see e.g. Edmonds 1957) and the radial part having the form,

$$\left[\frac{\mathrm{d}^2}{\mathrm{d}r^2}-\frac{l(l+1)}{r^2}-\frac{2M_\mathrm{c}}{\hbar^2}(V-E)\right]u(r)=0, \tag{2.2}$$

where M_c is the reduced mass $M_1M_2/(M_1+M_2)$ for the relative motion in the channel and $\hbar$ is Planck's constant divided by 2π.

The radial Schrödinger equation for the channel has a general solution composed of a regular component (with zero value at the origin) denoted by $F(r)$ and an irregular component (with a singularity at the origin) denoted by $G(r)$. These may be combined to form functions for ingoing waves $I(r)$ and outgoing waves $O(r)$. For particles without Coulomb interaction, $V = 0$, (e.g. if one of the pair is a neutron),

$$I(r) = G(r)-\mathrm{i}F(r), \tag{2.3a}$$

$$O(r) = G(r)+\mathrm{i}F(r). \tag{2.3b}$$

If the relative orbital angular momentum is l, the regular and irregular components of the solution are related to the spherical Bessel and Neumann functions by

$$F_l(r) = krj_l(kr) \tag{2.3c}$$

$$G_l(r) = -krn_l(kr) \tag{2.3d}$$

where k is the wave-number in the channel,

$$k = \surd(2M_\mathrm{c}E)/\hbar. \tag{2.4}$$

The numerical value of k is $0{\cdot}21968\ M_\mathrm{c}^{\frac{1}{2}}E^{\frac{1}{2}}$ fm^{-1}, the unit of M_c being the neutron mass and E being in MeV. The inverse of the wave-number k is the de Broglie wavelength divided by 2π, $\lambda\!\!\!^{-}$.

In this book we shall mostly be concerned with s-wave neutron channels in which the orbital angular momentum is zero. To a lesser extent p-wave channels ($l = 1$) will also be considered, and d-wave channels ($l = 2$) are on the very fringe of our subject. For these cases F and G are related to the simple trigonometrical functions in the following way:

$$F_0 = \sin(kr), \tag{2.5a}$$

$$G_0 = \cos(kr), \tag{2.5b}$$

$$F_1 = \sin(kr)/(kr) - \cos(kr), \tag{2.5c}$$

$$G_1 = \cos(kr)/(kr) + \sin(kr), \tag{2.5d}$$

$$F_2 = 3\sin(kr)/(kr)^2 - 3\cos(kr)/(kr) - \sin(kr), \tag{2.5e}$$

$$G_2 = 3\cos(kr)/(kr)^2 + 3\sin(kr)/(kr) - \cos(kr). \tag{2.5f}$$

The asymptotic forms of the ingoing and outgoing waves at large radial separation are

$$I_l \sim \exp(-\mathrm{i}kr + \tfrac{1}{2}\mathrm{i}l\pi), \tag{2.6a}$$

$$O_l \sim \exp(+\mathrm{i}kr - \tfrac{1}{2}\mathrm{i}l\pi). \tag{2.6b}$$

For negative energy channels there is a physical boundary condition of vanishing wave-function at infinite radius. The solutions of the radial wave-equation correspond only to outgoing waves, and are related, for zero Coulomb field, to the modified Bessel function of the second kind

$$O_l^- = (2\kappa r/\pi)^{\frac{1}{2}} K_{l+\frac{1}{2}}(\kappa r), \tag{2.7}$$

where $\kappa = (2M_c|E_c|)^{\frac{1}{2}}/\hbar$. For s, p, and d waves this is related to the decaying exponential function by

$$O_0^- = e^{-\kappa r} \tag{2.8a}$$

$$O_1^- = e^{-\kappa r}(1+1/\kappa r) \tag{2.8b}$$

$$O_2^- = e^{-\kappa r}\{1+1/(\kappa r)+1/(\kappa r)^2\} \tag{2.8c}$$

(b) Penetration and shift factors

Important functions of the radial waves are the penetration and shift factors, P and S respectively. These are related to the logarithmic derivative of the outgoing wave at the channel radius, a, by

$$L_l = S_l + \mathrm{i}P_l = \left(\frac{\rho}{O_l}\frac{dO_l}{d\rho}\right)_{r=a}, \tag{2.9}$$

where $\rho = ka$. For s-, p-, and d-wave neutron channels they have the simple forms

$$P_0 = \rho, \tag{2.10a}$$

$$S_0 = 0, \tag{2.10b}$$

$$P_1 = \rho^3/(1+\rho^2), \tag{2.10c}$$

$$S_1 = -1/(1+\rho^2), \tag{2.10d}$$

$$P_2 = \rho^5/(9+3\rho^2+\rho^4), \tag{2.10e}$$

$$S_2 = -3(6+\rho^2)/(9+3\rho^2+\rho^4). \tag{2.10f}$$

For negative energy channels the penetration factors are zero. The shift factors for s-, p-, and d-wave neutron channels are

$$S_0 = -\rho, \tag{2.11a}$$

$$S_1 = -\rho-1/(1+\rho), \tag{2.11b}$$

$$S_2 = -\rho-(3\rho+6)/(\rho^2+3\rho+3), \tag{2.11c}$$

where now $\rho = \kappa a$.

Another function of the radial waves that we shall require, for positive energy channels, is the hard-sphere scattering-phase shift ϕ_l given by

$$\phi_l = \arctan(F_l/G_l). \tag{2.12}$$

For the lowest neutron waves

$$\phi_0 = kr \tag{2.13a}$$

and

$$\phi_1 \approx -(kr)^3/3- \dots \tag{2.13b}$$

for small kr.

(c) Charged-particle channels

The solutions of the radial Schrödinger equation (eqn. 2.2) in the case of a Coulomb interaction ($V = Z_1Z_2e^2/r$, where e is the proton charge and Z_1Z_2 the charge numbers of target and projectile) have been studied particularly thoroughly by Bloch *et al.* (1950, 1951). Convenient asymptotic forms for the incoming and outgoing waves are found to be

$$I_c \sim \exp\{-\mathrm{i}(\rho-\eta \ln 2\rho-\tfrac{1}{2}l\pi+\sigma_0)\}, \tag{2.14a}$$

$$O_c \sim \exp\{\mathrm{i}(\rho-\eta \ln 2\rho-\tfrac{1}{2}l\pi+\sigma_0)\}, \tag{2.14b}$$

where $\eta = Z_1Z_2e^2M_c/\hbar^2k$ and the Coulomb phase shift $\sigma_l = \arg \Gamma(l+1+\mathrm{i}\eta)$. The regular and irregular solutions of eqn. (2.2) have the asymptotic forms

$$F_l \sim \sin(\rho-\eta \ln 2\rho-\tfrac{1}{2}l\pi+\sigma_l) \tag{2.14c}$$

$$G_l \sim \cos(\rho-\eta \ln 2\rho-\tfrac{1}{2}l\pi+\sigma_l). \tag{2.14d}$$

These functions, and the penetration and shift factors derived from them, normally have to be computed by direct numerical integration of eqn. (2.2). Tabulations of the results of such computations are presented by Bloch *et al.* (1951). Occasionally conditions are suitable for applying the JWKB approximation for the calculation of the penetrability of potential barriers (see e.g. Mott and Sneddon 1948). In this a local wave-number is computed at the radial distance r,

$$\kappa_l(r) = \left\{k^2 - \frac{2M_c}{\hbar^2}V(r) - \frac{l(l+1)}{\hbar^2}\right\}^{\frac{1}{2}}. \tag{2.15a}$$

The classical distance of closest approach r_0 for particles of angular momentum l is given by $\kappa_l(r) = 0$. The WKB approximation gives for particles passing above the barrier

$$(V(a)+\hbar^2 l(l+1)/2M_c < \hbar^2 k_c^2/2M_c)$$

$$P_l \approx a\kappa_l(a) \tag{2.15b}$$

$$S_l \approx -\tfrac{1}{2}a\{\kappa'_l(a)/\kappa_l(a)\}. \tag{2.15c}$$

For particles tunnelling through the barrier

$$(V(a)+\hbar^2 l(l+1)/2M_c > \hbar^2 k_c^2/2M_c^2)$$

$$P_l \approx a\kappa_l(a)\exp\left\{-2\int\limits_a^{r_0}\kappa_l(r)\,dr\right\}. \tag{2.15d}$$

$$S_l \approx -a\{\kappa_l(a)+\tfrac{1}{2}\kappa'_l(a)/\kappa_l(a)\}. \tag{2.15e}$$

Equation (2.15d) exhibits the well-known Gamow factor for potential tunnelling. These formulae are fairly accurate if $2\rho\eta+l(l+1)$ is large compared with ρ^2 and with η.

2. Channel functions

The complete wave-function of relative motion in the channel has the form

$$\psi = r^{-1}u(r)\mathrm{i}^l Y_m^{(l)}(\theta, \phi). \tag{2.16}$$

The radial functions u have already been considered above. The $Y_m^{(l)}(\theta, \phi)$ are the usual spherical harmonics of the angular variables θ and ϕ.

A wave-function giving a complete description of the channel must also include the internal wave-functions of the particles and their combined spin, the channel spin. These are usually lumped together into a channel-spin function $\psi_{\alpha s\nu}$. These in turn are combined with the function of relative motion, omitting the radial function, to give the channel surface functions

$$\varphi_{\alpha slvm} = r^{-1}\psi_{\alpha sv}(\mathrm{i}^l Y_m^{(l)}), \tag{2.17}$$

which have the property of orthonormality over the surface corresponding to all save the radial coordinate of the channel particles.

The complete channel wave-functions corresponding to ingoing and outgoing waves of unit flux crossing a sphere with its centre at the origin are respectively:

$$\mathscr{I}_{\alpha svlm} = \varphi_{\alpha svlm} I_{\alpha l}/v_\alpha^{\frac{1}{2}}, \tag{2.18a}$$

$$\mathscr{O}_{\alpha svlm} = \varphi_{\alpha svlm} O_{\alpha l}/v_\alpha^{\frac{1}{2}}. \tag{2.18b}$$

An alternative set of channel-surface functions, also with the property of orthonormality, is obtained by coupling the $\varphi_{\alpha svlm}$ with different v and m to obtain the functions $\varphi_{\alpha slJM}$ with given total angular momentum J and projection M.

3. Eigenfunctions of the internal region for R-matrix theory

Eigenfunctions for the internal region are defined as solutions of the nuclear Schrödinger equation in the internal region,

$$HX_\lambda = E_\lambda X_\lambda \tag{2.19}$$

with energy-independent, real boundary conditions applied to the surface. The application of such boundary conditions causes the eigenvalues E_λ to be discrete (and real) even in the continuum region. The eigenfunctions are also real.

The projection of the value of an eigenfunction X_λ upon the surface at the entrance to a particular channel c is denoted by $\gamma_{\lambda(\mathrm{c})}$ and may be expressed

$$\gamma_{\lambda(\mathrm{c})} = \left(\frac{\hbar^2}{2M_\mathrm{c}a_\mathrm{c}}\right)^{\frac{1}{2}} \int\limits_{r_\mathrm{c}=a_\mathrm{c}} \varphi_\mathrm{c}^* X_\lambda \mathrm{d}\mathscr{S}_\mathrm{c} \tag{2.20a}$$

with a suitable normalization constant $\sqrt{(\hbar^2/2M_\mathrm{c}a_\mathrm{c})}$. The projection of the radial derivative of X_λ with respect to r at the entrance to the same channel is

$$\delta_{\lambda(\mathrm{c})} = \gamma_{\lambda(\mathrm{c})} + \left(\frac{a_\mathrm{c}\hbar^2}{2M_\mathrm{c}}\right)^{\frac{1}{2}} \int\limits_{r_\mathrm{c}=a_\mathrm{c}} \varphi_\mathrm{c}^* \,\mathrm{grad}_\mathrm{n} X_\lambda \mathrm{d}\mathscr{S}_\mathrm{c}. \tag{2.20b}$$

The real boundary conditions applied to the states X_λ at the surface $\mathscr{S}_c$ of the internal region at channel c have the form

$$\delta_{\lambda(c)}/\gamma_{\lambda(c)} = B_c. \tag{2.20c}$$

The important property of the orthogonality of the X_λ is established by the use of Green's theorem (in many-dimensional configuration space). The Schrödinger equation is written down for two energies, E_1 and E_2:

$$H\Psi_1 = E_1\Psi_1,\ H\Psi_2 = E_2\Psi_2. \tag{2.19a}$$

The equation

$$(E_2-E_1)\int_\tau \Psi_2^*\Psi_1\,d\tau = \int_\tau \{(H\Psi_2)^*\Psi_1-\Psi_2^*H(\Psi_1)\}\,d\tau \tag{2.21}$$

is obtained by multiplying the first equation by $\Psi_2{}^*$, the complex conjugate of the second by Ψ_1, and integration of the difference over the internal region τ. Assuming the usual self-adjoint property of the potential energy terms V of the Hamiltonian H,

$$\int_\tau \{(V\Psi_2)^*\Psi_1-\Psi_2^*V\Psi_1\}\,d\tau = 0, \tag{2.22}$$

the integral involving the kinetic energy terms of eqn. (2.21), is reduced, by means of Green's theorem, to a surface integral. Thus, eqn. (2.21) becomes

$$(E_2-E_1)\int_\tau \Psi_2{}^*\Psi_1 d\tau = \int_{\mathscr{S}} \left(\frac{\hbar^2}{2M_c}\right)(\Psi_2^*\nabla_n\Psi_1-\Psi_1\nabla_n\Psi_2^*)\,d\mathscr{S}, \tag{2.23}$$

where $\mathscr{S}$, the entire surface of the internal region, is bounded by the radii $r_c = a_c$.

By choosing E_1 and E_2 to be eigenvalues (with eigensolutions X_1 and X_2) it is evident that

$$(E_2-E_1)\int_\tau X_2^*X_1\,d\tau = \sum_c(\gamma_{2(c)}^*\delta_{1(c)}-\gamma\delta_{2(c)}^*) \tag{2.24}$$

and application of the boundary condition, eqn. (2.20c), leads to the required orthogonality

$$\int_\tau X_\mu^*X_\lambda\,d\tau = \delta_{\lambda\mu}. \tag{2.25}$$

D. RELATION OF THE CROSS-SECTION TO THE INTERNAL EIGENFUNCTIONS: THE R-MATRIX THEORY

1. Expansion of the internal wave-function

Because of the orthogonality of the internal basis functions X_λ, it is possible to expand the wave-function, at energy E, in the internal region in terms of them:

$$\Psi = \sum_\lambda A_\lambda X_\lambda. \tag{2.26}$$

In the usual way (multiplication of both sides of eqn. (2.26) by X_λ^* and integration) it may be shown that the expansion coefficients A_λ have the form

$$A_\lambda = \int_\tau \mathrm{d}\tau X_\lambda^* \Psi. \tag{2.27}$$

These can be related to the derivatives D_c of Ψ at the entrances to the channels c by use of the Green's theorem relation of eqn. (2.23) to obtain

$$A_\lambda = (E_\lambda - E)^{-1} \sum_c \hat{D}_c \gamma_{\lambda(c)}, \tag{2.28}$$

where $D_c = D_c - B_c V_c$, V_c being the projected value of Ψ at the channel entrance; these projected values and derivatives are formally related to Ψ by relations perfectly analogous to eqn. (2.20). Equation (2.26) thus leads to the R-matrix relation between the values and derivatives of the internal wave-function at the channel entrances,

$$V_{c'} = \sum_c R_{c'c} \hat{D}_c, \tag{2.29}$$

where

$$R_{c'c} = \sum_\lambda \gamma_{\lambda(c)} \gamma_{\lambda(c')} / (E_\lambda - E). \tag{2.30}$$

In matrix notation eqn. (2.29) is written

$$\mathbf{V} = \mathbf{R}\hat{\mathbf{D}}, \tag{2.29a}$$

$\mathbf{V}$ and $\hat{\mathbf{D}}$ being column and row matrices (vectors) respectively, while $\mathbf{R}$ is a square matrix.

2. Matching of internal and channel wave-functions

(a) Expansion of a plane wave into spherical components

An incident plane wave of neutral particles moving in the z-direction has the well-known expansion (see e.g. Blatt and Weisskop 1952)

$$\frac{1}{v^{\frac{1}{2}}}\exp(ikz)\psi_{\alpha s\nu} = \frac{\pi^{\frac{1}{2}}}{krv^{\frac{1}{2}}}\sum_{l=0}^{\infty}(2l+1)^{\frac{1}{2}}\mathrm{i}^{l}(I_l - O_l)\,Y_0^{(l)}\psi_{\alpha s\nu}$$

$$= \frac{\pi^{\frac{1}{2}}}{k}\sum_{l=0}^{\infty}(2l+1)^{\frac{1}{2}}(\mathscr{I}_{\alpha s\nu l0} - \mathscr{O}_{\alpha s\nu l0}). \tag{2.31}$$

The constant involving v, the relative wave velocity, on the left-hand side has the effect of normalizing the wave to unit flux.

Equation (2.31) is the expansion of a plane wave of particles of given type, excitation, and polarization. It is convenient to be able to express this expansion in terms of components of given total angular momentum J and projection M. In fact, since the orbital angular momentum projection is zero, the total projection M is just that of the channel spin. We have

$$\frac{1}{v^{\frac{1}{2}}}\exp(ikz)\psi_{\alpha s\nu(=M)}$$

$$= \frac{\pi^{\frac{1}{2}}}{k}\sum_{l=0}^{\infty}(2l+1)^{\frac{1}{2}}\sum_{J=|l-s|}^{l+s}C_{JM(ls,0\nu)}(\mathscr{I}_{\alpha slJM} - \mathscr{O}_{\alpha slJM}), \tag{2.32}$$

where $C_{JM(lsm\nu)}$ is the Clebsch–Gordan coefficient for vector coupling (see e.g. Edmonds 1957).

(b) *Modification of a spherical component by scattering*

If there is a scattering centre at the origin, $r = 0$, the amplitudes of the outgoing waves of the expansion (2.31) or (2.32) will be disturbed. This is described by the introduction of a coefficient $U_{cc}(=U_{\alpha slJM,\alpha slJM})$ before the outgoing wave term $\mathscr{O}_c$.

If there is not only scattering but reaction at the origin, outgoing waves will be produced in other channels c′ not included in the spherical analysis of the plane wave. Their amplitudes, relative to those of the incoming waves c, are described by the coefficients $U_{c'c}$,

$$\Psi_{c'} = -U_{c'c}\mathscr{O}_{c'} \tag{2.33a}$$

If the channel c′ has a negative energy it is necessary to use the quantity $\mathscr{U}_{c'c}$ to define the wave-function in channel c′. The collision matrix element is related to $U_{c'c}$ by

$$U_{c'c} = \surd(v_{c'}/v_c)\mathscr{U}_{c'c} \tag{2.33b}$$

and the wave-function is written

$$\Psi_{c'} = -\mathscr{U}_{c'c}\varphi_c\mathscr{O}_c/v_c^{\frac{1}{2}}. \tag{2.33c}$$

(c) The collision matrix

The relative amplitudes $U_{c'c}$ collectively form the collision matrix. The general solution of the wave-function in the external region can be expressed in terms of them and the coefficients of the incoming waves, y_c:

$$\Psi = \sum_{cc'} (\delta_{c'c}\mathscr{I}_c - U_{c'c}\mathscr{O}_{c'})y_c. \tag{2.34}$$

We see from eqn. (2.32) that, for a plane wave of neutral particles of unit flux, the coefficients y_c have the form

$$y_c = y_{\alpha slJM(=\nu)} = \frac{\pi^{\frac{1}{2}}}{k}(2l+1)^{\frac{1}{2}}C_{JM(ls,0M)}. \tag{2.35}$$

The scattered wave in any channel c′ may be defined as the difference between the actual wave-function Ψ in the channel and the incident plane wave,

$$\Psi_{\text{scat, in c}'} = \sum_c y_c(\delta_{c'c} - U_{c'c})\mathscr{O}_{c'}. \tag{2.36}$$

The collision matrix has important general properties that can be established without the use of a particular reaction theory. One is the property of unitarity which expresses the conservation of probability flux in the stationary wave representation of the nuclear reaction. It may be established by use of Green's theorem, eqn. (2.23), for a very large surface $\mathscr{S}$. The explicit form of the relation is

$$\sum_c U^*_{cc'} U_{cc''} = \delta_{c'c''}. \tag{2.37}$$

The collision matrix also has the property of symmetry, $U_{cc'} = U_{c'c}$; this follows from the condition of time reversibility of the system.

(d) Cross-sections (for electrically-neutral incident particles)

Cross-sections may be obtained from the collision matrix elements $U_{c'c}$. A cross-section is defined as the ratio of number of events of a given kind per unit time per nucleus to the number of incident particles per unit area per unit time.

The scattered flux for a particular element of solid angle $d\Omega_c$ may be obtained from the well-known expression of quantum mechanics for the probability flux at a radial distance r_c:

$$N_{c'}\mathrm{d}\Omega_{c'} = \frac{\hbar}{2iM_{c'}} \int\limits_{\substack{\text{all except}\\ c' \text{ spatial co-ordinates}}} \mathrm{d}\tau$$

$$\left(\frac{\partial\Psi_{\text{scat, in }c'}}{\partial r_{c'}}\Psi^*_{\text{scat, in }c'} - \frac{\partial\Psi^*_{\text{scat, in }c'}}{\partial r_{c'}}\Psi_{\text{scat, in }c'}\right) r^2\mathrm{d}\Omega_{c'}. \quad (2.38)$$

Substituting from eqns. (2.35), (2.36), and (2.16) we find the scattered flux for neutral particles, for given channel spin s and total angular momentum J, M. Since the expressions have been written down for unit flux, this expression is the cross-section for the reaction c, c′, and since the orbital angular momentum of the reaction products is not to be distinguished we must sum over l' to obtain

$$\mathrm{d}\sigma_{\alpha s\nu,\alpha' s'\nu'}(J, M) = \frac{\pi}{k_\alpha^2} \sum_{l'=|J-s'|}^{J+s'} \left| \sum_{l=|J-s|}^{J+s} (2l+1)^{\frac{1}{2}} C_{JM(ls,0\nu)} \right.$$

$$\left. \times (\delta_{\alpha' s' l' JM,\alpha s l JM} - U_{\alpha' s' l' JM,\alpha s l JM}) Y_{m'}^{(l')} \right|^2 \quad (2.39)$$

where $\nu' = M - m'$. This expression is for *open* channels. Equation (2.38) gives zero if c′ is a closed channel.

If the cross-section for unpolarized particles is required, eqn. (2.39) must be averaged over the orientations $\nu = M$ of the incident particles and summed over the orientations ν' of the outgoing particles:

$$\frac{\mathrm{d}\sigma_{\alpha s,\alpha' s'}(J)}{\mathrm{d}\Omega_{\alpha'}} = \frac{1}{2s+1} \sum_{\nu,\nu'} \frac{\mathrm{d}\sigma_{\alpha s\nu,\alpha' s'\nu'}}{\mathrm{d}\Omega_{\alpha'}}. \quad (2.40)$$

Reference to the channel spins of the particles is excluded by averaging over s and summing over s';

$$\frac{\mathrm{d}\sigma_{\alpha,\alpha'}(J)}{\mathrm{d}\Omega_{\alpha'}} = \frac{1}{(2i+1)(2I+1)} \sum_{ss'\nu\nu'} \frac{\mathrm{d}\sigma_{\alpha s\nu,\alpha' s'\nu'}}{\mathrm{d}\Omega_{\alpha'}}. \quad (2.41)$$

Cross-sections integrated over the solid angle $\Omega_{\alpha'}$ are obtained by using certain relations of the Clebsch–Gordan coefficients. The result, for the component of total angular momentum J, is:

$$\sigma_{\alpha,\alpha'}(J) = \frac{\pi}{k_\alpha^2} \frac{(2J+1)}{(2i+1)(2I+1)} \sum_{s,s'=|I-i|}^{I+i} \sum_{l=|J-s|}^{J+s} \sum_{l'=|J-s'|}^{J+s'}$$

$$\times |\delta_{\alpha' s' l',\alpha s l} - U_{\alpha' s' l',\alpha s l}(J)|^2. \quad (2.42)$$

The total cross-section, the sum of the above over all α', is obtained from the unitarity of U. It is

$$\sigma_{\alpha,\mathrm{T}}(J) = \frac{2\pi}{k_\alpha^2} g_J \sum_{s=|I-i|}^{I+i} \sum_{l=|J-s|}^{J+s} \{1-\mathrm{Re}\, U_{\alpha sl,\alpha sl}(J)\}, \tag{2.43}$$

where g_J is the spin-weighting factor $(2J+1)/\{(2i+1)(2I+1)\}$.

In eqns. (2.42) and (2.43) explicit reference to one important quantum number has been omitted. This is parity: its effect is to provide a further limitation on the orbital angular momenta l and l' occurring in the sums. Thus, the label α denoting type and excitation of bombarding particle and target also includes the products of their parities (π_α, say). We shall often require the cross-section for the process to have gone through a compound system with given parity π_c as well as total angular momentum J. In this case the orbital angular momenta l, l' will be limited by the requirements

$$\pi_\alpha(-)^l = \pi_\mathrm{c} = \pi_{\alpha'}(-)^{l'}. \tag{2.44}$$

Implicitly, of course, parity is necessarily included in eqns. (2.39)–(2.43) by virtue of the quantum numbers α, s, l, and J.

(e) *Relation between the R-matrix and collision matrix*

In the external region the wave-function is a superposition of incoming and outgoing waves as expressed by eqn. (2.34). The 'value' and 'derivative' quantities for this wave-function (analogous to the $\gamma_{\lambda(\mathrm{c})}$ and $\delta_{\lambda(\mathrm{c})}$ of eqns. (2.20) for the internal eigenfunction) at the entrance to a channel c are

$$V_\mathrm{c} = \left(\frac{\hbar^2}{2M_\mathrm{c}a_\mathrm{c}}\right)^{\frac{1}{2}} \frac{1}{v_\mathrm{c}^{\frac{1}{2}}} \left\{y_\mathrm{c} I_\mathrm{c} - \left(\sum_{\mathrm{c}'} y_{\mathrm{c}'} U_{\mathrm{cc}'}\right) O_\mathrm{c}\right\}, \tag{2.45}$$

$$D_\mathrm{c} = \left(\frac{\rho_\mathrm{c}{}^2\hbar^2}{2M_\mathrm{c}a_\mathrm{c}}\right)^{\frac{1}{2}} \frac{1}{v_\mathrm{c}^{\frac{1}{2}}} \left\{y_\mathrm{c} \frac{\partial I_\mathrm{c}}{\partial \rho_\mathrm{c}} - \left(\sum_{\mathrm{c}'} y_{\mathrm{c}'} U_{\mathrm{cc}'}\right) \frac{\partial O_\mathrm{c}}{\partial \rho_\mathrm{c}}\right\}. \tag{2.46}$$

In order to match smoothly with the internal wave-function at the channel entrance, these quantities must satisfy the same R-matrix relation, eqn. (2.29), satisfied by the internal wave-function at the same energy E. Substitution of eqns. (2.45) and (2.46) into eqn. (2.29) and rearrangement with the use of eqn. (2.9) leads to the relation between the collision matrix and R-matrix

$$\mathbf{U} = \mathbf{\Omega} \mathbf{P}^{\frac{1}{2}} \{\mathbf{1} - \mathbf{R}(\mathbf{L} - \mathbf{B})\}^{-1} \{\mathbf{1} - \mathbf{R}(\mathbf{L}^* - \mathbf{B})\} \mathbf{P}^{-\frac{1}{2}} \mathbf{\Omega}. \tag{2.47}$$

Here, $\Omega_c = (I_c/O_c)_{r_c=a_c}$. For neutral particles this is simply $\Omega_c = \exp(-i\phi_c)$. The matrices $\mathbf{\Omega}$, $\mathbf{P}$, $\mathbf{L}$, and $\mathbf{B}$ are to be thought of as square diagonal matrices in eqn. (47), i.e. Ω_c is the element Ω_{cc} of $\mathbf{\Omega}$ etc., and the off-diagonal elements are zero. The establishment of eqn. (2.47) finally allows us to express the cross-sections in terms of the eigenvalues E_λ and eigenfunctions X_λ of the internal region.

It is easy to establish by matrix multiplication of the right-hand side of eqn. (2.47) into its complex conjugate that, because of the reality of $\mathbf{R}$, the R-matrix expression for the collision matrix has the necessary property of unitarity as expressed in eqn. (2.37). It can also be shown that, as a consequence of the symmetry of $\mathbf{R}$, the form of the collision matrix in eqn. (2.47) has the property of symmetry.

E. ALTERNATIVE FORMULATIONS AND APPROXIMATIONS TO THE R-MATRIX THEORY

1. The level matrix formulation

Equation (2.47) is, in general, much too complicated for practical use. In the usual case of nuclear reactions there are very many channels available as well as an infinite number of eigenstates. Usually, many of the channels will be closed but this fact is not expressed in the R-matrix and formally we are faced with the problem of inverting the matrix of very large order $\{\mathbf{1}-\mathbf{R}(\mathbf{L}-\mathbf{B})\}$.

It is possible, however, to transform the collision matrix from its form in eqn. (2.47) to a form involving the inversion of a level matrix. The procedure is to assume that

$$\left\{\mathbf{1}-\mathbf{R}(\mathbf{L}-\mathbf{B})\right\}^{-1}_{\mathrm{ab}} = \delta_{\mathrm{ab}}+\sum_{\mu\nu}\gamma_{\mu(\mathrm{a})}(L_{\mathrm{b}}-B_{\mathrm{b}})\gamma_{\nu(\mathrm{b})}A_{\mu\nu}$$

and then to find the form of $\mathbf{A}$ that satisfies this expression. We give the result here and refer to Thomas (1955) and Lane and Thomas (1958) for the mathematical details. The new form of the collision matrix is

$$U_{\mathrm{ab}} = \Omega_{\mathrm{a}}\Omega_{\mathrm{b}}\left\{\delta_{\mathrm{ab}}+2\mathrm{i}P^{\frac{1}{2}}_{\mathrm{a}}\sum_{\lambda\mu}\gamma_{\lambda(\mathrm{a})}\gamma_{\mu(\mathrm{b})}A_{\lambda\mu}P^{\frac{1}{2}}_{\mathrm{b}}\right\}, \tag{2.48}$$

where the reciprocal level matrix $\mathbf{A}$ is the inverse of $\mathbf{C}$ which has elements

$$C_{\lambda\mu} = (E_\lambda-E)\delta_{\lambda\mu}-\sum_{\mathrm{c}}L_{\mathrm{c}}\gamma_{\lambda(\mathrm{c})}\gamma_{\mu(\mathrm{c})}, \tag{2.49a}$$

$$=(E_\lambda-E)\delta_{\lambda\mu}-\Delta_{\lambda\mu}-\tfrac{1}{2}\mathrm{i}\Gamma_{\lambda\mu}. \tag{2.49b}$$

In the last line $\Delta_{\lambda\mu} = \sum_c S_c \gamma_{\lambda(c)}\gamma_{\mu(c)}$, $\Gamma_{\lambda\mu} = \sum_c 2P_c \gamma_{\lambda(c)}\gamma_{\mu(c)}$. The abbreviations Δ_λ, Γ_λ are normally adopted for $\Delta_{\lambda\lambda}$ and $\Gamma_{\lambda\lambda}$. Although formally the level matrix $\mathbf{C}$ is of infinite order it is easy in many actual physical situations to justify its approximation by a small finite section of it referring to only a few levels.

Approximations of this type can be made more general by making a preliminary division of the R-matrix into two parts,

$$\mathbf{R} = \mathbf{R}^\circ + \mathbf{R}' \tag{2.50}$$

of which $\mathbf{R}'$ is to be treated by the level-matrix method. The matrix product $(\mathbf{1}-\mathbf{R}\hat{\mathbf{L}})^{-1}\mathbf{R}$ can be written

$$(\mathbf{1}-\mathbf{R}\hat{\mathbf{L}})^{-1}\mathbf{R} = (\mathbf{1}-\mathbf{R}^\circ\hat{\mathbf{L}})^{-1}\mathbf{R}^\circ + (\mathbf{1}-\mathbf{R}^\circ\hat{\mathbf{L}})^{-1}(\mathbf{1}-\mathbf{R}'\hat{\mathbf{L}}')^{-1}\mathbf{R}'(\mathbf{1}-\hat{\mathbf{L}}\mathbf{R}^\circ)^{-1}, \tag{2.51}$$

in which $\hat{\mathbf{L}} = \mathbf{L}-\mathbf{B}$ and $\hat{\mathbf{L}}' = \hat{\mathbf{L}}(\mathbf{1}-\mathbf{R}^\circ\hat{\mathbf{L}})^{-1} = \mathbf{S}'+\mathrm{i}\mathbf{P}'$. If $\mathbf{R}^\circ$ is diagonal the terms of the type $\mathbf{1}-\mathbf{R}^\circ\hat{\mathbf{L}}^\circ$ are perfectly straight-forward to invert. In this case the result for the collision matrix is

$$U_{\mathrm{ab}} = \Omega_{\mathrm{a}}\Omega_{\mathrm{b}}\left[\delta_{\mathrm{ab}} + 2\mathrm{i}P_{\mathrm{a}}^{\frac{1}{2}}P_{\mathrm{b}}^{\frac{1}{2}}\left\{(1-R^\circ_{\mathrm{aa}}L_{\mathrm{a}})^{-1}R^\circ_{\mathrm{aa}}\delta_{\mathrm{ab}} + \frac{1}{(1-R^\circ_{\mathrm{aa}}\hat{L}_{\mathrm{a}})(1-R^\circ_{\mathrm{bb}}\hat{L}_{\mathrm{b}})}\sum_{\lambda\mu}\gamma_{\lambda(\mathrm{a})}\gamma_{\mu(\mathrm{b})}A_{\lambda\mu}\right\}\right], \tag{2.52}$$

for which the level matrix is obtained by substitution of $\hat{L}'$ (rather than $\hat{L}$) in eqn. (2.49).

The level matrix expansion also leads to a most useful result for the internal wave-function of the system when there is unit incoming flux in channel c (Lane and Thomas 1958). It is

$$\Psi^{(c)} = -\mathrm{i}\hbar^{\frac{1}{2}}\mathrm{e}^{-\mathrm{i}\phi_c}\sum_{\lambda\mu}A_{\lambda\mu}\Gamma^{\frac{1}{2}}_{\mu(c)}X_\lambda \tag{2.53}$$

This follows by establishing the derivatives D_c for unit incoming flux in a particular channel, using eqns. (2.46) and (2.52). These may then be used to calculate the expansion coefficients (eqn. (2.28)) for the expansion of the wave function Ψ in eqn. (2.26).

2. The reduced R-matrix formulation

An alternative method of dealing with the R-matrix is to introduce an auxiliary matrix of smaller order, the reduced R-matrix (Teichmann and Wigner 1952, Thomas 1955). In the practical analysis of a cross-section one is normally concerned with only a comparatively small number of channels for which, for example, the partial cross-sections may be available. In such a situation one requires only the section of the collision matrix referring to those particular channels, and explicit reference to all other channels may be eliminated. The channels included in this submatrix $(\mathbf{U})_{\mathrm{rr}}$ are named 'retained' and are denoted by the subscript r, while the remainder are named 'eliminated', denoted by subscript e. The relationship between values and derivatives for the retained channels is analogous to the full R-matrix relation, eqn. (2.29),

$$\mathbf{V}_{\mathrm{r}} = \mathscr{R}_{\mathrm{rr}}\hat{\mathbf{D}}_{\mathrm{r}}, \tag{2.54}$$

but here $\mathscr{R}_{\mathrm{rr}}$ is the *reduced* R-matrix and is related to the 'retained' and 'eliminated' submatrices of the full R-matrix by

$$\mathscr{R}_{\mathrm{rr}} = \mathbf{R}_{\mathrm{rr}}+\mathbf{R}_{\mathrm{re}}\hat{\mathbf{L}}_{\mathrm{e}}(\mathbf{1}-\mathbf{R}_{\mathrm{ee}}\hat{\mathbf{L}}_{\mathrm{e}})^{-1}\mathbf{R}_{\mathrm{er}}. \tag{2.55}$$

The retained collision sub-matrix bears the same relation to the reduced R-matrix as the full collision matrix does to the R-matrix (eqn. 2.47):

$$\mathbf{U}_{\mathrm{rr}} = \Omega_{\mathrm{r}}\mathbf{P}_{\mathrm{r}}^{\frac{1}{2}}(\mathbf{1}-\mathscr{R}_{\mathrm{rr}}\hat{\mathbf{L}}_{\mathrm{r}})^{-1}(\mathbf{1}-\mathscr{R}_{\mathrm{rr}}\hat{\mathbf{L}}_{\mathrm{r}}^{*})\mathbf{P}_{\mathrm{r}}^{-\frac{1}{2}}\Omega_{\mathrm{r}}. \tag{2.56}$$

These results are demonstrated by Lane and Thomas (1958).

The inversion of the matrix $(\mathbf{1}-\mathbf{R}_{\mathrm{ee}}\hat{\mathbf{L}}_{\mathrm{e}})$ which occurs in the expression for the reduced R-matrix, may be accomplished by the level-matrix method of Section II.E.1. The resulting expression for the reduced R-matrix is

$$(\mathscr{R}_{\mathrm{rr}})_{cc'} = \sum_{\lambda\mu}\gamma_{\lambda(c)}\gamma_{\mu(c')}A^{\mathrm{e}}_{\mu\lambda}. \tag{2.57}$$

The reciprocal level matrix $\mathbf{A}^{\mathrm{e}}$ has the same form as $\mathbf{A}$ of eqn. (2.48) but it and its inverse $\mathbf{C}^{\mathrm{e}}$ refer only to the eliminated channels:

$$C^{\mathrm{e}}_{\mu\lambda} = (E_{\lambda}-E)\delta_{\lambda\mu}-\sum_{\substack{c''\text{ only in}\\ \text{group e}}} L_{c''}\gamma_{\lambda(c'')}\gamma_{\mu(c'')}. \tag{2.58}$$

An important special case of the reduced R-matrix theory occurs if the group of eliminated channels includes only those with partial widths $2P_{c''}\gamma_{\lambda}^{2}{}_{(c'')}$ that are much smaller than the level spacings and with reduced width amplitudes that are uncorrelated in sign. Then, the off-diagonal elements of the matrix $\mathbf{C}^{\mathrm{e}}$ are negligible in comparison with the diagonal elements and a good approximation to the reciprocal level matrix $\mathbf{A}^{\mathrm{e}}$ is

$$A^{\mathrm{e}}_{\lambda\mu} = \delta_{\lambda\mu}(E_\lambda - E - \Delta^{\mathrm{e}}_\lambda - \tfrac{1}{2}\mathrm{i}\Gamma^{\mathrm{e}}_\lambda)^{-1} \tag{2.59}$$

where

$$\Delta^{\mathrm{e}}_\lambda = \sum_{\mathrm{c}'' \text{ in e}} \hat{\mathrm{S}}_{\mathrm{c}''}\gamma^2_{\lambda(\mathrm{c}'')}, \quad \Gamma^{\mathrm{e}}_\lambda = 2\sum_{\mathrm{c}'' \text{ in e}} P_{\mathrm{c}''}\gamma^2_{\lambda(\mathrm{c}'')}.$$

The reduced R-matrix thus has the simple form

$$(\mathscr{R}_{\mathrm{rr}})_{\mathrm{cc}'} \approx \sum_\lambda \frac{\gamma_{\lambda(\mathrm{c})}\gamma_{\lambda(\mathrm{c}')}}{E_\lambda - \Delta^{\mathrm{e}}_\lambda - \mathrm{E} - \frac{1}{2}\mathrm{i}\Gamma^{\mathrm{e}}_\lambda}, \tag{2.60}$$

the eliminated channels appearing as an 'absorption' width in the denominator of the conventional R-matrix form.

3. The Breit–Wigner single-level formula

(a) *Single level without background*

The Breit–Wigner single-level formula is of major importance in the study of low-energy nuclear reactions. We have already indicated in Chapter I that its use in the analysis of neutron spectroscopy data is most extensive, and we quoted the formula in the form most commonly used for s-wave neutron interactions. Here, we show how it may be derived from the general R-matrix reaction theory.

The essence of the single-level approximation is to replace the sum over levels for the element of the R-matrix (eqn. (2.30)) by a single term (that for $\lambda = 0$, say)

$$R_{\mathrm{ab}} = \frac{\gamma_{0(\mathrm{a})}\gamma_{0(\mathrm{b})}}{E_0 - E}. \tag{2.61}$$

This approximation to $\mathbf{R}$ has the property that repeated multiplications of the type $(\mathbf{R}\hat{\mathbf{L}})^n$ have the simple form

$$\{(\mathbf{R}\hat{\mathbf{L}})^n\}_{\mathrm{ab}} = T^{n-1}R_{\mathrm{ab}}\hat{L}_{\mathrm{bb}}, \tag{2.62}$$

where $T = \sum_{\mathrm{c}}\gamma^2_{0(\mathrm{c})}\hat{L}_{\mathrm{cc}}/(E_0 - E)$. This allows the evaluation of functions of $\mathbf{R}$, e.g.

$$\{(\mathbf{1} - \mathbf{R}\hat{\mathbf{L}})^{-1}\}_{\mathrm{ab}} = \delta_{\mathrm{ab}} + \frac{R_{\mathrm{ab}}\hat{L}_{\mathrm{bb}}}{1 - T}, \tag{2.63}$$

which can be checked, using eqn. (2.62) by multiplying $(\mathbf{1} - \mathbf{R}\hat{\mathbf{L}})$ into $(\mathbf{1} + \mathbf{R}\hat{\mathbf{L}}/(1 - T))$. Substitution of eqn. (2.63) into eqn. (2.47) leads to

$$U_{\mathrm{ab}} = \Omega_{\mathrm{a}}\Omega_{\mathrm{b}}\left\{\delta_{\mathrm{ab}}+\frac{\mathrm{i}\Gamma^{\frac{1}{2}}_{0(\mathrm{a})}\Gamma^{\frac{1}{2}}_{0(\mathrm{b})}}{E_0-\Delta_0-E-\frac{1}{2}\mathrm{i}\Gamma_0}\right\}, \tag{2.64}$$

where $\Gamma_{0(\mathrm{a})} = 2P_{\mathrm{a}}\gamma^2_{0(\mathrm{a})}$, $\Delta_0 = \sum_{\mathrm{c}} \hat{S}_{\mathrm{c}}\gamma^2_{0(\mathrm{c})}$, $\Gamma_0 = 2\sum_{\mathrm{c}} P_{\mathrm{c}}\gamma^2_{0(\mathrm{c})} = \sum_{\mathrm{c}}\Gamma_{0(\mathrm{c})}$.

The same result is obtained from eqn. (2.48) if the reciprocal level matrix **A** is restricted to order unity, referring only to the level $\lambda = 0$.

The substitution of eqn. (2.64) into eqn. (2.42) gives the Breit–Wigner formula for the elastic scattering cross-section,

$$\sigma_{\alpha\alpha} = \pi\lambda^2_{\alpha}\left\{\sum_{J'sl} 4g_{J'}\sin^2\phi_l - \frac{2g_J\sum'_{sl}\Gamma_{0(\alpha sl)}\{(E_0-\Delta_0-E)\sin 2\phi_l+\frac{1}{2}\Gamma_0(1-\cos 2\phi_l)\}}{(E_0-\Delta_0-E)^2+(\frac{1}{2}\Gamma_0)^2} + \frac{g_J\sum'_{sl}\Gamma_{0(\alpha sl)}\sum'_{s'l'}\Gamma_{0(\alpha s'l')}}{(E_0-\Delta_0-E)^2+(\frac{1}{2}\Gamma_0)^2}\right\} \tag{2.65}$$

The level $\lambda = 0$ has definite total angular momentum J and parity. Consequently, the values of channel spin and orbital angular momentum in the primed sums of the interference (second) and resonance (third) terms of the right-hand side of eqn. (2.65) are limited by the requirements of total angular momentum and parity conservation. This is also true for the reaction cross-section derived from eqn. (2.42). In this case, only the resonance term exists;

$$\sigma_{\alpha\alpha'} = \pi\lambda^2_{\alpha}g_J\frac{\sum'_{ls}\Gamma_{0(\alpha sl)}\sum'_{l's'}\Gamma_{0(\alpha's'l')}}{(E_0-\Delta_0-E)^2+(\frac{1}{2}\Gamma_0)^2}. \tag{2.66}$$

Equations (2.65) and (2.66) show the characteristic features exhibited by the data (see Chapter I). The resonance cross-section has the form of a peak in the cross-section centred about the energy $E_{\mathrm{R}} = E_0-\Delta_0(E = E_{\mathrm{R}})$. The maximum value of the cross-section is

$$\sigma_{\alpha\alpha'}(E = E_{\mathrm{R}}) = 4\pi\lambda^2_{\alpha}g_J\left(\sum'_{ls}\Gamma_{0(\alpha sl)}\right)\left(\sum'_{l's'}\Gamma_{0(\alpha's'l')}\right)\Big/\Gamma^2_0.$$

The width of the peak at half of its maximum value is Γ_0, the sum of all the partial widths.

A simple physical interpretation of the widths is of interest here. Below eqn. (2.64) it is seen that the partial widths are each essentially the product of the penetration factor P_c and the quantity $\gamma^2_{0(c)}$ known as the reduced width. This latter quantity was first introduced in the form of its square root, known as the reduced-width amplitude, in eqn. (2.20a), which shows that it is the value of the internal eigenfunction X_0 at the entrance to channel c. This indicates clearly that it is the primary factor governing the leakage of flux from the internal region into the channel. The other factor governing this leakage is the penetrability through the external Coulomb and centrifugal potential barriers in the channel; this is the role played by the penetration factor P_c introduced in eqn. (2.9). (The other quantity introduced in eqn. (2.9), the shift factor S_c, influences the matching of the eigenfunction to the channel function and therefore appears in the formula for the position of the resonance peak.) It is clear that the total width Γ_0 is a measure of the total leakage of flux into all channels and therefore governs the decay of the internal wave-function. The width of the resonance indicates the spreading of the internal wave-function over energy, and this is related to the lifetime of the decaying state by the Heisenberg uncertainty principle in the form $\Gamma \sim \hbar/T_{\frac{1}{2}}$.

The resonance peak in the scattering cross-section is superimposed on a very slowly varying background, the potential scattering cross-section, of value $4\pi\lambda\!\!\!^{-}_{\alpha}{}^2\sum_{Jsl}4g_J\sin^2\phi_l$, and is distorted by the interference between resonance and potential scattering. At very low energies (less than a few keV) the potential scattering cross-section reduces to the limiting s-wave value of $4\pi a^2\sum_{J=|I-i|}^{I-i}g_J$; this is independent of energy. In applications of the Breit–Wigner formula it is necessary to bear in mind that the partial widths, the total width, Γ_0, and the level shift Δ_0 are all energy dependent through the penetration and shift factors. The level shift Δ_0 can be made zero at the resonance energy (by adjustment of the boundary conditions B_c to equal the shift factors S_c at the energy E_R) but the energy dependence is not thereby removed. In practice, however, the energy-dependence of the level shift is often neglected (see Sec. F.3).

At very low energies ($E \ll E_R$ and $\frac{1}{2}\Gamma_0 \ll E_R$) the s-wave neutron scattering cross-section tends to the form

$$\sigma_{nn} = 4\pi a^2\sum_J g_J - 4\pi\lambda\!\!\!^{-}_n a g_J\frac{\Gamma_{0(n)}}{E_R} + \pi\lambda\!\!\!^{-2}_n g_J\frac{\Gamma^2_{0(n)}}{E^2_R}. \tag{2.65a}$$

This assumes that the energy variation of Δ_0 is negligible compared with E_0, and since $\Gamma_{0(n)}$ is proportional to $\sqrt{E}$ through the penetration factor ka and $\lambda\!\!\!^{-}_{n}$ is inversely proportional to $\sqrt{E}$ this equation is asymptotically independent of energy. The single level s-wave cross-section of a strongly exothermic reaction, on the other hand, shows the limiting behaviour

$$\sigma_{n\alpha} = g_J \pi \lambda\!\!\!^{-2}_{n}(E = E_R)\sqrt{\left(\frac{E_R}{E}\right)} \cdot \frac{\Gamma_{0(n)}(E = E_R)\Gamma_{0(\alpha)}}{E_R{}^2}. \qquad (2.66a)$$

with the well-known $1/\sqrt{E}$ increase as the energy tends to zero.

(b) Single-level formula with background

Rather more general equations can be obtained if the R-matrix element is subdivided into an explicit level term and a background term,

$$R_{ab} = \frac{\gamma_{0(a)}\,\gamma_{0(b)}}{E_0 - E} + R^{\infty}_{ab}. \qquad (2.67)$$

Single-level formulae can be obtained either from the assumption that $\mathbf{R}^{\infty}$ is always small (Feshbach *et al.* 1954) or, from eqn. (2.52), by assuming that $\mathbf{R}^{\infty}$ is diagonal (Lane and Thomas 1958).

Alternatively, it may be assumed that all partial widths, except the entrance-channel width, are small compared with the level spacing. Then we may consider a reduced R-matrix of only one element, the inversion of which is trivial:

$$\mathscr{R}_{aa} = \frac{\gamma^2_{0(a)}}{E_0 - \Delta^e_0 - E - \frac{1}{2}i\Gamma^e_0} + \mathscr{R}^{\infty}_{aa} \qquad (2.68)$$

The cross-section may be calculated for the cases of $\mathscr{R}^{\infty}_{aa}$ either real (Lane and Lynn 1958) or complex (Lynn 1963*a*). We quote here the result of Lane and Lynn for the total cross-section,

$$\sigma_{\alpha T} = \pi\lambda\!\!\!^{-2}_{\alpha}\left[\sum_{J'sl} 4g_{J'}\sin^2(\phi_l + \beta^{J'}_{sl}) - \frac{2g_J {\sum_{sl}}' \hat{\Gamma}_{0(\alpha sl)}[(E_0 - \hat{\Delta}_0 - E)\sin(2\phi_l + 2\beta^J_{sl}) + \frac{1}{2}\hat{\Gamma}_0\{1 - \cos(2\phi_l + 2\beta^J_{sl})\}]}{(E_0 - \hat{\Delta}_0 - E)^2 + (\frac{1}{2}\hat{\Gamma}_0)^2} + \frac{g_J {\sum_{ls}}' \hat{\Gamma}_{0(\alpha sl)}\hat{\Gamma}_0}{(E_0 - \hat{\Delta}_0 - E)^2 + (\frac{1}{2}\hat{\Gamma}_0)^2}\right]. \qquad (2.69)$$

In this equation

$$\beta^J_{sl} = \arg\{1-\hat{L}_{\alpha l}\mathscr{R}^{\infty}_{\alpha sl,\alpha sl}(J)\}, \tag{2.69a}$$

$$\hat{\Gamma}_{0(\alpha sl)} = \frac{2P_{\alpha l}\gamma^2_{0(\alpha sl)}}{|1-\hat{L}_{\alpha l}\mathscr{R}^{\infty}_{\alpha sl,\alpha sl}(J)|^2}, \tag{2.69b}$$

$$\hat{\Gamma}_0 = \hat{\Gamma}_{0(\alpha sl)} + \Gamma^{\mathrm{e}}_0; \tag{2.69c}$$

$$\hat{\Delta}_0 = \frac{\hat{S}_{\alpha sl} - \mathscr{R}^{\infty}_{\alpha sl,\alpha sl}(J)(\hat{S}^2_{\alpha sl}+P^2_{\alpha sl})}{|1-\hat{L}_{\alpha l}\mathscr{R}^{\infty}_{\alpha sl,\alpha sl}(J)|^2}\gamma^2_{0(\alpha sl)} + \Delta^{\mathrm{e}}_0, \tag{2.69d}$$

showing that not only is the potential scattering cross-section modified by the background but so also are the partial widths and level shifts of the entrance channel.

F. DEFINITION OF THE R-MATRIX EIGENVALUE SET; CHOICE OF BOUNDARY CONDITIONS AND CHANNEL RADII

1. Bound states

The appearance of an eigenvalue E_λ and a channel radius a in the formal R-matrix statement of the single-level Breit–Wigner formula explicitly draws attention to these formally arbitrary elements in the theory. It is essential, therefore, to discuss the choice of boundary conditions and channel radii to obtain the most useful set of eigenvalues.

First, it is useful to compare the R-matrix eigenvalues with the usual eigenvalues corresponding to the states of a bound system. The latter are formed by solving the Schrödinger equation with the physical boundary conditions of vanishing wave function at infinite values of the channel radii. It turns out that the logarithmic derivative of the radial wave-function at very large channel radius is $-\kappa a$. This, then, is an energy-dependent boundary condition, yet orthogonality of the eigenfunctions is retained by virtue of their vanishing at infinite radius (see eqn. 2.24). This kind of physical boundary condition at infinity in all channels cannot be used to obtain a set of real eigenvalues useful for resonance reactions when the system becomes unbound in one or more channels, for then a continuum of eigenvalues results.

If it is required to discuss a particular bound state within the framework of R-matrix theory it is possible to take finite channel radii, and to place at them boundary conditions equal to the shift factors at the energy of the bound state. These shift factors are in fact just the ratios of derivative to value of the exponentially decaying tails of the radial wave-function at the chosen channel radii (see eqns. 2.9, 2.11) with an additional radius factor. Thus, the R-matrix eigenvalue coincides with the physical eigenvalue for that particular state although the eigenfunction of the latter includes all the channel functions as well as the internal wave-function. However, with the imposition of these particular boundary conditions, the neighbouring R-matrix eigenvalues will not coincide exactly with the energies of the corresponding physical bound states. The internal wave-functions of the formal eigenstates may approximate to those of the physical states but, if joined smoothly to channel functions, the latter would diverge with increasing distance of separation. Thus, so far as bound states are concerned, the formal eigenvalues of R-matrix theory can have a physical interpretation only within the single-level approximation when it is insisted that all channel radii be finite.

2. Unbound states

This interpretation can be extended to unbound states (i.e. resonances) by generalizing the above condition, namely, that the boundary conditions be set equal to the shift factors at the resonance energy for unbound as well as bound channels; this condition we have already seen (Section E.3(a)) as a formal convenience for defining the resonance energy of the single-level Breit–Wigner formula without background. It amounts to the assumption that the penetrability can be neglected when matching the internal wave-function to outgoing waves in the channels.

3. Dependence of the level shift on energy

When the boundary conditions are thus adjusted so that a particular resonance energy coincides with an eigenvalue there will not be coincidence of other resonance energies with eigenvalues. A rough estimate of the level shift for neighbouring resonances can be obtained by using a sum rule to be introduced in Chapter VI; this provides an estimate for the sum of the reduced widths over all channels for a level λ, $\sum_{c}\gamma_{\lambda}{}^{2}{}_{(c)} \approx \langle\hbar^2/M_c a_c^2\rangle$ (with the channel radii taken close to the nuclear surface). Let us refer to the unbound channels by c′, to the well-bound channels by c″ and to the nearly unbound channels by c‴. At low channel energies the energy variation of a shift factor (with no Coulomb barrier) is mostly contained in the factor $\rho^2{}_{c'}/(2l-1)$ for $l \geqslant 1$ (see eqn.

2.10), and decreases with increasing energy. The contribution to the change in the level shift between energies E_1 and E_2 from these channels is therefore approximately $-\sum_{c'}\{\rho_{c'}^2(E_2)-\rho_{c'}^2(E_1)\}\gamma_{\lambda(c')}^2/(2l'-1)$. The contribution to this change from the nearly unbound channels is similar but of formally opposite sign, i.e.

$$-\sum_{c'''}\{\rho_{c'''}^2(E_1)-\rho_{c'''}^2(E_2)\}\gamma_{\lambda(c''')}^2/(2l'''-1).$$

The shift factor of the well-bound channels is approximately $-\rho$ (see eqns. 2.11) so their contribution to the change in level shift is

$$-\sum_{c''}\{\rho_{c''}(E_1)-\rho_{c''}(E_2)\}\gamma_{\lambda(c'')}^2.$$

The wave-numbers of the bound channels are given by $(2M)^{\frac{1}{2}}(E_{\text{th,c}}-E)^{\frac{1}{2}}/\hbar$ where $E_{\text{th,c}}$ is the threshold energy of channel c. For $E_{\text{th,c}} \gg E$, this is approximated by $(2ME_{\text{th,c}})^{\frac{1}{2}}\ (1-E/2E_{\text{th,c}})/\hbar$. Thus, the change in level shift can now be written

$$\begin{aligned}
\Delta(E_1)-\Delta(E_2) \approx & -\sum_{c'}\frac{2M_{c'}a_{c'}^2}{\hbar^2}(E_2-E_1)\frac{\gamma_{\lambda(c')}^2}{2l'-1} \\
& -\sum_{c''}\frac{(2M_{c''}E_{\text{th},c''})^{\frac{1}{2}}a_{c''}}{\hbar}\frac{(E_2-E_1)}{2E_{\text{th,c}}}\gamma_{\lambda(c'')}^2 \\
& -\sum_{c'''}\frac{2M_{c'''}a_{c'''}^2}{\hbar^2}(E_2-E_1)\frac{\gamma_{\lambda^2(c''')}}{2l'''-1} \\
= & -(E_2-E_1)\Bigg\{\sum_{c'}\frac{2M_{c'}a_{c'}^2}{\hbar^2}\frac{\gamma_{\lambda(c')}^2}{(2l'-1)}+\sum_{c'''}\frac{2M_{c'''}a_{c'''}^2}{\hbar^2}\frac{\gamma_{\lambda(c''')}^2}{(2l'''-1)} \\
& +\sum_{c''}\left(\frac{M_{c''}}{2\hbar^2E_{\text{th},c''}}\right)^{\frac{1}{2}}a_{c''}\gamma_{\lambda(c'')}^2\Bigg\}. \qquad (2.70)
\end{aligned}$$

If the channel radii are all taken close to the surface, and the sum rule mentioned above is applied, the change in level shift turns out to be nearly of the same order as the change in energy. This is quite useless for practical employment of the R-matrix formalism. It is clear that the only way to avoid this is to introduce very large channel radii in all or most of the bound channels. In this way their contribution to the level shift change can be made vanishingly small. At low energies there are few open channels. In Chapter VI theoretical estimates and experimental evidence for the reduced widths of such channels are presented, and from these it becomes clear that their contribution to the level shift change ranges from 10^{-3} to 10^{-7} times the energy difference; this is quite negligible for practical purposes. As we have already indicated, the price of using indefinitely large channel radii in the bound states is to introduce a high density (a near-continuum) of formal states, which do not correspond to resonances, above the channel thresholds. For consideration of resonance cross-sections in a localized energy-interval this is of little import, but it does suggest that as each new threshold is approached the channel radii and hence the eigenvalues ought to be redefined so that the new eigenvalue structure will correspond to the resonances in the opening channel.

4. Change of boundary condition

It is important to know how the eigenvalues and reduced widths change with variation of the boundary condition in an open channel. For this, we follow an argument due to Teichmann and Wigner (1952). First, suppose that the eigenvalues are known for a certain set of boundary conditions in all channels. In the channel c″, where we are going to change the boundary condition, the initial condition for the basic set is assumed to be $B_{c''} = 0$. We have, at all energies E, the R-matrix relation between value and derivative quantities at the channel entrances, eqn. (2.29),

$$V_{c'} = \sum_{c \neq c''} R_{c'c}(D_c - B_c V_c) + R_{c'c''}(D_{c''} - B_{c''} V_{c''}). \tag{2.29}$$

We now wish to determine the energies $E = E_\lambda(B_{c''}^{(a)})$ of the new eigenvalues for which the boundary conditions are now set as

$$\begin{aligned} B_c &= B_c, \; c \neq c'' \\ B_{c''} &= B_{c''}^{(a)}. \end{aligned} \tag{2.71}$$

At the new eigenvalues eqn. (2.20) holds, i.e.

$$\begin{aligned} D_c &= B_c V_c, \; c \neq c'' \\ D_{c''} &= B_{c''}^{(a)} V_{c''}. \end{aligned} \tag{2.72}$$

Therefore, at $E_\lambda(B_{c''}^{(a)})$,

$$V_{c'} = R_{c'c''} B_{c''}^{(a)} V_{c''} \tag{2.73a}$$

or

$$R_{c''c''} = \frac{1}{B_{c''}^{(a)}}, \tag{2.73b}$$

and the new eigenvalue set may be found from this last relation, which is illustrated in Fig. 2.1.

The behaviour of the reduced widths in channel c″ is found by starting from eqn. (2.26) for the expansion of the internal wave-function. With eqn. (2.28) it gives

$$\Psi = \sum_{\mu} \frac{1}{E_\mu - E} \sum_{c} (D_c - B_c V_c) \gamma_{\mu(c)} X_\mu \tag{2.74}$$

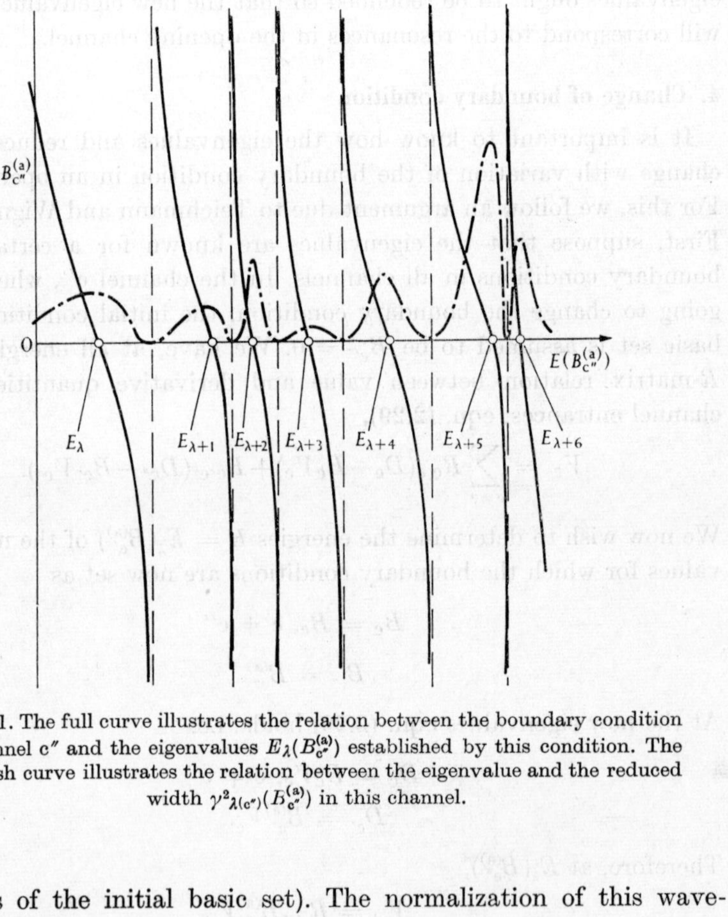

FIG. 2.1. The full curve illustrates the relation between the boundary condition in channel c″ and the eigenvalues $E_\lambda(B_{c''}^{(a)})$ established by this condition. The dot-dash curve illustrates the relation between the eigenvalue and the reduced width $\gamma^2{}_{\lambda(c'')}(B_{c''}^{(a)})$ in this channel.

(in terms of the initial basic set). The normalization of this wave-function yields

$$1 = \int_\tau |\Psi|^2 d\tau = \sum_{c,c'} \sum_{\mu} \frac{\gamma_{\mu(c)}\gamma_{\mu(c')}}{(E_\mu - E)^2} (D_c - B_c V_c)^* (D_{c'} - B_{c'} V_{c'}). \tag{2.75}$$

If we now apply eqn. (2.72) at one of the new eigenvalues $E_\lambda(B^{(a)}_{c''})$ we obtain

$$1 = \sum_\mu \frac{\gamma^2_{\mu(c'')}}{(E_\mu - E_\lambda(B^{(a)}_{c''}))^2} B^2_{c''} V^2_{c''} = B^2_{c''} V^2_{c''} \left(\frac{\partial R_{c''c''}}{\partial E}\right). \tag{2.76}$$

From eqn. (2.20a) we obtain the reduced width of the new eigenfunction $E_\gamma(B^{(a)}_{c''})$:

$$\gamma_{\lambda(c)}(B^{(a)}_{c''}) = \left(\frac{\hbar^2}{2M_{c''}a_{c''}}\right)^{\frac{1}{2}} \int_{r_{c''}=a_{c''}} \varphi_{c''}{}^* \Psi(E_\lambda(B^{(a)}_{c''}))\, \mathrm{d}\mathscr{S}_{c''}$$

$$= \sum_\mu \frac{1}{E_\mu - E} B_{c''} V_{c''} \gamma^2_{\mu(c'')}. \tag{2.77a}$$

Substitution from eqn. (2.76) gives

$$\gamma_{\lambda(c'')}(B^{(a)}_{c''}) = R_{c''c''} \left(\frac{\partial R_{c''c''}}{\partial E}\right)^{-\frac{1}{2}}, \tag{2.77b}$$

which is also illustrated in Fig. 2.1.

5. Change of channel radius

Attention is drawn to the apparently ambiguous role of the channel radius by its explicit occurrence in the potential scattering term of the single-level formula, eqn. (2.65a). In the formal theory it is an arbitrary quantity, required only to lie beyond the range of the nuclear forces, yet in the single-level formula it is apparently playing an important physical role. The answer to this dilemma is of course provided by the fuller version of the single-level formula which includes a background term R^∞ in the potential scattering. Clearly, this must alter as the channel radius changes so as to keep the potential scattering term invariant. An instructive example of this is the case of zero interaction at the scattering centre, a system with no energy levels in the physical sense and no cross-section.

Suppose we consider the elastic scattering channel only, setting a channel radius a and a zero boundary condition. The formal eigenvalues of the system are given by

$$E_n = \frac{\hbar^2}{2M} \frac{(2n+1)^2\pi^2}{a^2} \tag{2.78}$$

and the reduced widths have the common value

$$\gamma_n^2 = \frac{\hbar^2}{Ma^2} \tag{2.79}$$

With a channel radius of nuclear dimensions ($a \approx 10^{-12}$cm), and with the neutron mass, E_1 is found to be about 0·5 MeV, E_2 about 4·5 MeV, and these energies reduce rapidly with increasing radius. If, in the single-level formula, we ignore the resonance and interference terms (there being no 'physical' eigenvalue) and compute the potential scattering cross-section we find

$$R^\infty = \sum_n \frac{\gamma_n{}^2}{E_n - E} = \sum_n \frac{1}{\frac{1}{2}(2n+1)^2\pi^2 - Ma^2E/\hbar^2} = (ka)^{-1}\tan(ka) \tag{2.80a}$$

(see Titchmarsh 1939) and hence

$$\beta = \operatorname{atan}\left(-\frac{P_0}{ka}\tan ka\right), \tag{2.80b}$$

$$\sigma_{\text{pot}} = 4\pi\lambda\!\!\!^{-2}\sin^2(\phi_0+\beta) = 0. \tag{2.80c}$$

It is now clear that the introduction of a non-physical channel radius into the theory can lead to the appearance of 'fictitious' energy levels to give the correct cross-sections.

Let us now consider a realistic physical situation, asking the extent to which such fictitious energy levels confuse the true resonance structure. Suppose the eigenvalues have been found in a typical nuclear-scattering case with the open channel radii adjusted to their minimum possible values outside the nuclear force range, and with the boundary condition in a particular s-wave neutron channel set at zero. The eigenvalues are marked on the energy scale in this channel by circles along the abscissa in Fig. 2.2. The new eigenvalues obtained by variation of the boundary condition (indicated by the ordinate axis) are shown by the full curves of this diagram; this behaviour has already been discussed in Section F.4. Now, if the channel radius is increased from its initial value a_0 to a new value a_1 and the boundary condition is kept at zero, we can determine the new eigenvalues from the conditions

$$\cos(ka_1+\delta) = 0$$

$$ka_0\tan(ka_0+\delta) = B(k) \tag{2.81a}$$

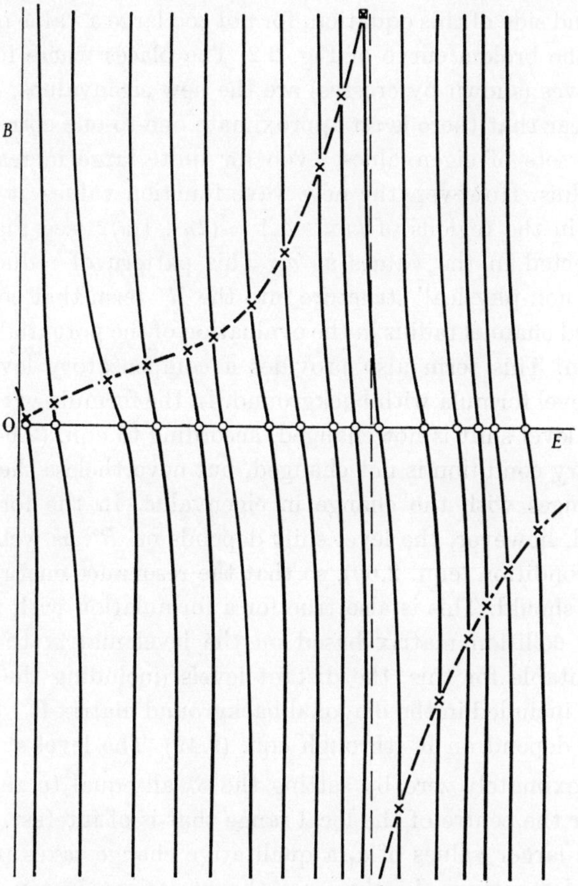

FIG. 2.2. The full lines show the variation of eigenvalue with the boundary condition in a given channel (as previously shown in Fig. 2.1) with channel radius chosen to be just outside the nuclear force radius. With boundary condition chosen to be zero the eigenvalues are indicated by the circles. If the channel radius is now changed to a much larger radius, and a boundary condition of zero is set at the new channel radius, the effective boundary condition at the old channel radius is indicated by the broken line. The abscissae of the curves with crosses where these intersect the full curves are the new eigenvalues for the new channel radius. There is almost a one-to-one correspondence between this set and the old set (only one extra 'level', shown by a square, is introduced in this diagram).

where the boundary condition $B(k)$ at channel radius a_0 is that required to place an eigenstate at wave number k as shown in Fig. 2.1. Equations (2.81a) are equivalent to

$$ka_0 \tan\{k(a_1-a_0)\} = B(k). \tag{2.81b}$$

The left-hand side of this equation, for not too large a value of a_1-a_0, is shown by the broken curve of Fig. 2.2. The places where it intersects the full curves (shown by crosses) are the new eigenvalues. This figure makes it clear that there is an approximate one-to-one correspondence of the two sets of eigenvalues, even for quite large increases in the channel radius. However, the new wave-function values at a_0 become very small in the regions of $k(a_1-a_0) = (2n+1)\pi/2$ (see Fig. 2.1) and this is reflected in the values at a_1. This pattern of reduced widths introduces 'non-physical' structure into the R^∞ term that compensates the increased channel radius in the evaluation of the potential scattering cross-section. This term also provides a compensatory level shift in the single-level formula with background. In the formula without background the level shift is not changed, according to eqn. (2.64), because the boundary condition is not changed, but nevertheless the resonance energy changes with the change in eigenvalue. In the formula with background, however, the level shift depends on R^∞ as well as on the boundary condition (eqn. 2.69), so that the resonance energy stays the same, as it should. This is also true for a formulation with many local levels. The collision matrix based on the level matrix through eqn. (2.52) is suitable for this, the distant levels (including the 'fictitious' ones) being included in the diagonal background matrix $\mathbf{R}^\circ$. In this, the level shifts depend on $\mathbf{R}^\circ$ through eqn. (2.49). The level shifts can be made approximately zero by setting the $\hat{S}_c$ all equal to zero at some energy near the centre of the local range that is of interest.

At much larger values of a_1 a qualitative change takes place in the formal level structure. In this case the variations in $\tan\{k(a_1-a_0)\}$ are more rapid than those in the relation between eigenvalue and boundary condition at a_0. This is shown in Fig. 2.3. There is no longer a one-to-one correspondence between the new eigenvalues and the eigenvalues defined with the low channel radius; the former are much denser and their density increases rapidly with channel radius. These are 'fictitious' eigenvalues in the sense of bearing no relation to the resonances. The critical radius separating these two schematic pictures is given by

$$\sqrt{\left(\frac{2M}{\hbar^2}\right)}\{\sqrt{(E+\bar{D})}-\sqrt{E}\}(a_c-a_0) \approx \pi \tag{2.82}$$

where $\bar{D}$ is the mean resonance spacing. At low energies this formula gives a critical radius far greater than the conventional nuclear radius; even for light nuclei, where the resonance spacing may be several

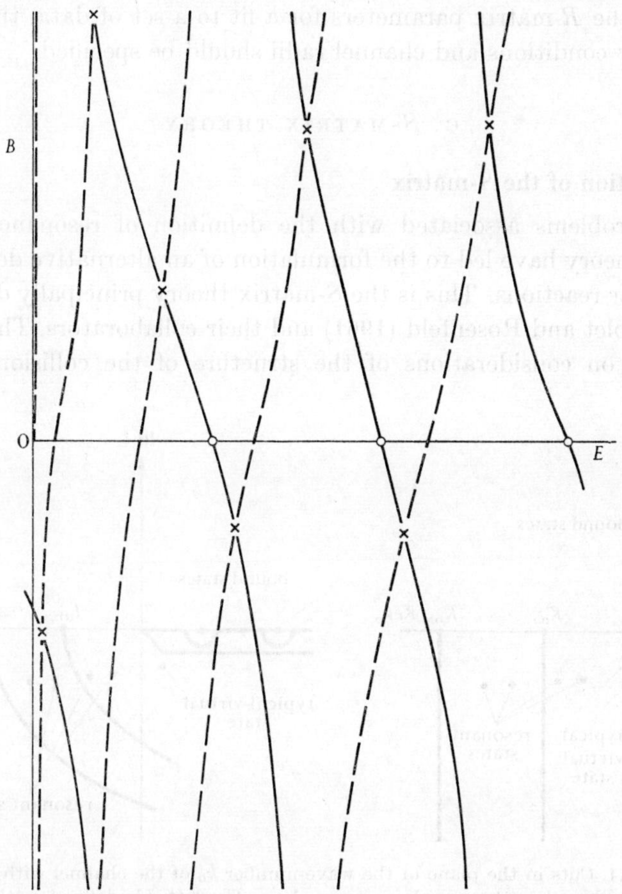

FIG. 2.3. This is similar to Fig. 2.2 but a portion of the energy scale has been magnified to show just a few of the eigenvalues determined at the small channel radius. The large channel radius is now very much increased so that the periodic variation of the boundary condition at the small radius is very much increased. It is now clear that the eigenvalue set for the very large channel radius is much denser than the 'physical' set determined at a small radius.

hundred keV, a_c is of the order of 20 fm, and it may be three orders of magnitude greater than this for heavy nuclei. Since nuclear forces are short-range forces, becoming effectively zero within a rather short distance beyond the nuclear radius, it is apparent that there is considerable freedom, in practice, in placing the open-channel radii so that the eigenvalue set has physical significance. In other words, R-matrix theory ought to be a very useful formalism for the description of low-energy nuclear reactions. It is clearly important, however, that, in quoting the R-matrix parameters for a fit to a set of data, the chosen boundary conditions and channel radii should be specified.

G. S-MATRIX THEORY

1. Definition of the S-matrix

The problems associated with the definition of resonances in R-matrix theory have led to the formulation of an alternative description of nuclear reactions. This is the S-matrix theory principally developed by Humblet and Rosenfeld (1961) and their collaborators. This theory is based on considerations of the structure of the collision matrix,

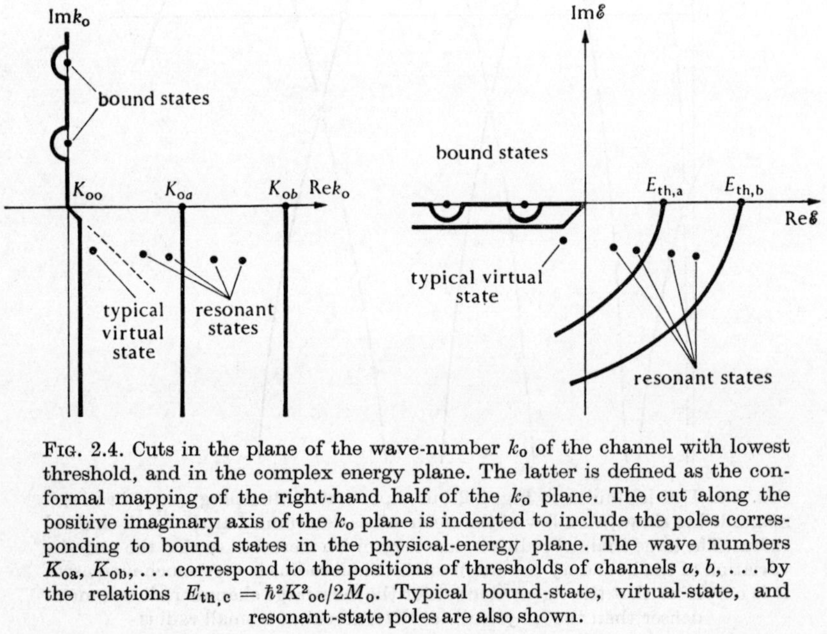

FIG. 2.4. Cuts in the plane of the wave-number k_0 of the channel with lowest threshold, and in the complex energy plane. The latter is defined as the conformal mapping of the right-hand half of the k_0 plane. The cut along the positive imaginary axis of the k_0 plane is indented to include the poles corresponding to bound states in the physical-energy plane. The wave numbers K_{0a}, K_{0b}, . . . correspond to the positions of thresholds of channels a, b, . . . by the relations $E_{th,c} = \hbar^2 K^2_{0c}/2M_0$. Typical bound-state, virtual-state, and resonant-state poles are also shown.

and in it the definition of a resonance arises naturally from this structure rather than from formal basis states required for the expansion of the solution of the Schrödinger equation. The theory has been developed using the elegant mathematics of functions of a complex variable.

The matrix element $S_{c'c}$ for the transition from channel c to channel c′ in the course of a reaction may be defined as the ratio of the amplitude of the outgoing flux in channel c′ (or the scattered flux if c′ = c) to that of the incoming flux in channel c. The S-matrix is thus related to the collision matrix (in the case of electrically-neutral incident particles) by

$$S_{c'c} = U_{c'c} - \delta_{c'c} \tag{2.83}$$

We consider the structure of the S-matrix in the complex energy plane (denoted by $\mathscr{E}$). The energy origin is taken as the threshold of the channel with highest kinetic energy. With respect to this, the thresholds of other channels c are denoted by $E_{\text{th,c}}$. The energy is related to the wave-number in channel c by

$$\mathscr{E} = \frac{\hbar^2}{2M_c} k_c^2 + E_{\text{th,c}}. \tag{2.84}$$

The S-matrix is more directly a function of the wave-numbers k_c, so eqn. (2.84) shows that the thresholds are actually branch points of the S-matrix in the complex energy plane. Systems of cuts through the branch points have to be made in order to define the physically important parts of the S-matrix: these have been discussed by Humblet and Rosenfeld (1961) and Humblet (1964b). The simplest set of cuts to achieve this object appears to be that defined by the latter author; they are shown schematically in Fig. 2.4.

2. Coefficients of incoming and outgoing waves

In order to establish their formalism Humblet and Rosenfeld work with very large channel radii; these nowhere appear, either explicitly or implicitly, in the final expressions. The external wave-function with respect to the complete set of channel radii is

$$\Psi_{\text{ext}} = \sum_c \varphi_c \frac{u_c(r_c)}{r_c} \tag{2.85}$$

where u_c is a superposition of incoming and outgoing waves:

$$u_c = x_c O_c + y_c I_c. \tag{2.86}$$

The values and derivatives of the interior wave-function at the surface $\mathscr{S}$ may be expanded in terms of the channel functions. For a definite type and excitation α of the particles in the channel we may write

$$(r_\alpha \Psi_{\text{int}})_{r_\alpha = a_\alpha} = \sum_{c(\alpha)} V_c \varphi_c \tag{2.87a}$$

$$\left\{\frac{\partial}{\partial r_\alpha}(r_\alpha \Psi_{\text{int}})\right\}_{r_\alpha = a_\alpha} = \sum_{c(\alpha)} D_c \varphi_c. \tag{2.87b}$$

The expansion coefficients V_c and D_c are closely related to, but are not quite the same, as the value and derivative quantities given the same symbol in eqns. (2.28) and (2.29). By matching eqns. (2.86) and (2.87) expressions for V_c and D_c are found,

$$V_c = x_c O_c(a_c,k_c) + y_c I_c(a_c,k_c) \tag{2.88a}$$

$$D_c = x_c O_c'(a_c,k_c) + y_c I_c'(a_c,k_c), \tag{2.88b}$$

which yield the amplitudes x_c, y_c for each channel

$$x_c = -\frac{1}{2ik_c} W(V_c, I_c; a_c) \tag{2.89a}$$

$$y_c = +\frac{1}{2ik_c} W(V_c, O_c; a_c). \tag{2.89b}$$

Here we have written V'_c for D_c in the Wronskian expressions of the type

$$W(V_c, I_c; a_c) = V_c' I_c - V_c I_c' \tag{2.90}$$

calculated at the channel radius a_c. Equations (2.89) result from applying the Wronskian condition, $W(I_c, O_c) = -2ik$, to the simultaneous solution of eqns. (2.88).

It is sufficient now to treat the case of a single entrance channel c, in which case the coefficients $V_{c'}$, $x_{c'}$, and $y_{c'}$ are denoted by a superscript c. In this case

$$y_{c'}^{(c)} = W(V_{c'}^{(c)}, O_{c'}) = 0, \; c' \neq c. \tag{2.91}$$

The relation between the coefficients $x_{c'}$ and $y_{c'}$ may be written, from the analogy with eqn. (2.34),

$$x_{c'}^{(c)} = -\mathcal{U}_{c'c} y_c^{(c)}, \tag{2.92}$$

where

$$\mathcal{U}_{c'c} = \frac{W(V_{c'}^{(c)}, I_{c'})/k_{c'}}{W(V_c^{(c)}, O_c)/k_c} \tag{2.93}$$

is simply related to the collision matrix element $U_{c'c}$ by eqn. (2.33b).

3. Green's theorem in the complex-energy plane

When we change from real energies to complex energies Green's theorem, eqn. (2.23), has to be modified. By going through the same procedure outlined in Section C.3, but with complex energies, we find

$$(\mathscr{E}_2^* - \mathscr{E}_1)\int_\tau \Psi_2^*\Psi_1 d\tau = \sum_c \frac{\hbar^2}{2M_c} W(V_{2c}^*, V_{1c}) \tag{2.94}$$

4. The definition of resonant states

The 'natural' definition of resonant states originally suggested by Siegert (1939), and adopted by Humblet and Rosenfeld, is to impose a boundary condition expressing the absence of incoming waves in any channel, i.e.

$$W(V_{c'}^{(c)}, O_c) = 0, \text{ all c}', \text{c}, \tag{2.95}$$

on the solutions of the Schrödinger equation in the complex energy plane. The condition of finite probability in the internal region ($|\Psi_{\text{int}}|^2$ is finite) is also required in order to express the condition that outgoing waves exist. From eqns. (2.95) and (2.93) it is apparent that the resonant states correspond to poles in the S-matrix at complex energies $\mathscr{E}_m$.

The eigenfunctions Ψ_m associated with these poles are clearly independent of any particular entrance channel c (by the symmetry of condition 2.95), and thus the radial coefficients V_{mc}, V'_{mc} of their expansions on the surface $\mathscr{S}$ are also independent of the entrance channel.

5. Interpretation of the resonant states

Suppose that the wave-number in channel c at the pole m is

$$k_{mc} = \kappa_{mc} - \mathrm{i}\gamma_{mc} \tag{2.96}$$

where κ_{mc} is zero or positive. (It can be shown that a pole at $-k_{mc}^{*}$ is associated with that at k_{mc} so that this condition is not restrictive.) The complex energy at the same pole will be denoted by

$$\mathscr{E}_m = E_m^{(\mathrm{H})} - \tfrac{1}{2}\mathrm{i}\Gamma_m^{(\mathrm{H})}, \tag{2.97a}$$

the superscript H being used to differentiate these quantities from the similar notation of R-matrix theory.

Thus, by eqn. (2.84),

$$E_m^{(\mathrm{H})} = \frac{\hbar^2}{2M_c}(\kappa_{mc}^2 - \gamma_{mc}^2) + E_{\text{th},c}, \tag{2.97b}$$

$$\Gamma_m^{(\mathrm{H})} = \frac{2\hbar^2}{M_c}\kappa_{mc}\gamma_{mc}. \tag{2.97c}$$

The Green's theorem relation, eqn. (2.94), may be used to prove that $\Gamma_m^{(\mathrm{H})}$ is positive or zero. By applying Green's theorem to the state Ψ_m with complex energy $\mathscr{E}_m$ we obtain

$$\mathrm{i}\Gamma_m^{(\mathrm{H})}\int_\tau |\Psi_m|^2 \mathrm{d}\tau = \sum_{\mathrm{c}} \frac{\hbar^2}{2M_{\mathrm{c}}}|V_{m\mathrm{c}}|^2 \left\{\frac{V'_{m\mathrm{c}}}{V_{m\mathrm{c}}} - \frac{V^{*\prime}_{m\mathrm{c}}}{V^*_{m\mathrm{c}}}\right\}. \tag{2.98}$$

The last factor is simply written in terms of the logarithmic derivatives of the outgoing wave in channel c; it is $L_{\mathrm{c}}(k_{m\mathrm{c}}) - L^*_{\mathrm{c}}(k_{m\mathrm{c}})$, which can be shown to be a positive imaginary number. The condition that $\Gamma_m^{(\mathrm{H})}$ be positive or zero imposes the condition on $\kappa_{m\mathrm{c}}$ and $\gamma_{m\mathrm{c}}$ that they be of the same sign, or one of them be zero, respectively.

The propagation (in distance and time) of a spherical outgoing wave in a channel c is governed asymptotically by the usual quantal factor, $\exp(\mathrm{i}kr)\exp(-\mathrm{i}Et/\hbar)$. For the resonant state at energy $\mathscr{E}_m$ this may be rewritten

$$\exp\{\mathrm{i}\kappa_{m\mathrm{c}}r_{\mathrm{c}} - \mathrm{i}(E_m^{(\mathrm{H})} - E_{\mathrm{th,c}})t/\hbar\}\exp(\gamma_{m\mathrm{c}}r_{\mathrm{c}} - \tfrac{1}{2}\Gamma_m^{(\mathrm{H})}t/\hbar). \tag{2.99}$$

It is clear from this that the state Ψ_m is either stationary or decays with logarithmic half-life $T_{\frac{1}{2}m} = \hbar/\Gamma_m^{(\mathrm{H})}$. States with purely real values of $k_{m\mathrm{c}}$ are physically excluded; they would consist entirely of undamped outgoing waves and would not be finite, therefore, in the interior region. Thus the stationary or bound states ($\Gamma_m^{(\mathrm{H})} = 0$) correspond to purely imaginary values of the wave-number in all channels. Thus, by eqn. (2.97b), the energy of such states, $E_m^{(\mathrm{H})}$ is less than the lowest threshold $E_{\mathrm{th,0}}$. In order that the wave-function of such states will attenuate with increasing radius in all channels it is necessary that all the $\gamma_{m\mathrm{c}}$ be less than zero.

Another class of states, the virtual states, also have energies less than $E_{\mathrm{th,0}}$ if $\gamma_{m0} > \kappa_{m0} > 0$, but have non-zero width and they therefore decay. The true resonant states in channel c lie above the threshold $E_{\mathrm{th,c}}$ ($\kappa_{m\mathrm{c}} > \gamma_{m\mathrm{c}} > 0$) and they also decay. The wave-function of such decaying states increases with increasing channel radius, corresponding to the fact that at the larger radius the wave was emitted from the source at earlier time when its strength was greater.

6. Threshold behaviour of the S-matrix

At the branch points $E_{\mathrm{th,c}}$ in the cut complex energy plane the S-matrix contains essential singularities. These give rise to characteristic energy-dependences of the cross-sections as the wave-number in a channel approaches zero from above. It is important that such threshold behaviour should be apparent explicitly in the formalism. From the mathematical behaviour of the functions involved in eqn. (2.93) Humblet and Rosenfeld deduced that for electrically neutral particles the essential singularity of $S_{c'c}$ at the threshold of channel c is contained in the factor

$$\mathscr{P}_{c} = k_{c}^{l_c+\frac{1}{2}}. \tag{2.100a}$$

The explicit threshold behaviour for charged-particle channels was deduced by Humblet (1964*a*); it is

$$\mathscr{P}_{c} = \varepsilon_{c} k_{c}^{l_c+\frac{1}{2}} \tag{2.100b}$$

where

$$\varepsilon_{c} = \frac{1}{l_{c}!}\left\{(l_{c}^{2}+\alpha_{c}^{2})\ldots(1+\alpha_{c}^{2})\frac{2\pi\alpha_{c}}{e^{2\pi\alpha_{c}}-1}\right\}^{\frac{1}{2}} \tag{2.100c}$$

where $\alpha_{c} = \eta_{c}/k_{c}$.

It is to be noted that these threshold factors are not the same as the penetration factors of Section C.1(b). The energy behaviour of the squares of the former become identical to the latter in the low wave-number limit, but the penetration factors are modified by a characteristic radial parameter at higher energies.

In addition to the factor $\mathscr{P}_{c}$, the threshold behaviour of the S-matrix in charged-particle channels makes it useful to factorize out the Coulomb phase shift factor $e^{i\sigma_c}$. Thus the S-matrix element may be written in terms of a T-matrix element, from which the essential singularities have been removed:

$$S_{c'c} = e^{i(\sigma_c+\sigma_{c'})}\mathscr{P}_{c}\mathscr{P}_{c'}T_{c'c}. \tag{2.101}$$

7. Expansion of the S-matrix about its poles

The only singularities now expected in the T-matrix introduced in the last section are the simple poles corresponding to the resonant states; this has been confirmed by detailed study of the case of elastic scattering in a spherically symmetric potential (Humblet 1952). Such a function can be expanded by means of the Mittag–Leffler theorem. The theorem can be stated in this form (see e.g. MacRobert 1947): it is possible to construct a meromorphic function (one that is analytic in a given domain except at isolated poles) provided that the series $\sum_{m=1}^{\infty}|\rho_m|/|a_m|^M$ is absolutely convergent for some integer M. Here the a_m are the poles (arranged so that $|a_1| < |a_2| < \ldots < |a_m| < |a_{m+1}|$

$<\ldots$) and the ρ_m are their residues. A function of the required type is

$$g(z) = \sum_{m=1}^{\infty} \frac{z^{M-1}}{z_m^{M-1}} \cdot \frac{\rho_m}{(z-z_m)} \tag{2.102}$$

A corollary to this theorem is that if $f(z)$ is a function with the same simple poles and residues as $g(z)$, $g(z)-f(z)$ is holomorphic (analytic) at all points in the domain and is therefore an integral function of z. Hence any meromorphic function can be put in the form

$$f(z) = E(z) + \sum_{m=1}^{\infty} \frac{z^{M-1}}{z_m^{M-1}} \cdot \frac{\rho_m}{(z-z_m)} \tag{2.103}$$

where $E(z)$ is an integral function of z.

The application of the theorem to the T-matrix gives

$$T_{c'c} = Q_{c'c}^{(M)}(\mathscr{E}) + \sum_m \left(\frac{\mathscr{E}}{\mathscr{E}_m}\right)^{M-1} \frac{\rho_{m,\, c'c}}{\mathscr{E}-\mathscr{E}_m} \tag{2.104}$$

where the background function $Q_{c'c}^{(M)}$ is an integral function of $\mathscr{E}$. To use this expansion it is necessary to know the minimum value of the integer M to secure the convergence of the series $\sum|\rho_{m,c'c}|/|\mathscr{E}_m|^M$. In the special case of elastic scattering by a central potential of limited range it can be shown that it is sufficient to have $M = 1$ (Humblet 1952), and it is assumed that this will also be so in the general case of nuclear reactions. With this specialization we drop the superscript M on the background function and write the expression for the S-matrix:

$$S_{c'c} = \mathscr{P}_{c'}\mathscr{P}_c e^{i(\sigma_{c'}+\sigma_c)} \left\{ Q_{c'c}(\mathscr{E}) + \sum_m \frac{\rho_{m,c'c}}{\mathscr{E}-\mathscr{E}_m} \right\}. \tag{2.105}$$

It remains to clarify the nature of the residues $\rho_{m,c'c}$. From eqns. (2.93), (2.33b) and (2.83) the S-matrix is

$$S_{c'c} = \sqrt{\left(\frac{M_c k_{c'}}{M_{c'} k_c}\right)} \frac{W(V_{c'}^{(c)}, I_{c'}-O_{c'})}{W(V_c^{(c)}, O_c)} \tag{2.106}$$

By using the first-order term in the Taylor expansion of the denominator about the pole at $\mathscr{E}_m$ the residue of $T_{c'c}$ is found to be

$$\rho_{m,cc'} = \{\mathscr{P}_{mc'}\mathscr{P}_{mc} e^{i(\sigma_{mc'}+\sigma_{mc})}\}^{-1} \sqrt{\left(\frac{M_c k_{mc'}}{M_{c'} k_{mc}}\right)} \frac{W(V_{mc'}^{(c)}, I_{mc'}-O_{mc'})}{\left\{\frac{d}{d\mathscr{E}} W(V_c^{(c)}, O_c)\right\}_{\mathscr{E}=\mathscr{E}_m}} \tag{2.107}$$

where the additional subscript m on quantities like k_c and $\mathscr{P}_c$ indicates that they are to be evaluated at the resonant state energy $\mathscr{E}_m$. By use of the condition (2.95) for the definition of the resonant state it is possible to eliminate $V'^{(c)}_{mc'}$ in the numerator, giving

$$W(V_{mc'}, I_{mc'} - O_{mc'}) = \frac{V_{mc'}}{O_{mc'}} W(O_{mc'}, I_{mc'})$$

$$= -2ik_{mc'}\frac{V_{mc'}}{O_{mc'}}. \tag{2.108}$$

Here, the superscripts c have been dropped, there being *no* ingoing wave at the resonant state. Now we may use the symmetry property of the collision matrix to show that $\rho_{m,cc'} = \rho_{m,c'c}$. Hence

$$\frac{k^2_{mc}}{M_c}\frac{V_{mc}}{O_{mc}}\left\{\frac{d}{d\mathscr{E}}W(V_c, O_c)\right\}_{\mathscr{E}=\mathscr{E}_m} = \frac{k^2_{mc'}}{M_{c'}}\frac{V_{mc'}}{O_{mc'}}\left\{\frac{d}{d\mathscr{E}}W(V_{c'}, O_{c'})\right\}_{\mathscr{E}=\mathscr{E}_m} \tag{2.109}$$

showing that the left- and right-hand sides of this equation are equal to some quantity, $\hat{q}_m$, say, independent of the channel c. Then,

$$\left\{\frac{d}{d\mathscr{E}}W(V_c, O_c)\right\}^{-1}_{\mathscr{E}=\mathscr{E}_m} = \frac{1}{\hat{q}_m}\cdot\frac{k^2_{mc}}{M_c}\cdot\frac{V_{mc}}{O_{mc}}, \tag{2.110}$$

and we obtain

$$\rho_{m,cc'} = -i\frac{G_{m(c)}G_{m(c')}}{|\mathscr{P}_{mc}||\mathscr{P}_{mc'}|}\exp\{i(\xi_{m(c)} + \xi_{m(c')})\}, \tag{2.111a}$$

where

$$G_{m(c)}e^{i\xi_{m(c)}} = k_{mc}\sqrt{\left(\frac{2k_{mc}}{\hat{q}_m M_c}\right)}\frac{V_{mc}}{O_{mc}}\cdot e^{-i(\xi_{m(c)} + \arg\mathscr{P}_{mc})}. \tag{2.111b}$$

Combining eqns. (2.105) and (2.111) we achieve the final form for the S-matrix in notation close to that of Mahaux (1966):

$$S_{c'c} = \mathscr{P}_{c'}\mathscr{P}_c e^{i(\sigma_c + \sigma_{c'})}\left\{Q_{c'c}(\mathscr{E}) - i\sum_m \frac{G_{m(c')}G_{m(c)}e^{i(\xi_{m(c')} + \xi_{m(c)})}}{|\mathscr{P}_{mc'}||\mathscr{P}_{mc}|(\mathscr{E} - E^{(H)}_m + \frac{1}{2}i\Gamma^{(H)}_m)}\right\}. \tag{2.112}$$

By eqn. (2.111b), the factors $G_{m(c)}$ are clearly a measure of the amplitude of state m leaking into the channels c. Thus they are proportional to the partial width amplitudes of state m, $\Gamma^{(H)\frac{1}{2}}_{m(c)}$. The proportionality constant for the relation between $G^2_{m(c)}$ and $\Gamma^{(H)}_{m(c)}$ is generally denoted by q_m; thus,

$$G_{m(c)} = \sqrt{\{q_m\Gamma^{(H)}_{m(c)}\}}. \tag{2.112a}$$

The expressions resulting for the cross-section (integrated over solid angle) from eqn. (2.112) are

$$\sigma_{\alpha\alpha'} = \frac{\pi}{k_\alpha^2}\sum_{J\pi} g_J \sum_{ls}{}' \sum_{l's'}{}' \Bigg\{ \mathscr{P}_c^2 \mathscr{P}_{c'}^2 |Q_{cc'}|^2$$

$$+\sum_m \frac{\mathscr{P}_c^2 \mathscr{P}_{c'}^2}{|\mathscr{P}_{mc}\mathscr{P}_{mc'}|^2} \cdot \frac{G_{m(c)}^2 G_{m(c')}^2}{(E-E_m^{(H)})^2+(\frac{1}{2}\Gamma_m^{(H)})^2}$$

$$-2|Q_{cc'}|\sum_m \frac{\mathscr{P}_c^2 \mathscr{P}_{c'}^2}{|\mathscr{P}_{mc}\mathscr{P}_{mc'}|} \cdot \frac{G_{m(c)} G_{m(c')}}{(E-E_m^{(H)})^2+(\frac{1}{2}\Gamma_m^{(H)})^2} \times$$

$$\{(E-E_m^{(H)})\sin\theta_{m(cc')} + \tfrac{1}{2}\Gamma_m^{(H)}\cos\theta_{m(cc')}\}$$

$$+2\sum_m \sum_{m'>m} \frac{\mathscr{P}_c^2 \mathscr{P}_{c'}^2}{|\mathscr{P}_{mc}\mathscr{P}_{mc'}\mathscr{P}_{m'c}\mathscr{P}_{m'c'}|} \times$$

$$\frac{G_{m(c)} G_{m(c')} G_{m'(c)} G_{m'(c')}}{\{(E-E_m^{(H)})^2+(\frac{1}{2}\Gamma_m^{(H)})^2\}\{(E-E_{m'}^{(H)})^2+(\frac{1}{2}\Gamma_{m'}^{(H)})^2\}} \times$$

$$[\{(E-E_m^{(H)})(E-E_{m'}^{(H)}) + \tfrac{1}{4}\Gamma_m^{(H)}\Gamma_{m'}^{(H)}\}\cos(\theta_{m'(cc')}-\theta_{m(cc')})$$

$$-\{\tfrac{1}{2}\Gamma_{m'}^{(H)}(E-E_m^{(H)}) - \tfrac{1}{2}\Gamma_m^{(H)}(E-E_{m'}^{(H)})\}\sin(\theta_{m'(cc')}-\theta_{m(cc')})]\Bigg\} \qquad (2.113)$$

where $\theta_{m(cc')} = \arg Q_{cc'} - \xi_{m(c)} - \xi_{m(c')}$.

The total cross-section is

$$\sigma_T = \frac{2\pi}{k_\alpha^2}\sum_{J\pi} g_J \sum_{ls}{}' \Bigg\{ -\mathscr{P}_c^2 \operatorname{Re} Q_{cc}$$

$$-\sum_m \frac{\mathscr{P}_c^2}{|\mathscr{P}_{mc}|^2} \cdot \frac{G_{m(c)}^2 \sin(2\xi_{m(c)})(E-E_m^{(H)})}{(E-E_m^{(H)})^2+(\frac{1}{2}\Gamma_m^{(H)})^2}$$

$$+\frac{1}{2}\sum_m \frac{\mathscr{P}_c^2}{|\mathscr{P}_{mc}|^2} \cdot \frac{G_{m(c)}^2 \Gamma_m^{(H)} \cos(2\xi_{m(c)})}{(E-E_m^{(H)})^2+(\frac{1}{2}\Gamma_m^{(H)})^2}\Bigg\}. \qquad (2.114)$$

The specializations to the single-level case are obvious.

H. THE RELATIONSHIP OF S-MATRIX THEORY TO R-MATRIX THEORY

1. S-matrix expansions of R-matrix expressions for the collision matrix

(a) *Single level without background*

Superficially, eqn. (2.64) for the single-level collision matrix from R-matrix theory already appears to be in the form of the one-level

S-matrix expansion. This is not quite so, however, for $E_m^{(H)}$ and $\Gamma_m^{(H)}$ are constants, independent of energy, whereas the level shift Δ_0 and total width Γ_0 of eqn. (2.64) are energy-dependent through the shift and penetration factors. Often, this energy-dependence is unimportant, but many cases do arise in which it must be considered. An approximate way of including the energy dependence of Δ_0 and Γ_0 is to assume a linear energy variation (Lane and Thomas 1958). Thus, making the abbreviation

$$\zeta_0 = \Delta_0 + \tfrac{1}{2}\mathrm{i}\Gamma_0, \tag{2.115}$$

Lane and Thomas obtain

$$E_0 - \Delta_0 - E - \tfrac{1}{2}\mathrm{i}\Gamma_0 = \{1 + (\mathrm{d}\zeta_0/\mathrm{d}E)_{E=E_0^\dagger}\}(E_0^{(H)} - E - \tfrac{1}{2}\mathrm{i}\Gamma_0^{(H)}), \tag{2.116}$$

where

$$E_0^\dagger = E_0 - \Delta_0(E_0^\dagger), \tag{2.116a}$$

$$E_0^{(H)} = E_0^\dagger - \frac{\tfrac{1}{2}\Gamma_0(E_0^\dagger)\mathrm{Im}(\mathrm{d}\zeta_0/\mathrm{d}E)}{\{1+\mathrm{Re}(\mathrm{d}\zeta_0/\mathrm{d}E)\}^2 + \{\mathrm{Im}(d\zeta_0/\mathrm{d}E)\}^2}, \tag{2.116b}$$

$$\Gamma_0^{(H)} = \left\{\frac{1+\mathrm{Re}(\mathrm{d}\zeta_0/\mathrm{d}E)}{\{1+\mathrm{Re}(\mathrm{d}\zeta_0/\mathrm{d}E)\}^2 + \{\mathrm{Im}(\mathrm{d}\zeta_0/\mathrm{d}E)\}^2}\right\}\Gamma_0(E_0^\dagger). \tag{2.116c}$$

To complete the S-matrix form it is apparent that

$$G_{0(c)} = \{(1+\mathrm{Re}(\mathrm{d}\zeta_0/\mathrm{d}E))^2 + (\mathrm{Im}(\mathrm{d}\zeta_0/\mathrm{d}E))^2\}^{-\frac{1}{4}}|\mathscr{P}_{mc}| \cdot \left(\frac{2^{\frac{1}{2}}P_c^{\frac{1}{2}}}{\mathscr{P}_c}\gamma_{0(c)}\right) \tag{2.117}$$

and

$$\xi_{0(c)} = -\phi_c - \tfrac{1}{2}\mathrm{atan}\left(\frac{\mathrm{Im}(\mathrm{d}\zeta_0/\mathrm{d}E)}{1+\mathrm{Re}(\mathrm{d}\zeta_0/\mathrm{d}E)}\right). \tag{2.118}$$

Notice that q_0 is, in general, greater than unity for this approximation.

(b) Narrow, non-interfering levels

S-matrix expansions are obtained by finding the poles and residues of R-matrix theory expressions for the collision matrix. The most convenient form of the collision matrix for this purpose is the level matrix form, eqn. (2.48). In the narrow, non-interfering level approximation, the off-diagonal elements of the level matrix, $\mathbf{C}$, given by eqn. (2.49), are assumed to be negligible. The inversion of $\mathbf{C}$, to obtain the reciprocal level matrix $\mathbf{A}$, is then perfectly simple, and we obtain for the collision matrix

$$U_{c'c}-\delta_{c'c} = (\Omega_{c'}\Omega_c-1)\delta_{c'c}+\mathrm{i}\sum_{\lambda}\frac{\Omega_{c'}\Gamma^{\frac{1}{2}}_{\lambda(c')}\Gamma^{\frac{1}{2}}_{\lambda(c)}\Omega_c}{E_\lambda-\Delta_\lambda-E-\frac{1}{2}\mathrm{i}\Gamma_\lambda}. \tag{2.119}$$

If we compare this with eqn. (2.112) and neglect the energy variation of wave numbers and penetration factors, it is apparent that, for $\lambda = m$,

$$E^{(\mathrm{H})}_m = E_\lambda-\Delta_\lambda, \tag{2.120a}$$

$$\Gamma^{(\mathrm{H})}_m = \Gamma_\lambda, \tag{2.120b}$$

$$G_{m(c)} = \frac{|\mathscr{P}_{mc}|}{\mathscr{P}_c}|\Gamma^{\frac{1}{2}}_{\lambda(c)}|, \tag{2.120c}$$

$$\exp(\mathrm{i}\sigma_c)\exp(\mathrm{i}\xi_{m(c)}) = \mathrm{sign}(\Gamma^{\frac{1}{2}}_{\lambda(c)})\Omega_c, \tag{2.120d}$$

$$\mathrm{e}^{\mathrm{i}(\sigma_c+\sigma_{c'})}\mathscr{P}_{c'}\mathscr{P}_cQ_{c'c} = (\Omega_{c'}\Omega_c-1)\delta_{c'c}, \tag{2.120e}$$

provided that the energy variation of Δ_λ and Γ_λ can be neglected.

(c) *The two-level formula*

When the off-diagonal elements of the reciprocal level matrix are not unimportant the relation of the collision matrix to the R-matrix theory parameters is not at all simple. The poles of the collision matrix may be found by solving the secular equation

$$\det(\mathbf{C}) = 0. \tag{2.121}$$

In the two-level case it turns out that

$$E^{(\mathrm{H})}_m-\tfrac{1}{2}\mathrm{i}\Gamma^{(\mathrm{H})}_m = E_1-\Delta_1-\tfrac{1}{2}\mathrm{i}\Gamma_1-Z_m \tag{2.122}$$

where

$$Z_m = \tfrac{1}{2}\{-b\pm\sqrt{(b^2+4C^2_{12})}\}, \tag{2.122a}$$

$$b = (E_2-E_1-\Delta_2+\Delta_1)-\tfrac{1}{2}\mathrm{i}(\Gamma_2-\Gamma_1). \tag{2.122b}$$

In eqn. (2.122a) the upper sign before the radicand refers to $m = 1$ and the lower to $m = 2$. The residues (divided by $-\mathrm{i}$) of the collision matrix at these poles are (omitting Coulomb phase shifts from now on)

$$\frac{\mathscr{P}_{c'}\mathscr{P}_{c}}{|\mathscr{P}_{mc'}\mathscr{P}_{mc}|}e^{i\xi_{m(c')}}G_{m(c')}G_{m(c)}e^{i\xi_{m(c)}}$$
$$= \frac{\Gamma^{\frac{1}{2}}_{1(c')}\Gamma^{\frac{1}{2}}_{1(c)}(b+Z_m)}{(b+2Z_m)}+\frac{\Gamma^{\frac{1}{2}}_{2(c')}\Gamma^{\frac{1}{2}}_{2(c)}Z_m}{(b+2Z_m)} \quad (2.123)$$
$$-\frac{C_{12}(\Gamma^{\frac{1}{2}}_{1(c')}\Gamma^{\frac{1}{2}}_{2(c)}+\Gamma^{\frac{1}{2}}_{2(c')}\Gamma^{\frac{1}{2}}_{1(c)})}{(b+2Z_m)}.$$

If the partial-level shifts $\Delta_{\lambda(c)}$ are assumed to be zero (by adjustment of the boundary conditions at the surface of the internal region) then it is readily seen, the term $4C_{12}^2$ in eqn. (2.122a) being negative, that the

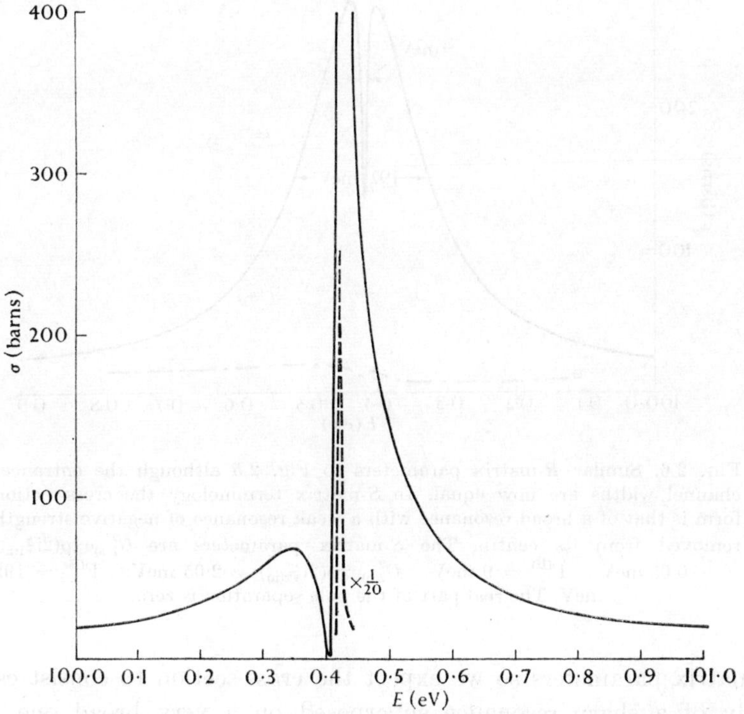

FIG. 2.5. The cross-section calculated for two R-matrix levels with the parameters $\Gamma_{1(n)} = 0{\cdot}01$ meV, $\Gamma_{1(r)} = 122$ meV, $\Gamma_1 = 122{\cdot}01$ meV, $E_2 = E_1+30$ meV, $\Gamma_{1(n)} = 2$ meV, $\Gamma_{2(r)} = 122$ meV, $\Gamma_2 = 124$ meV, i.e. almost identical total widths although the small entrance-channel widths are considerably different. The form of the cross-section is distinctly that of a narrow resonance superposed on a broad resonance although there is also some interference. The S-matrix parameters are $G^2_{1(n)}\exp(2i\xi_{1(n)}) = (0{\cdot}84-i0{\cdot}25)$ meV, $G_1{}^2{}_{(r)}$ exp $(2i\xi_{1(r)}) = (-3{\cdot}85+i0{\cdot}27)$ meV, $\Gamma^{(H)}_1 = 4{\cdot}6$ meV, $G^2_{2(n)}\exp(2i\xi_{2(n)}) = (1{\cdot}15+i0{\cdot}25)$ meV, $G^2_{2(r)}\exp(2i\xi_{2(r)}) = (248-i0{\cdot}27)$ meV, $\Gamma^{(H)}_2 = 241$ meV. The real separation of the poles is 0·1 meV.

energies $E_1^{(\mathrm{H})}$ and $E_2^{(\mathrm{H})}$ lie between the eigenvalues E_1 and E_2. In addition, one of the wdiths $\Gamma_1^{(\mathrm{H})}$, $\Gamma_2^{(\mathrm{H})}$ is less than the smaller of Γ_1 and Γ_2, and the other is greater than the larger of this pair.

These results can be used to illustrate the kind of situation in which the parameters of the two formalisms are very different. In the extreme case of two close broad R-matrix levels with the predominant parts of their widths in a single channel, the S-matrix poles consist of a narrow resonant state and a very broad resonant state. The cross-sections are much more directly related to the S-matrix parameters than to the

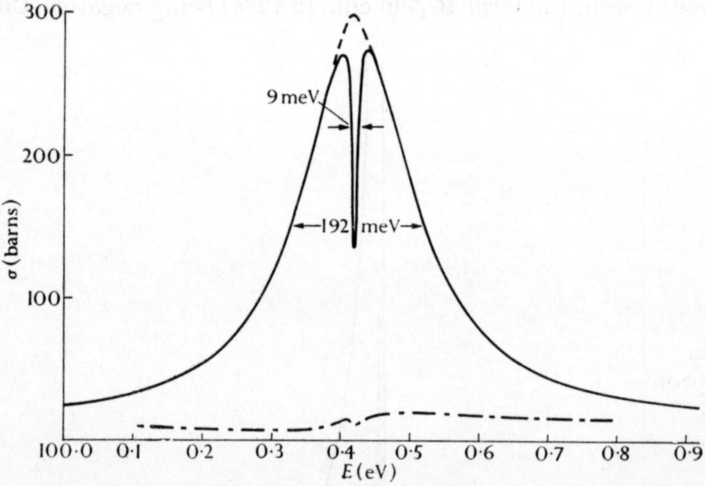

FIG. 2.6. Similar R-matrix parameters to Fig. 2.5 although the entrance-channel widths are now equal. In S-matrix terminology the cross-section form is that of a broad resonance with a weak resonance of negative strength removed from its centre. The S-matrix parameters are $G^2_{1(\mathrm{n})}\exp(2i\xi_{1(\mathrm{n})}) = -0{\cdot}05$ meV, $\Gamma_1^{(\mathrm{H})} = 9$ meV, $G^2_{2(\mathrm{n})}\exp(2i\xi_{2(\mathrm{n})}) = 2{\cdot}05$ meV, $\Gamma_2^{(\mathrm{H})} = 192$ meV. The real part of the pole separation is zero.

R-matrix parameters so we expect the cross-section to consist essentially of a sharp resonance superposed on a very broad one. The cross-section in a typical case is shown in Fig. 2.5 where it is clear that this is indeed the case. Occasionally the situation is not nearly so clear cut, however. The cross-section due to two identical R-matrix levels is shown in Fig. 2.6; now seems that the R-matrix parameters give a better idea of the form of the cross-section than the S-matrix parameters do. The reason is that the full entrance-channel width quantity $G^2_{m(\mathrm{c})}$ exp $\{2i\xi_{m(\mathrm{c})}\}$ for the narrow resonant state is negative and the corresponding resonance appears as a narrow dip in the broad resonance peak. In a more fundamental sense, however, there is still physical value in the S-matrix representation even in this extreme case. According to the Heisenberg uncertainty principle the energy spread of any feature in the cross-section is inversely proportional to the half-life of a term in the time development of the wave-function, the constant of proportionality being Planck's constant. This implies that for the sharpest distinct feature in the cross-section there ought to be a corresponding long-lived term in the wave-function expansion, whether the feature be a dip or a peak. Thus the minimum in Fig. 2.6, being much narrower than either maximum, ought to be represented in this picture by a long-lived resonant state in the wave-function expansion, and, as we have seen, this is so. Other examples of two-level cases can be found in Chapter VIII.

2. Unitarity of the *S*-matrix form

(a) Parametrization

If it is desired to fit a single partial cross-section using the single-level formula without background then, from eqn. (2.113), there are clearly three parameters available in S-matrix theory, namely $E_m^{(\mathrm{H})}$, $\Gamma_m^{(\mathrm{H})}$ and $G_{m(\mathrm{c})}^2 G_{m(\mathrm{c}')}^2$. It has been pointed out (Mahaux 1965) that in R-matrix theory there are more available parameters. If it is assumed that the boundary conditions are adjusted to give zero level shift, the parameters apparently required are E_λ, Γ_λ, $\gamma^2{}_{\lambda(\mathrm{c})}\gamma^2{}_{\lambda(\mathrm{c}')}$ and the energy variation of Δ_λ and Γ_λ. In actual fact, as illustrated by eqns. (2.116)–(2.118), only three combinations of these are actually available. If a complete set of partial cross-sections are to be fitted then, in principle, one fewer parameter is required for the R-matrix fit than for the S-matrix fit. This is also true for the representation of the total cross-section alone if the energy variation of the R-matrix level shift and width can be ignored. Then the R-matrix representation requires the parameters E_λ, Γ_λ, and $\Gamma_{\lambda(\mathrm{c})}$ while the S-matrix form demands $E_m^{(\mathrm{H})}$, $\Gamma_m^{(\mathrm{H})}$, $G_m{}^2{}_{(\mathrm{c})}$, and $\xi_{m(\mathrm{c})}$. If background is included the former theory requires, in addition, R_{cc}^∞ while the latter needs $\mathrm{Re}Q_{\mathrm{cc}}$.

If a set of partial cross-sections is to be fitted to more than one level, then the number of R-matrix parameters is, in principle, considerably fewer than the number of S-matrix parameters because of the various combinations of pole-channel phase factors required for the latter. The reason for the difference lies in the fact that in R-matrix

7

theory unitarity is built into the collision matrix, whereas in S-matrix theory this is not so.

(b) One-level collision matrix without background

The imposition of unitarity on the collision matrix of the S-matrix theory reveals various relationships among the parameters required by this theory. For example, the use of the unitarity relation, eqn. (2.37), on the single-level S-matrix form without background gives

$$2(E-E_m^{(\mathrm{H})})\sin(\xi_{m(\mathrm{c})}+\xi_{m(\mathrm{c}')})-\Gamma_m^{(\mathrm{H})}\cos(\xi_{m(\mathrm{c})}+\xi_{m(\mathrm{c}')})$$
$$+\sum_{\mathrm{c}''}\frac{\mathscr{P}^2_{\mathrm{c}''}}{|\mathscr{P}_{m\mathrm{c}''}|^2}G^2_{m(\mathrm{c}'')}\{\cos(\xi_{m(\mathrm{c})}-\xi_{m(\mathrm{c}')})+i\sin(\xi_{m(\mathrm{c})}-\xi_{m(\mathrm{c}')})\}=0. \tag{2.124}$$

If the dependence of the factors $\mathscr{P}_{\mathrm{c}}$ on energy are neglected this equation is valid for all E only if

$$\xi_{m(\mathrm{c})}=n\pi, \tag{2.124a}$$

where n is an integer or zero, for all c, and

$$\Gamma_m^{(\mathrm{H})}=\sum_{\mathrm{c}}\frac{\mathscr{P}^2_{\mathrm{c}}}{|\mathscr{P}_{m\mathrm{c}}|^2}G^2_{m(\mathrm{c})}. \tag{2.124b}$$

These conditions are obtained by equating the real and imaginary parts of the coefficients of the different powers of E on the left-hand side of eqn. (2.124) separately to zero.

An assumed linear energy dependence of the $\mathscr{P}^2_{\mathrm{c}}$ alters the results. Suppose

$$\mathscr{P}^2_{\mathrm{c}}(E)=\mathscr{P}^2_{\mathrm{c}}(E_m^{(\mathrm{H})})+(E-E_m^{(\mathrm{H})})\left\{\frac{\mathrm{d}}{\mathrm{d}E}(\mathscr{P}^2_{\mathrm{c}})\right\}_{E=E_m^{(\mathrm{H})}}, \tag{2.125}$$

then we find

$$\sin(\xi_{m(\mathrm{c})}-\xi_{m(\mathrm{c}')})=0, \tag{2.126}$$

$$\sin(2\xi_{m(\mathrm{c})})=-\frac{1}{2}\sum_{\mathrm{c}''}\frac{1}{|\mathscr{P}_{m\mathrm{c}''}|^2}\frac{\mathrm{d}}{\mathrm{d}E}(\mathscr{P}^2_{\mathrm{c}''})G^2_{m(\mathrm{c}'')}, \tag{2.127}$$

and

$$\Gamma_m^{(\mathrm{H})}=(1/\cos 2\xi_{m(\mathrm{c})})\sum_{\mathrm{c}''}\mathscr{P}^2_{\mathrm{c}''}(E_m^{(\mathrm{H})})G^2_{m(\mathrm{c}'')}/|\mathscr{P}_{m\mathrm{c}''}|^2. \tag{2.128}$$

These results are all in accord with those of subsection 2(a).

(c) One-level collision matrix with background

If the background matrix Q is assumed to be diagonal, and the energy variation of penetration factors is neglected, unitarity imposes the following conditions on the S-matrix parameters:

$$2\mathrm{Re}Q_{cc} = -\mathscr{P}_c^2|Q_{cc}|^2, \tag{2.129}$$

$$\xi_{m(c)} = \frac{1}{2}\arctan\left(\frac{\mathscr{P}_c^2\mathrm{Im}Q_{cc}}{\mathscr{P}_c^2\mathrm{Re}Q_{cc}+1}\right), \tag{2.130}$$

$$\Gamma_m^{(\mathrm{H})} = \sum_c \frac{\mathscr{P}_c^2}{|\mathscr{P}_{mc}|^2} G_{m(c)}^2. \tag{2.131}$$

(d) The low-energy asymptotic form of the single-level s-wave formula

If the proper energy-dependence of the threshold factors is taken into account some real difficulties are found in using the single-level formula with background. These are well exemplified by the s-wave neutron case, and we confine our discussion to this.

Let us refer back to eqns. (2.113) and (2.114) for the cross-sections as given by S-matrix theory. If the incoming channel c is that of an s-wave neutron (the energy being low enough so that all other terms in the sum over l are negligible) the threshold factor $\mathscr{P}_c$ is just $k^{\frac{1}{2}}$. Then the background term in the elastic scattering cross-section is just $\pi\sum_J g_J|Q_{cc}|^2$, and if it is assumed that $|Q_{cc}|^2$ is independent of energy within the slow neutron region this provides the observed constancy of potential scattering as the neutron energy tends to zero. This asymptotic energy behaviour is also true of the interference and resonance terms of eqn. (2.113) provided that within the asymptotic range the energy E is much less than $|E_m^{(\mathrm{H})}|$.

If eqn. (2.113) is applied to a reaction cross-section of high Q-value, the threshold factors for the reaction channels c′ do not vary significantly as the neutron energy is changed to zero in the s-wave range. It is then obvious that the cross-section has the experimentally observed $1/\sqrt{E}$ behaviour. In these respects eqn. (2.113) appears entirely satisfactory.

The total cross-section, eqn. (2.114), is not so satisfactory in this way, however. Equation (2.114) is not deduced from the sum of eqns. (2.113) but is obtained from the relation (2.43) based on unitarity of the collision matrix. It would seem desirable that in the s-wave region the background constant $\mathrm{Re}Q_{cc}$ should be energy independent, but if this assumption is made the contribution of the background term to the total cross-section is proportional to $1/\sqrt{E}$ even though physical intuition would suggest that it should represent the constant potential scattering cross-section. Constant behaviour can of course be obtained by making $\mathrm{Re}Q_{cc}$ proportional to $\sqrt{E}$, but this does not affect the behaviour of the remaining terms on the right-hand side of eqn. (2.114). The second term should clearly represent the interference between resonance and potential scattering and therefore should also have an asymptotic independence of energy. In fact, its behaviour is again proportional to $1/\sqrt{E}$, which is a very serious difficulty impeding the use of eqn. (2.114). The third or resonance term of eqn. (2.114) also has the asymptotic behaviour of proportionality to $1/\sqrt{E}$. In this case the behaviour should be a mixture of the $1/v$ term and a constant term, the former resulting from reaction and the latter from elastic scattering. In the case of pure elastic scattering, the energy-dependence of this term in eqn. (2.114) is again quite wrong.

The reason for this curious paradox resulting from a well-founded theory lies in the fact that the term involving $\mathrm{Re}Q_{cc}$ cannot be regarded as just a potential scattering term, nor can it be regarded as having a 'simple' energy-dependence. This does not necessarily clash in practice with regarding the term due to $|Q_{cc}|^2$ in eqn. (2.113) as a potential scattering term, for it can be shown (from eqn. 2.129) that in the low wave-number region $|\mathrm{Re}Q_{cc}|^2$ is much smaller than $|Q_{cc}|^2$.

Let us assume that $\mathrm{Re}Q_{cc}$ and $\mathrm{Im}Q_{cc}$ can be written in series form

$$|k_{mc}|\,\mathrm{Re}Q_{cc} = \sum_n b_n E^n, \tag{2.132a}$$

$$\mathrm{Im}Q_{cc} = \sum_n c_n E^n. \tag{2.132b}$$

Then, after including the $\sqrt{E}$ dependence of $\mathscr{P}_c^2$ in the unitarity equation for the one-level form with background and separating the coefficients of different powers of $\sqrt{E}$, the following equations are found for the coefficients b_n:

$$b_0 = \frac{\left\{2E_m \sin 2\xi_{m(c)} - \sum_{c'\neq c} G^2_{m(c')} + \Gamma_m \cos 2\xi_{m(c)}\right\} G_{m(c)}}{2(E_m^2 + \frac{1}{4}\Gamma_m^2)}, \tag{2.133a}$$

$$b_1 = \frac{4E_m b_0 - 2G^2_{m(c)} \sin 2\xi_{m(c)}}{2(E^2 + \frac{1}{4}\Gamma^2)}, \tag{2.133b}$$

$$b_2 = \frac{4E_m b_1 - 2b_0}{2(E_m^2 + \frac{1}{2}\Gamma_m^2)}, \tag{2.133c}$$

$$b_n = \frac{4E_m b_{(n-1)} - 2b_{(n-2)}}{2(E_m^2 + \frac{1}{2}\Gamma_m^2)}. \tag{2.133d}$$

This expansion for Re Q renders the entire elastic scattering contribution to the total cross-section equal to zero. The implication here is that for this particular asymptotic situation the convergence coefficient, $M = 1$, chosen for the Mittag-Leffler expansion, eqn. (2.104), is not high enough. The most satisfactory expansion for this special case is probably one in the wave-number plane with $M = 2$ (Humblet and Rosenfeld 1961).

(e) Two-level collision matrix without background

There is even more complication in the formulae for more than one level. Here we confine ourselves to two levels without background. In the same way as before we find that an important condition imposed by unitarity on the two-level collision matrix (again assuming that energy-dependence of the penetration factors is unimportant) is

$$\sum_m \frac{\mathscr{P}_c \mathscr{P}_{c'}}{|\mathscr{P}_{mc}\mathscr{P}_{mc'}|} G_{m(c)} G_{m(c')} \sin(\xi_{m(c)} + \xi_{m(c')}) = 0. \tag{2.134a}$$

This can be interpreted as either all pole-channel phase factors being zero or, less stringently, that

$$\frac{|\mathscr{P}_{2c}\mathscr{P}_{2c'}|}{|\mathscr{P}_{1c}\mathscr{P}_{1c'}|} G_{1(c)} G_{1(c')} \sin(\xi_{1(c)} + \xi_{1(c')}) = -G_{2(c)} G_{2(c')} \sin(\xi_{2(c)} + \xi_{2(c')}). \tag{2.134b}$$

This condition results from setting the coefficient of the highest power of the energy equal to zero in the unitarity equation. From the other terms, other, more complicated, relations can be found. It is possible to gain some idea of the magnitude of the channel-pole phase factor $\xi_{m(c)}$ by treating the other pole as if it were a background term. If the separation of the poles is large compared with their widths this procedure leads to

$$\xi_{m(c)} \approx \tfrac{1}{2}\,\mathrm{atan}\left\{\frac{-G^2_{m'(c)}\cos 2\xi_{m'(c)}}{(E_m - E_{m'})}\right\}. \tag{2.135a}$$

non-diagonal terms being ignored. In the other extreme ($\Gamma_{m'}$ much greater than the separation) the phase is given very roughly by

$$\xi_{m(c)} = \tfrac{1}{2}\,\mathrm{atan}\left\{\frac{-G^2_{m'(c)}\sin 2\xi_{m'(c)}}{\frac{1}{2}\Gamma_{m'} - G^2_{m'(c)}\cos 2\xi_{m'(c)}}\right\}. \tag{2.135b}$$

(*f*) *Many levels without background*

The same application of unitarity reveals an overall correlation among all the phase factors associated with the residues of the poles:

$$\sum_m G_{m(c)} G_{m(c')} \sin(\xi_{m(c)} + \xi_{m(c')}) = 0. \tag{2.136}$$

Such an overall correlation is expected to be superimposed on stronger correlations exhibiting themselves, for example, as approximate satisfactions of eqn. (2.134) on pairs of close states.

3. Conclusions

From the foregoing discussions it is clear that the S-matrix formulation of nuclear reaction theory has the advantage of a physically clear definition of resonance energy and rather simple expressions for the cross-sections. Much of the latter advantage is lost, however, by the greater number of parameters and the complicated correlations that implicitly exist among them. Because of this, it seems that R-matrix theory, which has the great advantage of having unitarity built into it, is simpler in practice to handle in spite of its more-complicated formulae. Finally, the complementarity of the two theories ought to be stressed; the difficulty of resonance definition in the dynamical R-matrix formalism can be avoided by relating the R-matrix parameters for the collision matrix to the resonant states dominating the structure of the S-matrix.

I. OTHER REACTION THEORIES

Although the two foregoing theories are the only ones we shall use in this book there are several alternatives available. Two of the most important are due to Kapur and Peierls (1938) and Feshbach (1962). The former employs two sets of eigenstates and eigenvalues. The boundary conditions required for their definition require the logarithmic derivatives of the interior wave-function at each channel entrance to be equal to the logarithmic derivative of the radial outgoing or ingoing wave-function, respectively, in that channel. These two sets of eigenstates are mutually, but not separately, orthogonal, and the necessary expansions must be made in terms of both of them. The resulting cross-section expressions are very similar in form to those of the S-matrix theory, but the parameters are all energy dependent. Adler and Adler (1966) have shown how the R-matrix theory may be transformed into the Kapur–Peierls formalism.

Feshbach's formalism is based on the use of suitable projection operators to select from the complete wave-function the part that is of physical interest. One such operator partitions the wave-function into closed and open channel segments, but no channel radii need be defined in order to do this. From this partition an effective Hamiltonian for the open channels is derived and from the analysis of its structure various aspects of nuclear reaction theory such as direct and compound-nucleus processes may be obtained. By the use of other projection operators the R-matrix formalism, the Kapur–Peierls expansion, and the Humblet–Rosenfeld expansion can be demonstrated.

III

THE SINGLE-PARTICLE MODEL OF NEUTRON REACTIONS

A. FORMAL CONSIDERATIONS

ALTHOUGH the single-particle model is far from being a valid description of neutron reactions it is a very useful basis for more realistic discussions of the subject. In the single-particle model the entire interaction between projectile and target is assumed to be a central potential field varying smoothly with radial distance from the centre. Elastic scattering is obviously the only particle reaction that can be treated by such a model.

The usual way of analysing the scattering by a potential field is to use the phase-shift method described in several texts on quantum mechanics (e.g. see Schiff 1949), but it is more expedient in the present case to use the R-matrix formalism. Suppose, for simplicity, that there is no spin-orbit coupling term in the potential field so that the collision function will depend only on the orbital angular momentum l and not on the projectile-target channel spin s with which it is coupled to give total angular momentum J. Then the total cross-section for a partial wave with orbital angular momentum quantum number l coupled to total spin quantum number J is written in terms of the collision function $U(J, l)$ (from eqn. 2.43)

$$\sigma_{\mathrm{T}}(J, l) = 2\pi\lambda\!\!\!^{-2} \sum_{s=|J-l|}^{J+l} g_J\{1-\mathrm{Re}\,U(J, l)\}. \tag{3.1}$$

The collision function is itself a function of the derivative or R-function which is the ratio of the wave function in the interior region to its derivative, both these quantities being evaluated at a radial distance a where the potential energy has become asymptotically zero (in the absence of a Coulomb force). The R-function has a simple expansion in terms of the discrete eigenvalues and eigenfunctions of the solution of the Schrödinger equation with a real, constant boundary condition on the radial wave-functions $u_{\mathrm{p}}(r)$ at the radius a (cf. eqn. (2.30)): it is

$$R(J) = \sum_{\mathrm{p}} \frac{\gamma_{\mathrm{p}}^2}{E_{\mathrm{p}}-E} \tag{3.2}$$

where p refers to the eigenvalues for the solution with total angular momentum quantum number J and parity $(-)^l$, γ_p is the product of the eigenfunction value at radius a and the factor $(\hbar^2/2Ma)^{\frac{1}{2}}$. The collision function is related to the R-function through the equation

$$U(J,l) = \mathrm{e}^{-2\mathrm{i}\phi_l}\cdot\frac{1-(L_l^*-B_l^J)R(J)}{1-(L_l-B_l^J)R(J)} \tag{3.3}$$

which is simply the scalar form of eqn. (2.47). Here $-\phi_l$ is the phase shift for l-wave particles scattered from a hard sphere of radius a. The quantity B_l^J is the boundary condition imposed on the eigensolutions of the Schrödinger equation

$$B_l^J = (r/u_\mathrm{p})(du_\mathrm{p}/dr)_{r=a}.$$

Since the R-function is real in the potential-well model (the radial wave-functions and eigenvalues being real), the collision function may be expressed in the form

$$U(J,l) = \exp[-2\mathrm{i}\{\phi_l-\mathrm{atan}(P_l R(J)/(1-\hat{S}_l^J R(J))\}], \tag{3.4}$$

where $\hat{S}_l = S_l - B_l$ may be called the *modified shift factor*. From eqns. (3.1) and (3.4) it is found that the condition for maximum cross-section is

$$\phi_l-\mathrm{atan}\left(\frac{P_l R(J)}{1-\hat{S}_l^J R(J)}\right) = \frac{(2\mathrm{p}+1)\pi}{2} \tag{3.5}$$

with p an integer.

For the purposes of low-energy neutron spectroscopy we may confine further discussion to the limit of very low energy ($\phi_l \ll 1$). From eqn. (3.5) it then becomes apparent that the energy of maximum cross-section will differ from the eigenvalue E_p by a 'level-shift' quantity $\Delta_{\mathrm{p}(l)} = -\hat{S}_l^J\gamma_\mathrm{p}^2$. This quantity tends to zero in the limit of low energy provided that the boundary condition is chosen to be $B_l = -l$. This is also the boundary condition, in the limit of zero energy, of the bound single-particle states, which are properly determined by using the physical boundary condition of vanishing wave-function in the limit of very large radial coordinate.

The eigenvalues E_p of a square potential well with $V(r) = V_0$ where $r < a$ and $V(r) = 0$ where $r \geqslant a$ are given (with the boundary condition $B_l = -l$) by

$$E_\mathrm{p} = V_0+(\hbar^2/2Ma^2)\mu_{\mathrm{p}l} \tag{3.6}$$

where μ_{pl} is the pth root of the equation for the spherical Bessel function $j_{l-1}(\mu_{pl}) = 0$. For s-waves ($l = 0$) the recursion formula leading to this result breaks down; in this case $\mu_{p0} = \pi^2(\mathrm{p}-\frac{1}{2})^2$. The reduced width amplitudes γ_p are equal to $(\hbar^2/Ma^2)^{\frac{1}{2}}$.

To obtain numerical estimates of the eigenvalues and reduced width amplitudes, it is necessary to know the dimensions of the potential well. Analyses of nuclear size suggest a relation of the following type for the dependence of nuclear radius R on mass number, A:

$$R = r_0 A^{\frac{1}{3}} \tag{3.7}$$

with r_0 a constant. Electrical measures of the nuclear size (such as high-energy electron scattering and the energies of μ-mesonic X-rays) give the estimate, $r_0 = (1{\cdot}20 \pm 0{\cdot}01)$fm (Hill 1956). This determines the radius of the proton distribution and, by assumption, the neutron distribution. The nuclear force region is expected to be larger than this by the nuclear force range b giving a potential-well radius of the form

$$a = r_0 A^{\frac{1}{3}} + b. \tag{3.8}$$

Neutron scattering at 90 MeV may be interpreted with the values $r_0 = 1{\cdot}23$ fm and $b = 0{\cdot}8$ fm for these constants (Hill 1956). The form of eqn. (3.7) has often been used for the potential radius. In this case r_0 turns out to be about 1·35 fm.

For order-of-magnitude numerical formulae we accept the form of eqn. (3.7) and this last estimate of r_0. The numerical form of eqn. (3.6) for the eigenvalues with $l = 0$ is

$$E_\mathrm{p} = V_0 + \frac{0{\cdot}20\times 10^{-23}}{r_0^2 A^{\frac{2}{3}}}(\mathrm{p}-\tfrac{1}{2})^2 \text{ MeV}$$

$$= V_0 + \frac{113}{A^{\frac{2}{3}}}(\mathrm{p}-\tfrac{1}{2})^2 \text{ MeV}. \tag{3.9}$$

The integer p will not usually be larger than 3 or 4 for an eigenvalue close to the top of the well, so that the spacing of such eigenvalues will be of the order of 30 MeV. The numerical estimate of the reduced width is

$$\gamma_\mathrm{p}^2 = \frac{\hbar^2}{Ma^2} = \frac{0{\cdot}4165\times 10^{-24}}{r_0^2 A^{\frac{2}{3}}} \text{MeV} = \frac{22{\cdot}8}{A^{\frac{2}{3}}} \text{MeV}. \tag{3.10}$$

The use of a nuclear force field with a sharp cut-off at a given radius is very crude. In all sophisticated work a milder radial dependence of the potential field is assumed. The usual form adopted for the nuclear potential is that due to Eckart (1930):

$$V(r) = \frac{V_0}{1+\exp\{(r-a)/d\}}. \tag{3.11}$$

Proton-scattering measurements yield $d = 0{\cdot}5$ fm and neutron-scattering measurements have given values of the same order of magnitude. Such diffuseness of the nuclear surface does not greatly affect the eigenvalues of the well (Vogt 1962) but has a considerable effect on the reduced widths. Vogt (1962) gives the following empirical formula for the reduced widths:

$$\gamma_{\mathrm{p}}^2 = \frac{\hbar^2}{Ma^2}(1+6{\cdot}7d^2), \tag{3.12}$$

where d is in units of fm, giving increases in the reduced widths, for reasonable values of d, of a factor of up to about 3 above the square well estimates.

It is necessary to add here only some remarks concerning the shape of the cross-section in the single-particle model. Although the single-level approximation to eqn. (3.2) suggests that the cross-section should exhibit a resonance peak with a total width $\Gamma_{\mathrm{p(T)}} \approx \Gamma_{\mathrm{p(n)}} = 2P_l\gamma_{\mathrm{p}}^2$ this does not necessarily occur. An $l = 0$ single-particle resonance in the continuum does not reveal itself as a maximum in the cross-section when plotted against energy but appears as a size resonance if the cross-section at a given low energy is viewed as a function of the potential-well radius. The resonances due to higher l do appear as maxima if the energy is low enough to render the penetration factor P_l very low and thus give a small value of $\Gamma_{\mathrm{p(T)}}$ across the resonance, i.e. when the virtual single-particle state is classically bound by the centrifugal barrier.

B. ANALYSIS OF NEUTRON CROSS-SECTION DATA

1. Low-energy elastic scattering data

The single-particle model already appears to correlate very low-energy neutron cross-section data. This was found by Bohm and Ford (1950) who analysed the coherent scattering lengths of a large number of nuclei at thermal neutron energy. The coherent scattering length is the weighted addition to the scattering lengths, $\alpha_{J(\mathrm{n})} = |1-U(J)|/2k$

for the total angular momenta possible in the interaction at very low energies (i.e. with zero orbital angular momentum, $l = 0$):

$$\alpha_{\text{coh}} = \sum_{J=|I-\frac{1}{2}|}^{I+\frac{1}{2}} g_J |1-U(J)|/2k. \tag{3.13}$$

These quantities, rather than the scattering cross-sections, were analysed because the latter are ambiguous inasmuch as they do not reveal the sign of the scattering length. Bohm and Ford plotted α_{coh} as a function

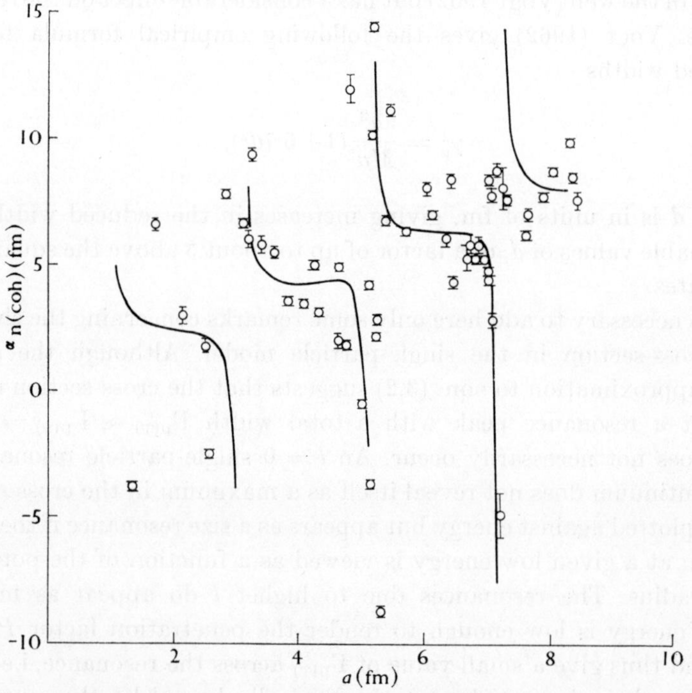

Fig. 3.1. Coherent scattering length plotted against the potential radius $a(=1{\cdot}35\ A^{\frac{1}{3}}\text{fm})$. The full curve is calculated from the single-particle model with square well potential, $\Gamma_0 = 1{\cdot}35 \times 10^{-13}$ cm, $V_0 = -50$ MeV.

of nuclear radius (from eqn. 3.7; they used $r_0 = 1{\cdot}45$ fm) and showed that there were strong discontinuities at mass number $A = 10$, 55, and 150, or radii $a = 3{\cdot}0$, $5{\cdot}6$, $7{\cdot}8$ fm. They took these to be the radii of the potential well at which the single-particle s-wave states lie at zero energy. From these radii they determined the depth of the well to be $V_0 = -45$ MeV. A revised version of Bohm and Ford's diagram is given in Fig. 3.1 using data compiled by Hughes and Schwartz (1958). The discontinuous curve which follows the general trend of the data is the scattering length calculated from eqns. (3.13), (3.2), (3.9), and (3.10) using $r_0 = 1{\cdot}35$ fm and $V_0 = -50$ MeV.

It is useful to study the low-energy cross-sections of the lightest nuclei in more detail, for in general their resonances are found to be broad and widely spaced. The low-energy values of the total (coherent plus diffuse) and coherent elastic scattering cross-sections σ_{n} and $\sigma_{\mathrm{n(coh)}}$ of some of these nuclei are listed in Table 3.1. The two quantities are related to the s-wave scattering lengths $\alpha_J = |1-U(J)|/2k$ for the states of total angular momentum J by

$$\sigma_{\mathrm{n(coh)}} = 4\pi\left(\sum_{J=|I-\frac{1}{2}|}^{I+\frac{1}{2}} g_J\alpha_J\right)^2, \tag{3.14}$$

$$\sigma_{\mathrm{n}} = 4\pi \sum_{J=|I-\frac{1}{2}|}^{I+\frac{1}{2}} g_J\alpha_J^2. \tag{3.15}$$

The scattering lengths deduced from these equations are also listed in the table. By using the nuclear radius, given by eqn. (2.8) with $r_0 = 1{\cdot}35$ fm, the R-function, $\sum_\lambda \gamma^2_{\lambda(\mathrm{n})}/(E_\lambda - E)$, is determined for zero neutron energy. If it is assumed that $R(J)$ is due essentially to one level, the single-particle s-wave state, it is apparent that the eigenvalue E_λ changes sign between ^{8}Li and ^{10}Be (taking the neutron separation energy as zero), and with the exception of ^{14}N it appears to become of decreasing importance as the mass number increases. This state would be assumed, in the single-particle picture, to be the 2s state of the nuclear potential well, the 1s state being filled by nucleons.

There is some evidence that in ^{10}Be this may indeed be approximately the single-particle state. The (d, p) reaction on ^{9}Be has revealed two states, one of spin $J = 1$ at 5·96 MeV excitation, the other with $J = 2$ at 6·26 MeV, both of which cause angular distribution patterns that correspond to an orbital angular momentum of zero for the captured neutron. The reduced widths of these states have been reported as approximately 1·4 MeV (Macfarlane and French 1960), which approaches the order of magnitude expected in the single-particle model (5.3 MeV according to eqn. (3.10)). Substitution of the excitation energies into the R-function values of Table 3.1 gives reduced width values of 1·4 and 1·0 MeV, respectively, confirming the analysis of the (d, p) work.

2. Radiative capture

Elastic scattering is the only particle reaction that is allowed in the single-particle model, but if the weak interaction of the system with

TABLE 3.1

The thermal scattering and coherent scattering properties of light nuclei, and deduced values of the R-function

Target nucleus	Nuclear radius a (10^{-13} cm)	Scattering cross-section, σ_n(barns)	Coherent cross-section, $\sigma_{n(coh)}$(barns)	Sign of coherent scattering amplitude	Angular momentum of scattering state, J	$\frac{\|1-U(J)\|}{2k}$ (10^{-13} cm)	$R(J)$
^{7}Li	2·58	1·4	0·8	(−)	1	0·298 or −5·34	0·88 or 3·07
					2	4·22 or −0·83	−0·64 or 0·68
^{9}Be	2·81	7·54	7·53	(+)	1	8·11 or 7·38	−1·88 or −1·63
					2	7 2 or 7·96	−1·68 or −1·83

^{13}C	3·16	5·5	4·5	(+)	0	10·9	−2·45
						or	or
						1·1	0·65
					1	4·4	−0·39
						or	or
						7·6	−1·4
^{14}N	3·25	11·4	11·0	(+)	½	11·9	−2·66
						or	or
						6·9	−1·15
					3/2	8·1	−1·49
						or	or
						10·6	−2·26
^{19}F	3·6	4·0	3·8	(+)	0	7·7	−1·14
						or	or
						3·3	0·08
					1	4·8	−0·33
						or	or
						6·2	−0·72

the electromagnetic field is considered then there is the possibility of capture of the bombarding particle accompanied by emission of radiation. The usual perturbation theory is adequate for the description of this phenomenon. The subject of radiative capture is dealt with more fully in Chapter VII, so we give here only the briefest summary of the relevant theory.

The cross-section for radiative capture is the sum of the transition probabilities from a plane wave Ψ_i of unit flux, undergoing scattering in the potential field, to a bound state (with wave function Ψ_f normalized to unity) in the same potential field. The transition probabilities for emission of electric multipole radiation carrying $\mathscr{L}$ units of angular momentum, $\mathscr{M}$ units of the projection of angular momentum upon an arbitrary axis and parity $(-)^{\mathscr{L}}$ are

$$T_{\mathrm{E}}(\mathscr{L},\mathscr{M}) = \frac{8\pi(\mathscr{L}+1)\kappa^{2\mathscr{L}+1}}{\mathscr{L}\{(2\mathscr{L}+1)!!\}^2\hbar}|\mathrm{Q}_{\mathscr{L}\mathscr{M}}|^2 \tag{3.16}$$

where the wave-number, κ, associated with the emitted photon is given in terms of the circular frequency ω and velocity of light c by $\kappa = \omega/c = \varepsilon_\gamma/\hbar c$. The quantity ε_γ is the energy emitted in the transition. In the long-wavelength approximation the semi-classical expression for the matrix element $\mathrm{Q}_{\mathscr{L}\mathscr{M}}$ reduces to

$$\mathrm{Q}_{\mathscr{L}\mathscr{M}} = e' \int \mathrm{d}\tau r^{\mathscr{L}} Y_{\mathscr{M}}^{(\mathscr{L})*}(\theta,\phi)\Psi_i^*\Psi_f \tag{3.17}$$

with the usual notation $Y_{\mathscr{M}}^{(\mathscr{L})}$ for the spherical harmonics, e' denoting the effective electric charge of the system.

We consider here only the most important term in the electric multipole expansion, the electric dipole term ($\mathscr{L} = 1$). For neutron bombardment of a target with electric charge Ze the cross-section for electric dipole capture is calculated from eqns. (3.16) and (3.17) to be

$$\sigma_{\gamma,E1} = \frac{2}{3}\frac{\varepsilon_\gamma^3}{(\hbar c)^3}\frac{e^2}{\hbar}\left(\frac{Z}{A}\right)^2 \sum_l (l+l_f+1)\left|\int_0^\infty \mathrm{d}r r^2 u_f \Psi_l\right|^2. \tag{3.18}$$

In deriving this equation it is assumed that there is no spin-orbit coupling term in the potential energy. The final state has orbital angular momentum l_f and can be separated into radial and angular parts:

$$\Psi_f = u_f(r) Y_m^{(l_f)}(\theta,\phi)/r. \tag{3.19}$$

The function ψ_l is proportional to the radial component of the lth term in the expansion of the scattered plane wave (cf. eqns. 2.34 and 2.35)

$$\psi_l = i\pi^{\frac{1}{2}}k^{-1}(I_l - U(l)O_l). \tag{3.20}$$

The numerical equivalent of eqn. (3.18) is

$$\sigma_{\gamma,E1} = 1{\cdot}8983\times10^{16}\varepsilon_\gamma^3\left(\frac{Z}{A}\right)^2\sum_l (l+l_f+1)\left|\int_0^\infty dr\,r^2 u_f \psi_l\right|^2, \tag{3.21}$$

the result being in barns if ε_γ is given in MeV; the wave functions in the radial matrix element are calculated using a basic length unit of 10^{-12}

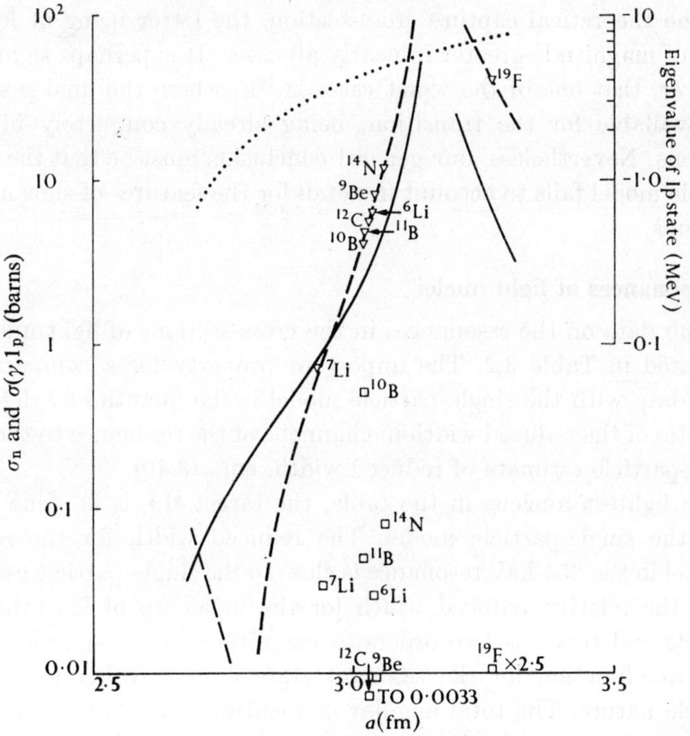

FIG. 3.2. Neutron scattering and radiative capture at thermal energies in the single-particle model compared with data. Dot curve indicates eigenvalue of the 1-p state; dash curve is model scattering cross-section, full curve is model capture cross-section, ∇ scattering cross-section data, □ capture cross-section data.

cm (10 fm). Notice that for E1 capture the values of l are limited by the selection rule $l = |l_f \pm 1|$.

Computations of the electric dipole capture cross-section have been carried out using eqn. (3.21) with an Eckart potential (eqn. 3.11) of depth $V_0 = -42$ MeV and diffuseness constant $d = 0{\cdot}058 \times 10^{-12}$ cm. Neutron capture data for light nuclei is generally available only at thermal neutron energies at which only s-waves ($l = 0$) are scattered. Thus the computation is limited to the case where the final state is a bound p-wave state ($l = 1$). The computations are compared with the data in Fig. 3.2. The radius assumed for each nucleus has been adjusted so that its scattering cross-section agrees with the calculation. Where the capture cross-section to a known final p-wave state is not available the total capture cross-section has been plotted instead. Even so, it is apparent that there is no agreement between the data and the theoretical capture cross-section, the latter being at least an order of magnitude greater in nearly all cases. It is perhaps significant, however, that one of the worst cases is ^{19}F, where the final p-state is not available for the transition, being already completely filled by nucleons. Nevertheless, our general conclusion must be that the single-particle model fails to account in detail for the features of slow neutron reactions.

3. Resonances of light nuclei

Some data on the resonances in the cross-sections of light nuclei are presented in Table 3.2. The important property for a comparison of these data with the single-particle model is the quantity θ_c^2 defined as the ratio of the reduced width in channel c of the resonance to the crude single-particle estimate of reduced width, eqn. (3.10).

The lightest nucleus in the table, the target ^{6}Li, is in some accord with the single-particle model. The reduced width for the neutron channel in the 255-keV resonance is close to the single-particle estimate, while the relative reduced width for the break up of ^{7}Li into an α-particle and triton is two orders of magnitude lower, suggesting that the wave-function for the resonant state is of a rather pure single-particle nature. The total angular momentum and parity of the state correspond to its excitation by p-wave neutrons, which is quite reasonable for this nucleus at the bottom of the $1p$ shell. No other resonances are observed at higher energies. The reduced neutron width for the resonance at 260 keV in the cross-section of ^{7}Li is somewhat smaller but not excessively so. Again this is a p-wave resonance.

The p-wave resonances of the nuclei above the lithium isotopes have considerably smaller neutron widths, but the appearance of d-wave excited resonances in the cross-sections of ^{11}B and heavier nuclei again suggests some validity in the single-particle model. The 1280 keV

TABLE 3.2

Some resonances in the neutron cross-sections of light nuclei. Details are taken from Stehn et al. (1964) *and Lane* (1960). *The channel-radius convention of the latter,* $a_c = 1{\cdot}45\,(A_{c_1}^{1/3}+A_{c_2}^{1/3})$ fm, *is employed in deducing* $\theta^2_{(c)}$

Target nucleus	$I\pi$	Compound nucleus	E_R (keV)	$J\pi$	$\Gamma_{R(n)}$ (keV)	l_n	$\theta^2_{(n)}$	Charged-particle channels		
								alpha-triton break-up		
								$\Gamma_{R(\alpha)}$ (keV)	l_α	$\theta^2_{(\alpha)}$
^{6}Li	1^+	^{7}Li	255	$5/2^-$	61	1	0·39	38	3	0·012
^{7}Li	$3/2^-$	^{8}Li	260	3^+	28	1	0·11			
^{9}Be	$3/2^-$	^{10}Be	620	3^+	23	1	0·021			
			810	2^+	7	1	0·0051			
^{11}B	3^-	^{12}B	430	2^+	37	1	0·054			
			1280	3^-	120	2	0·42			
^{12}C	0^+	^{13}C	2076	$5/2^+$	7	2	0·008			
			2950	$3/2^+$	90	2	0·04			
			3600	$3/2^+$	700	2	0·28			
^{13}C	$\frac{1}{2}^-$	^{14}C	153	1^+	13	1	0·076			
								proton channel		
								$\Gamma_{R(p)}$ (keV)	l_p	$\theta^2_{(p)}$
^{14}N	1^+	^{15}N	430	$\frac{1}{2}^-$	1·5	1	0·002	9·7	1	0·03
			640	$\frac{1}{2}^+$	24	0	0·014	15	0	0·005
			820	$\frac{1}{2}^+$	18	0	0·014	500	0	0·23
			910	$3/2^+$	34	0	0·02	0·5	2	0·003
			1020	$5/2^-$	22	1	0·01	0·03	3	0·002
			1100	$\frac{1}{2}^-$	20	1	0·009	0·3	1	0·0003
			1230	$5/2^-$	16	1	0·007	0·8	3	0·03
			1280	$5/2^+$	36	2	0·008	14	2	0·04
			1440	$3/2^+$	2·1	0	0·0007	0·3	2	0·006
^{16}O	0^+	^{17}O	442	$3/2^-$	42	1	0·057			
			1000	$3/2^+$	95	2	0·39			
			1312	$3/2^-$	33	1	0·014			
			1910	$\frac{1}{2}^-$	28	1	0·0084			
			2370	$\frac{1}{2}^+$	110	0	0·020			
			3330	$3/2^+$	210	2	0·075			
			3600	$3/2^-$	750	1	0·120			

resonance in the ^{11}B cross-section has a particularly strong single-particle component and so does the 1000-keV resonance in the ^{16}O case. However, the ^{13}C compound nucleus is already showing the break-up of the single-particle d-wave state with the appearance of two resonances with spin and parity $3/2^+$ at 2950 keV and 3600 keV and one resonance at 2076 keV with $J^\pi = 5/2^+$ and a very small relative reduced width.

In the cross-section of ^{14}N there are numerous resonances of several angular momentum and parity combinations all with small reduced neutron widths and with reduced proton widths of the same order of magnitude. The breakdown of the single-particle model in this and heavier nuclei is now quite clear. The strong fluctuations in reduced widths from resonance to resonance, even of the same spin and parity class, is also striking.

A discussion of the reduced widths of resonance states in light nuclei in terms of nuclear structure models is given by Lane (1960).

C. SYSTEMATICS OF SINGLE-PARTICLE STATES

Although the single-particle model does not give a good description of neutron cross-sections it is most useful as a basis for more accurate theoretical discussions of neutron spectroscopic data. For this purpose we should expect, as a first approximation, to use a potential well similar to that used in the shell-model theory for explanation of the properties of the low-lying states of nuclei. It is well known that neither a simple harmonic oscillator potential nor a square well potential can give the correct ordering of eigenvalues to allow the closed shell or 'magic' nuclei to contain the observed numbers of protons and neutrons. The addition of a large spin-orbit term to a potential well that is intermediate in shape between oscillator and square will give the correct shell closures (Mayer 1949, Haxel *et al.* 1949).

A suitable intermediate form of potential is the Eckart potential (eqn. 3.11). To this must be added a spin-orbit coupling term which is usually taken to be proportional to the relativistic Thomas term of atomic physics (Thomas 1926),

$$(\hbar^2/4M^2c^2) \,.\, (1/r \,.\, \partial V/\partial r)\boldsymbol{\sigma} \,.\, \mathbf{l}.$$

The eigenvalues of the operator $\boldsymbol{\sigma} \,.\, \mathbf{l}$ on operating on states with intrinsic spin and orbital angular momenta coupled to $j = l+\frac{1}{2}$ and

$j = l-\frac{1}{2}$ are l and $-(l+1)$ respectively. The radial Schrödinger wave equation to be solved for neutrons is thus

$$-\frac{\hbar^2}{2M}\frac{1}{r^2}\frac{\mathrm{d}}{\mathrm{d}r}\left(r^2\frac{\mathrm{d}u}{\mathrm{d}r}\right)+\left[\frac{V_0}{1+\exp\{(r-a)/\mathrm{d}\}}+\frac{\hbar^2}{2M}\cdot\frac{l(l+1)}{r^2}\right.$$
$$\left.+\lambda\cdot\frac{\hbar^2}{4M^2c^2}\cdot\frac{V_0\exp\{(r-a)/d\}}{rd[1+\exp\{(r-a)/d\}]^2}\cdot(-)^{\delta_{j,l-\frac{1}{2}}}(l+\delta_{j,l-\frac{1}{2}})\right]u = Eu. \tag{3.22}$$

For protons the equation contains, in addition, a Coulomb repulsion term. Parameters have been established for this form of potential that

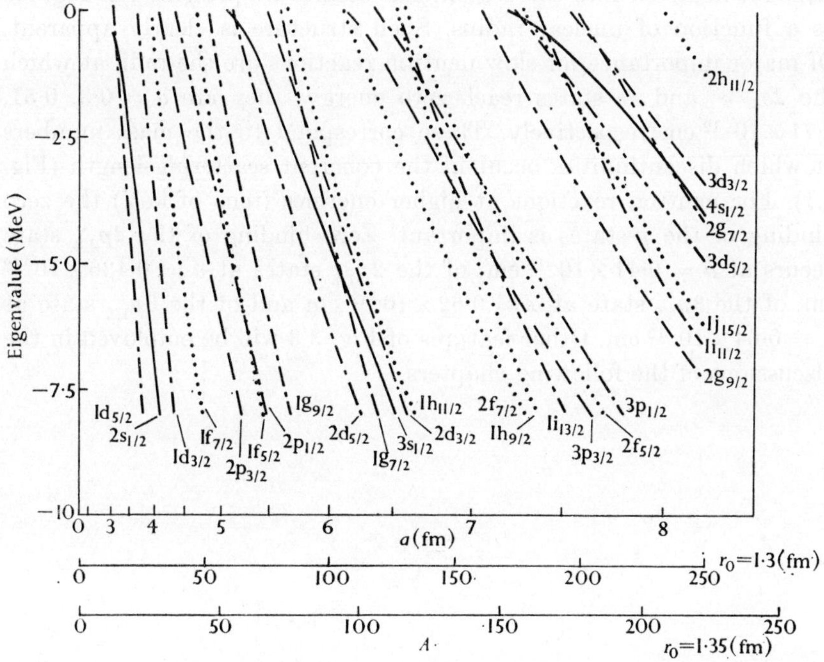

FIG. 3.3. Eigenvalues above the Fermi energy in the real potential of Ross *et al.* (1956). The upper mass-number scale is related to the radius scale through $a = 1{\cdot}3A^{\frac{1}{3}}$ fm and the lower through $a = 1{\cdot}35A^{\frac{1}{3}}$ fm.

give approximately correct values for the level sequence (as inferred from the ground-state angular momenta of odd-mass nuclei) and the binding energies of the last-filled level of the well (Ross *et al.* 1956). With the radius parameter taken to be $r_0 = 1{\cdot}3$ fm, the well depth for neutrons is $V_0 = -42{\cdot}8$ MeV, the diffuseness constant $d = 0{\cdot}69$ fm, and the spin-orbit coupling constant $\lambda = 39{\cdot}5$. For protons the well is somewhat deeper. A change in the radius parameter will lead to changes in the other parameters according to the transformation

$$V_0' r_0'^2 = V_0 r_0^2,\ \lambda' V_0' = \lambda V_0,\ r_0'/d' = r_0/d,$$
$$E' r_0'^2 = E r_0^2, \tag{3.23}$$

to which eqn. (3.22) is invariant.

In the paper of Ross *et al.* (1956) eigenvalues have been calculated to just above the Fermi energy. In the study of neutron reactions we are more interested in the single-particle levels between the Fermi energy and the neutron separation energy so we have extended their calculations for neutrons into this region. The results are presented in Fig. 3.3 as a function of nuclear radius. Shell structure is clearly apparent. Of major importance for slow neutron reactions are the radii at which the 2*s*, 3*s*, and 4*s* states reach zero energy; they are $a = 0{\cdot}3$, $0{\cdot}51$, $0{\cdot}71\times10^{-12}$ cm respectively. These correspond to the mass numbers at which discontinuities occur in the coherent scattering length (Fig. 3.1). For neutron reactions at higher energies (tens of keV) the zero binding of the *p*-states is important. Zero binding of the $2p_{3/2}$ state occurs at $a = 0{\cdot}41\times10^{-12}$ cm, of the $2p_{1/2}$ states at $a = 0{\cdot}436\times10^{-12}$ cm, of the $3p_{3/2}$ state at $a = 0{\cdot}62\times10^{-12}$ cm and of the $3p_{1/2}$ state at $a = 0{\cdot}64\times10^{-12}$ cm. Other features of Fig. 3.3 will be employed in the discussions of the following chapters.

IV

THE SPACING OF NEUTRON RESONANCES

A. LEVEL-DENSITY DATA

THE immediately obvious failure of the single-particle model is its inability to explain the order of magnitude of resonance spacings. Resonances of given spin and parity would be spaced at intervals of several MeV in a single-particle system of the size of the nucleus. Observed spacings are very rarely as large as this. In the cross-sections of most nuclei they are many orders of magnitude smaller. This implies that the neutron–nucleus system has many more degrees of freedom than the three of the single-particle picture. A large number of degrees of freedom is a primary feature of the compound-nucleus theory, which must be greatly favoured therefore as a starting-point for the discussion of the neutron-resonance phenomenon.

Neutron-resonance data constitute the most detailed source of knowledge concerning the level densities of highly excited nuclei. The resonances in the low-energy region are observed to be mostly very narrow. Their widths are measures of the lifetimes of the corresponding nuclear states according to the Heisenberg uncertainty relation between energy and time, $\Delta E \sim \hbar/\Delta t$. Hence these states are very long-lived and may be compared with the bound nuclear states in the energy region just below the particle thresholds of the composite nucleus formed by adding a neutron to the target. The main qualitative difference is that the resonance states have somewhat shorter lifetimes than the bound states owing to the possibility of particle emission in addition to radiation. The states that are thus revealed by neutron-resonance spectroscopy have narrowly selected values of angular momentum and parity quantum numbers. The values of the total angular momentum J are selected by the vectorial addition of the ground-state spin of the target I, the spin of the neutron i, and the orbital angular momentum of the neutron relative to the target, l. It is conventional first to combine the target and neutron spins to form a channel spin s (eqn. 2.1). The combinations of the channel spin and orbital angular momentum then give the total angular momenta

$$\mathbf{J} = \mathbf{s}+\mathbf{l}. \tag{4.1}$$

The parity π_C of the compound-nucleus state is the product of the parity of the ground state of the target π_T and the parity of the relative motion of target and projectile $(-)^l$

$$\pi_C = (-)^l \pi_T. \tag{4.2}$$

The resonances in the total neutron cross-section of a nucleus are superimposed on a very slowly varying background known as the *potential scattering cross-section*, which, at low energies, is predominantly due to s-wave neutron interaction. The strength of a resonance may be taken as the integral, over neutron energy, of the cross-section under the resonance after subtracting the potential scattering. For resonances that are narrow compared with the level spacing (which is the usual case for low-energy cross-sections), the strength S_λ is related to the neutron width $\Gamma_{\lambda(n)}$ of a resonance λ by

$$S_\lambda = 2\pi^2 \lambda\!\!\!^{-2} \Gamma_{\lambda(n)} g_J. \tag{4.3}$$

The neutron width is a product of two factors, one of which, the reduced neutron width $\gamma^2_{\lambda(n)}$, is related to the wave-function at the edge of the nucleus and the other is a penetration factor P_l that depends on the centrifugal barrier to be overcome by the entering neutron (see Chapter II):

$$\Gamma_{\lambda(n)} = 2P_l \gamma^2_{\lambda(n)}. \tag{4.4}$$

For all but s-wave neutrons P_l is very small at low energies; therefore resonances that can be excited by s-wave neutrons are expected to have a much greater strength than other resonances. For even-target nuclei ($I = 0$, π_T even) only one value of the channel spin can be formed, and hence the total spin and parity of the states excited by s-wave bombardment are unique: $J = \frac{1}{2}$, π_C even. For other nuclei there are two possible channel spins in general, $s = I+\frac{1}{2}$, $I-\frac{1}{2}$, and hence two sets of compound-nucleus states can be excited: $J = I+\frac{1}{2}$, $I-\frac{1}{2}$, $\pi_C = \pi_T$. Of course some, or all, of these states (according to the value of I) can be excited by d-wave or higher even l-wave bombardment but the penetration factors are so small that their contributions to the neutron width are negligible. The states excited by p-wave bombardment of an even nucleus are limited to those with $J = \frac{1}{2}$, $\frac{3}{2}$, π_C odd. If the target is not even, then there may be up to four values of J of the excited states with parity $\pi_C = \pi_T$. Again it may be possible to excite some or all of these states by bombardment with higher odd l-waves but again with extremely small penetration factors.

It is only with the most careful experimental techniques that it is possible to observe some of the p-wave resonances. The strength of such resonances is so small owing to the low value of the penetration factor P_1 that they are scarcely detectable against the potential scattering cross-section. Thus most of the resonances observed in low-energy neutron cross-sections are believed to be excited by s-wave bombardment. Many can be positively identified as such by the observation of an asymmetry in the shape of the resonance due to interference between the resonance and potential scattering cross-sections. The division of a penetration factor into the neutron width often eliminates a p-wave assignment by showing that this assumption would yield a reduced width $\gamma^2_{(n)}$ greater than the single-particle estimate (eqn. 3.10). This would violate a sum rule (Teichmann and Wigner 1952; see Chapter VI, Section A). Techniques have also been introduced to identify the parity of the compound state from the capture γ-ray emission spectrum to low-lying final states of known spin and parity; these are based on the assumed weakness of magnetic dipole transitions (carrying even parity) relative to electric dipole transitions (with odd parity). For comparison with neutron-resonance data, which give the spacings of states with only one or two values of spin and parity, it is desirable, therefore, that nuclear level-density theories should be capable of giving results for the densities of states as a function of total angular momentum and parity as well as of energy.

The nuclear level spacings that are deduced from the neutron-resonance data suffer from a number of sources of error. The strengths of the resonances even of one class of spin and parity vary greatly from one to another so that, from measurements of the cross-section over a given energy region, it cannot be certain that all the resonances (of s-wave character) have been detected. Conversely, if positive means of identification have not been used, it cannot be certain that one or more of the resonances that have been detected are not of p-wave character. These two errors tend to be compensatory. Finite instrumental resolution, which may lead to failure to separate two resonances in a cross-section, can give rise to an underestimate of the nuclear level density. For the mean spacing over a large interval there is also a source of uncertainty of a statistical nature that is due to the irregularity in spacing between individual levels (see Chapter V). For small energy intervals containing n level spacings the variance of the observed spacing D resulting from this irregularity is usually taken to be

$$\text{var}\, D = 0{\cdot}27\,\frac{D^2}{n}. \tag{4.5}$$

These sources of error all apply to an even-target nucleus. They also apply to other targets with some modification. The instrumental resolution effect is stronger because two resonances with different spin are more likely to have a small spacing than two with the same spin (see Chapter V, Section C). There is an additional source of error in that the spins of resonances of these nuclei have been measured in only a small minority of cases. The level density that is extracted from most such data is usually the sum of the densities for the two spins. In addition to the uncertainty to which this gives rise in comparing the data with theory the statistical uncertainty of eqn. (4.5) is increased and becomes approximately

$$\text{var}\, D = 0{\cdot}54\,\frac{D^2}{n}. \tag{4.6}$$

The statistical uncertainties expressed by eqns. (4.5) and (4.6) require much discussion and qualification, which are given in Chapter V, Section D. Nevertheless they are generally adopted here for the purpose of quoting errors on observed level densities. The quoted error is the square root of var D. For small values of n this is rather less than the limits that include 34 per cent of the frequency distribution on each side of the mean; this latter definition is employed by some writers as the analogue of the standard deviation of a normal distribution.

The neutron-resonance spacing data are summarized in Table 4.1. In column 1 the target nucleus is listed; its spin and parity are in column 2. In columns 3 and 4 the same things are listed for the compound nucleus formed by the absorption of s-wave neutrons. In column 5 the excitation energy of the compound nucleus (its neutron-separation energy) is given. The observed mean resonance spacing is in column 6. This quantity is assumed to be the average over s-wave resonances, and known p-wave resonances have been excluded in calculating it. In some cases only a lower limit or an order of magnitude is available. Remarks on such points, and references, are made in column 7. The reciprocal of the resonance spacing, the density, occupies column 8, and

TABLE 4.1

Summary of experimental data on s-wave resonance densities at just above the neutron separation energy

Target nucleus	I^π	Compound nucleus	J^π (*s*-waves assumed)	Neutron separation energy, $E_{\mathrm{th,n}}$ (MeV)	Observed resonance spacing, D (eV)	References and remarks	Resonance density $\rho(E_{\mathrm{th,n}})$ (MeV^{-1})	$\frac{\rho(E_{\mathrm{th,n}})}{2(2I+1)}$
$^{23}_{11}$Na	3/2+	$^{24}_{11}$Na	1+, 2+	6·959	$(2·7\pm1·4)\times10^5$	1, 2, 3; (a)	$3·7\pm1·8$	$0·46\pm0·23$
$^{27}_{13}$Al	5/2+	$^{28}_{13}$Al	2+, 3+	7·724	$(5·4\pm4)\times10^4$	4, 5; (b)	19 ± 15	$1·6\pm1·2$
$^{32}_{16}$S	0+	$^{33}_{16}$S	$\frac{1}{2}$+	8·643	$(3·5\pm1·8)\times10^5$	6, 7; (a)	$2·9\pm1·5$	$1·4\pm0·7$
$^{35}_{17}$Cl	3/2+	$^{36}_{17}$Cl	1+, 2+	8·577	$(5·6\pm2·4)\times10^3$	8, 9, 10; (c)	$(1·8\pm0·9)\times10^2$	22 ± 11
$^{40}_{20}$Ca	0+	$^{41}_{20}$Ca	$\frac{1}{2}$+	8·361	$(4·9\pm1)\times10^4$	11, 12	20 ± 4	10 ± 2
$^{42}_{20}$Ca	0+	$^{43}_{20}$Ca	$\frac{1}{2}$+	7·93	$(2·85\pm0·4)\times10^4$	74; (h)	35 ± 5	$17·5\pm2·5$
$^{44}_{20}$Ca	0+	$^{45}_{20}$Ca	$\frac{1}{2}$+	7·42	$(5·0\pm1·2)\times10^4$	11	20 ± 5	10 ± 3
$^{45}_{21}$Sc	7/2−	$^{46}_{21}$Sc	3−, 4−	8·766	$>1\times10^3$	13; (d)	$<1\times10^3$	<63
$^{46}_{22}$Ti	0+	$^{47}_{22}$Ti	$\frac{1}{2}$+	8·887	$(3·0\pm0·6)\times10^4$	12	33 ± 7	16 ± 3
$^{48}_{22}$Ti	0+	$^{49}_{22}$Ti	$\frac{1}{2}$+	8·147	$(1·5\pm·23)\times10^4$	11, 12	67 ± 11	33 ± 5
$^{50}_{22}$Ti	0+	$^{51}_{22}$Ti	$\frac{1}{2}$+	6·36	$(1·2\pm0·5)\times10^5$	12; (a)	8 ± 3	4 ± 2
$^{50}_{23}$V	6(+)	$^{51}_{23}$V	11/2(+), 13/2(+)	11·04	$(1·1\pm0·3)\times10^3$	75	$(9·1\pm2·2)\times10^2$	35 ± 9
$^{50}_{24}$Cr	0+	$^{51}_{24}$Cr	$\frac{1}{2}$+	9·249	$(1·65\pm0·2)\times10^4$	74; (h)	61 ± 7	$30\pm3·5$
$^{51}_{23}$V	7/2−	$^{52}_{23}$V	3−, 4−	7·304	$(3·6\pm0·9)\times10^3$	14	$(2·8\pm0·7)\times10^2$	17 ± 4
$^{52}_{24}$Cr	0+	$^{53}_{24}$Cr	$\frac{1}{2}$+	7·943	$(4·4\pm0·8)\times10^4$	12	23 ± 4	11 ± 2
$^{54}_{24}$Cr	0+	$^{55}_{24}$Cr	$\frac{1}{2}$+	6·02	$(2·35\pm0·4)\times10^4$	74; (h)	42 ± 10	21 ± 5
$^{54}_{26}$Fe	0+	$^{55}_{26}$Fe	$\frac{1}{2}$+	9·300	$(2·5\pm0·4)\times10^4$	11, 12	40 ± 6	20 ± 3
$^{55}_{25}$Mn	5/2−	$^{56}_{25}$Mn	2−, 3−	7·270	$(2·1\pm0·8)\times10^3$	15	$(4·8\pm2·0)\times10^2$	40 ± 17
$^{56}_{26}$Fe	0+	$^{57}_{26}$Fe	$\frac{1}{2}$+	7·641	$(2·9\pm0·4)\times10^4$	11, 12	35 ± 5	18 ± 3
$^{58}_{28}$Ni	0+	$^{59}_{28}$Ni	$\frac{1}{2}$+	9·001	$(2.7\pm0·5)\times10^4$	11	37 ± 7	19 ± 4
$^{59}_{27}$Co	7/2−	$^{60}_{27}$Co	3−, 4−	7·497	960 ± 210	16	$(1·0\pm0·2)\times10^3$	65 ± 12
$^{60}_{28}$Ni	0+	$^{61}_{28}$Ni	$\frac{1}{2}$+	7·823	$(2·3\pm0·4)\times10^4$	11	43 ± 6	21 ± 3
$^{62}_{28}$Ni	0+	$^{63}_{28}$Ni	$\frac{1}{2}$+	6·841	$(1·95\pm0·25)\times10^4$	74; (h)	51 ± 6	$25·5\pm3$

TABLE 4.1 (cont.)

Summary of experimental data on s-wave resonance densities at just above the neutron separation energy

Target nucleus	I^π	Compound nucleus	J^π (*s*-waves assumed)	Neutron separation energy, $E_{\mathrm{th,n}}$ (MeV)	Observed resonance spacing, D (eV)	References and remarks	Resonance density $\rho(E_{\mathrm{th,n}})$ (MeV^{-1})	$\frac{\rho(E_{\mathrm{th,n}})}{2(2I+1)}$
$^{63}_{29}$Cu	3/2−	$^{64}_{29}$Cu	1−, 2−	7·916	$(1{\cdot}2\pm0{\cdot}3)\times10^3$	17	$(8{\cdot}3\pm1{\cdot}7)\times10^2$	$(1{\cdot}0\pm0{\cdot}2)\times10^2$
$^{64}_{28}$Ni	0+	$^{65}_{28}$Ni	$\frac{1}{2}$+	6·13	$(2{\cdot}85\pm0{\cdot}4)\times10^4$	74; (h)	35 ± 5	$17{\cdot}5\pm2{\cdot}5$
$^{64}_{30}$Zn	0+	$^{65}_{30}$Zn	$\frac{1}{2}$+	7·99	$(1{\cdot}8\pm1{\cdot}4)\times10^3$	18	$(5{\cdot}6\pm4{\cdot}2)\times10^2$	$(2{\cdot}8\pm2)\times10^2$
$^{65}_{29}$Cu	3/2−	$^{66}_{29}$Cu	1−, 2−	7·06	$(2{\cdot}0\pm1{\cdot}0)\times10^3$	17	$(5{\cdot}0\pm2{\cdot}5)\times10^2$	61 ± 31
$^{66}_{30}$Zn	0+	$^{67}_{30}$Zn	$\frac{1}{2}$+	7·04	$(5{\cdot}0\pm1{\cdot}3)\times10^3$	17	$(2{\cdot}0\pm0{\cdot}5)\times10^2$	$(1{\cdot}0\pm0{\cdot}3)\times10^2$
$^{67}_{30}$Zn	5/2−	$^{68}_{30}$Zn	2−, 3−	10·20	700 ± 370	18	$(1{\cdot}4\pm0{\cdot}7)\times10^3$	$(1.2\pm0{\cdot}6)\times10^2$
$^{68}_{30}$Zn	0+	$^{69}_{30}$Zn	$\frac{1}{2}$+	6·41	>260	18; (d)	$<3{\cdot}9\times10^3$	$<2\times10^3$
$^{69}_{31}$Ga	3/2−	$^{70}_{31}$Ga	1−, 2−	7·71	340 ± 95	19, 20	$(2{\cdot}9\pm0{\cdot}6)\times10^3$	$(3{\cdot}6\pm0{\cdot}8)\times10^2$
$^{70}_{32}$Ge	0+	$^{71}_{32}$Ge	$\frac{1}{2}$+	7·30	$(1{\cdot}7\pm0{\cdot}3)\times10^3$	17	$(5{\cdot}9\pm0{\cdot}9)\times10^2$	$(3.0\pm0{\cdot}5)\times10^2$
$^{71}_{31}$Ga	3/2−	$^{72}_{31}$Ga	1−, 2−	7·1	170 ± 63	19, 20	$(5{\cdot}9\pm2)\times10^3$	$(7{\cdot}4\pm3)\times10^2$
$^{72}_{32}$Ge	0+	$^{73}_{32}$Ge	$\frac{1}{2}$+	6·46	$(2{\cdot}1\pm0{\cdot}4)\times10^3$	17	$(4{\cdot}7\pm0{\cdot}7)\times10^2$	$(2{\cdot}3\pm0{\cdot}4)\times10^2$
$^{74}_{34}$Se	0+	$^{75}_{34}$Se	$\frac{1}{2}$+	7·96	250 ± 130	21, 22	$(4{\cdot}0\pm2{\cdot}0)\times10^3$	$(2{\cdot}0\pm1{\cdot}0)\times10^3$
$^{74}_{32}$Ge	0+	$^{75}_{32}$Ge	$\frac{1}{2}$+	6·43	$(8{\cdot}5\pm1{\cdot}0)\times10^3$	76	$(1{\cdot}2\pm0{\cdot}15)\times10^2$	60 ± 8
$^{75}_{33}$As	3/2−	$^{76}_{33}$As	1−, 2−	7·33	87 ± 14	20, 23	$(1.1\pm0{\cdot}2)\times10^4$	$(1{\cdot}4\pm0{\cdot}3)\times10^3$
$^{76}_{32}$Ge	0+	$^{77}_{32}$Ge	$\frac{1}{2}$+	5·8	$(8\pm1)\times10^3$	76	$(1{\cdot}4\pm0{\cdot}2)\times10^2$	70 ± 10
$^{76}_{34}$Se	0+	$^{77}_{34}$Se	$\frac{1}{2}$+	7·416	$(1{\cdot}2\pm0{\cdot}3)\times10^3$	21, 22, 23	$(8{\cdot}3\pm1{\cdot}7)\times10^2$	$(4{\cdot}1\pm0{\cdot}9)\times10^2$
$^{77}_{34}$Se	$\frac{1}{2}$−	$^{78}_{34}$Se	0−, 1−	10·48	100 ± 25	22, 23, 24	$(1{\cdot}0\pm0{\cdot}3)\times10^4$	$(2{\cdot}5\pm0{\cdot}8)\times10^3$
$^{78}_{34}$Se	0+	$^{79}_{34}$Se	$\frac{1}{2}$+	6·52	$3{\cdot}7\times10^3$	76	$(2{\cdot}7\pm0{\cdot}5)\times10^2$	$(1{\cdot}3\pm0{\cdot}3)\times10^2$
$^{79}_{35}$Br	3/2−	$^{80}_{35}$Br	1−, 2−	7·88	57 ± 19	21	$(1{\cdot}8\pm0{\cdot}6)\times10^4$	$(2{\cdot}3\pm0{\cdot}8)\times10^3$
$^{80}_{34}$Se	0+	$^{81}_{34}$Se	$\frac{1}{2}$+	6·82	$(4{\cdot}3\pm1{\cdot}0)\times10^3$	76	$(2{\cdot}3\pm0{\cdot}6)\times10^2$	$(1{\cdot}2\pm0{\cdot}3)\times10^2$
$^{80}_{36}$Kr	0+	$^{81}_{36}$Kr	$\frac{1}{2}$+	7·8	530 ± 280	25	$(1{\cdot}9\pm1)\times10^3$	$(1{\cdot}0\pm0{\cdot}5)\times10^3$
$^{81}_{35}$Br	3/2−	$^{82}_{35}$Br	1−, 2−	7·77	51 ± 26	21	$(2{\cdot}0\pm1)\times10^4$	$(2{\cdot}5\pm1{\cdot}2)\times10^3$
$^{82}_{34}$Se	0+	$^{83}_{34}$Se	$\frac{1}{2}$+	~6·7	$(7\pm1)\times10^3$	76	$(1{\cdot}4\pm0{\cdot}2)\times10^2$	70 ± 10

Table 4.1 (cont.)

Summary of experimental data on s-wave resonance densities at just above the neutron separation energy

Target nucleus	I^π	Compound nucleus	J^π (s-waves assumed)	Neutron separation energy, $E_{th,n}$ (MeV)	Observed resonance spacing, D (eV)	References and remarks	Resonance density $\rho(E_{th,n})$ (MeV^{-1})	$\frac{\rho(E_{th,n})}{2(2I+1)}$
$^{82}_{36}$Kr	0^+	$^{83}_{36}$Kr	$\frac{1}{2}^+$	7·52	>20	25; (d)	$<5\times10^4$	$<2·5\times10^4$
$^{83}_{36}$Kr	$9/2^+$	$^{84}_{36}$Kr	$4^+, 5^+$	10·50	200 ± 150	25	$(5·0\pm3·7)\times10^3$	$(2·5\pm1·8)\times10^2$
$^{84}_{36}$Kr	0^+	$^{85}_{36}$Kr	$\frac{1}{2}^+$	6·92	~200	25; (e)	$\sim5\times10^3$	$\sim2·5\times10^3$
$^{85}_{37}$Rb	$5/2^-$	$^{86}_{37}$Rb	$2^-, 3^-$	8·82	130 ± 20	77; (i)	$(7·7\pm1·3)\times10^3$	$(6·4\pm1·2)\times10^2$
$^{87}_{37}$Rb	$3/2^-$	$^{88}_{37}$Rb	$1^-, 2^-$	6·24	$(1·2\pm0·5)\times10^3$	26	$(8·3\pm3)\times10^2$	$(1·0\pm0·4)\times10^2$
$^{87}_{38}$Sr	$9/2^+$	$^{88}_{38}$Sr	$4^+, 5^+$	11·14	$>1·8$	27	$<5·6\times10^5$	$<2·8\times10^4$
$^{88}_{38}$Sr	0^+	$^{89}_{38}$Sr	$\frac{1}{2}^+$	6·5	$(5·5\pm1·9)\times10^4$	11	18 ± 6	9 ± 3
$^{89}_{39}$Y	$\frac{1}{2}^-$	$^{90}_{39}$Y	$0^-, 1^-$	6·85	$(1\pm0·25)\times10^3$	11, 24, 28	$(1·0\pm0·3)\times10^3$	$(2·5\pm0·8)\times10^2$
$^{90}_{40}$Zr	0^+	$^{91}_{40}$Zr	$\frac{1}{2}^+$	7·2	$(4·5\pm1·6)\times10^3$	29	$(2·2\pm0·8)\times10^2$	$(1·1\pm0·4)\times10^2$
$^{91}_{40}$Zr	$5/2^+$	$^{92}_{40}$Zr	$2^+, 3^+$	8·66	315 ± 85	23, 29, 30; (f)	$(3·2\pm0·8)\times10^3$	$(2·7\pm0·7)\times10^2$
$^{92}_{40}$Zr	0^+	$^{93}_{40}$Zr	$\frac{1}{2}^+$	6·69	$(1·2\pm0·4)\times10^3$	29	$(8·3\pm2·8)\times10^2$	$(4·1\pm1·4)\times10^2$
$^{93}_{41}$Nb	$9/2^+$	$^{94}_{41}$Nb	$4^+, 5^+$	7·20	70 ± 10	31, 30, 80, (f)	$(1·4\pm0·2)\times10^4$	$(7·0\pm1·0)\times10^2$
$^{94}_{40}$Zr	0^+	$^{95}_{40}$Zr	$\frac{1}{2}^+$	6·42	$(2·4\pm0·9)\times10^3$	29	$(4·2\pm1·4)\times10^2$	$(2·1\pm0·7)\times10^2$
$^{95}_{42}$Mo	$5/2^+$	$^{96}_{42}$Mo	$2^+, 3^+$	9·16	>11	30; (d, f)	$<9\times10^4$	$<7·5\times10^3$
$^{96}_{40}$Zr	0^+	$^{97}_{40}$Zr	$\frac{1}{2}^+$	5·6	$(1·0\pm0·3)\times10^3$	29	$(1·0\pm0·3)\times10^3$	$(5·0\pm1·5)\times10^2$
$^{96}_{42}$Mo	0^+	$^{97}_{42}$Mo	$\frac{1}{2}^+$	6·9	>66	32; (d)	$<1·5\times10^4$	$<7·5\times10^3$
$^{97}_{42}$Mo	$5/2^+$	$^{98}_{42}$Mo	$2^+, 3^+$	8·3	170 ± 70	32, 33	$(5·9\pm2·5)\times10^3$	$(5·0\pm2·0)\times10^2$
$^{98}_{42}$Mo	0^+	$^{99}_{42}$Mo	$\frac{1}{2}^+$	4·3	>240	32; (d)	$<4·2\times10^3$	$<2·1\times10^3$
$^{99}_{44}$Ru	$5/2^+$	$^{100}_{44}$Ru	$2^+, 3^+$	9·4	>55	34; (d)	$<1·8\times10^4$	$<1·5\times10^3$
$^{99}_{43}$Tc	$9/2^+$	$^{100}_{43}$Tc	$4^+, 5^+$	6·3	24 ± 6	35	$(4·2\pm1·0)\times10^4$	$(2·1\pm0·5)\times10^3$
$^{100}_{42}$Mo	0^+	$^{101}_{42}$Mo	$\frac{1}{2}^+$	5·6	>180	32; (d)	$<5·6\times10^3$	$<2·8\times10^3$
$^{101}_{44}$Ru	$5/2^+$	$^{102}_{44}$Ru	$2^+, 3^+$	9·2	16 ± 5	34	$(6·3\pm2·0)\times10^4$	$(5·2\pm1·7)\times10^3$

TABLE 4.1 (cont.)

Summary of experimental data on s-wave resonance densities at just above the neutron separation energy

Target nucleus	I^π	Compound nucleus	J^π (*s*-waves assumed)	Neutron separation energy, $E_{\mathrm{th,n}}$ (MeV)	Observed resonance spacing, D (eV)	References and remarks	Resonance density $\rho(E_{\mathrm{th,n}})$ (MeV^{-1})	$\frac{\rho(E_{\mathrm{th,n}})}{2(2I+1)}$
$^{102}_{44}$Ru	0^+	$^{103}_{44}$Ru	$\frac{1}{2}^+$	9·32	>100	34; (d)	$<1\times10^4$	$<5\times10^3$
$^{103}_{45}$Rh	$\frac{1}{2}^-$	$^{104}_{45}$Rh	$0^-, 1^-$	6·79	19 ± 4	36, 37	$(5·3\pm1·1)\times10^4$	$(1·3\pm0·3)\times10^4$
$^{104}_{46}$Pd	0^+	$^{105}_{46}$Pd	$\frac{1}{2}^+$	6·8	>93	38; (d)	$<1·1\times10^4$	$<5·5\times10^3$
$^{105}_{46}$Pd	$5/2^+$	$^{106}_{46}$Pd	$2^+, 3^+$	9·5	13 ± 4	38	$(7·7\pm2·5)\times10^4$	$(6·4\pm2·0)\times10^3$
$^{106}_{46}$Pd	0^+	$^{107}_{46}$Pd	$\frac{1}{2}^+$	6·38	>140	38; (d)	$<7·0\times10^3$	$<3·5\times10^3$
$^{107}_{47}$Ag	$\frac{1}{2}^-$	$^{108}_{47}$Ag	$0^-, 1^-$	7·22	$13·5\pm1·3$	39, 89	$(7·4\pm0·7)\times10^4$	$(1·8\pm0·2)\times10^4$
$^{108}_{46}$Pd	0^+	$^{109}_{46}$Pd	$\frac{1}{2}^+$	6·21	57 ± 40	38	$(1·8\pm1·4)\times10^4$	$(9·0\pm7·0)\times10^3$
$^{109}_{47}$Ag	$\frac{1}{2}^-$	$^{110}_{47}$Ag	$0^-, 1^-$	6·81	$12·8\pm1·3$	39, 89	$(7·8\pm0·8)\times10^4$	$(1·9\pm0·2)\times10^4$
$^{110}_{46}$Pd	0^+	$^{111}_{46}$Pd	$\frac{1}{2}^+$	6·1	>6	38; (d)	$<1·7\times10^5$	$<8·5\times10^4$
$^{110}_{48}$Cd	0^+	$^{111}_{48}$Cd	$\frac{1}{2}^+$	7·3	>45	19	$<2·2\times10^4$	$<1·1\times10^4$
$^{111}_{48}$Cd	$\frac{1}{2}^+$	$^{112}_{48}$Cd	$0^+, 1^+$	9·48	26 ± 5	83	$(3·8\pm0·8)\times10^4$	$(0·95\pm0·2)\times10^3$
$^{112}_{48}$Cd	0^+	$^{113}_{48}$Cd	$\frac{1}{2}^+$	6·38	200 ± 50	83	$(5·0\pm1·2)\times10^3$	$(2·5\pm0·6)\times10^3$
$^{112}_{50}$Sn	0^+	$^{113}_{50}$Sn	$\frac{1}{2}^+$	7·97	108 ± 100	32	$(5·5\pm3·0)\times10^3$	$(2·7\pm1·5)\times10^3$
$^{113}_{48}$Cd	$\frac{1}{2}^+$	$^{114}_{49}$Cd	$0^+, 1^+$	9·05	25 ± 5	83	$(4·0\pm0·8)\times10^4$	$(1·0\pm0·2)\times10^4$
$^{113}_{49}$In	$9/2^+$	$^{114}_{49}$In	$4^+, 5^+$	7·31	$6·5\pm2$	32	$(1·5\pm0·5)\times10^5$	$(7·5\pm2·5)\times10^3$
$^{114}_{48}$Cd	0^+	$^{115}_{48}$Cd	$\frac{1}{2}^+$	6·16	160 ± 50	83	$(6·2\pm0·2)\times10^3$	$(3·1\pm1)\times10^3$
$^{114}_{50}$Sn	0^+	$^{115}_{50}$Sn	$\frac{1}{2}^+$	7·53	150 ± 60	42	$(6·7\pm2·6)\times10^3$	$(3·4\pm1·3)\times10^3$
$^{115}_{49}$In	$9/2^+$	$^{116}_{49}$In	$4^+, 5^+$	6·62	$6·7\pm2$	32, 33	$(1·5\pm0·5)\times10^5$	$(7·5\pm2·5)\times10^3$
$^{115}_{50}$Sn	$\frac{1}{2}^+$	$^{116}_{50}$Sn	$0^+, 1^+$	9·4	50 ± 30	42	$(2·0\pm1·2)\times10^4$	$(5·0\pm3·0)\times10^3$
$^{116}_{50}$Sn	0^+	$^{117}_{50}$Sn	$\frac{1}{2}^+$	7·2	180 ± 50	42	$(5·5\pm1·5)\times10^3$	$(2·8\pm0·8)\times10^3$
$^{117}_{50}$Sn	$\frac{1}{2}^+$	$^{118}_{50}$Sn	$0^+, 1^+$	9·14	25 ± 5	42	$(4·0\pm0·8)\times10^4$	$(1·0\pm0·2)\times10^4$
$^{118}_{50}$Sn	0^+	$^{119}_{50}$Sn	$\frac{1}{2}^+$	6·66	180 ± 50	42	$(5·6\pm1·6)\times10^3$	$(2·8\pm0·8)\times10^3$

TABLE 4.1 (cont.)

Summary of experimental data on s-wave resonance densities at just above the neutron separation energy

Target nucleus	I^π	Compound nucleus	J^π (*s*-waves assumed)	Neutron separation energy, $E_{th,n}$ (MeV)	Observed resonance spacing, D (eV)	References and remarks	Resonance density $\rho(E_{th,n})$ (MeV^{-1})	$\frac{\rho(E_{th,n})}{2(2I+1)}$
$^{119}_{50}Sn$	$\frac{1}{2}^+$	$^{120}_{50}Sn$	$0^+, 1^+$	8·98	30 ± 8	42	$(3·3\pm0·8)\times10^4$	$(8·1\pm2·0)\times10^3$
$^{120}_{50}Sn$	0^+	$^{121}_{50}Sn$	$\frac{1}{2}^+$	6·29	200 ± 70	42	$(5·0\pm1·7)\times10^3$	$(2·5\pm0·8)\times10^3$
$^{121}_{51}Sb$	$5/2^+$	$^{122}_{51}Sb$	$2^+, 3^+$	6·78	14 ± 4	34, 19, 27	$(7·1\pm2·0)\times10^4$	$(6·0\pm1·7)\times10^3$
$^{122}_{50}Sn$	0^+	$^{123}_{50}Sn$	$\frac{1}{2}^+$	5·97	400 ± 200	42	$(2·5\pm1·2)\times10^3$	$(1·2\pm0·6)\times10^3$
$^{122}_{52}Te$	0^+	$^{123}_{52}Te$	$\frac{1}{2}^+$	6·98	>36	43; (d)	$<2·8\times10^4$	$<1·4\times10^4$
$^{123}_{51}Sb$	$7/2^+$	$^{124}_{51}Sb$	$3^+, 4^+$	6·46	28 ± 12	19	$(3·6\pm1·5)\times10^4$	$(2·3\pm1·0)\times10^3$
$^{123}_{52}Te$	$\frac{1}{2}^+$	$^{124}_{52}Te$	$0^+, 1^+$	9·40	39 ± 14	43	$(2·6\pm0·9)\times10^4$	$(6·5\pm2·2)\times10^3$
$^{124}_{50}Sn$	0^+	$^{125}_{50}Sn$	$\frac{1}{2}^+$	5·78	400 ± 200	42	$(2·5\pm1·2)\times10^3$	$(1·2\pm0·6)\times10^3$
$^{124}_{52}Te$	0^+	$^{125}_{52}Te$	$\frac{1}{2}^+$	6·52	>21	43; (d)	$<4·9\times10^4$	$<2·5\times10^4$
$^{124}_{54}Xe$	0^+	$^{125}_{54}Xe$	$\frac{1}{2}^+$	7·4	$>2·5$	25; (d)	$<4·0\times10^5$	$<2·0\times10^4$
$^{125}_{52}Te$	$\frac{1}{2}^+$	$^{126}_{52}Te$	$0^+, 1^+$	8·9	65 ± 25	43	$(1·5\pm0·6)\times10^4$	$(3·7\pm1·5)\times10^3$
$^{126}_{52}Te$	0^+	$^{127}_{52}Te$	$\frac{1}{2}^+$	6·30	>100	43; (d)	$<1\times10^4$	$<5\times10^3$
$^{127}_{53}I$	$5/2^+$	$^{128}_{53}I$	$2^+, 3^+$	6·71	$13\pm0·5$	78	$(7·7\pm0·3)\times10^4$	$(6·4\pm0·3)\times10^3$
$^{129}_{53}I$	$7/2^+$	$^{130}_{53}I$	$3^+, 4^+$	6·58	18 ± 6	44	$(5·6\pm1·8)\times10^4$	$(3·5\pm1·1)\times10^3$
$^{129}_{54}Xe$	$\frac{1}{2}^+$	$^{130}_{54}Xe$	$0^+, 1^+$	9·34	82 ± 55	25	$(1·2\pm0·8)\times10^4$	$(3·0\pm2·0)\times10^3$
$^{130}_{52}Te$	0^+	$^{131}_{52}Te$	$\frac{1}{2}^+$	6·1	$(3·5\pm0·6)\times10^3$	11	$(2·9\pm0·5)\times10^2$	$(1·5\pm0·3)\times10^2$
$^{131}_{54}Xe$	$3/2^+$	$^{132}_{54}Xe$	$1^+, 2^+$	8·93	31 ± 16	25	$(3·2\pm1·6)\times10^4$	$(4·0\pm2·0)\times10^3$
$^{133}_{55}Cs$	$7/2^+$	$^{134}_{55}Cs$	$3^+, 4^+$	6·70	20 ± 1	78	$(4·6\pm0·2)\times10^4$	$(2·9\pm0·2)\times10^3$
$^{135}_{56}Ba$	$3/2^+$	$^{136}_{56}Ba$	$1^+, 2^+$	9·21	51 ± 14	27, 38	$(2·0\pm0·6)\times10^4$	$(2·5\pm0·8)\times10^3$
$^{136}_{56}Ba$	0^+	$^{137}_{56}Ba$	$\frac{1}{2}^+$	6·96	$(8\pm4)\times10^3$	11, 38	$(1·2\pm0·6)\times10^2$	60 ± 30
$^{137}_{56}Ba$	$3/2^+$	$^{138}_{56}Ba$	$1^+, 2^+$	8·59	200 ± 150	38	$(5·0\pm3·7)\times10^3$	$(6·2\pm4·5)\times10^2$
$^{138}_{56}Ba$	0^+	$^{139}_{56}Ba$	$\frac{1}{2}^+$	4·66	$(10\pm4)\times10^3$	11	$(1·0\pm0·4)\times10^2$	50 ± 20
$^{138}_{57}La$	$5^{(-)}$	$^{139}_{57}La$	$9/2^{(-)}, 11/2^{(-)}$	8·78	23 ± 7	85	$(4·3\pm1·2)\times10^4$	$(2·0\pm0·6)\times10^3$

TABLE 4.1 (cont.)

Summary of experimental data on s-wave resonance densities at just above the neutron separation energy

Target nucleus	I^π	Compound nucleus	J^π (*s*-waves assumed)	Neutron separation energy, $E_{th,n}$ (MeV)	Observed resonance spacing, D (eV)	References and remarks	Resonance density $\rho(E_{th,n})$ (MeV^{-1})	$\frac{\rho(E_{th,n})}{2(2I+1)}$
$^{139}_{57}$La	$7/2^+$	$^{140}_{57}$La	$3^+, 4^+$	4·99	73 ± 50	27	$(1{\cdot}4\pm1{\cdot}0)\times10^4$	$(8{\cdot}7\pm6{\cdot}0)\times10^2$
$^{141}_{59}$Pr	$5/2^+$	$^{142}_{59}$Pr	$2^+, 3^+$	5·65	51 ± 16	28, 46, 23, 47	$(2{\cdot}0\pm0{\cdot}6)\times10^4$	$(1{\cdot}7\pm0{\cdot}5)\times10^3$
$^{142}_{58}$Ce	0^+	$^{143}_{58}$Ce	$\frac{1}{2}^+$	5·31	~1000	48	$\sim10^3$	$\sim5\times10^2$
$^{143}_{60}$Nd	$7/2^-$	$^{144}_{60}$Nd	$3^-, 4^-$	7·81	72 ± 50	28	$(1{\cdot}4\pm1{\cdot}0)\times10^4$	$(8{\cdot}7\pm6{\cdot}0)\times10^2$
$^{145}_{60}$Nd	$7/2^-$	$^{146}_{60}$Nd	$3^-, 4^-$	7·56	33 ± 13	28	$(3{\cdot}0\pm1{\cdot}2)\times10^4$	$(1{\cdot}9\pm0{\cdot}7)\times10^3$
$^{147}_{61}$Pm	$7/2^{(+)}$	$^{148}_{61}$Pm	$3^+, 4^+$	6·0	$5{\cdot}2\pm1{\cdot}4$	49	$(1{\cdot}9\pm0{\cdot}5)\times10^5$	$(1{\cdot}2\pm0{\cdot}3)\times10^4$
$^{147}_{62}$Sm	$7/2^-$	$^{148}_{62}$Sm	$3^-, 4^-$	8·1	$8{\cdot}0\pm1{\cdot}7$	38	$(1{\cdot}2\pm0{\cdot}3)\times10^5$	$(7{\cdot}5\pm1{\cdot}9)\times10^3$
$^{149}_{62}$Sm	$7/2^-$	$^{150}_{62}$Sm	$3^-, 4^-$	8·00	$2{\cdot}4\pm0{\cdot}6$	50	$(4{\cdot}2\pm1{\cdot}0)\times10^5$	$(2{\cdot}6\pm0{\cdot}6)\times10^4$
$^{150}_{62}$Sm	0^+	$^{151}_{62}$Sm	$\frac{1}{2}^+$	5·53	>10	38; (d)	$<1\times10^5$	$<5\times10^4$
$^{151}_{62}$Sm	$7/2^-$	$^{152}_{62}$Sm	$3^-, 4^-$	8·3	$1{\cdot}3\pm0{\cdot}4$	44	$(7{\cdot}7\pm2{\cdot}4)\times10^5$	$(4{\cdot}8\pm1{\cdot}6)\times10^4$
$^{151}_{63}$Eu	$5/2^{(+)}$	$^{152}_{63}$Eu	$2^{(+)}, 3^{(+)}$	6·4	$0{\cdot}75\pm0{\cdot}15$	51, 52	$(1{\cdot}3\pm0{\cdot}3)\times10^6$	$(1{\cdot}1\pm0{\cdot}3)\times10^5$
$^{152}_{62}$Sm	0^+	$^{153}_{62}$Sm	$\frac{1}{2}^+$	6·0	>4	53	$<2{\cdot}5\times10^5$	$<1{\cdot}2\times10^5$
$^{153}_{63}$Eu	$5/2^{(+)}$	$^{154}_{63}$Eu	$2^{(+)}, 3^{(+)}$	6·4	$1{\cdot}4\pm0{\cdot}4$	51, 52	$(7{\cdot}1\pm2{\cdot}4)\times10^5$	$(5{\cdot}9\pm2{\cdot}0)\times10^4$
$^{155}_{64}$Gd	$3/2^-$	$^{156}_{64}$Gd	$1^-, 2^-$	8·45	$2{\cdot}1\pm0{\cdot}2$	54	$(4{\cdot}9\pm0{\cdot}5)\times10^5$	$(6{\cdot}1\pm0{\cdot}6)\times10^4$
$^{157}_{64}$Gd	$3/2^-$	$^{158}_{64}$Gd	$1^-, 2^-$	7·92	12 ± 6	54	$(8{\cdot}3\pm4{\cdot}2)\times10^4$	$(1{\cdot}0\pm0{\cdot}5)\times10^4$
$^{159}_{65}$Tb	$3/2^{(+)}$	$^{160}_{65}$Tb	$1^{(+)}, 2^{(+)}$	6·3	$3{\cdot}9\pm0{\cdot}6$	47, 32	$(2{\cdot}6\pm0{\cdot}4)\times10^5$	$(3{\cdot}2\pm0{\cdot}5)\times10^4$
$^{161}_{66}$Dy	$5/2^{(+)}$	$^{162}_{66}$Dy	$2^{(+)}, 3^{(+)}$	8·18	$2{\cdot}1\pm0{\cdot}4$	38	$(4{\cdot}8\pm0{\cdot}8)\times10^5$	$(4{\cdot}0\pm0{\cdot}7)\pm10^4$
$^{162}_{66}$Dy	0^+	$^{163}_{66}$Dy	$\frac{1}{2}^+$	6·28	130 ± 50	38	$(7{\cdot}7\pm2{\cdot}0)\times10^3$	$(3{\cdot}8\pm1{\cdot}0)\times10^3$
$^{163}_{66}$Dy	$5/2^{(+)}$	$^{164}_{66}$Dy	$2^{(+)}, 3^{(+)}$	7·63	11 ± 3	38	$(9{\cdot}1\pm2{\cdot}0)\times10^4$	$(7{\cdot}6\pm1{\cdot}7)\times10^3$
$^{164}_{66}$Dy	0^+	$^{165}_{66}$Dy	$\frac{1}{2}^+$	6	>70	38, (d)	$<1{\cdot}4\times10^4$	$<7{\cdot}0\times10^3$
$^{165}_{67}$Ho	$7/2^{(-)}$	$^{166}_{67}$Ho	$3^{(-)}, 4^{(-)}$	6·09	$6{\cdot}1\pm1{\cdot}2$	32	$(1{\cdot}6\pm0{\cdot}2)\times10^5$	$(1{\cdot}0\pm0{\cdot}1)\times10^4$
$^{167}_{68}$Er	$7/2^{(+)}$	$^{168}_{68}$Er	$3^{(+)}, 4^{(+)}$	7·76	$3\pm1{\cdot}5$	38	$(3{\cdot}3\pm1{\cdot}6)\times10^5$	$(2{\cdot}1\pm1{\cdot}0)\times10^4$

TABLE 4.1 (cont.)

Summary of experimental data on s-wave resonance densities at just above the neutron separation energy

Target nucleus	I^{π}	Compound nucleus	J^{π} (*s*-waves assumed)	Neutron separation energy, $E_{\mathrm{th,n}}$ (MeV)	Observed resonance spacing, D (eV)	References and remarks	Resonance density $\rho(E_{\mathrm{th,n}})$ (MeV^{-1})	$\frac{\rho(E_{\mathrm{th,n}})}{2(2I+1)}$
$^{169}_{69}$Tm	$\frac{1}{2}^+$	$^{170}_{69}$Tm	$0^+, 1^+$	6·4	$6\pm1·5$	55	$(1·7\pm0·4)\times10^5$	$(4·2\pm1·0)\times10^4$
$^{174}_{72}$Hf	0^+	$^{175}_{72}$Hf	$\frac{1}{2}^+$	6·8	>15	32; (d)	$<6·7\times10^4$	$<3·3\times10^4$
$^{175}_{71}$Lu	$7/2^+$	$^{176}_{71}$Lu	$3^+, 4^+$	6·3	$3·7\pm0·7$	32	$(2·7\pm0·4)\times10^5$	$(1·7\pm0·3)\times10^4$
$^{176}_{71}$Lu	$7^{(-)}$	$^{177}_{71}$Lu	$13/2^{(-)}, 15/2^{(-)}$	6·84	$2·3\pm0·4$	56	$(4·4\pm0·7)\times10^5$	$(1·5\pm0·2)\times10^4$
$^{177}_{72}$Hf	$7/2^-$	$^{178}_{72}$Hf	$3^-, 4^-$	7·59	$2·9\pm0·7$	32	$(3·4\pm0·6)\times10^5$	$(2·1\pm0·4)\times10^4$
$^{178}_{72}$Hf	0^+	$^{179}_{72}$Hf	$\frac{1}{2}^+$	6·17	$>3·9$	32; (d)	$<2·6\times10^5$	$<1·3\times10^5$
$^{179}_{72}$Hf	$9/2^+$	$^{180}_{72}$Hf	$4^+, 5^+$	7·36	$4·0\pm0·7$	32	$(2·5\pm0·4)\times10^5$	$(1·2\pm0·2)\times10^4$
$^{180}_{72}$Hf	0^+	$^{181}_{72}$Hf	$\frac{1}{2}^+$	5·8	>36	32; (d)	$<2·8\times10^4$	$<1·4\times10^4$
$^{180}_{73}$Ta	$>6^-$	$^{181}_{73}$Ta	$>11/2^-$	7·64	$>0·2$	57; (d, g)	$<5\times10^6$	$<2\times10^5$
$^{181}_{73}$Ta	$7/2^+$	$^{182}_{73}$Ta	$3^+, 4^+$	6·059	$4·4\pm0·4$	58	$(2·3\pm0·2)\times10^5$	$(1·4\pm0·1)\times10^4$
$^{182}_{74}$W	0^+	$^{183}_{74}$W	$\frac{1}{2}^+$	6·29	55 ± 18	59, 60	$(1·8\pm0·4)\times10^4$	$(9·0\pm2·0)\times10^3$
$^{183}_{74}$W	$\frac{1}{2}^-$	$^{184}_{74}$W	$0^-, 1^-$	7·42	15 ± 4	59, 60	$(6·7\pm1·6)\times10^4$	$(1·7\pm0·4)\times10^4$
$^{184}_{74}$W	0^+	$^{185}_{74}$W	$\frac{1}{2}^+$	5·77	>90	60	$<1·1\times10^4$	$<5·0\times10^3$
$^{185}_{75}$Re	$5/2^+$	$^{186}_{75}$Re	$2^+, 3^+$	6·23	$3·8\pm0·8$	38	$(2·6\pm0·4)\times10^5$	$(2·2\pm0·3)\times10^4$
$^{186}_{74}$W	0^+	$^{187}_{74}$W	$\frac{1}{2}^+$	5·24	150 ± 80	60	$(6·7\pm3·5)\times10^3$	$(3·3\pm1·7)\times10^3$
$^{187}_{75}$Re	$5/2^+$	$^{188}_{75}$Re	$2^+, 3^+$	5·95	$4·5\pm1·2$	38	$(2·2\pm0·5)\times10^5$	$(1·8\pm0·4)\times10^4$
$^{191}_{77}$Ir	$3/2^+$	$^{192}_{77}$Ir	$1^+, 2^+$	6·14	$3·1\pm0·6$	43, 38	$(3·2\pm0·5)\times10^5$	$(4·0\pm0·6)\times10^4$
$^{192}_{78}$Pt	0^+	$^{193}_{78}$Pt	$\frac{1}{2}^+$	6·25	~20	38; (e)	$\sim5\times10^4$	$\sim2·5\times10^4$
$^{193}_{77}$Ir	$3/2^+$	$^{194}_{77}$Ir	$1^+, 2^+$	5·96	$8·2\pm1·6$	43, 38	$(1·2\pm0·2)\times10^5$	$(1·5\pm0·3)\times10^4$
$^{195}_{78}$Pt	$\frac{1}{2}^-$	$^{196}_{78}$Pt	$0^-, 1^-$	7·92	18 ± 4	24	$(5·5\pm1·0)\times10^4$	$(1·4\pm0·3)\times10^4$
$^{197}_{79}$Au	$3/2^+$	$^{198}_{79}$Au	$1^+, 2^+$	6·495	$16·8\pm1·6$	58	$(6·0\pm0·6)\times10^4$	$(7·5\pm0·7)\times10^3$
$^{198}_{78}$Pt	0^+	$^{199}_{78}$Pt	$\frac{1}{2}^+$	5·7	>48	61; (d)	$<2·1\times10^4$	$<1·0\times10^4$
$^{198}_{80}$Hg	0^+	$^{199}_{80}$Hg	$\frac{1}{2}^+$	6·68	99 ± 30	62	$(1·0\pm0·3)\times10^4$	$(5·0\pm1·7)\times10^3$

TABLE 4.1 (cont.)

Summary of experimental data on s-wave resonance densities at just above the neutron separation energy

Target nucleus	I^π	Compound nucleus	J^π (s-waves assumed)	Neutron separation energy, $E_{\text{th,n}}$ (MeV)	Observed resonance spacing, D (ev)	References and remarks	Resonance density $\rho(E_{\text{th,n}})$ (MeV^{-1})	$\dfrac{\rho(E_{\text{th,n}})}{2(2I+1)}$
$^{199}_{80}$Hg	$\frac{1}{2}^-$	$^{200}_{80}$Hg	$0^-, 1^-$	8·01	70 ± 28	62, 63	$(1\cdot4\pm0\cdot4)\times10^4$	$(3\cdot5\pm1\cdot0)\times10^3$
$^{200}_{80}$Hg	0^+	$^{201}_{80}$Hg	$\frac{1}{2}^+$	6·24	$(2\cdot2\pm0\cdot7)\times10^3$	62	$(4\cdot5\pm1\cdot0)\times10^2$	$(2\cdot2\pm0\cdot5)\times10^2$
$^{201}_{80}$Hg	$3/2^-$	$^{202}_{80}$Hg	$1^-, 2^-$	7·76	100 ± 40	62, 63	$(1\cdot0\pm0\cdot4)\times10^4$	$(1\cdot2\pm0\cdot5)\times10^3$
$^{202}_{80}$Hg	0^+	$^{203}_{80}$Hg	$\frac{1}{2}^+$	6·07	$(2\cdot4\pm1\cdot3)\times10^3$	62	$(4\cdot2\pm2\cdot0)\times10^2$	$(2\cdot1\pm1\cdot0)\times10^2$
$^{203}_{81}$Tl	$\frac{1}{2}^+$	$^{204}_{81}$Tl	$0^+, 1^+$	6·54	$(2\pm1)\times10^3$	64	$(5\cdot0\pm2\cdot5)\times10^2$	$(1\cdot2\pm0\cdot6)\times10^2$
$^{205}_{81}$Tl	$\frac{1}{2}^+$	$^{206}_{81}$Tl	$0^+, 1^+$	6·52	$(1\cdot0\pm0\cdot3)\times10^4$	64	100 ± 30	25 ± 7
$^{206}_{82}$Pb	0^+	$^{207}_{82}$Pb	$\frac{1}{2}^+$	6·737	$\sim5\times10^4$	65; (h)	~20	~10
$^{207}_{82}$Pb	$\frac{1}{2}^-$	$^{208}_{82}$Pb	$0^-, 1^-$	7·374	$\sim8\times10^3$	65; (h)	~120	~30
$^{208}_{82}$Pb	0^+	$^{209}_{82}$Pb	$\frac{1}{2}^+$	3·93	$>3\cdot5\times10^5$	11	$<2\cdot9$	$<1\cdot5$
$^{209}_{83}$Bi	$9/2^-$	$^{210}_{83}$Bi	$4^-, 5^-$	4·58	$(3\cdot5\pm1\cdot2)\times10^3$	88	300 ± 100	15 ± 5
$^{231}_{91}$Pa	$3/2^-$	$^{232}_{91}$Pa	$1^-, 2^-$	5·67	$1\cdot0\pm0\cdot2$	67, 73	$(1\cdot0\pm0\cdot2)\times10^6$	$(1\cdot2\pm0\cdot3)\times10^5$
$^{232}_{90}$Th	0^+	$^{233}_{90}$Th	$\frac{1}{2}^+$	5·13	$17\cdot5\pm0\cdot7$	68	$(5\cdot7\pm0\cdot2)\times10^4$	$(2\cdot8\pm0\cdot1)\times10^4$
$^{232}_{92}$U	0^+	$^{233}_{92}$U	$\frac{1}{2}^+$	5·90	$7\cdot6\pm1\cdot5$	69	$(1\cdot3\pm0\cdot2)\times10^5$	$(6\cdot5\pm1\cdot0)\times10^4$
$^{233}_{91}$Pa	$3/2^-$	$^{234}_{91}$Pa	$1^-, 2^-$	5·0	$0\cdot8\pm0\cdot2$	82	$(1\cdot25\pm0\cdot3)\times10^6$	$(1\cdot56\pm0\cdot35)\times10^5$
$^{234}_{92}$U	0^+	$^{235}_{92}$U	$\frac{1}{2}^+$	5·24	13 ± 2	70	$(7\cdot7\pm1\cdot0)\times10^4$	$(3\cdot8\pm0\cdot5)\times10^4$
$^{236}_{92}$U	0^+	$^{237}_{92}$U	$\frac{1}{2}^+$	5·42	17 ± 3	70	$(5\cdot9\pm0\cdot9)\times10^4$	$(2\cdot9\pm0\cdot5)\times10^4$
$^{238}_{92}$U	0^+	$^{239}_{92}$U	$\frac{1}{2}^+$	4·76	$17\cdot7\pm0\cdot7$	68	$(5\cdot6\pm0\cdot2)\times10^4$	$(2\cdot8\pm0\cdot1)\times10^4$
$^{238}_{94}$Pu	0^+	$^{239}_{94}$Pu	$\frac{1}{2}^+$	5·6	13 ± 4	86	$(7\cdot7\pm2)\times10^4$	$(3\cdot4\pm1)\times10^4$
$^{240}_{94}$Pu	0^+	$^{241}_{94}$Pu	$\frac{1}{2}^+$	5·52	13 ± 2	81	$(7\cdot7\pm1\cdot2)\times10^4$	$(3\cdot4\pm0\cdot6)\times10^4$
$^{241}_{95}$Am	$5/2^-$	$^{242}_{95}$Am	$2^-, 3^-$	5·5	$0\cdot77\pm0\cdot15$	87	$(1\cdot3\pm0\cdot3)\times10^6$	$(1.1\pm0\cdot3)\times10^5$
$^{242}_{94}$Pu	0^+	$^{243}_{94}$Pu	$\frac{1}{2}^+$	5·02	15 ± 2	79, 90	$(6\cdot6\pm1\cdot6)\times10^4$	$(3\cdot3\pm0\cdot8)\times10^4$
$^{243}_{95}$Am	$5/2^-$	$^{244}_{95}$Am	$2^-, 3^-$	5·15	$1\cdot4\pm0\cdot3$	71	$(7\cdot1\pm1\cdot2)\times10^5$	$(6\cdot0\pm1\cdot0)\times10^4$
$^{244}_{96}$Cm	0^+	$^{245}_{96}$Cm	$\frac{1}{2}^+$	6·27	13 ± 3	72	$(7\cdot7\pm1\cdot5)\times10^4$	$(3\cdot8\pm0\cdot8)\times10^4$

TABLE 4.1 (cont.)

Summary of experimental data on s-wave resonance densities at just above the neutron separation energy

Remarks

(a) From spacing of 3 resonances observed to be *s*-wave.
(b) From spacing of 2 resonances observed to be *s*-wave.
(c) From spacing of 4 resonances believed to be *p*-wave.
(d) From energy of lowest observed resonance with confidence limit of 99 per cent (see Section B of Chapter V).
(e) Remark (d) applies with extra information from one spacing.
(f) Parities assigned in last reference.
(g) Isotope not identified beyond doubt.
(h) With identification of *s*-wave resonances.
(i) This may include several weak *p*-wave resonances.

All target nucleus ground state spins and parities listed in this table have been taken from the *Landolt–Börnstein Tables* (1961). Neutron separation energies up to mass number 210 have also been taken from the *Landolt–Börnstein Tables*, and above this from Everling *et al.* (1960)

References

1. Stelson and Preston (1952)
2. Lynn *et al.* (1958)
3. Block (1958*a*)
4. Toller and Newson (1955)
5. Block *et al.* (1958)
6. Adair *et al.* (1949)
7. Peterson *et al.* (1950)
8. Bilpuch *et al.* (1959)
9. Brugger *et al.* (1956)
10. Popov and Shapiro (1961)
11. Bilpuch *et al.* (1961)
12. Bowman *et al.* (1961)
13. Marshak and Newson (1957)
14. Firk *et al.* (1963*a*)
15. Coté *et al.* (1964*b*)
16. Morgenstern *et al.* (1964)
17. Good and Miller (1958)
18. Dahlberg and Bollinger (1956)
19. Palmer and Bollinger (1956)
20. Julien *et al.* (1964)
21. Leblanc *et al.* (1959)
22. Coté *et al.* (1964*c*)
23. Julien *et al.* (1962*a*)
24. Julien *et al.* (1962*b*)
25. Mann *et al.* (1959)
26. Good *et al.* (1958)
27. Stolovy and Harvey (1957)
28. Bianchi *et al.* (1963)
29. Moskaler *et al.* (1964)
30. Jackson (1963)
31. Saplakoglu *et al.* (1958)
32. Harvey *et al.* (1955)
33. Radkevich *et al.* (1956)
34. Bolotin and Chrien (1963)
35. Slaughter *et al.* (1958)
36. Ribon *et al.* (1961)
37. Wang *et al.* (1963)
38. Hughes *et al.* (1959)
39. Rae *et al.* (1958)
40. Simpson and Fluharty (1957*a*)
41. Carter *et al.* (1954)
42. Fuketa *et al.* (1963)
43. Bolotin and Chrien (1960)
44. Harvey *et al.* (1958*a*)
45. Harvey *et al.* (1959)
46. Corge *et al.* (1961)
47. Wang *et al.* (1964)
48. Newson *et al.* (1959)
49. Block *et al.* (1958*b*)
50. Marshak and Sailor (1958)
51. Sailor *et al.* (1954)
52. Domani and Patronis (1959)
53. Bernabei *et al.* (1962)
54. Simpson and Fluharty (1957*b*)

TABLE 4.1 (cont.)

Summary of experimental data on s-wave resonance densities at just above the neutron separation energy

55. Singh (1964)
56. Harvey *et al.* (1958*b*)
57. Evans *et al.* (1955)
58. Desjardins *et al.* (1960)
59. Waters *et al.* (1959)
60. Firk and Moxon (1959)
61. Waters (1960)
62. Carpenter and Bollinger (1960)
63. Bird *et al.* (1959)
64. Newson *et al.* (1961)
65. Macklin *et al.* (1964)
66. Nichols *et al.* (1959)
67. Patterson and Harvey (1962)
68. Garg *et al.* (1964)
69. James (1964)
70. Harvey and Hughes (1958)
71. Coté *et al.* (1959)
72. Coté *et al.* (1964*a*)
73. Simpson *et al.* (1962)
74. Farrell *et al.* (1966)
75. Good and Block (1966)
76. Biggerstaff and Farrell (1966)
77. Iliescu *et al.* (1965)
78. Garg *et al.* (1965)
79. Auchampaugh *et al.* (1966)
80. Le Poittevin *et al.* (1965)
81. Byers *et al.* (1966)
82. Simpson *et al.* (1964)
83. Adamchuk *et al.* (1966)
84. Kalebin *et al.* (1966)
85. Harvey and Slaughter (1966)
86. Bowman *et al.* (1966)
87. Gerasimov (1966)
88. Firk *et al.* (1963*c*)
89. Muradin and Adamchuk (1966)
90. Böckhoff *et al.* (1966)

TABLE 4.2

Summary of experimental data on s-wave resonance densities for specified values of the total angular momentum

Target nucleus	I	Compound nucleus	Energy interval (eV)	No. of resonances observed with (a) $J = I-\frac{1}{2}$	(b) $J = I+\frac{1}{2}$	References
^{77}Se	$\frac{1}{2}$	^{78}Se	0–1500	3	6	Julien *et al.* (1962*a*) Coté *et al.* (1964*c*)
^{107}Ag	$\frac{1}{2}$	^{108}Ag	0–100	1	2	Rae *et al.* (1958)
^{109}Ag	$\frac{1}{2}$	^{110}Ag	0–300	2	9	Rae *et al.* (1958) Desjardins *et al.* (1960)
^{169}Tm	$\frac{1}{2}$	^{170}Tm	0–160	5	9	Singh (1964)
^{183}W	$\frac{1}{2}$	^{184}W	0–110	2	3	Waters *et al.* (1959) Firk and Moxon (1959)
^{195}Pt	$\frac{1}{2}$	^{196}Pt	0–310	6	13	Waters (1960) Julien *et al.* (1962)
^{199}Hg	$\frac{1}{2}$	^{200}Hg	0–900	2	5	Landon and Rae (1957) Bird *et al.* (1959) Carpenter and Bollinger (1960)
^{75}As	3/2	^{76}As	0–4000	11	14	Julien *et al.* (1962*a*) Julien *et al.* (1964)
^{155}Gd	3/2	^{156}Gd	0–7	1	3	Stolovy (1964)
^{159}Tb	3/2	^{160}Tb	0–50	2	5	Wang *et al.* (1964)
^{55}Mn	5/2	^{56}Mn	0–9000	2	3	Coté *et al.* (1964*b*)
^{105}Pd	5/2	^{106}Pd	0–400	12	14	Bollinger *et al.* (1965)
^{141}Pr	5/2	^{142}Pr	0–1000	3	6	Corge *et al.* (1961) Wang *et al.* (1964)
^{151}Eu	5/2	^{152}Eu	0–3·5	1	3	Stolovy (1964)
^{51}V	7/2	^{52}V	0–30000	4	3	Firk *et al.* (1963*a*)
^{59}Co	7/2	^{60}Co	0–25000	5	6	Morgenstern *et al.* (1964)
^{149}Sm	7/2	^{150}Sm	0–20	3	4	Marshak *et al.* (1962)
^{165}Ho	7/2	^{166}Ho	0–60	5	4	Alfimenkov *et al.* (1966)
^{177}Hf	7/2	^{178}Hf	0–15	4	4	Bollinger *et al.* (1965)
^{115}In	9/2	^{116}In	0–10	1	2	Dabbs *et al.* (1955) Stolovy (1959)
^{209}Bi	9/2	^{210}Bi	0–15000	3	2	Firk *et al.* (1963*b*)

finally, in column 9, the density divided by $2(2I+1)$ is given. This last quantity is assumed (see Section B.4) to be the equivalent density of levels with the target-nucleus parity and total angular momentum equal to zero. We use the adjective 'equivalent' here because the compound nucleus formed from an even-mass target nucleus cannot have levels with integral spin quantum number.

The angular momentum has been measured for a small minority of the levels observed in neutron spectroscopy. The methods used in these measurements include the direct observation of the transmission of polarized neutrons through polarized targets, the measurements of the peak total cross-section of predominantly elastic scattering resonances, the determination of the statistical spin factor g_J by combination of transmission, elastic scattering, and total capture measurements, and observations on various features of the capture γ-ray spectrum. A summary of the results of all this work is contained in Table 4.2.

B. THE INDEPENDENT-PARTICLE MODEL

1. Direct counting methods

In order to compute the level density of the compound nucleus, the independent-particle model has generally been used as a starting-point. The potential energy terms of the nuclear Hamiltonian are divided into a central part, which is a smooth function of the radial coordinate and is an average (in the Hartree–Fock sense) over the nucleon–nucleon interactions, and a part that is the sum of the residual interactions. The single-particle energy levels in the average central field can be used to build the independent-particle states by taking one or more nucleons out of the ground-state configuration and placing them in higher unoccupied levels. When the residual interactions are included in the description the independent-particle states will be mixed to a great extent. The mixing of the few single-particle states into the many other states of the pure independent-particle system permits the excitation of all the states by particle bombardment of the target. The central assumption of the model is that the shifting of energy levels also resulting is of a fairly random character with no large overall shift to either lower or higher energies. Consequently, in order to calculate the average level density of the compound nucleus it is necessary only to calculate that of the independent-particle model. Of course, the assumption of random shifting is very much open to question. It is known, for example, that residual short-range pairing forces will considerably lower certain states of the correct symmetry (Bohr *et al.* 1958), and this effect is certainly strong enough to make it necessary to adjust semi-empirically the excitation energy of the independent-particle level density formulae according to the odd or even character of the compound nucleus. Other strong 'shifting' forces are the short-range particle-hole coupling responsible for the elevation of the photonuclear dipole state (Brown and Bolsterli 1959) and the long-range quadrupole force which lowers the 'vibrational' 2^+ state of spherical nuclei near closed shells (Ferrell 1957) and gives the rotational states of deformed nuclei (Elliott 1958). Of a more general character is the energy due to the effect of nuclear exchange forces acting in states of different symmetry character (Wigner 1937).

It is possible to compute the level density of the independent-particle model directly. Indeed, the simplest possible version of the model, in which the single-particle states are non-degenerate and equally spaced, is a combinatorial problem of ancient origin that was solved by Euler. In a practical calculation it is necessary to take account of degeneracies of the single-particle states, for the only degeneracy that is expected to remain in highly excited compound-nucleus states is that due to the projection of the total angular momentum on an arbitrary axis. Such a programme has been carried out by Critchfield and Oleksa (1951) for the states of ^{20}Ne up to excitation of 25 MeV. The model employed for the single-particle states was a square-well potential of radius 3·07 fm and of sufficient depth (the same for neutrons and protons) to give a neutron separation energy of 16·8 MeV. An additional potential energy term was included in the description of the independent-particle states; this depended on the symmetry of the wave functions of these states, the states of maximum symmetry having zero potential energy from this source, and those of less symmetry having a positive contribution to allow for the effect of exchange forces (Wigner 1937). The independent-particle states were classified according to their total orbital angular momenta and their symmetry character, and the possible spins of the latter were combined with the angular momenta to form states of definite total spin J. There are high degeneracies in the states thus computed but these are removed in reality by forces that have not been considered in the model. The results show that the increase in the density of nuclear states with excitation energy has an exponential character. The numbers of states with angular momentum $J = 0$ in the energy ranges 0–5 MeV, 5–10 MeV, 10–15 MeV, 15–20 MeV, and 20–25 MeV are 1, 5, 13, 15, and 107 respectively. Thus the density of states with $J = 0$ at the neutron-separation energy is of the order of 3 MeV^{-1}. This is about the order of magnitude of the density of states observed in ^{20}Ne by the ^{19}F (p, n) reaction.

2. Methods of statistical thermodynamics

The usual way of computing the density of levels of a nuclear model is to adopt the methods of statistical mechanics. As a result of this a certain amount of thermodynamic terminology has crept into nuclear reaction theory. The method starts from the grand partition function

$$\exp(-\beta F) = \sum_{l} \exp\Big(-\beta E_{l} + \sum_{k} \beta\mu_{k} C_{kl}\Big) \tag{4.7}$$

where the E_l are the energy eigenvalues of the levels l of the system, C_{kl} are values of other constants of the motion for these levels, the constant β plays the part of the inverse temperature (in energy units) in statistical mechanics, and the μ_k are parameters associated with the other constants of the motion. The constants of the motion that are usually considered in nuclear level-density theory are the projection of the total angular momentum, the number of nucleons in the nucleus, and the charge of the nucleus. The sum in the grand partition function may be expressed as an integral over energy by introduction of the level density $\rho(E, C_1, \ldots, C_k, \ldots, C_K)$; thus

$$\exp(-\beta F) = \sum_{k=1}^{K} \sum_{C_k} \int_{0}^{\infty} dE \rho(E, C_1, \ldots C_k, \ldots, C_K) \exp\Big(-\beta E + \sum_{k=1}^{K} \beta\mu_k C_k\Big) \tag{4.8}$$

The level density can now be expressed in terms of the partition function by inversion of the Laplace transform

$$\rho(E, C_1, \ldots, C_k, \ldots, C_K) = \frac{1}{(2\pi \mathrm{i})^{K+1}} \int d\beta dx_1 \ldots dx_K \exp\Big(\beta E - \sum_{k} x_k C_k + \Phi\Big) \tag{4.9}$$

with the integrals taken along contours from $-\mathrm{i}\infty$ to $+\mathrm{i}\infty$. We have replaced the product $\beta\mu_k$ with the notation x_k and $-\beta F$ by Φ.

If we ignore, for the moment, the constants of the motion C_k and consider only the integral in β, we see that the integrand has a saddle point at the value β_0 defined by

$$E = -\mathrm{d}\Phi/\mathrm{d}\beta. \tag{4.10}$$

In statistical mechanics the function F is the free energy, and other thermodynamic quantities may be derived from it. Thus, in eqn. (4.9), linking the free energy and the energy of the system, β_0 is equal to $1/kT$, the inverse product of Boltzmann's constant and the temperature of the system. The exponent of the integrand at the saddle point is the entropy $S = \beta_0(E-F)$, which leads to the usual relation between entropy and temperature, $dS/dE = \beta_0$. Evaluation of the integral by the method of steepest descents gives the expression for the level density

$$\rho(E) = \frac{e^S}{\sqrt{\left\{-2\pi\left(\frac{dE}{d\beta}\right)_{\beta=\beta_0}\right\}}}. \tag{4.11}$$

If the energy variation of the denominator is neglected in this equation the very simple level-density formula

$$\rho(E) \propto e^S \propto e^{E/kT} \tag{4.12}$$

is obtained. This is the standard form used in statistical mechanics to calculate evaporation properties and has been much used in nuclear reaction theory for determining the spectra of inelastically scattered neutrons (e.g. see Blatt and Weisskopf 1952). From eqn. (4.11) a relation between level density and temperature is found:

$$\frac{d\ln\rho(E)}{dE} = \frac{d}{dE}\left\{S-\frac{1}{2}\ln\left(-\frac{dE}{d\beta}\right)\right\} \tag{4.13a}$$

$$= \frac{1}{kT}-\frac{1}{2}\frac{d}{dE}\ln\left(kT^2\frac{dE}{dT}\right). \tag{4.13b}$$

The second term on the right-hand side of this equation is usually dropped and Boltzmann's constant is incorporated in T to give the definition of the nuclear temperature in energy units.

Finally, we remark that integration of the complete integral of eqn. (4.9) by the saddle-point method gives

$$\rho(E, C_1, \ldots, C_k, \ldots, C_K) = \frac{\exp\left(\beta_0 E-\sum_k x_{k0}C_k+\Phi\right)}{(2\pi)^{(K+1)/2}(\det A)^{\frac{1}{2}}} \tag{4.14}$$

where the saddle-point conditions for the values β_0 and x_{k0} are

$$E+\partial\Phi/\partial\beta = 0, \tag{4.15a}$$

$$C_k-\partial\Phi/\partial x_k = 0. \tag{4.15b}$$

The elements of the determinant det A are the second derivatives of Φ at the saddle point with respect to β and the x_k,

$$a_{11} = \partial^2\Phi/\partial\beta^2,\ a_{12} = \partial^2\Phi/\partial\beta\ \partial x_1,\ \text{etc.} \tag{4.16}$$

3. General equations for the independent-particle model

Further evaluation of the level density expression in eqn. (4.14) requires the assumption of a nuclear model. Most studies have started from the independent-particle model and have differed in the degree of detail that they include. In a nuclear system the neutron may occupy the available single-particle levels of energy ε_{ns} and the protons may occupy single-particle levels of energy ε_{ps}. If the occupation numbers of these levels are denoted by n_s and z_s, the total energy E, the total neutron number N and the total charge number Z are

$$E = \sum_s (n_s \varepsilon_{ns} + z_s \varepsilon_{ps}), \tag{4.17}$$

$$N = \sum_s n_s, \tag{4.18}$$

$$Z = \sum_s z_s. \tag{4.19}$$

Lang and Le Couteur (1953) limit themselves to these constants of the motion but others can be introduced. For example, Newton (1956) considers also the projection of the total angular momentum of the system upon an arbitrary spatial axis. If the projections of the angular momenta of the single-particle levels are denoted by m_{ns} and m_{ps} for neutrons and protons respectively, the projection of the total angular momentum is

$$M = \sum_s n_s m_{ns} + \sum_s z_s m_{ps}. \tag{4.20}$$

Bloch (1954) generalizes the notation for introducing constants of the motion. Thus, if $c_1, \ldots, c_k, \ldots, c_K$ represent a set of K commuting constants of the motion of a single nucleon in a suitable independent-particle model, the values C_k of the constants of motion of the whole system are the sums of the values of the c_k for the individual nucleons. In this model the grand partition function can be calculated in terms of the properties of the single-particle states.

In the expression for the free energy,

$$-\beta F \equiv \Phi = \ln \sum_l \exp\Big(-\beta E_l + \sum_k x_k C_{kl}\Big), \tag{4.7}$$

the independent-particle model substitutions are made:

$$E_l = \sum_i n_i^{(l)} \varepsilon_i \tag{4.21a}$$

$$C_{kl} = \sum_i n_i^{(l)} c_{ki}. \tag{4.21b}$$

Here the $n_i^{(l)}$ are the occupation numbers of the single-particle levels i in the independent-particle state l. The result of the substitutions is

$$\Phi = \ln \sum_l \exp\left(-\beta \sum_i n_i^{(l)} \varepsilon_i + \sum_k x_k \sum_i n_i^{(l)} c_{ki}\right) \tag{4.22a}$$

$$= \ln \prod_i \sum_{n_i=0}^{n_{i,\max}} \exp\left(-\beta n_i \varepsilon_i + \sum_k x_k n_i c_{ki}\right). \tag{4.22b}$$

For fermions $n_{i,\max} = 1$ giving

$$\Phi = \ln \prod_i \left\{1 + \exp\left(-\beta \varepsilon_i + \sum_k x_k c_{ki}\right)\right\} \tag{4.23a}$$

$$= \sum_i \ln\left\{1 + \exp\left(-\beta \varepsilon_i + \sum_k x_k c_{ki}\right)\right\}. \tag{4.23b}$$

4. The Fermi gas model

(a) The continuous approximation

The simplest method of evaluating the level density of the independent-particle model is to use the continuous approximation. The expression (4.23b) for Φ is approximated by an integration, i.e. the level density of single-particle states ρ_s is treated as a continuous function of energy. In order to carry out this approximation the single-particle levels must be divided into components (Bloch 1954), each of which is specified by a particular set of values of the constants of the motion c_k. Thus, levels of the component α will have values of the constants

$$c_1 = m_{1\alpha},\ c_2 = m_{2\alpha},\ \ldots,\ c_k = m_{k\alpha},\ \ldots,\ c_K = m_{K\alpha}. \tag{4.24}$$

A level, i, will have a weighting $g_{i\alpha}$ in a component α. Provided that the constants of the motion c_1 to c_K fully account for the degeneracies of the levels, $g_{i\alpha}$ will be either one or zero. The function Φ can now be subdivided amongst the components α; thus, $\Phi = \sum_\alpha \Phi_\alpha$ where

$$\Phi_\alpha = \sum_i g_{i\alpha} \ln\left\{1 + \exp\left(\sum_k x_k m_{k\alpha} - \varepsilon_i \beta\right)\right\}. \tag{4.25}$$

In the continuous approximation

$$\Phi_\alpha(\beta, x_k) = \int_0^\infty d\varepsilon\, \rho_{s\alpha}(\varepsilon) \ln\Big\{1+\exp\Big(\sum_k x_k m_{k\alpha} - \varepsilon\beta\Big)\Big\}. \tag{4.26}$$

The important values of ε in this integral are those less than the energy $\varepsilon_\alpha = \sum_k x_k m_{k\alpha}/\beta$, particularly if β is small. If the integral is divided into two parts with ε less than and greater than ε_α then, using the expansions of the logarithms that become possible,

$$\Phi_\alpha = \beta\int_0^{\varepsilon_\alpha} d\varepsilon\, \rho_{s\alpha}(\varepsilon)(\varepsilon_\alpha - \varepsilon) + \int_0^{\varepsilon_\alpha} d\varepsilon\, \rho_{s\alpha}(\varepsilon) \sum_{n=1}^{\infty} \frac{(-)^n}{n} \exp\{n\beta(\varepsilon-\varepsilon_\alpha)\}$$
$$+\int_{\varepsilon_\alpha}^{\infty} d\varepsilon\, \rho_{s\alpha}(\varepsilon) \sum_{n=1}^{\infty} \frac{(-)^n}{n} \exp\{n\beta(\varepsilon_\alpha-\varepsilon)\}. \tag{4.27}$$

In the last two integrals of this equation the leading term of a Taylor expansion about ε_α is used to approximate $\rho_{s\alpha}(\varepsilon)$. This leads to the result

$$\Phi_\alpha = \beta(\varepsilon_\alpha N_\alpha - W_\alpha) + \frac{\pi^2}{6\beta}\rho_{s\alpha}(\varepsilon_\alpha), \tag{4.28}$$

where $N_\alpha(\varepsilon_\alpha) = \int_0^{\varepsilon_\alpha} d\varepsilon\, \rho_{s\alpha}(\varepsilon)$ and $W_\alpha(\varepsilon_\alpha) = \int_0^{\varepsilon_\alpha} d\varepsilon\, \varepsilon\rho_{s\alpha}(\varepsilon)$.

Partial differentiation of this result for Φ leads to values of the energy and constants of the motion:

$$E = \sum_\alpha \{W_\alpha + (\pi^2/6\beta^2)(\rho_{s\alpha} + \varepsilon_\alpha \rho'_{s\alpha})\}, \tag{4.29a}$$

$$M_k = \sum_\alpha m_{k\alpha}\{N_\alpha + (\pi^2/6\beta^2)\rho'_{s\alpha}\}. \tag{4.29b}$$

The prime indicates differentiation with respect to the energy ε. All functions of ε are understood to be evaluated at $\varepsilon = \varepsilon_\alpha$. The ground-state energy E_1 for specified constants of the motion M_k is obtained by setting $\beta = \infty$. The excitation energy, $U_1 = E - E_1$, measured with respect to the energy E_1, is

$$U_1 = (\pi^2/6\beta^2)\sum_\alpha \rho_{s\alpha}(\varepsilon_\alpha) \tag{4.30}$$

to first approximation. The constant of the motion M_1 is now specified to be the mass number A. The other constants of the motion are now assumed to have values, for each single nucleon state, that are symmetric about zero. The second derivatives of Φ with respect to the x_k are given by

$$\frac{\partial^2\Phi}{\partial x_k^2} = \sigma_k^2 = \frac{1}{\pi}\overline{m_k^2}\left(\frac{6U_1}{\delta_s}\right)^{\frac{1}{2}}, \tag{4.31}$$

where $\overline{m_k^2} = \sum_\alpha m_{k\alpha}^2 \rho_{s\alpha}(\varepsilon_\alpha)/\sum_\alpha \rho_{s\alpha}(\varepsilon_\alpha)$ and δ_s is the single-particle level spacing at the Fermi energy; $\delta_s = 1/\sum_\alpha \rho_{s\alpha}(\varepsilon_\alpha)$. Then the level density in the first approximation is

$$\rho(E, M_k) = \{(2\pi)^{(K-1)/2}(\surd 48)U_1\sigma_2 \ldots \sigma_K\}^{-1}\exp\{\pi(2U_1/3\delta_s)^{\frac{1}{2}}\}. \tag{4.32}$$

Provided that the derivatives of the single-particle density are negligible the difference between the true ground-state energy E_0 of a system of mass A, with zero values of the other constants, and the energy E_1 is determined from the average values of m_k^2 for single-nucleon levels. If a single nucleon is lifted from the true ground-state and placed in the next higher level, the average value of M_k^2 in the new state is $2\overline{m_k^2}$ (the sum of the contributions from both the 'particle' and 'hole' created in the ground state 'vacuum'). It is now easy to see that

$$E_1 - E_0 = \delta_s \sum_{k=1}^{K} M_{kl}^2/2\overline{m_k^2}. \tag{4.33}$$

This is also the difference between the true excitation energy U, measured from E_0, and the excitation U_1. The substitution of U in eqn. (4.32) leads approximately to the Gaussian law for the distribution of the constants M_k:

$$\rho(U, M_k) = \rho(U)\{(2\pi)^{(K-1)/2}\sigma_2 \ldots \sigma_k\}^{-1}\exp\left(-\sum_{k=2}^{K} M_{kl}^2/2\sigma_k^2\right) \tag{4.34a}$$

where

$$\rho(U) = \{U\surd(48)\}^{-1}\exp\{\pi(2U/3\delta_s)^{\frac{1}{2}}\}. \tag{4.34b}$$

In practice this formula can be used for describing the level densities of light nuclei where one of the constants of the motion is the isotopic spin and the ground state (of a supermultiplet) normally has isotopic spin zero. Coulomb forces become more important for heavier nuclei and even though these may not cause the breakdown of isotopic spin as a good quantum number (Lane and Soper 1962) this number is no longer zero for the ground state. For heavier nuclei, therefore, it is necessary to introduce charge number as well as mass number explicitly at the start of the calculation. This leads in the continuous approximation (Lang and Le Couteur 1954) to level-density expressions

$$\rho(U,M_k) = \rho(U)\{(2\pi)^{(K-2)/2}\sigma_3\sigma_4\ldots\sigma_K\}^{-1}\exp\left(-\sum_{k=3}^{K} M_k^2/2\sigma_k^2\right), \tag{4.35a}$$

$$\rho(U) = \frac{\rho_s}{2}(\rho_s^2\delta_{sn}\delta_{sp})^{\frac{1}{2}}\frac{6^{\frac{1}{4}}}{12(\rho_s U)^{\frac{5}{4}}}\exp\{\pi(2U/3\delta_s)^{\frac{1}{2}}\}, \tag{4.35b}$$

where δ_{sn} and δ_{sp} are the single neutron and proton level-spacings respectively and $\delta_{sn}^{-1}+\delta_{sp}^{-1} = \delta_s^{-1}$.

(*b*) *Application to the Fermi gas model*

The continuous approximation is often used for calculation of the level density of a Fermi gas model of the nucleus (Bethe 1937) in which the nucleons (neutrons and protons of both spin projections) are confined to move independently within the nuclear volume of radius $R = r_0 A^{\frac{1}{3}}$. In a sufficiently large system of this kind the sum of particle states below energy ε is given (Courant 1931) by

$$z(\varepsilon) = \frac{2^{\frac{1}{2}}}{3\pi^2}\left(\frac{M\varepsilon}{\hbar^2}\right)^{\frac{3}{2}} V \tag{4.36}$$

where V is the volume occupied by the gas. In the ground state of the system these states are filled to the Fermi energy ε_0 which is found by equating the number of cells in the occupied phase space

$$V\left\{\int_0^{\varepsilon_0} 4\pi p^2(dp/d\varepsilon)d\varepsilon/h^3\right\}$$

to the number of particles of given type ($A/4$ neglecting the difference between numbers of neutrons and protons.) The Fermi energy turns out to be

$$\varepsilon_0 = \left(\frac{\pi}{3}\right)^{\frac{2}{3}}\frac{9}{4}\frac{\hbar^2}{2Mr_0^2}, \tag{4.37}$$

where M is the nucleon mass. Using this in connexion with eqn. (4.36) we find the density of particle states at the Fermi energy to be

$$\rho_{\mathrm{S}} = \frac{3}{2}\frac{A}{\varepsilon_0}. \tag{4.38}$$

This, together with the approximate relations $\rho_{\mathrm{sn}} = \rho_{\mathrm{sp}} = \frac{1}{2}\rho_{\mathrm{S}}$ may be substituted in eqn. (4.35b).

The resulting equation is to be compared with the experimental data on neutron-resonance densities (Table 4.1). It is convenient to make a graphical comparison and for this purpose the experimental values are 'normalized' to a common excitation energy $U_{\mathrm{N}} = 6{\cdot}5$ MeV by use of eqns. (4.35b), (4.37), and (4.38):

$$\rho(U_{\mathrm{N}}) = \rho(U) \,.\, \left(\frac{U}{U_{\mathrm{N}}}\right)^{\frac{5}{4}} \exp\left\{2\left(\frac{\pi}{3}\right)^{\frac{1}{3}}\left(\frac{2Mr_0^2 A}{\hbar^2}\right)^{\frac{1}{2}}(U_{\mathrm{N}}^{\frac{1}{2}} - U^{\frac{1}{2}})\right\} \tag{4.39a}$$

$$= \rho(U) \,.\, \left(\frac{U}{U_{\mathrm{N}}}\right)^{\frac{5}{4}} \exp\{0{\cdot}56A^{\frac{1}{2}}(U_{\mathrm{N}}^{\frac{1}{2}} - U^{\frac{1}{2}})\}. \tag{4.39b}$$

To obtain eqn. (4.39b) the radius constant for the charge distribution, $r_0 = 1{\cdot}2\times10^{-13}$, has been used. The comparison is shown in Fig. 4.1. The experimental points due to even, odd-mass, and odd nuclei are distinguished and the full curve is eqn. (4.35b), with the substitution of eqn. (4.38) for δ_{S}, evaluated at $U = 6{\cdot}5$ MeV as a function of mass number. An arbitrary constant, $K_{\mathrm{f}} = 0{\cdot}12$, which allows for the fact that the observed densities are for specified angular momentum ($J = 0$), is multiplied into eqn. (4.35b) so that it runs through the broad mass of data. The overall agreement in trend is not too bad considering the simplicity of the model and the mathematical approximations used in deriving eqn. (4.35), but it could be improved by one of the following devices: (i) decrease of the single-particle level density; a possible cause of such a decrease is velocity-dependence of the nuclear forces (Johnson and Teller 1955), the simplest way of representing this being the use of an effective mass equal to about half the nucleon mass M in eqns. (4.36)–(4.38); (ii) allowing the constant K_{f} to be dependent on mass number; it will be seen in Section B.6 that K_{f} should be proportional roughly to $A^{-7/4}$, which is in the right direction for improvement of the fit. The significance of the arbitrary constant K_{f} will be considered further in Section B.6.

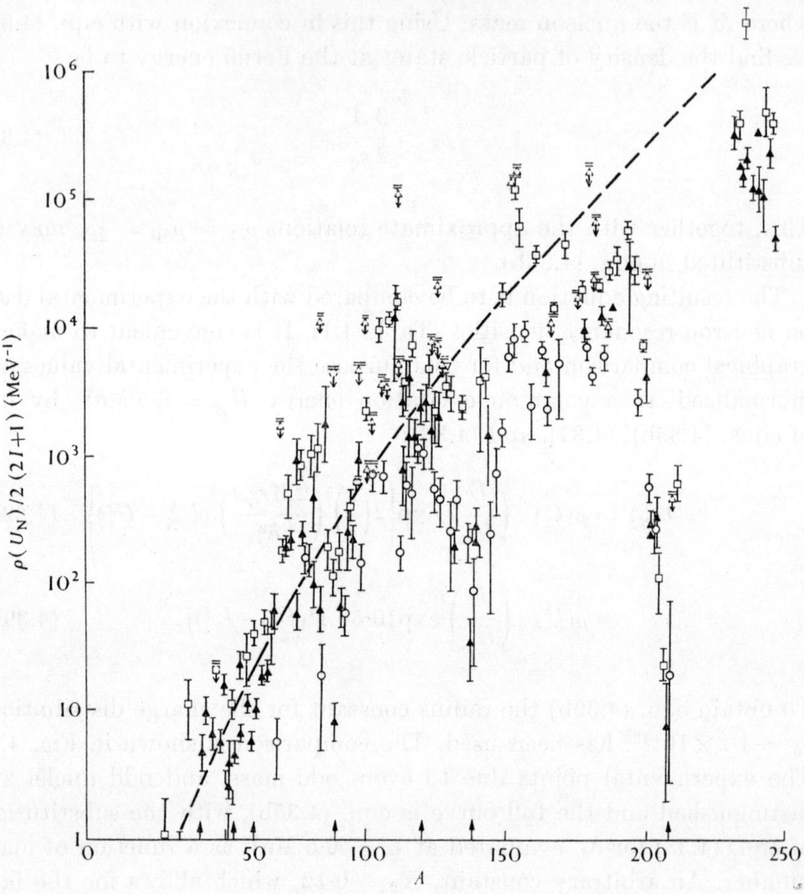

FIG. 4.1.

(c) *The odd-even effect*

The major discrepancies between the model and the data occur near the nucleon shell closures. Nuclear shell-model calculations of the level density are described in Section B.5. Apart from the shell effect there is a much smaller but systematic discrepancy between the level densities of odd and even compound nuclei that is not explained by the Fermi gas model. Unlike the shell effect this difference is not explicable by a more refined version of the independent-particle model. The odd-even effect is a manifestation of the breakdown of the random level shift assumption that underlies the use of the independent-particle model in calculating level densities. In an even nucleus the ground state, with spin and parity 0^+, is considerably depressed below the other states by the short-range component of the nuclear force (Bohr *et al.* 1958). Although there is usually a vibrational or rotational band of collective excitations based on the ground state there is a significant energy gap before the relatively dense onset of states that are considered to be intrinsic excitations of individual nucleons. In an

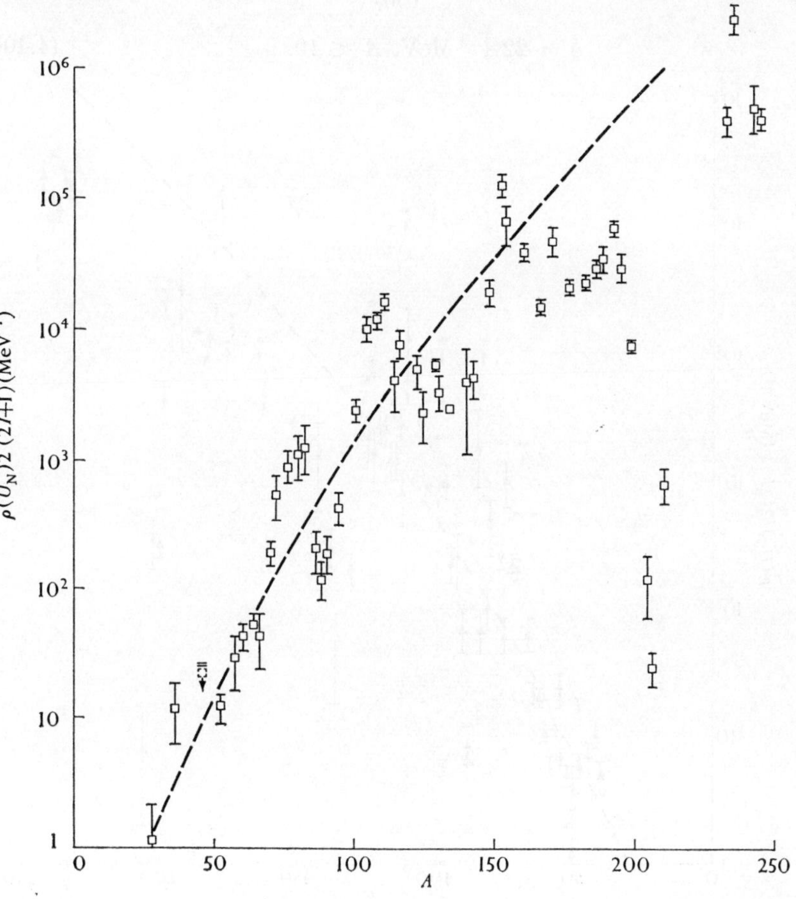

FIG. 4.2. (*a*)

odd nucleus this energy gap does not exist. In an odd-mass nucleus it covers a less dense region of states that are essentially single-particle excitations. The device first used by Hurwitz and Bethe (1951) to cope with this situation within the framework of an independent-particle model is to use a modified excitation energy measured from a characteristic level at an energy above the ground state equal to δ

for an even nucleus, $\frac{1}{2}\delta$ for an odd-mass nucleus, and zero for an odd nucleus. Various prescriptions have been given for δ. That given by Newton (1956), as a result of nuclear mass analysis, seems as good as any; it is

$$\delta = 0{\cdot}82\left(4 - \frac{A}{100}\right) \text{ MeV}, \; A \geqslant 40 \tag{4.40a}$$

$$\delta = 22A^{-\frac{1}{2}} \text{ MeV}, \; A < 40. \tag{4.40b}$$

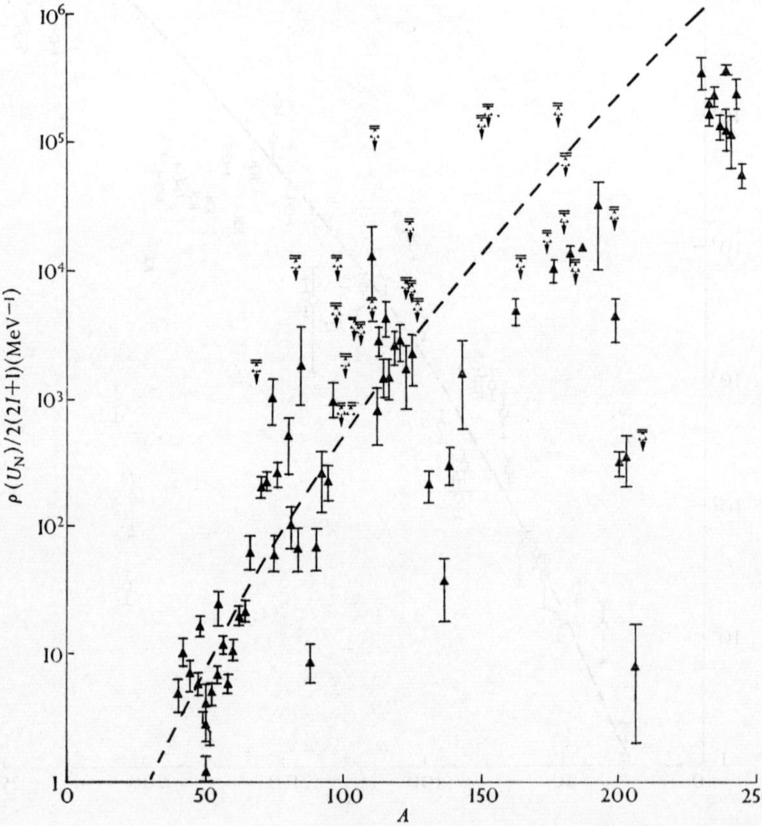

FIG. 4.2. (b)

In Fig. 4.2 (a to c) the experimental data normalized to 6·5 MeV are again shown but they are compared with eqn. (4.35b) calculated for the modified excitation energy of 6·5 MeV, 6·5 MeV $-\frac{1}{2}\delta$, and 6·5 MeV $-\delta$ for odd, odd mass, and even-compound nuclei respectively. It is apparent that this device is partially effective in explaining the odd–even effect. The constant, K_f, used in these figures is 0·23.

(d) *Exchange forces*

The effect of exchange forces on the level density have been included in the Fermi gas model in a semi-empirical way by Critchfield and Oleksa (1951) as deductions from direct calculations (see Section B.1) on ^{20}Ne (isotopic spin projection $T^{\zeta} = 0$), ^{20}F ($T^{\zeta} = 1$), ^{20}Na ($T^{\zeta} = -1$), ^{20}O ($T^{\zeta} = 2$), and ^{20}Mg ($T^{\zeta} = -2$). They found that the last

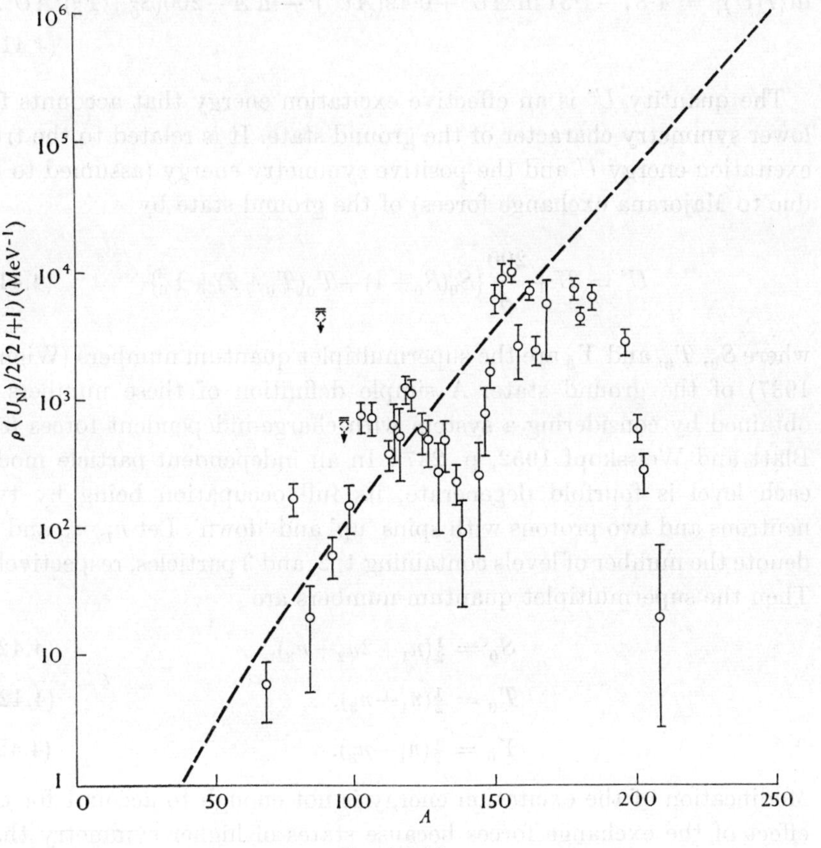

FIG. 4.2 (*c*)

four of these nuclei have higher level densities than ^{20}Ne in spite of the fact that states of lower isotopic spin do not contribute; this is because the lowest states have lower symmetry than those of ^{20}Ne and this allows higher supermultiplets to contribute at a given excitation energy. From all these calculations and with the aid of the Fermi gas formula (eqn. (4.35)) to obtain the mass number dependence they derived a semi-empirical formula for the level density of levels with zero angular momentum and given parity at an excitation energy U:

$$\rho(U) = \frac{1}{2U'}\left\{0{\cdot}245(AU')^{\frac{1}{2}}+200\frac{(S_0^2+T_0^2)}{AU'}-1{\cdot}31\right\}I(U) \quad (4.41a)$$

where

$$\ln\{I(U)\} = 4{\cdot}87-1{\cdot}31\ln AU'+0{\cdot}49(AU')^{\frac{1}{2}}-\ln A-200(S_0^2+T_0^2)/AU'. \quad (4.41b)$$

The quantity U' is an effective excitation energy that accounts for lower symmetry character of the ground state. It is related to the true excitation energy U and the positive symmetry energy (assumed to be due to Majorana exchange forces) of the ground state by

$$U' = U+\frac{200}{A}\{S_0(S_0+4)+T_0(T_0+2)+Y_0^2\}, \quad (4.41c)$$

where S_0, T_0, and Y_0 are the supermultiplet quantum numbers (Wigner 1937) of the ground state. A simple definition of these numbers is obtained by considering a system with charge-independent forces (see Blatt and Weisskopf 1952, p. 237). In an independent-particle model each level is fourfold degenerate, its full occupation being by two neutrons and two protons with spins 'up' and 'down'. Let n_1, n_2, and n_3 denote the number of levels containing 1, 2, and 3 particles, respectively. Then the supermultiplet quantum numbers are

$$S_0 = \tfrac{1}{2}(n_1+2n_2+n_3), \quad (4.42a)$$

$$T_0 = \tfrac{1}{2}(n_1+n_3), \quad (4.42b)$$

$$Y_0 = \tfrac{1}{2}(n_1-n_3). \quad (4.42c)$$

Modification of the excitation energy is not enough to account for the effect of the exchange forces because states of higher symmetry than the ground state cannot be present in the system. The absence of these states is accounted for by the final term on the right-hand side of eqn. (4.41b).

Equations (4.41) are expected to be valid for values of AU' up to 800. They may be of value, therefore, for the representation of neutron resonance data up to mass numbers of 100. We have tested this against the experimental data for a few nuclei up to mass number 110 (see Table 4.3). The agreement is reasonable up to about mass number 60.

TABLE 4.3

Comparison of resonance density data of medium weight nuclei with the semi-empirical formula of Critchfield and Oleksa (1951)

Target nucleus	Compound nucleus	Neutron separation energy (MeV)	S_0	T_0 (of compound nucleus)	Y_0	Calculated level density (MeV^{-1})	Observed level density, $\rho(E_{\text{th}}, n)/2(2I+1)$ (MeV^{-1})
^{23}Na	^{24}Na	6·96	1	1	0	0·92	0·46±0·23
^{27}Al	^{28}Al	7·72	1	1	0	1·53	1·6±1·2
^{32}S	^{33}S	8·64	$\frac{1}{2}$	$\frac{1}{2}$	$\frac{1}{2}$	2·43	1·4±0·7
^{45}Sc	^{46}Sc	8·77	1	2	0	8·61	<63
^{51}V	^{52}V	7·30	1	3	0	7·42	17±4
^{58}Ni	^{59}Ni	9·00	$\frac{1}{2}$	3/2	$\frac{1}{2}$	19·3	19±4
^{60}Ni	^{61}Ni	7·82	$\frac{1}{2}$	5/2	$\frac{1}{2}$	12·9	21±3
^{75}As	^{76}As	7·33	1	5	0	65·4	1400±300
^{88}Sr	^{89}Sr	6·5	$\frac{1}{2}$	13/2	$\frac{1}{2}$	159	9±3
^{109}Ag	^{110}Ag	6·81	1	8	7	$4{\cdot}88\times10^5$	$(1{\cdot}2\pm0{\cdot}4)\times10^4$

5. The shell model

(*a*) *Use of the continuous approximation*

It is clear from the comparison of neutron resonance data with the Fermi gas model that such a simple theory is an inadequate explanation of nuclear level densities at moderate excitation energies. Simple study of the data shows strong correlations with nuclear magic numbers and some quantitative studies have shown that an independent-particle shell model appears to give a good description of level densities at the neutron separation energy.

Newton (1956) adapted the continuous approximation to the evaluation of level densities of the shell model. Newton uses three constants of the motion in his study; neutron number, proton number, and angular momentum projection. He notes that in the integral approximations for Φ and its derivatives (eqn. 4.26), the integrand is a product of the single-particle level density and a function with a sharp maximum at the Fermi energy, and is of a width roughly equal to the nuclear temperature. Instead of using the Fermi gas level-density in the formulae for the continuous approximation, Newton uses the discrete levels of the shell model averaged over the width of this maximum.

In the spherical-shell model, the Fermi energies correspond to the energy of the last unfilled subshells for neutrons and protons. If the angular momenta of these subshells are j_N and j_Z respectively, the single-particle level densities are proportional to (j_N+j_Z+1) at very low temperature. At higher temperatures this proportionality is modified by the averaging procedure; the result can be represented by using a notation of effective angular momenta $\overline{j_N}$, $\overline{j_Z}$. Newton shows that the spherical-shell model calculation results in more structure in the level density at excitations equivalent to neutron separation energies than the resonance data reveal. The structure between the major shells is removed by using the spheroidal model of Nilsson (1955) in the mass number regions where nuclei are known to be deformed.

The effective angular momenta calculated by Newton using the spherical-shell model close to magic nucleon numbers and the speroidal model in the deformed region are given in Table 4.4. The final formula for the density of levels of zero angular momentum and one parity is

$$\rho(U, J=0) = K_S(\rho_N \rho_Z)^{-\frac{1}{2}}(2U+3T)^{-2}\exp\left\{\left(\frac{2\pi^2}{3}\rho_S U\right)^{\frac{1}{2}}\right\}. \tag{4.43}$$

The dependence of the level density on angular momentum is assumed to be proportional to $2J+1$. The single-particle level densities are

$$\rho_N = \alpha(2\overline{j_N}+1)A^{\frac{2}{3}}, \tag{4.44a}$$

$$\rho_Z = \alpha(2\overline{j_Z}+1)A^{\frac{2}{3}}, \tag{4.44b}$$

$$\rho_S = \rho_N+\rho_Z = 2\alpha(\overline{j_N}+\overline{j_Z}+1)A^{\frac{2}{3}}. \tag{4.44c}$$

The mass number dependence is roughly that of the reciprocal of the spacing between subshells in the spherical-shell model. The numerical values determined by Newton for the proportionality constants α and K_S by fitting eqn. (4.43) to the neutron resonance spacings of 52 nuclei are

$$\alpha = 0{\cdot}01886 \tag{4.45a}$$

$$K_S = \frac{3{\cdot}0}{A}. \tag{4.45b}$$

Newton has tested eqns. (4.43) and (4.44) by the following statistical criterion. The quantity γ was defined as the logarithm of the ratio of the observed level spacing to the calculated spacing:

$$\gamma = \ln(\bar{D}_{obs}(J=0)/\bar{D}_{calc}(J=0)). \tag{4.46}$$

TABLE 4.4

Effective angular momenta of nucleons at the Fermi level of a nucleus at the neutron threshold temperature, according to Newton (1956)

N or Z	$2\bar{j}_Z+1$	$2\bar{j}_N+1$	N or Z	$2\bar{j}_Z+1$	$2\bar{j}_N+1$
1	2	2	77	6	6·4
2	2·67	2·67	78	5	5·2
3	3·33	3·33	79	3·6	3·6
4–5	4	4	80	3·2	3·2
6	3·33	3·33	81	4·4	4
7	2·67	2·67	82	5·6	4·8
8	3·33	3·33	83	6·8	5·6
9	4·67	4·67	84	8·4	6·8
10–13	6	6	85–88	10	8
14	4·67	4·67	89	10	8·4
15	3·33	3·33	90	10	8·8
16	2·67	2·67	91	9·867	9·2
17	3·33	3·33	92	9·733	9·6
18–19	4	4	93	9·6	10
20	5·33	5·33	94	9·467	10
21	6·67	6·67	95–98	9·33	10
22–27	8	8	99–100		10
28	6·67	6·67	101–106		10
29	5·33	5·33	107–118		10
30–31	4	4	119		8·8
32	4·67	4·67	120		7·6
33	5·33	5·33	121		6·4
34–37	6	6	122		5·2
38	4·67	4·67	123		3·6
39	3·33	3·33	124		3·2
40	4·67	4·67	125		4·4
41	7·33	7·33	126		5·6
42–48	10	10	127		6·8
49	9·6	9·2	128		8·4
50	9·2	8·4	129–134		10
51	8·8	7·6	135		10·4
52	8·4	6·8	136		10·8
53–54	8	6	137		11·2
55	8	6·8	138		11·6
56	8	7·6	139–148		12·0
57	8·2	8·4			
58	8·4	9·2			
59	8·6	10			
60	8·8	10			
61–64	9	10			
65–74	9	10			
75	8	8·8			
76	7	7·6			

Then the quantity $\chi^2 = (n-1)^{-1}\sum_k \gamma_k^2$ was formed, where n is the number of nuclei for which γ was determined. For 52 nuclei (the data available in 1956) χ^2 was found to be 1·21; this is to be compared with a value of $\chi^2 = 5{\cdot}4$ found in fitting the same data to a Fermi gas form. The former value is equivalent to an expected error of a factor 3.

The data in Table 4.2 are much more extensive than those that were available to Newton. We have compared them indirectly with eqn. (4.43) in a way that was also used by Newton. The resonance density

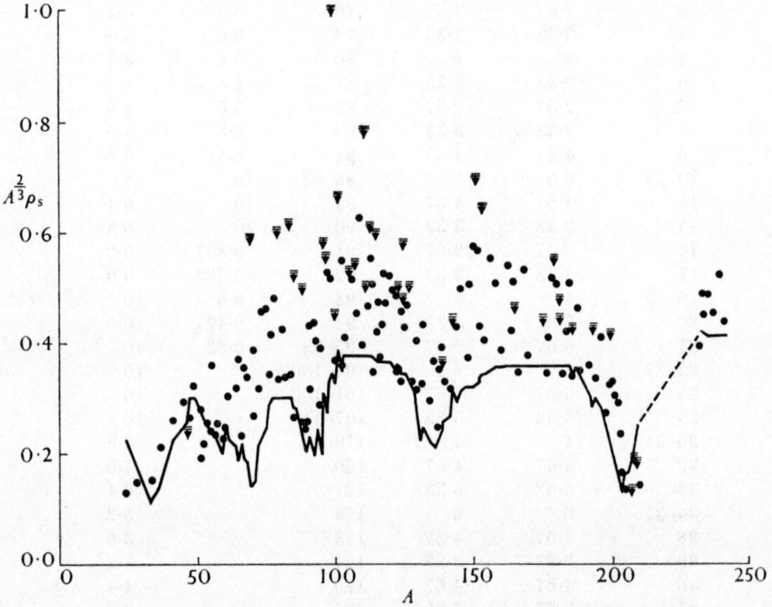

Fig. 4.3. Single-particle level densities ρ_s, derived from neutron resonance-density data by the use of the shell-model level-density theory of Newton (1956) and compared with the theoretical curve of the same paper.

data are reduced to single-particle level densities by inversion of eqn. (4.43) and these are compared with eqns. (4.44) and (4.45a) in Fig. 4.3. Most of the data lie above the theoretical curve by a considerable factor; only at some of the closed shells and amongst the lighter nuclei is there reasonable agreement. It is quite obvious that overall agreement cannot be obtained by simple adjustment of the constant α. Improved agreement is obtained, however, by the choice $\alpha = 0{\cdot}0227$ (Lang 1961).

Cameron (1958) has attempted to improve the calculation by using a more empirical method of determining the single-particle level density. He computed these densities by taking appropriate averages of the second differences of adjacent atomic masses. We refer the reader to Cameron's paper for this formula for the single-particle level density and the extensive table of parameters that it requires.

(*b*) *Occupation of subshells*

By its very nature the continuous approximation, even as adapted by Newton, allows no statement of the dependence of the level density on the occupation number of a subshell in the ground state. According to the continuous approximation the level density of two nuclei differing only in their place in the subshell should be affected only by the small change in the single-particle level density.

A simple model which demonstrates the subshell effect on the level density has been studied (Rosenzweig 1957). The model consists of a system of N non-interacting fermions occupying a set of uniformly spaced single-particle levels. Each level has a p-fold degeneracy. The lowest level is taken as the energy origin. The number of distinct ways in which the N particles can occupy the levels so as to give a total energy E is denoted by $C_p(N, E)$, which is used to represent the level density at energy E. At zero excitation energy $C_p(N, E)$ is just $p!/\{n!(p-n)!\}$ where n is the number of particles in the highest occupied level, the Fermi level, in the ground state of the system. For a degenerate Fermi system, in which the energy is insufficient to excite more than one particle out of the lowest single-particle level, it is sometimes more convenient to use the subshell occupation number n in place of the total number N. Rosenzweig obtained the exact solutions for $C_p(n, E)$ for low excitations. They are:

$$C_p(n, 0) = \tfrac{1}{2}F(0), \tag{4.47a}$$

$$C_p(n, 1) = pF(1), \tag{4.47b}$$

$$C_p(n, 2) = p^2F(0)+pF(1)+\binom{p}{2}F(2), \tag{4.47c}$$

$$C_p(n, 3) = p^2F(0)+p\left\{1+\binom{p}{2}\right\}F(1)+p^2F(2)+\binom{p}{3}F(3), \tag{4.47d}$$

where

$$F(\sigma) = \binom{p}{n-\sigma}+\binom{p}{n+\sigma}. \tag{4.47e}$$

The unit of excitation energy here is the single-particle level spacing. These results have the feature that a system with n particles has the same level density as one with $p-n$ particles (n holes).

For higher excitation energies an asymptotic formula has to be developed. This may be obtained from eqn. (4.14), the result of saddle-point integration of the inversion of the Laplace transform in eqn. (4.9). The logarithm of the partition function for the present model is clearly (from eqn. 4.23b)

$$\Phi = p\sum_{m=0}^{\infty} \ln(1+\mathrm{e}^{x_1-\beta m}), \tag{4.48}$$

with m referring to energy units and the only constant of the motion being the number of particles in the system. Rosenzweig applies the Euler–Maclaurin formula to the evaluation of Φ:

$$\sum_{m=0}^{\infty} \ln(1+\mathrm{e}^{x_1-\beta m}) = \int_0^{\infty} \ln(1+e^{x_1-\beta\varepsilon})d\varepsilon+\tfrac{1}{2}\ln(1+e^{x_1}) + \frac{\beta}{12(1+e^{-x_1})}+\zeta(x_1,\beta), \tag{4.49}$$

where the remainder ζ is of order e^{-x_1} and β^2. In the limits of $x_1 \to \infty$ and $\beta \to 0$

$$\Phi = E\beta - Nx_1 + \frac{p}{\beta}\left(\frac{x_1^2}{2}+\frac{\pi^2}{6}\right)+p\left(\frac{x_1}{2}+\frac{\beta}{12}\right). \tag{4.50}$$

The relation between the energy E and the excitation energy U of the model is

$$E-\frac{1}{2p}(N-\tfrac{1}{2}p)^2 = U-\frac{1}{2p}(n-\tfrac{1}{2}p)^2. \tag{4.51}$$

The level density $\rho(U,n)$ may now be expressed as

$$\rho(U,n) = C_p(N,E) \approx (\surd(48)U_\mathrm{e})^{-1}\exp\left\{\pi\left(\frac{2pU_\mathrm{e}}{3}\right)^{\frac{1}{2}}\right\}, \tag{4.52a}$$

where the effective excitation energy is

$$U_\mathrm{e} = U+\frac{p}{12}-\frac{1}{2p}(n-\tfrac{1}{2}p)^2. \tag{4.52b}$$

The equation of state of the system is obtained from the derivative of Φ with respect to β; it is

$$U_e = p\pi^2/6\beta^2. \tag{4.53}$$

The relation between number of particles and the chemical potential $\mu \equiv x_1/\beta$ is

$$N = p\mu + \tfrac{1}{2}p. \tag{4.54}$$

Although eqn. (4.52a) is an asymptotic formula for $\beta \to 0$ or (from eqn. 4.53) as $U_e \to \infty$ direct calculation shows that it is a fairly good approximation to the level density even at quite low energies (Rosenzweig 1957). For a given excitation energy it is most accurate for high degeneracy. Using this formula Rosenzweig shows that the ratio of level densities for the half-filled and the unfilled (or completely filled) shells is

$$R \approx \exp\left\{\frac{p}{6}\left(\frac{p}{U}\right)^{\frac{1}{2}}\right\} \tag{4.55}$$

provided that $p/U \ll 12$. This equation shows that the level density becomes independent of the occupation of the shell at very large values of the excitation energy, in which case eqn. (4.52a) becomes the usual formula from the continuous approximation.

At excitations of the order of the neutron-separation energy, however, the ratio R may still be quite large if the degeneracy p of the subshell is large. Using his generalization of eqn. (4.52) for a system of both neutrons (subshell spacing δ_n, degeneracy p) and protons (subshell spacing δ_p, degeneracy q) Rosenzweig gives estimates of R. The complete level-density formula is

$$\rho(n, p, U) = \frac{\exp[\pi\{\frac{2}{3}(p/\delta_n + q/\delta_p)U_e\}^{\frac{1}{2}}]}{4\{216U_e^5(p/\delta_n)^2(q/\delta_p)^2/(p/\delta_n + q/\delta_p)^3\}^{\frac{1}{4}}} \tag{4.56a}$$

$$U_e = U + \frac{p\delta_n}{12} - \frac{\delta_n}{2p}(n - \tfrac{1}{2}p)^2 + \frac{q\delta_p}{12} - \frac{\delta_p}{2q}(m - \tfrac{1}{2}q)^2 \tag{4.56b}$$

where n, m are the subshell occupation numbers for neutrons and protons.

It is difficult to confirm the existence of this effect in the data. The isotopes of tin would appear to provide the ideal test. In these isotopes the $1g_{9/2}$ proton subshell is full and it is believed that the $1h_{11/2}$ neutron subshell is in the course of filling. If this is so then the ratio R is expected to be about 13. Among all the odd mass compound nuclei of tin listed in Table 4.1 the level densities do not differ by more than a factor of 3, however, even when they are normalized to the same excitation energy by using eqn. (4.39b). In the same mass-number region the nuclei with proton numbers $Z = 44$ to 50 (filling of the $1g_{9/2}$ proton subshell) might also be expected to provide a test (Rosenzweig *et al.* 1958). Again there is no appreciable difference of level densities in the sequences of compound nuclei ${}^{102}_{49}$Ru, ${}^{106}_{46}$Pd, ${}^{112}_{48}$Cd, ${}^{116}_{50}$Sn or ${}^{104}_{45}$Rh, ${}^{110}_{47}$Ag, ${}^{116}_{49}$In within which the members have the same even or odd character. Near the shell closures at lead, Rosenzweig points out that if the $7i_{13/2}$, $4p_{3/2}$, and $4p_{1/2}$ neutron shells are considered coincident the level densities of ^{198}Au and ^{208}Pb should differ by a factor of about 10^4. The observed difference is of the order of 10^3 (or rather less if the odd-even effect is taken into account). Since this difference is already partly accounted for by Newton's theory (see Fig. 4.3), which considers only the effective single-particle level density, it seems that residual forces obliterate much of the degeneracy effect within subshells. On the other hand the failure of Newton's model between the shell closures, which is also shown in Fig. 4.3, could be due to the Rosenzweig effect operating in the major shells.

A generalization of eqn. (4.56a) now exists for the case in which the shells of nucleons are spread uniformly over a constant energy interval or band with uniform separation (Rosenzweig 1965). This may prove more fruitful in the analysis of level-density data.

6. The dependence of the level density on angular momentum

(a) General

In Section B.4 the formal derivation of the level-density law using the continuous approximation was described, following the procedure of Bloch (1954) which leads to a Gaussian law for scalar constants of the motion:

$$\rho(U, M) = \rho(U)\{\sigma_M\sqrt{(2\pi)}\}^{-1}\exp(-M^2/2\sigma_M^2) \qquad (4.57)$$

where $\sigma_M{}^2 = (1/\pi)\overline{m^2}(6U/\delta_S)^{\frac{1}{2}}$. This law can also be established by statistical arguments (Ericson 1960).

A physical explanation can also be given for a Gaussian type of law for the angular momentum projection (Lang and Le Couteur 1954). If the system of particles is in rotation as a whole about a given axis, the kinetic energy of the rotation is the ratio of the square of the angular momentum component parallel to the axis of rotation, L_z, to twice the moment of inertia of the system, $\mathscr{I}$, about this axis:

$$E_{\text{kin,rot}} = \frac{L_z^2}{2\mathscr{I}}. \tag{4.58}$$

This kinetic energy is not available for internal excitation of the particles of the system. The effective excitation energy U_{eff} for the level density therefore will be the true excitation minus the kinetic energy of rotation $E_{\text{kin,rot}}$. For a quantal system

$$U_{\text{eff}} = U - \frac{\hbar^2 M^2}{2\mathscr{I}}. \tag{4.59}$$

The level density of a system carrying this angular momentum projection can now be calculated from that for a system with zero spin projection provided that the rotation energy term is small compared to the excitation energy, E. Equation (4.59) for U_{eff} is substituted in the main exponential term $\exp(U\beta)$ of eqn. (4.11) in the formula for the zero spin system; thus

$$\rho(U, M) = \rho(U, M = 0)\exp(-\hbar^2 M^2 \beta/2\mathscr{I}). \tag{4.60}$$

According to this, the dispersion of the projection quantum number is

$$\sigma_{\text{M}}^2 = \mathscr{I}/(\hbar^2\beta). \tag{4.61}$$

The density of levels with total angular momentum J is derived from eqn. (4.57) referring to the projection by the observation (Bethe 1937) that

$$\rho(U, J) = \rho(U, M = J) - \rho(U, M = J+1) \tag{4.62a}$$

$$= \frac{1}{\sigma_{\text{M}}\sqrt{(2\pi)}}\left\{\exp\left(-\frac{J^2}{2\sigma_{\text{M}}^2}\right) - \exp\left(-\frac{(J+1)^2}{2\sigma_{\text{M}}^2}\right)\right\}\rho(U) \tag{4.62b}$$

$$\approx \frac{\exp\{-J(J+1)/2\sigma_{\text{M}}^2\}}{\sigma_{\text{M}}\sqrt{(2\pi)}} \cdot \frac{(2J+1)}{2\sigma_{\text{M}}^2} \cdot \rho(U). \tag{4.62c}$$

The approximation leading to eqn. (4.62c) can be made if quantities like $J/4\sigma_{\text{M}}^2$ and $J^3/24\sigma_{\text{M}}^3$ are small compared to unity. Maximization of eqn. (4.62c) gives $\sigma_{\text{M}} - \frac{1}{2}$ as the value of J for which the level density is greatest. If σ_{M} is greater than unity it would appear that (4.62c) is reasonably valid to nearly this value of J.

That σ_{M} is indeed greater than unity is suggested theoretically by the numerical work of Critchfield and Oleksa (1951), in which the level density was found to increase with increasing angular momentum and pass through a maximum. A least-squares fit of their results to eqn. (4.62c) gave values of σ_{M}^2 with the behaviour shown in Fig. 4.4. There does not appear to be any appreciable dependence on excitation energy and the average value of σ_{M}^2 is about 12. Experimentally, the data, summarized in Table 4.2, from direct observation of the angular momenta of neutron resonances, show no evidence that σ_{M}^2 is appreciably

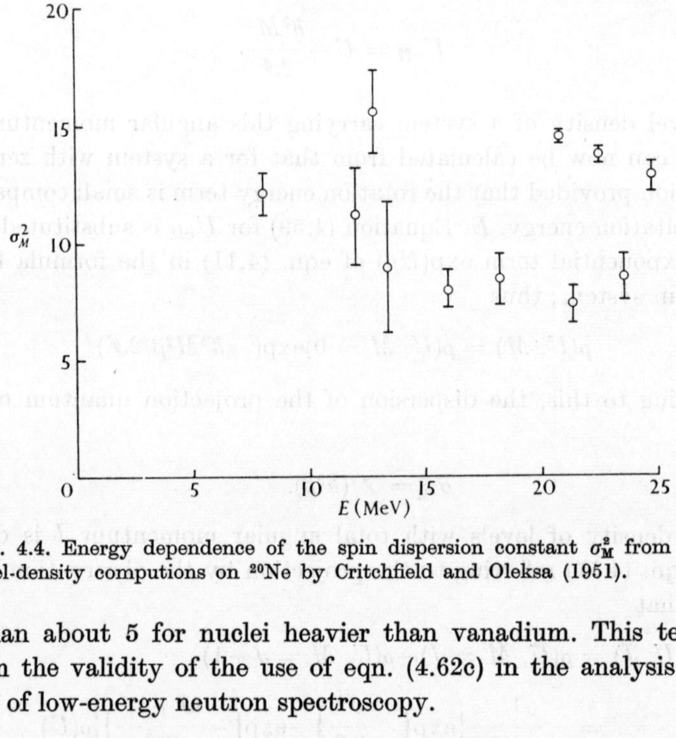

Fig. 4.4. Energy dependence of the spin dispersion constant σ_{M}^2 from the level-density computions on ^{20}Ne by Critchfield and Oleksa (1951).

less than about 5 for nuclei heavier than vanadium. This tends to confirm the validity of the use of eqn. (4.62c) in the analysis of the results of low-energy neutron spectroscopy.

(b) *Fermi gas model*

Bethe (1937) used the WKB approximation to obtain an estimate of the spin dispersion factor σ_{M}^2 appropriate to a gas of fermions occupying a spherical potential well of radius R. He established that the single-particle level density for states of given orbital angular momentum l and projection m at energy ε is

$$\rho_{\mathrm{S}}(\varepsilon, l, m) = \frac{1}{\pi\varepsilon}\left(\frac{2M_{\mathrm{n}}\varepsilon R^2}{\hbar^2} - (l+\tfrac{1}{2})^2\right)^{\frac{1}{2}} \tag{4.63}$$

where M_n is the nucleon mass. The integral of this over the angular momentum l from $l = |m|$ upwards gives the density for a given angular momentum projection $\rho_S(\varepsilon, m)$. This may be used to establish that σ_M^2 is given by the expression

$$\sigma_M^2 = \frac{2}{5}(M_n R^2/\hbar^2\beta)A. \tag{4.64}$$

This is equivalent to a moment of inertia $\mathscr{I}$ that is appropriate to a rigid body (through eqn. 4.61):

$$\mathscr{I} = \frac{2}{5}AM_n R^2. \tag{4.65}$$

A rigid body with the dimensions of a heavy nucleus would have a spin dispersion factor σ_M^2 of the order of $150T$. At the neutron separation energy, the temperature will be of the order of 1 MeV (from eqn. (4.13b)). The dependence of σ_M^2 on mass number is obtained from eqns. (4.64) and (4.30): it is proportional to $A^{7/6}$. Such high values of σ_M^2 would render the exponential factor of eqn. (4.62c) relatively unimportant for the levels studied in low-energy neutron spectroscopy. Thus, the density of neutron resonances is expected to be very nearly proportional to the factor $(2J+1)$ according to the Fermi gas model.

This has been confirmed for the lowest values of J. The first part of Table 4.2 displays the available data on the low-energy resonances of some target nuclei with ground-state angular momentum $I = \frac{1}{2}$. The number of resonances observed with $J = 1$ ranges from twice to three times the number with $J = 0$; the expected ratio is 3. For target nuclei with $I = \frac{3}{2}$ the observed ratios of the numbers of $J = 2$ resonances to $J = 1$ resonances range from 1·0 to 3 while the expectation is 1·67.

A more stringent test of the Fermi gas model is provided by the constant K_f evaluated in the rough fitting of eqn. (4.35b) to the resonance density data of Table 4.1. It is apparent from eqn. (4.62c) that this constant, for $J = 0$ levels, is

$$K_f = \frac{1}{(2\sigma_M^2)^{\frac{3}{2}}\pi^{\frac{1}{2}}} \tag{4.66}$$

Substitution of $K_f = 0{\cdot}23$ leads to $\sigma_M^2 \approx 0{\cdot}9$ which implies a serious breakdown of the model. If we allow K_f to be dependent on mass number, however, a considerably smaller value will be required for the actinide nuclei than elsewhere. The deduced value of σ_M^2 is correspondingly higher and the model becomes more acceptable for these nuclei; indeed, it is to be expected that the Fermi gas approximation would be more valid for a large system than for a small one. A general decrease of K_f can be achieved only by increasing the exponent in the level-density equation (4.35b), i.e. by increasing the single-particle level density; this appears to be physically unacceptable.

Notice also that the comparisons of the data with the Fermi gas model that are illustrated in Figs. 4.1 and 4.2 have implicitly assumed the validity of the $(2J+1)$ rule (all densities have been divided by $2\times(2I+1)$ to normalize them to $J = 0$). Even so, the data of the odd nuclei (corresponding to odd-mass targets often with high spin) generally lie above those of odd-mass, even-charge nuclei (from even targets with zero spin). If the $(2J+1)$ rule were not valid the difference between the overall trends of these classes of data would be even greater and it would not be possible to reconcile them by the simple odd–even effect described in Section 4(c).

(c) *The shell model*

The calculation of the spin dispersion coefficient of the independent-particle shell model involves averaging the mean square spin projection $\overline{m^2} = j(j+1)(2j+1)/3$ for a level with spin j over the single-particle levels within a region centred on the Fermi energy with width approximately equal to the temperature. Most of the naturally available target nuclei have even nucleon numbers or odd mass numbers. Their ground-state angular momenta, therefore, will normally be either zero or have the spin j of the Fermi level in the spherical-shell model. For low temperatures, substitution of the Fermi level mean square projection $\overline{m^2}$ into eqn. (4.31), together with the use of Newton's (1956) estimate of the single-particle level spacing, indicates that the exponential attenuation factor governing the density of s-wave resonances of odd-mass targets is close to unity. We conclude that in the independent-particle model the density of s-wave resonances of angular momentum J is proportional to $(2J+1)$.

There is some evidence available to test this rule but not enough to test it rigorously. The angular momenta of the first states of one of the highest spin targets ^{209}Bi ($I = 9/2$) have been measured (Firk *et al.* 1963*b*). Two of these were found to have $J = 5$ and three to have $J = 4$. Taking into account the non-uniform distribution of level spacings (see Chapter V) it can be shown that these data are fully consistent with the $(2J+1)$ rule. They also set a lower limit of about 5 on the possible value of σ_M^2 for ^{210}Bi at the neutron separation energy. This is the worst case in Table 4.2. It follows that the data from the other high-spin targets are also consistent with the $(2J+1)$ rule in agreement with the theory.

There are also a few data for odd-target nuclei with high angular momenta. They form odd-mass compound nuclei and their resonance densities may be compared with those of neighbouring odd compound nuclei. The most important case is the target $^{176}_{71}\text{Lu}$ with $I = 7$, which has a resonance density twice as high as its neighbour $^{175}_{71}\text{Lu}$ $(I = 7/2)$ (Harvey *et al.* 1958*b*). The compound nucleus ^{177}Lu has an excitation energy about 0·5 MeV higher than its neighbour but the effect of this ought to be cancelled by the odd–even difference. There is no evidence, therefore, that levels with $J = 13/2$ or $15/2$ are appreciably less dense than those with $J = 3$ or 4. This suggests that in heavy nuclei σ_{M}^2 may be of the order of magnitude of 50 or greater.

Evidence on σ_{M}^2 in lighter nuclei is provided by the cross-section of ^{50}V. The mean resonance spacing in this cross-section is $1{\cdot}1 \pm 0{\cdot}3$ keV (Good and Block 1966). Thus the resonance density (presumably of states with $J = 11/2$, $13/2$) in ^{51}V is three times as great as that of the $J = 3$ and 4 states in the neighbouring compound nucleus ^{52}V and about 10 times that of the $J = \frac{1}{2}$ states in ^{51}Cr. The excitation energies in these three nuclei are 11·04, 7·304, and 9·249 MeV, respectively. ^{51}V and ^{51}Cr are odd-mass nuclei while ^{52}V is odd. The effective excitation energies adjusted for the odd–even effect are therefore 9·5 MeV for ^{51}V, 7·75 MeV for ^{51}Cr, and 7·3 MeV for ^{52}V. After adjustment to a standard excitation energy, using the extrapolation formula, eqn. (4.39b), it is found that the density of $J = 11/2$ and $13/2$ states in ^{51}V is about the same as that of $J = 3$ and 4 states in ^{52}V and four times that of $J = \frac{1}{2}$ states in ^{51}Cr, whereas the $(2J+1)$ formula would give ratios of 13:8 and 13:1 respectively. From the discrepancies it is deduced that σ_{M}^2 is in the range 18 to 27 in these nuclei.

On the other hand, the values of the spin dispersion coefficient that may be deduced from the empirical constant of proportionality given by Newton (1956) and Cameron (1958) are very low. The constant is related to the dispersion coefficient by

$$K_{\text{S}} = \frac{\pi}{(12\overline{m^2})^{\frac{3}{2}}} = \frac{(6U\rho_{\text{S}})^{\frac{3}{2}}}{12^{\frac{3}{2}}\pi^{\frac{1}{2}}\sigma_{\text{M}}^3} \tag{4.67}$$

By using eqn. (4.45b) for K_{S} we find that σ_{M}^2 is only of the order of 10 even for nuclei where the single-particle level density is high. Cameron's value is even smaller (or the order of 2). This throws considerable doubt on the validity of the independent-particle model as a quantitative and self-consistent explanation of neutron resonance spacings.

Malyshev (1963) has analysed the neutron resonance data to obtain σ_M^2 and ρ_S for individual nuclei with the requirement that $\overline{m^2} = 0{\cdot}146A^{2/3}$. His values for σ_M^2 are much higher than those of Newton and Cameron and his values for ρ_S are in general agreement with those of Lang (1961). The relation for $\overline{m^2}$, however, is from the work of Jensen and Luttinger (1952); it is a calculation that applies to the whole nucleus, whereas, according to eqn. (4.57), level-density theory requires the mean square spin projection in the region of the Fermi level. To the extent that this differs from $\overline{m^2}$ for the whole nucleus Malyshev's analysis is uncertain.

7. Parity

The earlier development of neutron spectroscopy was concerned exclusively with *s*-wave resonances. More recently *p*-wave resonances have been measured but at the time of writing insufficient of these have been identified to establish reliable values of *p*-wave level spacings. It is probably worth mentioning here, however, that according to the independent-particle model there could be a small dependence of level density on parity at excitations of the order of the neutron separation energy (Ericson 1960). This dependence decreases rapidly with increasing energy.

One compound nucleus in which there appears to be little dependence of the level density on parity is ^{53}Cr. The target ^{52}Cr has spin and parity 0^+, so states with $J^\pi = \frac{1}{2}^+$ are excited by *s*-wave neutrons and states with $J^\pi = \frac{1}{2}^-, \frac{3}{2}^-$ are excited by *p*-waves. Most of the *s*-wave resonances can be identified by their strong interference with potential scattering, and their cumulative histogram as a function of neutron energy is shown in Fig. 4.5 (after Newson 1965). The slope of this gives the density of the $J^\pi = \frac{1}{2}^+$ states. The cumulative histogram of the remaining resonances (starting at an arbitrary point) is plotted above this curve. Its slope over a range of 300 keV is consistent with a density of three times that of $\frac{1}{2}^+$ states. This is consistent with the assumptions that the unidentified resonances are excited by *p*-waves, that few are missed, that the $(2J+1)$ dependence of level density is valid, and that there is no parity-dependence.

8. Validity of the continuous approximation

The review of this section has revealed that most of the work on the independent-particle model of level densities has employed the continuous approximation for the density of single-particle states at the Fermi energy. While direct numerical comparison for a system with discrete equidistant single-particle states (Lang and Le Conteur 1954, Ericson 1960) shows that the level density is quite accurately computed in the continuous approximation at excitations somewhat greater than

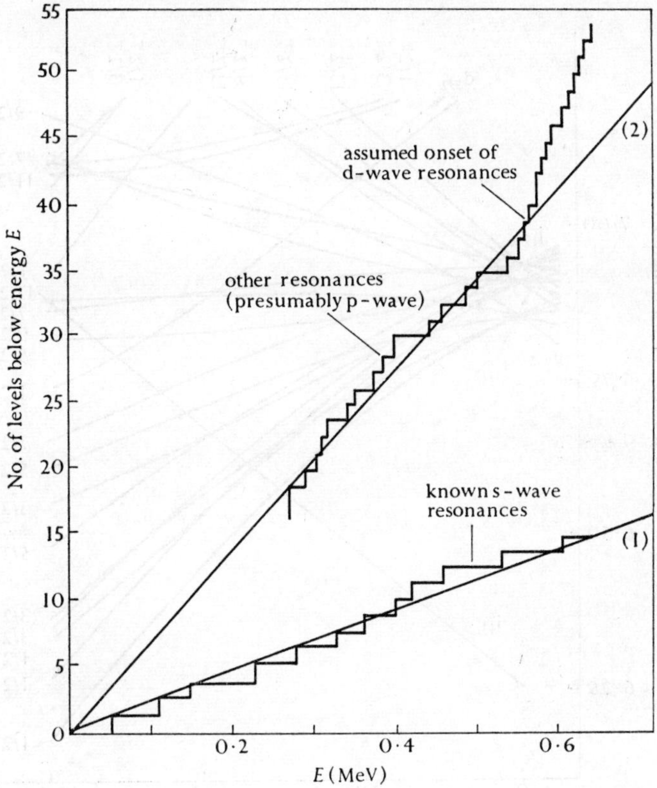

Fig. 4.5. This shows the density of known *s*-wave resonances in the cross-section of ^{52}Cr. The slope of line (1) is proportional to this density. The upper stepped curve indicates the positions of other resonances (starting at an arbitrary number) and the slope of the lower portion of this curve (curve 2) is three times that of curve (1) (after Newson 1965).

one level spacing, other computations reveal that a nuclear shell model with its highly irregular spacings and degeneracies is not so well treated by this approximation.

The main evidence for this statement comes from the work of Critchfield and Oleksa (1951), which was described in Section B.1, and of Bloch (1954). Critchfield and Oleksa found that their direct computation of the level density of ^{20}Ne agreed with an estimate derived from the continuous approximation, but their work included terms in the potential well to represent the effect of exchange forces while the continuous approximation estimate did not. Bloch used the saddle-point method to evaluate the level density of ^{20}Ne. His evaluation of the grand partition function Φ depends on a power series expansion in

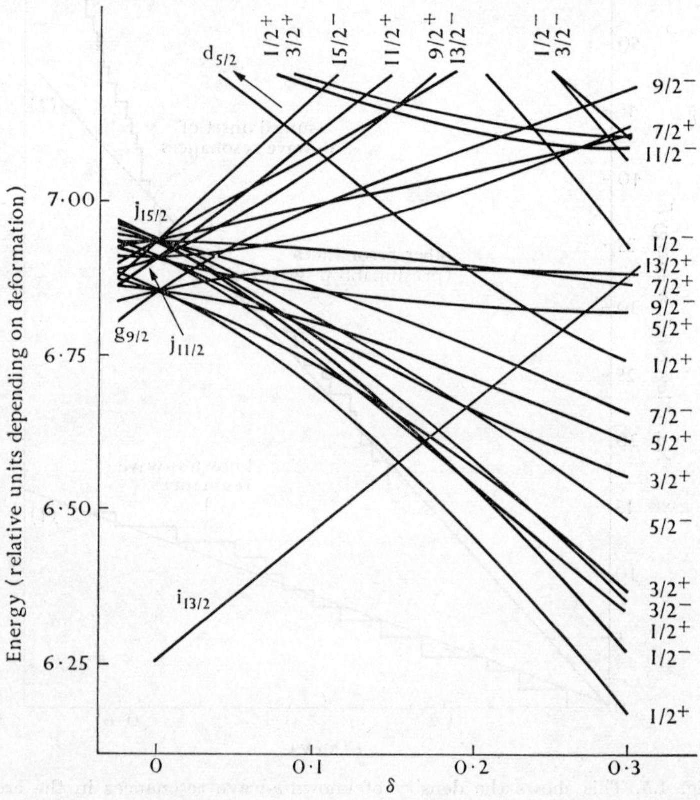

FIG. 4.6. Dependence of the energies of single-particle levels on the deformation δ of the potential energy well from spherical. The total and orbital angular momenta of the levels in the sphere are indicated as well as the projection of angular momentum along the cylindrical-symmetry axis (Nilsson 1955).

terms of the potentials x_k but treats the dependence on temperature exactly. His comparison between this method and the continuous approximation (Bardeen and Feenberg 1938), both including the effect of exchange forces, reveals that the continuous approximation leads to an underestimate of the level density by a factor of about 10 at an excitation energy of 25 MeV. The discrepancy is greater at lower energies and smaller at higher energies. Bloch ascribes the difference to a term in the entropy involving the number of particles and holes in the last unfilled level of the ground-state configuration. This term is absent in the equations derived from the continuous approximation. It is closely related to the Rosenzweig effect described in Section B.5.

Not only is the absolute magnitude of the level density doubtful in the continuous approximation but so is the equation of state. The continuous approximation leads to the form

$$U = aT^2 \tag{4.68}$$

where the constant of proportionality is $a = \pi^2\rho_S/6$. Newton's (1956) use of the continuous approximation clearly involves a temperature-dependent effective single-particle spacing. This naturally leads to a dependence of the level density on energy that is considerably different from the one given by the standard treatment. The general conclusion to be drawn from these considerations is that the continuous approximation is unreliable for estimating the level density of spherical nuclei. Strongly deformed nuclei, however, have a very different single-particle level structure (Nilsson 1955) with the disappearance of the strong degeneracies associated with the subshells of the spherical-shell model (see Fig. 4.6). It is probable that the continuous approximation leads to a reasonable estimate of the level density law of such nuclei provided that the independent-particle model is valid in this context.

C. MODELS WITH COLLECTIVE FEATURES

1. The liquid-drop model

The liquid-drop model can be considered to be the opposite extreme to the independent-particle model. The strong short-range forces between the nucleons are believed, in this model, to give rise to strong correlations among their motions; in particular, fluctuations in the density are assumed to be very improbable, i.e. the nuclear fluid is almost incompressible. In such a model only surface waves will be excited at relatively low energies. Surface waves on a spherical drop of mass M_D may be expanded in terms of a set of normal modes. The amplitude, q, of the displacement of the surface from the mean radius R has the expansion

$$q(\theta, \phi) = \sum_{l=0}^{\infty} \sum_{m=-l}^{l} q_{lm} Y_m^{(l)}(\theta, \phi), \tag{4.69}$$

where the $Y_m^{(l)}$ are spherical harmonics and the q_{lm} are the normal coordinates of the expansion. The circular frequency ω_l of the normal mode associated with the latter is (Rayleigh 1879)

$$\omega_l = \left\{\frac{4\pi\alpha}{3M_D}l(l-1)(l+2)\right\}^{\frac{1}{2}}. \tag{4.70}$$

Here, α is the surface tension coefficient. It may be calculated, for a nuclear fluid, from the surface energy term, E_S, of the Weizsäcker semi-empirical mass formula. This term has the form $E_S = u_S A^{2/3}$. A recent estimate of the coefficient u_S is 17·97 MeV (Green 1958); the coefficient $\alpha = u_S A^{2/3}/(4\pi R^2)$. This leads to energies, $\hbar\omega_l$, of the order of a few MeV for a normal mode of low angular momentum, l, in a heavy nucleus. This estimate is reduced if the effect of Coulomb repulsion is considered. The reduction factor is as high as $\sqrt{2}$ for a heavy nucleus. For this reason we employ an effective surface tension coefficient, u_s', in the following equations; this may be as low as one-half of the value of u_s. The coefficient u_s' really depends on l;

$$u_s' = \left\{1 - \frac{20x}{(2l+1)(2l+2)}\right\}u_S, \tag{4.71a}$$

where $2x$ is the ratio of the Coulomb energy, $E_C = 3(Z_e)^2/5R$, to the surface energy E_S,

$$x = \frac{E_C}{2E_S} = \frac{3}{10}\cdot\frac{e^2/r_0}{u_S}\cdot\frac{Z^2}{A} = 0{\cdot}02Z^2/A. \tag{4.71b}$$

From eqn. (4.70) an approximate expression may be derived for the density in energy of the normal modes, ε_S (Bethe 1937):

$$g(\varepsilon)\mathrm{d}\varepsilon = 3^{-1/3}\,.\,4(u_s'\hbar^2/M_n r_0^2)^{-2/3}A^{2/3}\varepsilon^{1/3}\mathrm{d}\varepsilon. \tag{4.72}$$

The energy levels of the liquid-drop nucleus are built up from the superposition of these normal modes (phonons). The problem of finding the level density is solved by the use of the statistical mechanics governing a system consisting of an indefinite number of bosons. The partition function for such a system is (see, for example, Schrödinger 1948)

$$\mathrm{e}\Phi = \prod_s (1-\mathrm{e}^{-\beta\varepsilon_s}). \tag{4.73}$$

From the partition function we are led to the equation of state relating the excitation energy to the temperature of the system

$$U = 4{\cdot}7(u_s'\hbar^2/M_n r^2)^{-2/3}A^{2/3}T^{7/3} \tag{4.74}$$

and from this to the level density relation (Bethe 1937)

$$\rho(U) = 0{\cdot}364\left(\frac{AM_{\mathrm{n}}r_0^2}{u'_{\mathrm{s}}\hbar^2}\right)^{1/7} U^{-5/7}\exp\left\{3{\cdot}39\left(\frac{AM_{\mathrm{n}}r_0^2U^2}{u'_{\mathrm{s}}\hbar^2}\right)^{2/7}\right\}. \quad (4.75)$$

Using recent values for the constants that occur in this equation we find that eqn. (4.75) falls some orders of magnitude short of the level density of heavy nuclei at the neutron-separation energy. Equation (4.72) clearly overestimates the low-energy density of the normal modes of a spherical liquid drop; since these are the most important modes involved in the formation of states of the system at low and moderate excitation energies, we would expect that eqn. (4.75) is a gross over-estimate of the level density of the liquid drop. On the other hand, the observed nuclear states with apparently vibrational character lie at much lower energies than those given by eqn. (4.70) using the constants determined from the semi-empirical mass formula. It is arguable that this observation implies that a high-density approximation to the normal-mode density should indeed be used. This invites the speculation that the highly excited resonance states could be simple superpositions of the low-energy vibrational modes. In this picture the correlation of the resonance spacings with shell structure would be explained by the 'stiffness' of nuclei very near the shell closures to surface oscillations. In particular, it is known that the first excited 2^+ state of even nuclei (the state carrying one phonon of quadrupole character) increases in energy near the shell closures. It follows that the density of normal modes and, therefore, the density of highly excited states decreases. However, such a speculation has not been tested quantitatively.

Lang and Le Couteur (1954) have used a composite picture of an independent-particle model and a surface oscillation model to analyse nuclear level densities. To obtain the level-density formula for this system they approximate the equation of state by simply adding the equation of state of the two models:

$$U = aAT^2 - bT + cA^{2/3}T^{7/3}. \quad (4.76)$$

From data on neutron evaporation spectra at excitation energies of 10, 50, and 200 MeV the constant a was determined as 0·091 with the constants b and c fixed at 1·0 and 0·125 (close to the value of the charged liquid drop) respectively; this agrees reasonably well with the single-particle level density deduced for the Fermi gas model (see eqns. 4.30, 4.38, and 4.37). With a moment of inertia of about 55 per cent of the rigid body value (eqn. (4.65)) (this agrees roughly with the value deduced from the low-lying rotational spectra of heavy even nuclei) the density of levels with zero total angular momentum is found to be

$$\rho(U, J = 0) = 9{\cdot}1A^{-2}(U+T)^{-2} \exp\{2(0{\cdot}091AU)^{\frac{1}{2}}+0{\cdot}465U^{2/3}\}(\text{MeV}^{-1}). \tag{4.77}$$

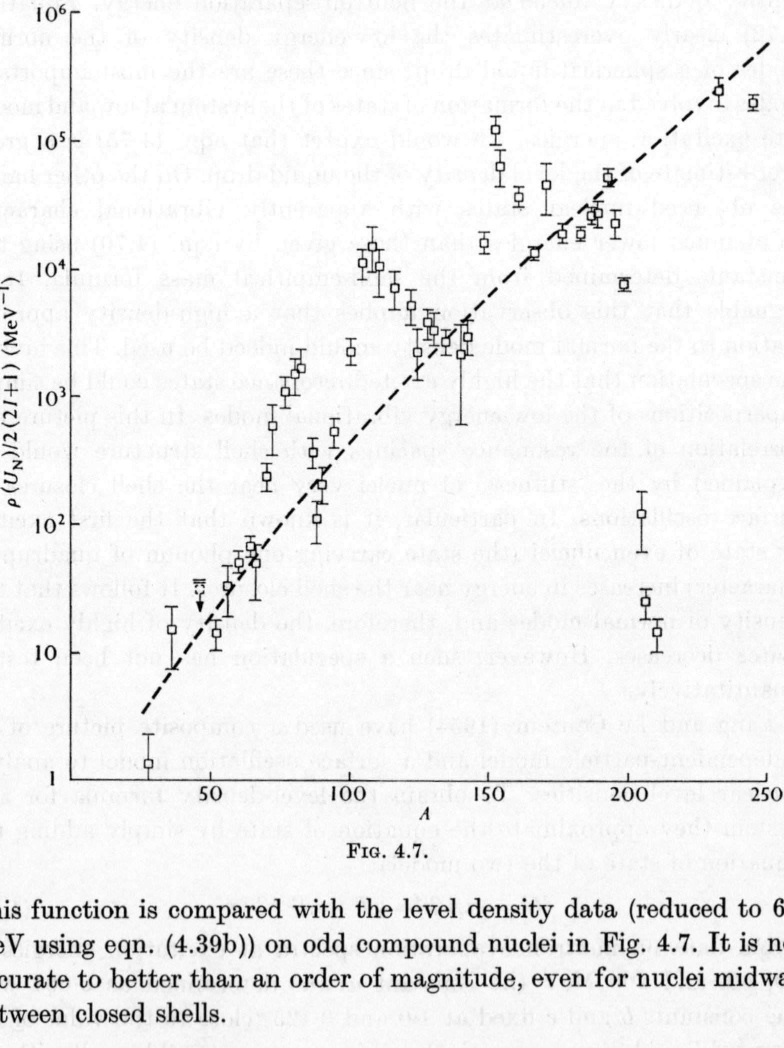

FIG. 4.7.

This function is compared with the level density data (reduced to 6·5 MeV using eqn. (4.39b)) on odd compound nuclei in Fig. 4.7. It is not accurate to better than an order of magnitude, even for nuclei midway between closed shells.

2. Pairing-energy model

All writers on nuclear level densities have found it ncessary to admit the deficiency of the independent-particle model in being unable to explain the observed differences between the densities of odd, even, and odd-mass nuclei. In the use of this model the adjustment of the excitation energy described in Section B.4 has usually been employed. This is at best only a device but there have been some calculations of the level density of a model that is thought to account for the observed differences. This is the pairing-energy model, in which a certain amount of energy (other than that given by the differences in eigenvalues of the single-particle states) is required to break a pair of nucleons occupying degenerate states differing only in the signs of the angular momentum projection on a nuclear symmetry axis. In the shell model the pairing energy has some theoretical foundation. It results from the short-range residual attraction between two strongly overlapping states and is found to be proportional to the single-particle angular momentum j (Edmonds and Flowers 1952). If treated properly, however, the short-range forces give rise to the pairing correlation model, which is discussed in its relation to level density in Section C.3. The present simpler pairing-energy model differs from this in the possibility of building states from superpositions of simple pairs. In the extreme form of the model (Newson and Duncan 1959) the pairing energy is effectively infinite and *only* states that are superpositions of pairs can be excited.

Ericson (1958) calculates the level density of this model by remarking that it is the sum of the densities of levels that consist of prescribed numbers, n of neutrons and z of protons in unpaired occupation of single-particle levels:

$$\rho(U) = \sum_{n,z} \rho(U, n, z). \tag{4.78}$$

The densities $\rho(U, n, z)$ may be calculated from a pure independent-particle model, but the effective excitation energy is reduced by the amount $\mu\tilde{\Delta}$ where μ is the number of broken pairs, simply calculated from n and z, and $\tilde{\Delta}$ is the energy needed to break a pair. The dependence of $\tilde{\Delta}$ on the angular momentum j is ignored. If spin projections and parities are also ignored the result is

$$\rho(U, n, z) =$$
$$\frac{\rho_{\mathrm{sn}}^{n-\frac{1}{2}}\rho_{\mathrm{sp}}^{z-\frac{1}{2}}\pi^{\nu-\frac{3}{2}}U_{\mathrm{e}}^{\nu-2}\exp 2\left\{\frac{\pi^2}{24}\rho_{\mathrm{s}}U_{\mathrm{e}}+\left(\frac{\nu-1}{2}\right)^2\right\}^{\frac{1}{2}}}{n!\,z!\,2^{2\nu}\left\{\left(\frac{\pi^2}{24}\rho_{\mathrm{s}}U_{\mathrm{e}}+\left(\frac{\nu-1}{2}\right)^2\right)^{\frac{1}{2}}+\frac{\nu-1}{2}\right\}^{\nu-2}\left\{\frac{\pi^2}{24}\rho_{\mathrm{s}}U_{\mathrm{e}}+\left(\frac{\nu-1}{2}\right)^2\right\}^{\frac{1}{4}}}, \tag{4.79a}$$

where U_e is the effective excitation energy given by

$$U_e = U - \frac{2}{\pi^2}\left\{\frac{n(n-1)}{\rho_{sn}} + \frac{z(z-1)}{\rho_{sp}}\right\} - \mu\tilde{\Delta}, \quad (4.79b)$$

and $\nu = n+z$.

An alternative formulation of the model (Lang and Le Couteur 1960) commences with the evaluation of the general partition function. This takes advantage of the specified twofold degeneracy of the single-particle states so that there are three terms in every single-particle factor of the partition function, corresponding to occupation numbers of 0, 1, and 2. In the case of unit occupation there is an addition to the single-particle energy of half the pairing energy. This term also contains a factor of 2 to allow for the two alternative ways of putting a single particle in the level. Thus the partition function for a neutron–proton assembly is

$$e^{\Phi} = \prod_s [1+2\exp\{x_1 - \beta(\varepsilon_{ns} + \tilde{\Delta}/2)\} + \exp\{2x_1 - 2\beta\varepsilon_{ns}\}]$$
$$\times[1+2\exp\{x_2 - \beta(\varepsilon_{ps} + \tilde{\Delta}/2)\} + \exp\{2x_2 - 2\beta\varepsilon_{ps}\}], \quad (4.80)$$

where n and p refer to single neutron and proton states respectively. In the continuous approximation, inversion of the partition function and integration by the method of steepest descents yield the level density (over all quantum numbers except specified neutron and proton numbers N and Z)

$$\rho(U) = \frac{\beta^2\exp\{4(\rho_{sn}+\rho_{sp})(\frac{1}{6}\pi^2 - \frac{1}{2}\lambda^2)T - 1\}}{(2\pi)^{3/2}[16\rho_{sn}\rho_{sp}\{(\rho_{sn}+\rho_{sp})(\frac{1}{6}\pi^2 - \frac{1}{2}\lambda^2)T - 1\}]^{\frac{1}{2}}}, \quad (4.81)$$

the relation between excitation energy and temperature being

$$U = \rho_s T^2(\tfrac{1}{6}\pi^2 - \tfrac{1}{2}\lambda^2) + \tfrac{1}{2}T\rho_s\tilde{\Delta}\lambda\cot\lambda - T - (U - E^*) \quad (4.82)$$

where $\cos\lambda = \exp(-\frac{1}{2}\beta\tilde{\Delta})$ and $E^* = U$ for even nuclei, $E^* = U - \frac{1}{2}\tilde{\Delta}$ for odd-mass nuclei, $E^* = U - \tilde{\Delta}$ for odd nuclei.

A good approximation to this equation at high energies is

$$\rho(U) = \frac{\exp\left\{\frac{1}{3}\pi^2\rho_s T - 1 - \frac{1}{2}\rho_s\tilde{\Delta} + \frac{\rho_s\tilde{\Delta}^3}{180T^2} + \frac{\rho_s\tilde{\Delta}^4}{2520T^3} + \dots\right\}}{12(\pi T)^{5/2}\left(\frac{1}{6}\rho_s\right)^{3/2}} \quad (4.83a)$$

$$U = \frac{1}{6}\pi^2\rho_s T^2 - T - \frac{\rho_s\tilde{\Delta}^2}{12} + \frac{\rho_s\tilde{\Delta}^2}{90T} + \frac{\rho_s\tilde{\Delta}^4}{1680T^2} + \dots - (U - E^*) \quad (4.83b)$$

Further approximation gives

$$\rho(U) \approx \frac{\exp\{2(\frac{1}{6}\pi^2\rho_s U_e)^{\frac{1}{2}} - \frac{1}{2}\rho_s\tilde{\Delta}\}}{12(\frac{1}{6}\rho_s)^{\frac{1}{4}}(U_e+T)^{5/4}}, \tag{4.84a}$$

$$U_e = U + (U - E^*) + \tfrac{1}{12}\rho_s\tilde{\Delta}^2. \tag{4.84b}$$

These results show that the pairing energy cannot be incorporated simply into the independent-particle model by straightforward correc-

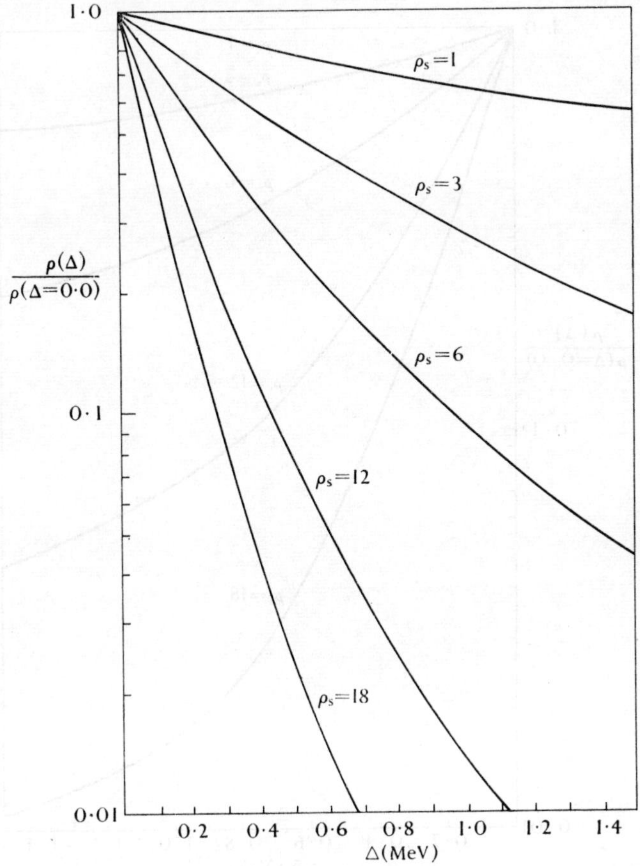

FIG. 4.8. The dependence of level density on the pairing energy in the pairing-energy model of an even nucleus at an excitation energy of 6·5 MeV.

tion of the excitation energy according to eqn. (4.40). At high energy this is only the first term in the approximation; an additional term common to all classes of nuclei, $\rho_s\tilde{\Delta}^2/12$, is necessary, as well as an adjustment, by a factor $\exp(-\rho_s\tilde{\Delta}/2)$, to the proportionality constant.

The corrections are essential if calculations to better than an order of magnitude are required. The dependence of the level density on $\tilde{\Delta}$, as given by eqn. (4.84), is displayed in Fig. 4.8 for an even nucleus and in Fig. 4.9 for an odd nucleus. The dependence is clearly smaller in the latter case but is by no means negligible for a high single-particle level density.

Lang and Le Couteur (1960) derive the distribution of levels over angular momentum in this model by considering the occupation num-

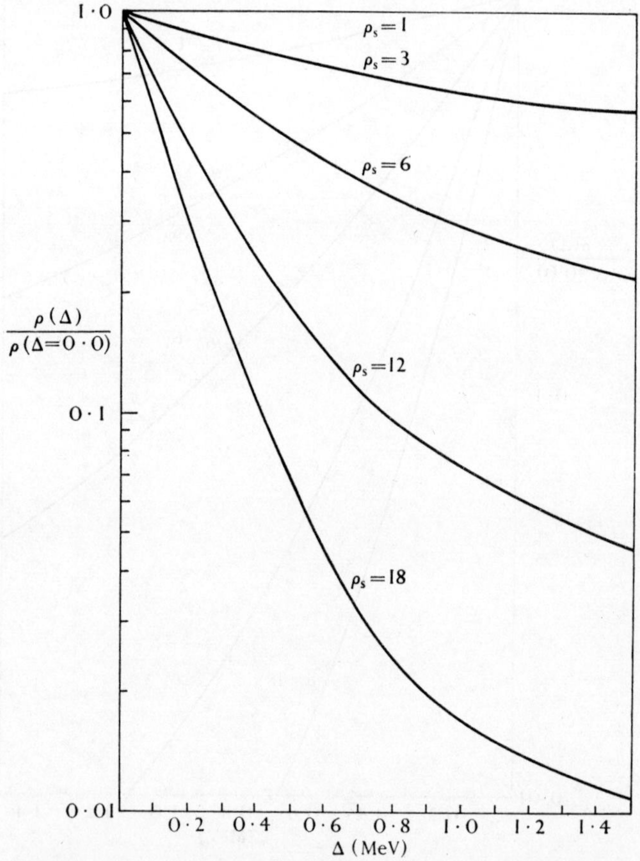

FIG. 4.9. The dependence of level density on the pairing energy in the pairing-energy model of an odd nucleus at an excitation energy of 6·5 MeV.

bers of the single-particle levels. These are simply obtained from the expressions for $\partial\Phi/\partial x_1$ (giving the neutron number) and $\partial\Phi/\partial x_2$ (giving the proton number) at the saddle point. These expressions can readily be interpreted as the sums of the probabilities that in each level s

there is a particle with either positive or negative spin projection but not both, p_s (+ or −), and that there are two particles in the level, $p_s(+-)$. This interpretation gives (for neutrons say)

$$p_s\,(+\text{ or }-) = \frac{2\exp\{x_1-\beta(\varepsilon_s+\tilde{\Delta}/2)\}}{1+2\exp\{x_1-\beta(\varepsilon_s+\tilde{\Delta}/2)\}+\exp\{2x_1-2\beta\varepsilon_s\}}, \tag{4.85a}$$

$$p_s(+-) = \frac{\exp\{2x_1-2\beta\varepsilon_s\}}{1+2\exp\{x_1-\beta(\varepsilon_s+\tilde{\Delta}/2)\}+\exp\{2x_1-2\beta\varepsilon_s\}}. \tag{4.85b}$$

It can be seen that for each state s the mean value of $\sum_s m_s$ is zero, and that the mean value of $(\sum_s m_s)^2$ is equal to $m_s^2 p_s$ (+ or −). Thus the mean square angular momentum projection is

$$\sigma_{\mathrm{M}}^2 = \sum_s m_s^2 p_s(+\text{ or }-). \tag{4.86}$$

For even nuclei this is calculated from the model to be

$$\sigma_{\mathrm{M}}^2 = \lambda \overline{m^2} \rho_{\mathrm{S}} T \cot \lambda. \tag{4.87}$$

At zero excitation energy it reduces to zero, as expected, because of the finite energy required to break a pair and thus produce a non-zero contribution to the angular momentum projection. Odd-mass and odd nuclei already contain one and two unpaired nucleons respectively which add contributions of $\overline{m^2}$ and $2\overline{m^2}$ to the mean square projection at zero excitation. Thus

$$\sigma_{\mathrm{M}}^2 = \lambda \overline{m^2} \rho_{\mathrm{S}} T \cot \lambda + \begin{cases} 0 \text{ for even nuclei,} \\ \overline{m^2} \text{ for odd-mass nuclei,} \\ 2\overline{m^2} \text{ for odd nuclei.} \end{cases} \tag{4.88}$$

In the pure independent-particle model the dispersion constant $\sigma_{\mathrm{M}}^2 = \overline{m^2}\rho_{\mathrm{S}} T$. The first term on the right-hand side of eqn. (4.88) represents a reduction of this constant by a factor of $\lambda \cot \lambda$ which tends to zero at low excitation energies and to unity at high energy.

Some explicit calculations of the level density in the shell model with pairing energy have been made for gold and some neighbouring nuclei. In these calculations the use of the continuous approximation has been avoided; the integration of the Laplace transform of the free energy has been calculated directly, using the saddle-point method, on an electronic digital computer. The partition function employed was an extended form of eqn. (4.80), the extra constants of the motion being the projection of angular momentum and parity. If the subscript i denotes a single-particle level of specific energy, neutron, proton, and parity character and specific modulus of total angular momentum projection, the total angular momentum projection of a state l of the model is

$$C_{pl} \equiv M_l = \sum_i \delta_{n_i^{(l)}1}(\pm|m_i|). \tag{4.89}$$

There will always be two states l (degenerate) similar in every respect except for opposite projection of m_j for a specific level j with $n_j^{(l)} = 1$, i.e.

$$M_{l_1} = \sum_{i\neq j} \delta_{n_i^{(l)}1}(s_i^{(l)}|m_i|)+|m_j| \tag{4.90a}$$

$$M_{l_2} = \sum_{i\neq j} \delta_{n_i^{(l)}1}(s_i^{(l)}|m_i|)-|m_j| \tag{4.90b}$$

where $s_i^{(l)}$ indicates the appropriate sign of m_i in state l. Thus, the grand partition function may be written

$$\begin{aligned} e\Phi = \prod_i \Bigg\{1 &+ \exp\Bigg(-\beta\varepsilon_i + \sum_{k\neq p} x_k c_{ki} + x_p|m_i|\Bigg) \\ &+ \exp\Bigg(-\beta\varepsilon_i + \sum_{k\neq p} x_k c_{ki} - x_p|m_i|\Bigg) \\ &+ \exp\Bigg(-\beta(2\varepsilon_i - \tilde{\Delta}_i) + 2\sum_{k\neq p} x_k c_{ki}\Bigg)\Bigg\}. \end{aligned} \tag{4.91}$$

The numerical calculation of the level density for a specific nucleus starts with guessed values of the temperature and parameters x_k. The first and second partial derivatives of Φ are then explicitly calculated; from the first derivatives the constants of the motion are calculated (from eqns. (4.15a) and (4.15b)), and from these and the second derivatives the level density is calculated (using eqns. (4.14) and (4.16)). The changes required in the temperature and the x_k to achieve the desired constants of the motion are calculated using a first-order Taylor expansion:

$$\delta E = \frac{\partial E}{\partial \beta}\delta\beta + \sum_k \frac{\partial E}{\partial x_k}\delta x_k, \tag{4.92a}$$

$$\delta C_k = \frac{\partial C_k}{\partial \beta}\delta\beta + \sum_{k'} \frac{\partial C_k}{\partial x_{k'}}\delta x_{k'}. \tag{4.92b}$$

With successive approximations the desired constants can be achieved with specified accuracy.

For the calculations on $^{198}_{79}$Au the pairing energy $\tilde{\Delta}_i$ was assumed to be proportional to $(2j_i+1)$, and the single-particle energy levels were calculated using the parameters of Ross *et al.* (1956) (see Chapter III, Section C). Calculations were made with proportionality constants of 0·0, 0·015, 0·03, and 0·06 at an excitation energy of 6·5 MeV. The results shown in Fig. 4.10 agreed qualitatively with the behaviour

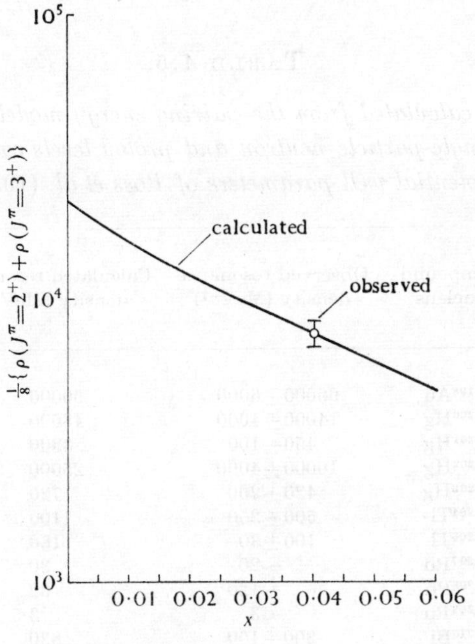

FIG. 4.10. Level density of ^{198}Au at the neutron-seperation energy with pairing energy $\tilde{\Delta}_i = x(2j_i+1)$.

shown in Fig. 4.9 with ρ_S assumed to be of the order of 15. Comparison of the summed level density for $J = 1$ and 2 and even parity with the resonance data on gold (see Table 4.2) shows that the constant of proportionality for $\tilde{\Delta}_i$ should be about 0·04. This is considerably less than the value of 0·3 that is suggested by a study of nucleon separation energies. With this value of $\tilde{\Delta}_i$ calculations of the level densities for the series of nuclei ^{200}Hg to ^{210}Bi have been made. The results are compared with the experimental data in Table 4.5. The striking feature here is the overall agreement in order of magnitude over such a wide range of level density. This leaves no doubt that the shell effect is broadly responsible for the major fluctations in level density. The second feature is that the discrepancies between the calculation and observation (up to a factor of 7 at worst, but generally better than a factor of 3) are not a systematic odd–even effect. Overall agreement could probably be improved by raising $\tilde{\Delta}_i$ by not more than a factor of 2. It appears that the pairing-energy model may be capable of giving a reasonable representation of neutron resonance densities, provided that the continuous approximation is not used for the single-particle level density. The same calculations yield reasonable values for the

TABLE 4.5

Level densities calculated from the pairing-energy model with $\tilde{\Delta}_i = 0{\cdot}04\,(2j_i+1)$ *and single-particle neutron and proton levels calculated from the potential well parameters of Ross et al.* (1956)

Compound nucleus	Observed resonance density (MeV^{-1})	Calculated resonance density (MeV^{-1})
^{198}Au	60000 ± 6000	60000
^{200}Hg	14000 ± 4000	48000
^{201}Hg	450 ± 100	3300
^{202}Hg	10000 ± 4000	25000
^{203}Hg	420 ± 200	720
^{204}Tl	500 ± 250	1100
^{206}Tl	100 ± 30	150
^{207}Pb	~ 20	30
^{208}Pb	~ 120	32
^{209}Pb	<3	3·5
^{210}Bi	300 ± 100	830

spin dispersion constant, the estimate for gold being $\sigma_M^2 \approx 40$ for $\Delta_i = 0{\cdot}04\,(2j_i+1)$.

3. The unified model

Before carrying on the discussion of pairing effects on level density with an account of the more elaborate pairing correlation theory (postponed to Section C.4), as would be natural, we interpose here a discussion of the unified model. This is because the pairing energy formalism introduced in the last section has been used as the basis for level-density calculations on this model.

The unified model of Bohr and Mottelson (1953) seeks to explain the properties of the low-lying levels of a large class of nuclei by combining many of the features of both the shell model and the collective rotational model. The class of nuclei dealt with includes those nuclei with large electric quadrupole moments and thus, by inference, shapes considerably deformed from the spherical. These nuclei are usually assumed to be spheroidal, i.e. to have axial symmetry. They occur mainly among the rare earths ($155 < A < 185$) and the actinide elements ($A > 225$) although some light nuclei ($A \approx 24$) have also been shown to have this property. The common feature of the nuclei in these groups is that they have several nucleons more or less than the nearest 'magic' nucleus. The closed shells of the 'magic' nuclei are expected to have spherical symmetry, and it is believed that the strongly deformed nuclei results from the polarizing action on the closed shell core of their loosely bound nucleons (Rainwater 1951).

The total angular momentum and orbital angular momentum of a particle in a spheroidal potential well are not constants of the motion, but their projections on the symmetry axis are such constants. In particular we can denote the projection of the total angular momentum of the particle by the quantum number Ω_s. If there are several independent particles in the well the projection of the total angular momentum of the system is denoted by K; it is the sum of the Ω_s over the occupied states of the potential well.

In addition to the motion of the nucleons in the potential well, the unified model includes the motion of the well itself. If the motion of the well is slow compared with that of the nucleons, the latter will be little affected by the former. There are two kinds of motion that are usually considered in the model, vibrations and rotations. Since the quanta associated with the vibrations usually carry a much greater energy than those associated with rotations we consider here only the latter. The Hamiltonian is thus approximately separable into a part due to the intrinsic motion of the nucleons in the well, H_{int}, and a part due to the kinetic energy of the rotation, T_{rot}. A term expressing the coupling between the intrinsic motion and the rotation has also been considered in work on the unified model but is neglected here. The rotational kinetic energy term, T_{rot}, is simply expressed in terms of the squares of the angular momentum projections and the corresponding moments of inertia $\mathscr{I}_3$ and $\mathscr{I}$ of the rotating body about the symmetry axis and an axis perpendicular to it. The moment of inertia $\mathscr{I}_3$ is zero in this nuclear model because the rotational motion of the nucleus is in fact the collective response of the nucleons to variations of the nuclear field; this is invariant with respect to rotations about the symmetry axis. Collective rotations, therefore, are about an axis perpendicular to the symmetry axis; this leads to the coupling scheme for the total angular momentum I shown in Fig. 4.11, in which I clearly must be greater than or equal to K. The expression for the energy $E_K^{(l)}(I)$ of a state with total angular momentum I and symmetry

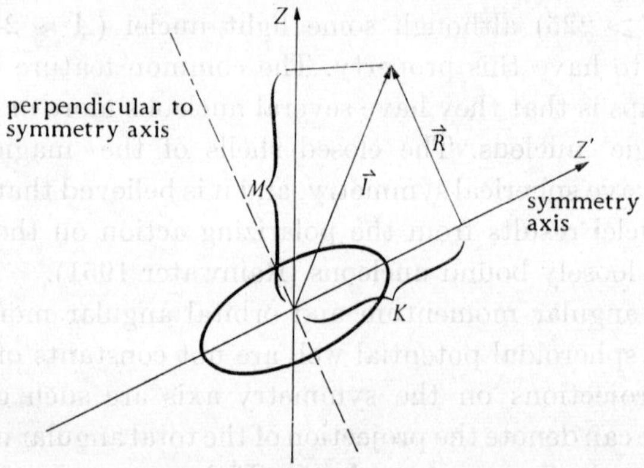

FIG. 4.11. Spin coupling scheme of a deformed nucleus.

projection K is found, from the application of this simplified Hamiltonian, to be

$$E\,(I) = E^{(l)} + \frac{\hbar^2}{2\mathscr{I}}\{I(I+1) - K^2\} \tag{4.93}$$

where $E^{(l)}$ is the energy due to the instrinsic motion alone. A typical spectrum of states which results from a given intrinsic state with specified K is illustrated in Fig. 4.12.

In calculations of the level density law of the unified model the intrinsic energy $E^{(l)}$ has been taken to include the pairing energy reductions $\tilde{\Delta}$ that result from the occupation of two single-particle levels identical in everything but the sign of the angular momentum projection on the symmetry axis. The calculation of the level density thus commences with a calculation of the level density of the pairing-energy model.

There are two different philosophies for the procedure beyond this point. Ericson (1958) takes the level density of the pairing-energy model to be the density of the intrinsic states of the unified model; each of these intrinsic states is the parent of a rotational band as shown in Fig. 4.12. Of course this picture cannot be true to an indefinitely high excitation energy. The degrees of freedom associated with the collective model can only come, ultimately, from the degrees of freedom of the nucleons themselves. In other words, the rotational states must consist of superpositions of independent-particle motions. Ericson's point of view is equivalent to assuming that the rotational states are derived from independent-particle states of very high excitation. In order to analyse the neutron-resonance data with Ericson's version of the unified-model level-density law it is assumed that these states are lowered from excitations very much greater than the neutron-separation energy.

Lang and Le Couteur (1960), on the other hand, take the view that the overall level density of the pairing-energy model, eqn. (4.83),

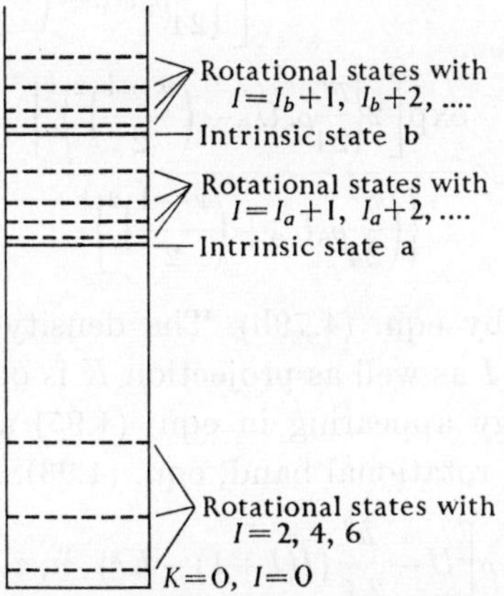

FIG. 4.12. Schematic level scheme of a nucleus with rotational motion.

includes both the intrinsic states and the rotational states of the unified model. They emphasize the fact, first pointed out by Bohr *et al.* (1958), that a difficulty of the simple pairing-energy model is that it gives no reason for the elevation of low-lying states which consist of excitation of pairs, yet, if rotational states are ignored, such states are not observed in the low-lying spectra of even nuclei. Lang and Le Couteur suggest that the pair states be identified with the rotational states so that the latter are included in the levels of the pairing-energy model.

After obtaining the level density of the pairing-energy model Ericson (1958) discusses the distribution of these levels over the angular momentum projection K. The available single-particle levels near the Fermi energy will have a maximum possible value of K, denoted by $K_{\mathrm{m}}-1$. This can be obtained, for a given nucleus, from the level scheme calculated by Nilsson (1955) for a spheroidal potential well with spin-orbit coupling. The variance of the distribution of K for a single unpaired nucleon among these levels can be shown to be $K_m^2/6$. Application of the central limit theorem of statistics to the distribution of K for ν unpaired particles gives the Gaussian law

$$p(U,\nu,K) = \frac{1}{K_m}\sqrt{\left(\frac{3}{\pi\nu}\right)}\exp\left(-\frac{3K^2}{K_m^2}\right)p(U,\nu). \tag{4.94}$$

With eqn. (4.79) this leads to the density of intrinsic states with n and z neutrons and protons excited, angular momentum projection K, and given parity π:

$$\rho(U,n,z,K,\pi) = \frac{\rho_{sn}^{n-\frac{1}{2}}\rho_{sp}^{z-\frac{1}{2}}}{2^{\nu+1}n!z!K_m}\left(\frac{3}{\nu}\right)^{\frac{1}{2}}\left[\frac{\pi U_e}{\left\{\frac{\pi^2}{24}\rho_s U_e+\left(\frac{\nu-1}{2}\right)^2\right\}^{\frac{1}{2}}+\frac{\nu-1}{2}}\right]^{\nu-2}$$

$$\times\frac{\exp\left[2\left\{\frac{\pi^2}{24}\rho_s U_e+\left(\frac{\nu-1}{2}\right)^2\right\}^{\frac{1}{2}}\right]}{\left\{\left(\frac{\pi^2}{24}\rho_s U_e+\left(\frac{\nu-1}{2}\right)^2\right)\right\}^{\frac{1}{4}}}\cdot\exp\left(-\frac{3K^2}{\nu K_m^2}\right) \tag{4.95}$$

where U_e is given by eqn. (4.79b). The density of states with total angular momentum I as well as projection K is obtained by modifying the excitation energy appearing in eqn. (4.95) according to the rule for the energies of a rotational band, eqn. (4.93), giving

$$\rho(U,I,K,n,z,\pi) = \rho\left[U-\frac{\hbar^2}{2\mathscr{I}}\{I(I+1)-K^2\},n,z,0,\pi\right]\cdot\exp\left(-\frac{3K^2}{\nu K_m^2}\right). \tag{4.94}$$

It is very probable that K will cease to be a good quantum number at high excitations owing to the effect of residual interactions. States of the model with the same total angular momentum but different projections on the symmetry axis will be mixed and an analysis of the data will require an expression for the density of levels of given angular momentum I and parity π with no reference to K. This is derived from the summation of eqn. (4.94) over all $K \leqslant I$ and the approximate result obtained by Ericson is

$$\rho(U,I,n,z,\pi) = \frac{(2I+1)}{2}\rho\left\{U-\frac{(I+\frac{1}{2})^2}{3}\left(\frac{\hbar^2}{\mathscr{I}}+\frac{3T}{\nu K_m^2}\right),n,z,0,\pi\right\} \tag{4.95a}$$

$$= \frac{(2I+1)}{2}\exp-\left\{\frac{2(I+\frac{1}{2})^2}{3T}\left(\frac{\hbar^2}{\mathscr{I}}+\frac{3T}{\nu K_m^2}\right)\right\}\rho(U,n,z,0,\pi). \tag{4.95b}$$

By comparison with eqn. (4.62c) it is seen that the effective moment of inertia term for the level-density law is

$$\mathscr{I}_{\text{eff}} = \frac{3\hbar^2}{4\left(\dfrac{\hbar^2}{\mathscr{I}}+\dfrac{3T}{\nu K_{\text{m}}^2}\right)}. \tag{4.96}$$

This tends to $\frac{3}{4}\mathscr{I}$ at low excitations and since $\mathscr{I}$ has been observed from experimental data on rotational bands to be about $\frac{1}{2}\mathscr{I}_{\text{rigid}}$, $\mathscr{I}_{\text{eff}}$ tends to $\frac{3}{8}\mathscr{I}_{\text{rigid}}$. As the temperature increases, the effective moment of inertia decreases, according to eqn. (4.96), tending to $\nu K_{\text{m}}^2\hbar^2/4T$ at very high energy. Such low values of $\mathscr{I}_{\text{eff}}$ indicate that a deviation from the $(2I+1)$ law should be observable for the s-wave resonances of heavy odd–mass target nuclei. As we have already seen from the data of Table 4.2 such deviations apparently do not occur.

Lang and Le Couteur (1960) also start from the pairing-energy model. Their result (eqn. 4.88) for the density of states with given angular momentum projection M on an arbitrary axis must be taken, in the unified model, to be the density of states with projection K on the symmetry axis. To obtain the density of states with total angular momentum J it is also necessary to know the density of states with given angular momentum projection on the plane x, y perpendicular to the symmetry axis. This projection will include contributions from the paired particles. In the case of an even nucleus Lang and Le Couteur assume that a system with precisely the mean occupation numbers of the pairing-energy model will have zero angular momentum in this plane, and hence non-zero values of the angular momentum arise from the statistical fluctuations of the actual occupation numbers away from the mean values. Thus, the average square of the angular momentum in the (x, y) plane is the sum of the average square angular momenta, $(j_x^2+j_y^2)(\langle n_s^2\rangle-\langle n_s\rangle^2)$, over all the single-particle states. The evaluation of this sum, using the expressions for the occupation number, eqn. 4.85, gives

$$\langle J_x^2+J_y^2\rangle = \overline{m^2}\rho_{\text{S}}T(1+\lambda\cot\lambda). \tag{4.97}$$

At very low excitation energies it is apparent that

$$\langle J^2\rangle = \overline{m^2}\rho_{\text{S}}T, \tag{4.98}$$

which corresponds to an effective moment of inertia of $\frac{1}{2}\mathscr{I}_{\text{rigid}}$, and, furthermore, the direction of the angular momentum is perpendicular to the symmetry axis as in a rotating axially-symmetric nucleus. This renders it more plausible that the excited pair states of the pairing-energy model correspond to the rotational states of the unified model. The distribution of levels over the total angular momentum is obtained from the Gaussian distributions for K, J_x, and J_y. It is

$$\rho(U,J) = \frac{2J+1}{\pi^{\frac{1}{2}}(2cT)^{\frac{3}{2}}}\cdot\exp\left\{-\frac{J(J+1)}{2cT}\right\}\rho(U) \qquad (4.99)$$

where $c = (\overline{m^2}\rho_S\lambda\cot\lambda)^{1/3}(\frac{1}{2}\overline{m^2}\rho_S+\frac{1}{2}\overline{m^2}\rho_S\lambda\cot\lambda)^{2/3}$. In contrast to Ericson's result (eqn. 4.95) this tends to zero at very low excitation energy and increases with temperature until it approaches $\mathscr{I}_{\text{rigid}}/\hbar^2$ at very high energy. This seems to be in better agreement with the neutron resonance data of Table 4.2.

4. Pairing correlations

A more fundamental explanation of the energy gap in the low-lying spectrum of even nuclei is provided by the study of pairing correlations (Bohr *et al.* 1958, Belyaev 1959; for a general review see Lane 1964). The first approximation to the behaviour of a system of particles interacting with two-body forces is to represent those forces by a smooth potential energy over the system. Such an approximation takes no account of the correlations amongst the motions of the particles which inevitably arise from the short-range components of the two-body forces. Explicit calculations suggest the nature of the effects of such correlations on the spectrum of states of the system. A residual δ-function force acting between two particles occupying a single-particle state with degeneracy $2l+1$ (due to orbital angular momentum) lowers the state with total angular momentum $J = 0$ below the states with $J = 1\ldots 2l$ by an amount proportional to $2l+1$. The remaining states are lowered to a much smaller extent. A similar effect occurs if, for the residual force, the so-called pairing force is used. This is a force which is very convenient mathematically. It is defined by the value of its matrix element between the initial and final states of the scattering of a pair of particles:

$$\langle(j_1j_2)J|v|(j_3j_4)J\rangle = \frac{(2j_1+1)^{\frac{1}{2}}(2j_3+1)^{\frac{1}{2}}}{2}G\delta_{J0}. \qquad (4.100)$$

If only the states of one configuration are considered, i.e. $j_1 = j_2 = j_3 = j_4 = j$, this force leads to the seniority principle which lies at the root of the pairing-energy model considered in Section C.3. States for an even number of particles of seniority quantum number $s = 2$ have two unpaired particles and lie together, degenerate, at an energy $(2j+1)G/2$, above the state with seniority $s = 0$ (no unpaired particles) and angular momentum $J = 0$. States with $s = 4$ and higher lie at still higher energies. If an odd number of particles belong to the configuration, the lowest has $s = 1$ and $J = j$, while the next levels, raised by an energy $(2j-1)G/2$, have seniority $s = 3$.

The quantum dynamics of a system with a Hamiltonian that includes the pairing force of eqn. (4.100) may be solved in more complicated situations in which the single-particle states are not degenerate. Thus, for a system containing an even number $2p$ of particles which may occupy any of Ω pair states α outside of the closed shells, the lowest state consists of superpositions of the states α with probabilities of occupation V_α^2 and of not being occupied U_α^2.

These probabilities may be expressed in terms of a 'gap' quantity Δ and a chemical potential λ which behaves as a modified 'Fermi level' for the system. To find Δ and λ the equations

$$\frac{G}{2}\sum_\alpha \frac{1}{\sqrt{\{(\varepsilon_\alpha-\lambda)^2+\Delta^2\}}} = 1, \tag{4.101a}$$

$$\sum_\alpha \left[1-\frac{\varepsilon_\alpha-\lambda}{\sqrt{\{(\varepsilon_\alpha-\lambda)^2+\Delta^2\}}}\right] = 2p, \tag{4.101b}$$

have to be solved simultaneously. Here, the ε_α are the energies of the particle states α. The probabilities U_α^2 and V_α^2 have the form

$$U_\alpha^2 = \frac{1}{2}\left[1+\frac{\varepsilon_\alpha-\lambda}{\sqrt{\{(\varepsilon_\alpha-\lambda)^2+\Delta^2\}}}\right] \tag{4.102a}$$

$$V_\alpha^2 = \frac{1}{2}\left[1-\frac{\varepsilon_\alpha-\lambda}{\sqrt{\{(\varepsilon_\alpha-\lambda)^2+\Delta^2\}}}\right], \tag{4.102b}$$

showing that in the ground-state pairs are distributed over the single-particle states around the chemical potential λ; states more than an energy interval Δ below the chemical potential are nearly fully occupied, and those more than the interval Δ above λ are almost empty. This distribution resembles that of a gas of independent fermions, in fact, at a temperature of the same order of magnitude as Δ. Equations (4.102) together with the gap equation (4.101) imply that $\Delta = G\sum_\alpha U_\alpha V_\alpha$.

It can be shown that the ground-state energy of an even system (above the energy of its closed shells) is just $2p\lambda$, expressing the fact that λ is the mean energy of the $2p$ paired particles. A simple excited state may be formed from the ground state by taking a pair, breaking it and placing each into unpaired-particle states α_1 and α_2. The energy of this state can be shown to be

$$E_2 = 2p\lambda+\sqrt{\{(\varepsilon_{\alpha_1}^2-\lambda)^2+\Delta^2\}}+\sqrt{\{(\varepsilon_{\alpha_2}^2-\lambda)^2+\Delta^2\}}. \tag{4.103}$$

It is clear that there is an energy gap of at least 2Δ between the ground and first excited of such a system. In an odd system with $2p+1$ particles outside the closed shells one particle cannot be paired and has to occupy a single-particle level on its own. The energy of such a state is

$$E_1 = (2p+1)\lambda+\sqrt{\{(\varepsilon_{\alpha_1}-\lambda)^2+\Delta^2\}}. \tag{4.104}$$

There is no energy gap in this case.

The simple additive nature of these results has been generalized by Belyaev (1959) in terms of a quasi-particle formalism, in which the ground state (of an even system) is considered as the vacuum state of the quasi-particles, and with respect to which the excited state energies are simply sums of the energies of the elementary quasi-particles:

$$e_\alpha = \sqrt{\{(\varepsilon_\alpha-\lambda)^2+\Delta^2\}}. \tag{4.105}$$

The level-density behaviour of systems that consist entirely of combinations of these quasi-particle excitations has been studied theoretically by Brovetto and Canuto (1963), Kluge (1964), and Sano and Yamasaki (1963). In particular, Kluge's method avoids the use of the saddle-point method at low energies, since this introduces a divergence at zero excitation energy. Using the continuous approximation for the single-particle level density he obtains for the partition function the expression

$$\Phi(\beta) = \int\limits_{-\infty}^{\infty} d\varepsilon\rho_S \ln[1+\exp\{-\beta(\Delta^2+\varepsilon^2)^{\frac{1}{2}}\}]-2\ln 2 \tag{4.106a}$$

$$= 2\rho_S\Delta\sum_{n=1}^{\infty}\frac{(-)^{n+1}K_1(n\beta\Delta)}{n}-\ln 4, \tag{4.106b}$$

where K_1 is the modified Bessel function of the second kind of order one. This relation is used to evaluate the level density numerically. The result for an even nucleus with $\rho_S\Delta = 10$ is shown in Fig. 4.13 in comparison with the level density of the Fermi gas model. A striking feature of the level density of the pairing-correlation model is the step-like behaviour at low excitation energies. It is also apparent from Fig. 4.13 that at higher energies the level density cannot be obtained from that of the Fermi gas by a simple modification of the excitation energy to be substituted in the expression for the latter. It is clear that the absolute difference between the level densities of the two models can be very large.

For odd-mass and odd nuclei the ground state contains one and two quasi-particles respectively, so that the ground-state energy is not

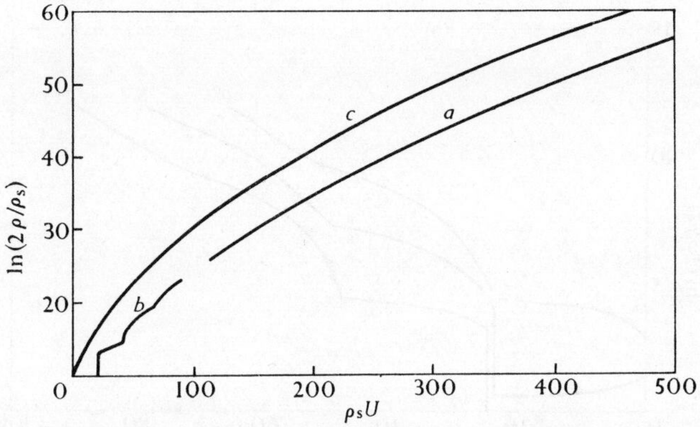

FIG. 4.13. Level density of the pairing-correlation model with $\rho_S\Delta = 10$ (curves (*a*) and (*b*)). Curve (*b*) is calculated numerically. The results are compared with the independent-particle model (curve *c*). (After Kluge, 1964)

zero but Δ and 2Δ in the two cases. The level density, as a function of excitation energy measured from the ground state, is correspondingly modified as shown in Fig. 4.14. The calculations show that the relations between the level densities of even, odd-mass, and odd nuclei

$$\rho_{\text{odd mass}}(U) = \rho_{\text{even}}(U+\Delta) \tag{4.107a}$$

$$\rho_{\text{odd}}(U) = \rho_{\text{even}}(U+2\Delta) \tag{4.107b}$$

are valid except for odd-mass nuclei at very low energies.

The results obtained above are valid only at relatively low excitation energies. At higher energies there is expected to be a phase transition analogous to that occurring in superconductors. The quantities Δ and λ should properly be recalculated for each state. The more unpaired particles that are included in each state the fewer are the available states for correlations among the paired particles. This 'blocking' effect eventually reduces Δ to zero. Kluge (1964) and Sano and Yamasaki (1963) have used the results of the theory of superconductivity (Bardeen *et al.* 1957) to estimate the effect of the phase transition on the level density. The phase transition is expected to occur at the temperature

$$T_c = 0{\cdot}57\Delta_0 \tag{4.108}$$

where Δ_0 is the energy-gap constant for the ground state.

Above this critical temperature the system simply behaves as a normal independent-particle system. Its excitation energy, however, differs from that of the independent-particle system because the ground

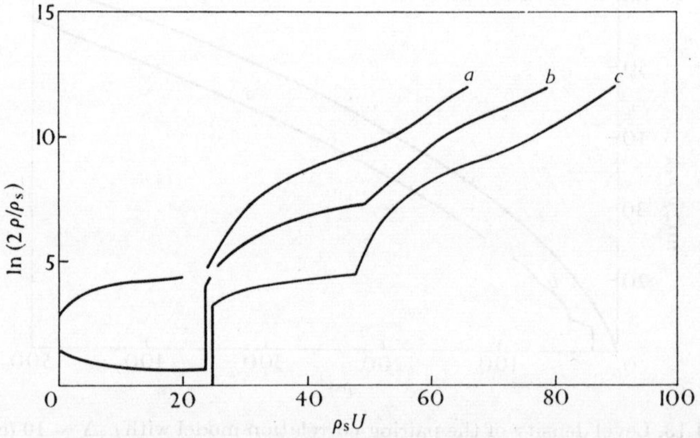

FIG. 4.14. Level density of pairing-correlation model for odd (curve *a*), odd mass (curve *b*), and even (curve *c*) nuclei (after Kluge 1964).

state that would belong to the latter lies above the true correlated ground state of the system in its 'superconducting' phase. The estimate of this difference obtained from the superconductivity model is $\frac{1}{4}\rho_s\Delta_0^2$. The level density for this phase is therefore just that for the independent-particle model $\rho_{\text{I.P.}}$ with the excitation modified by this amount:

$$\rho(U) = \rho_{\text{I.P.}}(U - \tfrac{1}{4}\rho_s\Delta_0^2). \tag{4.109}$$

Equation (4.109) with $\rho_s\Delta = 10$ is compared with the curve of Fig. 4.13 and with the independent-particle model in Fig. 4.15. The excitation energy corresponding to the critical temperature is, by these considerations and eqn. (4.30),

$$U_c = \tfrac{1}{4}\rho_s\Delta_0^2 + \tfrac{1}{6}\pi^2\rho_s T = 0{\cdot}77\rho_s\Delta_0^2. \tag{4.110}$$

These results have to be extended to levels of specified angular momentum before they can be compared usefully with neutron-resonance data. Such an extension has been made by Kammuri (1964). He finds that for fixed angular momentum projection the 'blocking'

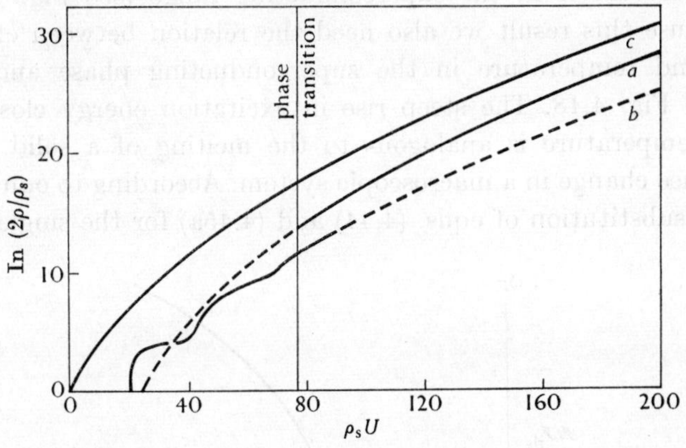

FIG. 4.15. Comparison of level densities of pairing-correlation model with phase transition into a non-superconducting phase (curve *a*) with the model without such a transition (curve *b*), and with the independent-particle model (curve *c*) (after Kluge 1964).

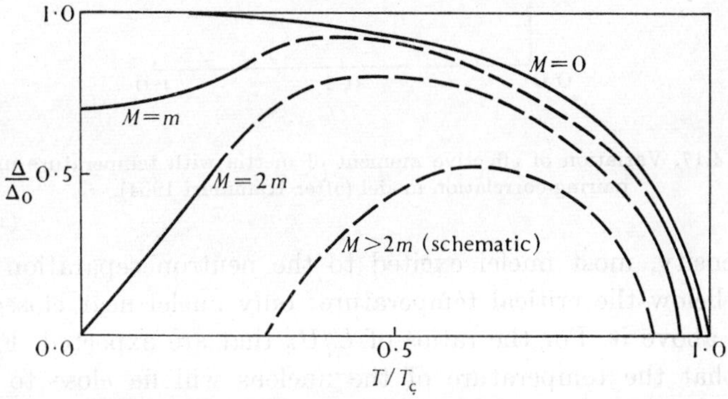

FIG. 4.16. Dependence of the energy gap Δ on temperature due to the blocking effect for different angular momentum projections M. The calculation was made (Kammuri 1964) for a simplified system with a continuous density of single-particle levels each with the same magnetic quantum number m. Δ_0 is the energy gap for $M = 0$ levels at zero temperature. T_c is the critical (phase transition) temperature.

effect operates even at zero temperature but is reduced at rather higher temperatures. At still higher energies a critical temperature is reached above which the nucleus is no longer analogous to a superconducting system; the critical temperature is rather insensitive to the value of the angular-momentum projection. The energy gap of such states relative to that of the ground state is shown as a function of temperature in Fig. 4.16. The result of this behaviour is that the effective moment of inertia of eqn. (4.59) is reduced below the rigid-body value when the temperature is in the superconducting range (see Fig. 4.17). In order to use this result we also need the relation between excitation energy and temperature in the superconducting phase and this is shown in Fig. 4.18. The steep rise in excitation energy close to the critical temperature is analogous to the melting of a solid or some other phase change in a macroscopic system. According to eqn. (4.110), with the substitution of eqns. (4.44) and (4.45a) for the single-particle

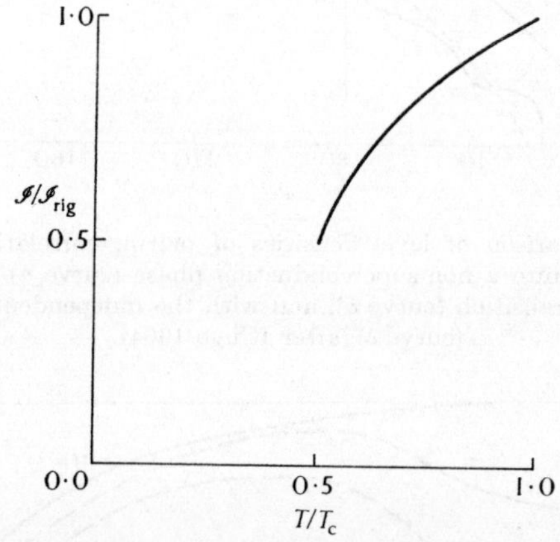

Fig. 4.17. Variation of effective moment of inertia with temperature in the pairing-correlation model (after Kammuri 1964).

level density, most nuclei excited to the neutron separation energy will lie below the critical temperature; only nuclei near closed shells may lie above it. For the ratios of U/U_c that are expected, Fig. 4.18 shows that the temperature of the nucleus will lie close to T_c. In consequence, the moment of inertia will not be greatly different from the independent-particle value (Fig. 4.17). It appears, therefore, that the level density, for specified angular momenta, of most nuclei at the neutron-separation energy will be much smaller than that expected in the independent-particle model (by about two or three orders of magnitude) and in the pairing-energy model (by more than about one order of magnitude). The agreement found in Section C.2 between the pairing-energy model with a rather small value of $\tilde{\Delta}$ and data in the gold region, suggests that these nuclei lie above the critical temperature; the pairing-correlation theory seems to fail, at least in this respect. On the other hand, Grin' and Strutinsky (1965) have calculated the value of Δ_0 from the observed level densities of some highly deformed nuclei in the rare earth and actinide regions using the superconductivity theory and find values agreeing within 20 per cent of those obtained by other methods (such as odd–even nuclear mass differences). In doing this they allow for the empirically observed 20 per cent greater value of Δ_0 for the proton system over that for the neutron system. An interesting feature of their results is that, allowing

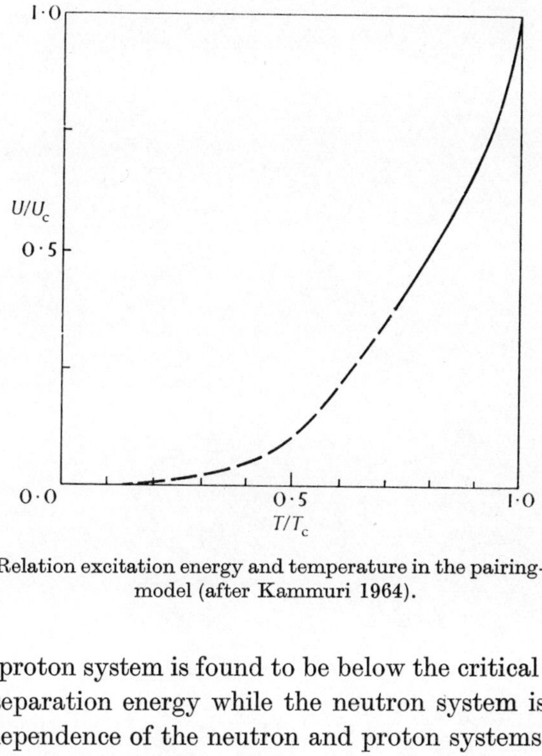

FIG. 4.18. Relation excitation energy and temperature in the pairing-correlation model (after Kammuri 1964).

for this, the proton system is found to be below the critical temperature at neutron-separation energy while the neutron system is above. The assumed independence of the neutron and proton systems is a difficult point in the pairing-correlation theory, and it would be well, therefore, not to read too much into this result. The assumed value of the single-particle level density for this work was taken from the Nilsson scheme, $\rho_S = A/12{\cdot}5\ \mathrm{MeV}^{-1}$. This work supports the theory, but perhaps the main evidence for it rests on the deduction of Ericson(1959) from low-energy level densities (from d, p and p,p') reactions that the nucleus is in a nearly constant temperature phase, as suggested by Fig. 4.18. The temperatures deduced by Ericson are 1·6 MeV for ^{28}Al and

^{33}S, 1·15 MeV for ^{56}Mn, and 1·2 MeV for ^{57}Fe. These temperatures are about 25 per cent lower than those suggested by eqn. (4.108) with the substitution of $\Delta = \delta$ from eqn. (4.40). We conclude that while the pairing-correlation theory may be qualitatively correct its quantitative details require further consideration.

V

THE STATISTICAL DISTRIBUTION OF RESONANCE SPACINGS

A. THE WIGNER DISTRIBUTION FOR ONE CLASS OF LEVELS

TO INFER the features of the statistical frequency function of the spacings of highly excited nuclear levels, considerations are required of a kind very different from those needed for a study of the mean values of the spacings. The independent particle model, for example, is of value in a study of the latter provided that it can be assumed that the neglected residual forces cause only random shifting of the independent-particle levels. Although they are neglected in the calculation the residual forces are necessary to the interpretation of the results for they remove the high degeneracies associated with the independent-particle states and allow their excitation by particle bombardment.

The theoretical study of the level spacing distribution commences from the matrix formulation of quantum mechanics. A suitable basis is chosen for the representation of dynamical quantities. This may consist of the eigenfunctions ψ_a of a simplified Hamiltonian with the correct number of degrees of freedom. In this basis the Hamiltonian H of the system is represented by the matrix

$$\mathbf{H} = \begin{pmatrix} H_{aa} & H_{ab} & \cdot & \cdot & H_{aq} \\ H_{ba} & H_{bb} & & & \\ \cdot & & \cdot & & \\ \cdot & & & \cdot & \\ \cdot & & & & \cdot \\ H_{qa} & & & & H_{qq} \end{pmatrix}, \tag{5.1a}$$

the elements of which are, typically,

$$H_{ab} = \langle a|H|b\rangle = \int \mathrm{d}\tau \psi_a{}^* H \psi_b \tag{5.1b}$$

From the required Hermitian property of a matrix that represents a dynamical variable, $H_{ab} = H^*_{ba}$. Throughout this section it is also assumed that the matrices are real, so, from the Hermitian property, they are also symmetric. This requirement implies time-inversion invariance of the dynamical system.

The eigenvalues of the Hamiltonian are found by solving the secular equation

$$||\mathbf{H}-\lambda\mathbf{I}|| = 0 \tag{5.2}$$

where **I** is the unit matrix. The q roots λ of this equation are the desired eigenvalues and from them the spacings of the eigenvalues are obtained. The Hamiltonian of a nuclear system is not nearly exactly known, of course, and the best that can be done is to determine the statistical distribution of the eigenvalue spacings that result from reasonable or plausible, or simply guessed, assumptions about the statistical nature of the matrix elements of **H**.

This line of enquiry was initiated by Wigner (1956) who began by studying the simplest possible case of a matrix of order 2. The secular equation in this case simplifies to

$$(H_{aa}-\lambda)(H_{bb}-\lambda)-|H_{ab}|^2 = 0, \tag{5.3a}$$

giving

$$\lambda = \frac{H_{aa}+H_{bb}}{2} \pm \tfrac{1}{2}\sqrt{\{(H_{aa}-H_{bb})^2+4|H_{ab}|^2\}}. \tag{5.3b}$$

The difference between the two eigenvalues, their spacing, is

$$|\lambda_1-\lambda_2| = \sqrt{\{(H_{aa}-H_{bb})^2+4|H_{ab}|^2\}}. \tag{5.4}$$

Suppose that the Hamiltonian matrix in the chosen basis is diagonal, i.e. $H_{ab} = H_{ba}{}^* = 0$. This will be the case, for instance, if some constant of the motion has different values for the different states. Take as the origin of the energy scale the position of the first level. We call the probability of not seeing a level between the origin and $E = D$, $P(D)$, and the probability of seeing a level between D and $D+\mathrm{d}D$, $f(D)\mathrm{d}D$. Clearly $P(D)$ is unity at $D = 0$ and decreases to zero as D tends to become indefinitely large. Now the probability, $p(D)\mathrm{d}D$ that the second level lies between D and $D+\mathrm{d}D$ is

$$p(D)\mathrm{d}D = P(D)f(D)\mathrm{d}D. \tag{5.6}$$

From this we derive $P(D)$, which is also the probability that the second level lies beyond D:

$$P(D) = \int\limits_D^\infty p(D')\mathrm{d}D' = \int\limits_D^\infty P(D')f(D')\mathrm{d}D'. \tag{5.7a}$$

This gives us

$$\frac{dP}{dD} = -P(D)f(D), \tag{5.7b}$$

and, by integration,

$$P(D) = \exp\left\{-\int_0^D f(D')\,dD'\right\}. \tag{5.8}$$

The statistical frequency function for the level spacing thus depends on the assumption to be made for the frequency function $f(D)$ for observing a level at D. In the absence of any detailed knowledge of the Hamiltonian of the system we can only assume that the diagonal elements of the matrix are distributed quite randomly. Thus, $f(D)=\rho$, the level density, and

$$p(D)\,dD = \rho e^{-\rho D}\,dD. \tag{5.9}$$

We may take this to be the distribution of spacing among levels each with a different set of values for the constants of the motion.

The spacing distribution for levels with the same values for constants of the motion may be discussed, following Wigner (1956), by considering eqn. (5.4). It is very unlikely that a basis would be chosen, making a random choice, which would result in a diagonal form of H in this case. We must assume that the non-diagonal elements are likely to be non-zero and thus the spacing between the two levels is unlikely to be zero; by contrast, eqn. (5.9) gives maximum likelihood for small values of the spacing. If the matrix of order 2 is used to determine the nature of the function $f(D)$ giving the probability of observing a level at D, it is obvious that $f(D)$ cannot be independent of D, as in the previous case, but must tend to zero. A more quantitative assessment is obtained be considering the plane of the variables $t = |H_{aa} - H_{bb}|$ and $u = 2|H_{ab}|$. Then D is the distance from the origin to a point (t, u) in this plane. The probability $f(D)\,dD$ of observing a level between D and $D+dD$ is the integral, over an annulus of radius D and thickness dD in the t, u plane, of the product of the frequency functions of t and u. The simplest, and not implausible, assumption about these latter frequencies is that they are independent, random, and equal to the same density. This clearly leads to the proportionality

$$f(D)\,dD \propto D\,dD, \tag{5.10}$$

and hence

$$p(D)\mathrm{d}D = \frac{\pi D}{2\bar{D}^2}\exp\left(-\frac{\pi D^2}{4\bar{D}^2}\right)\mathrm{d}D. \tag{5.11}$$

An alternative derivation treats the matrix of order 2 not as a means of surmising the density of levels at the energy D but as the entire Hamiltonian matrix of the system. It is plausible that two very close levels may be treated independently of the others in which case the order 2 matrix represents a sub-space that is approximately independent of the rest of the system. In either case the assumption that the variables t and u are distributed according to Gaussian laws of zero mean and equal variance leads to a density function $f(D)$ that is now identical to the frequency function $p(D)$ (simply because there are no more than two levels) given by eqn. (5.11).

It is a remarkable fact that the Wigner frequency function of eqn. (5.11), obtained from the study of such a very crude system, closely resembles the results of much more elaborate computations. It is particularly good, as we may expect, for small values of the spacings. Even at large spacings, however, it is sufficiently good that its very simple analytical form can be used in very many theoretical applications. The essential qualitative feature of eqn. (5.11) is its 'level repulsion' property, the unlikelihood of finding small level spacings. This feature was first remarked in the experimental data on neutron resonances by Lane *et al.* (1956) and Gurevich and Pevsner (1956).

Attempts have been made to improve the level spacing frequency function by studying the properties of a matrix of order three (Moldauer 1959, Porter and Rosenzweig 1960). With the same statistical assumptions that leads to eqn. (5.11), namely that the elements are independently distributed according to Gaussian laws with zero mean, the variance of the distribution of the diagonal elements being twice that for the non-diagonal elements, the frequency function for the spacings D between consecutive levels is

$$p(x)\mathrm{d}x = \frac{729}{128\pi^2}x\exp\left(-\frac{27x^2}{16\pi}\right)\left[\left(x^2-\frac{8\pi}{9}\right)\left\{\mathrm{erf}\left(\frac{3x}{4\sqrt{\pi}}\right)-1\right\} + \frac{4}{3}x\exp\left(-\frac{9x^2}{16\pi}\right)\right], \tag{5.12}$$

where $x = D/\bar{D}$. The variance of this distribution is var $x = 11\pi/27-1 = 0{\cdot}280$. The variance of the Wigner distribution is var $x = 4/\pi-1$

$= 0{\cdot}273$. The limiting value of eqn. (5.12) for small spacings is $p(x) \to 81x/16\pi$. This is very close to the behaviour of eqn. (5.11) but the limiting value for very large spacings is quite different, $p(x) \to (27/2\pi) \exp(-9x^2/4\pi)$. This difference is not so important as it may appear on first consideration for the total integrated probability of the 'tails' of the distributions are very small.

The qualitative form of the Wigner surmise has been confirmed by numerical computations on matrices of much higher order (up to 40) the matrix elements being selected independently and at random from Gaussian distributions with a factor of 2 between the variances of

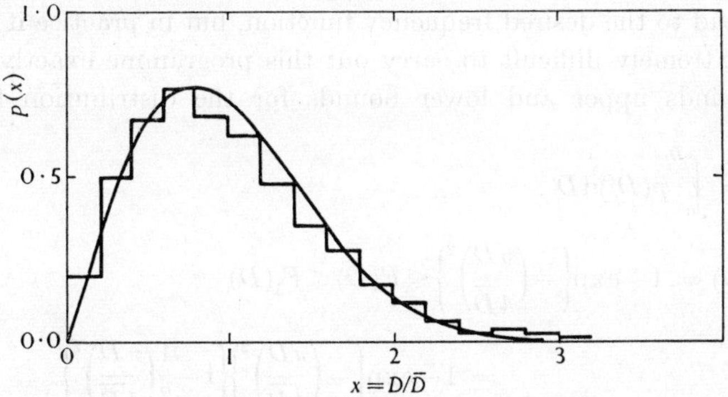

Fig. 5.1. Distribution of eigenvalue spacings from diagonalization of matrices with elements drawn randomly from Gaussian distributions, the variance of the diagonal distribution being twice that of the off-diagonal distribution. The histogram is compared with the Wigner frequency function (after Porter and Rosenzweig 1960).

diagonal and off-diagonal elements (Blumberg and Porter 1958, Rosenzweig 1958, Porter and Rosenzweig 1960). The spacings between consecutive ordered eigenvalues resulting from the diagonalization of such matrices were collected into histograms. A typical result from 180 matrices of order 20 is shown in Fig. 5.1 in comparison with eqn. (5.11). It is apparent that the latter is a very good representation of the histogram.

Analytical methods have also been employed to determine the level spacing distribution resulting from the Gaussian assumption for the matrix elements in the limit of very high order of the matrix. First of all, it can be shown that the joint frequency function of the eigenvalues of a matrix H of order n is the Wishart distribution (Wilks 1943),

$$p(E_1, E_2, \ldots, E_n) = \mu_0^{-1} \exp\{-(E_1^2 + \ldots + E_n^2)\} \prod_{i<j} |E_i - E_j|, \quad (5.13a)$$

where

$$\mu_0 = n!2^{-n(n-1)/4}\prod_{g=1}^{n}\Gamma(\tfrac{1}{2}g). \tag{5.13b}$$

To obtain the spacing distribution from this equation the integral

$$p(E_1, E_2) = \int' p(E_1, E_2, \ldots, E_n)\mathrm{d}E_3 \ldots \mathrm{d}E_n \tag{5.14}$$

must be found, the prime indicating that in integrating over $E_3 \ldots E_n$ the interval between E_1 and E_2 is excluded. Transformation to the new variables $D = E_1 - E_2$, $E_2 = E_2$ and integration over E_2 will, in principle, lead to the desired frequency function, but in practice it appears to be extremely difficult to carry out this programme exactly. Mehta (1960) finds upper and lower bounds for the distribution function

$$F(D) = \int_0^D p(D')\mathrm{d}D':$$

$$F_0(D) = 1-\exp\left\{-\left(\frac{\pi D}{4\bar{D}}\right)^2\right\} \leqslant F(D) \leqslant F_1(D)$$

$$= 1-\exp\left\{-\left(\frac{\pi D}{4\bar{D}}\right)^2\right\}\left\{1-\frac{1}{3}\left(\frac{\pi D}{4\bar{D}}\right)^2\right\}. \tag{5.15}$$

The Wigner surmise satisfies these bounds. However Mehta shows that the Wigner surmise cannot be exact by obtaining derivatives of the exact distribution function. Thus the quantities

$$(6\bar{D}^2/\pi^2)\,(\mathrm{d}^2F/\mathrm{d}D^2)_{D=0} \text{ and } (-10\bar{D}^4/\pi^4)\,(\mathrm{d}^4F/\mathrm{d}D^4)_{D=0}$$

have the values unity for the exact distribution function; for the Wigner surmise they have the values $3/\pi \approx 0{\cdot}955$ and $15/2\pi^2 \approx 0{\cdot}76$, respectively. Gaudin (1961) proceeds from Mehta's work to establish a rapidly converging infinite product for the distribution function of spacings, and uses this for a numerical evaluation. The results of this are shown in Table 5.1. It is apparent that, until the tail is reached at values of $D/\bar{D}$ greater than about 2·5, the exact frequency function $p(D)$ and the Wigner surmise $p_W(D)$ differ by only a few per cent. For the region $D/\bar{D} < 2$ Gaudin proposes, as an approximation to $p(D)$, the form

$$p(D) = \left(1+0{\cdot}078\frac{\pi^2 D^2}{4\bar{D}^2}\right)^{-1{\cdot}003} \exp\left(-\frac{\pi^2 D^2}{16\bar{D}^2}\right). \tag{5.16}$$

TABLE 5.1

The level spacing exact distribution and frequency functions, $F(D)$ and $p(D)$, according to Gaudin (1961), and the Wigner surmise for the same functions, $F_W(D)$ and $p_W(D)$

$D/\bar{D}$	$F(D)$	$F_W(D)$	$p(D)$	$p_W(D)$
0	0	0	0	0
0·064	0·00330	0·00317	0·104	0·0996
0·127	0·01321	0·01265	0·207	0·1974
0·191	0·02947	0·02824	0·303	0·2915
0·255	0·05168	0·04965	0·395	0·3801
0·318	0·07947	0·07649	0·477	0·4617
0·382	0·11219	0·10827	0·549	0·5350
0·446	0·14920	0·14441	0·6117	0·5989
0·509	0·18982	0·18430	0·6630	0·6525
0·573	0·23338	0·22727	0·7032	0·6954
0·637	0·27908	0·27262	0·7308	0·7273
0·764	0·37410	0·36768	0·7547	0·7587
0·891	0·46962	0·46414	0·7396	0·7502
1·018	0·56114	0·55730	0·6933	0·7083
1·146	0·64529	0·64346	0·6255	0·6417
1·273	0·71986	0·72007	0·5445	0·5598
1·400	0·78376	0·78575	0·4587	0·4713
1·528	0·83681	0·84014	0·3750	0·3836
1·655	0·87956	0·88372	0·2978	0·3023
1·782	0·91307	0·91749	0·2301	0·2308
1·910	0·93863	0·94300	0·1730	0·1709
2·037	0·95760	0·96159	0·1267	0·1229
2·164	0·97133	0·97476	0·0906	0·0857
2·292	0·98104	0·98384	0·0631	0·0581
2·419	0·98772	0·98991	0·0429	0·0383
2·546	0·99223	0·99386	0·0286	0·0245
2·674	0·99518	0·99635	0·0185	0·0153
2·801	0·99708	0·99789	0·0117	0·0092
2·928	0·9983	0·99881	0·0062	0·0054
3·055	0·9990	0·99934	0·0030	0·0031
3·183	0·9994	0·99965	0·002	0·0017

So far in this discussion no attempt has been made to justify the Gaussian assumption for the distribution of the matrix elements:

$$p_N(H_{11}, H_{12}, \ldots, H_{NN}) = C\exp\{-(H_{11}^2+2H_{12}^2+\ \ldots\ +H_{NN}^2)/4\sigma^2\}. \tag{5.17}$$

Porter and Rosenzweig (1960) have shown that the requirements of statistical independence of the matrix elements and rotational invariance of the form of the matrix element distribution are necessary to give eqn. (5.17). Rotational invariance means that the frequency function p_N must be independent of the orientation of the basis. This seems to be one of the most general statistical requirements that could be made.

Studies (Porter and Rosenzweig 1960) of the matrix elements of nuclear shell model calculations (Kurath 1956) would seem to verify eqn. (5.17).

Porter and Rosenzweig have also investigated the results of relaxation of eqn. (5.17) in the sense of allowing the ratio of the variances of the diagonal and non-diagonal matrix elements to differ from the value 2. If parameters β and α are introduced, where

$$\beta = \mathrm{e}^{\alpha} = (2\overline{H_{12}^2}/\overline{H_{11}^2})^{\frac{1}{2}}, \tag{5.18}$$

the frequency function for the level spacing resulting from a 2×2 matrix is

$$p(x;\alpha)\mathrm{d}x = \frac{\pi}{2}\{P_{\frac{1}{2}}(\cosh|\alpha|)\}^2 x \exp[-\frac{\pi}{4}\cosh|\alpha|\{P_{\frac{1}{2}}(\cosh|\alpha|)\}^2 x^2]\times$$
$$\times I_0\left[\frac{\pi}{4}\sinh|\alpha|\{P_{\frac{1}{2}}(\cosh|\alpha|)\}^2 x^2\right]\mathrm{d}x, \tag{5.19}$$

where $P_{\frac{1}{2}}$ is the Legendre function and I_0 the Bessel function. When β tends to unity this result tends to eqn. (5.11). When β tends to either zero or very large values eqn. (5.19) tends to the form

$$p(x) = \frac{2}{\pi}\exp\left(-\frac{x^2}{\pi}\right) \tag{5.20}$$

in which the absence of the level repulsion effect is to be remarked. The question was pursued numerically for matrices of higher order and diagonal elements identically equal to zero. For a matrix of order 3 the repulsion effect is already apparent and for higher orders the results rapidly tend to be indistinguishable from those obtained using the assumption of eqn. (5.17) (Porter and Rosenzweig 1960). This can be ascribed, not to unimportance of the rotational invariance requirement, but to the small number of diagonal compared with non-diagonal elements. Numerical diagonalization of matrices of order 20 with elements chosen randomly from *a*) a uniform distribution between -1 and 1, and *b*) a δ-function distribution at -1 and $+1$ also lead to nearest neighbour spacing distributions which are hardly distinguishable from those arising from eqn. (5.11).

Before we can compare the above theory with experimental data it is necessary to decide exactly what the parameters are that the mathematical model represents. The model in fact is meant to give the real eigenvalues of a system so complicated that it appears random no matter what representation it is presented in. The internal region of the highly excited nucleus would appear to be classifiable as such a system, and therefore the eigenvalues of the solutions of the Schrödinger equation with real boundary conditions imposed just outside the internal region, i.e. R-matrix eigenvalues, would be the correct parameters to compare with the model. The spacings of the real parts of the S-matrix poles do not necessarily qualify for this role because the S-matrix eigenstates belong to the whole configuration space. Thus, if the states as a whole have large partial widths because of large penetration factors for leakage into just one or a few channels there will be large non-random contributions to the Hamiltonian matrix elements making the above statistical model invalid. In the two-dimensional case, for example, it may be possible to choose a basis in which the difference in the diagonal elements is on average much larger than the non-diagonal elements, i.e. β of eqn. (5.18) is small. In this case the frequency function of the spacing will tend towards the simple Gaussian form, eqn. (5.20).

This can be seen in another way by studying the relationships between R-matrix and S-matrix parameters developed in Chapter II. In particular, the discussion of Section H.1.(c) of that chapter shows that two neighbouring R-matrix levels (defined 'physically' with vanishingly small level shifts) with large partial widths in few channels can give rise to S-matrix poles with a real separation considerably less than the level separation. The extreme case of two exactly similar levels is shown in Fig. 5.2; here the real pole separation becomes zero when the level width to level spacing ratio becomes more than 2. These simple considerations show that the Wigner repulsion effect must be considerably weakened in the frequency function of real spacings in cases where mean width to spacing ratios are large.

Fortunately this is not usually the condition in slow neutron cross-sections. In the cross-sections of the non-fissile nuclei the resonances up to a few keV neutron energy are very narrow compared with the spacing, and the resonance energies extracted by single-level fitting are very close to the set of R-matrix eigenvalues chosen with the physical set of channel radii and boundary conditions described in Section F of Chapter II as well as to the S-matrix pole energies. The spacings of these resonance energies can thus be compared directly with the mathematical models described here. The cross-section data of the fissile nuclei are not suitable for this purpose however; this is discussed further in Chapter VIII.

The experimental data essentially confirm eqn. (5.11). The data to be used in a comparison with theory must be of high quality. Experimental resolution must be very good so that two very close levels may be resolved and their small spacing observed. Instrumental sensitivity must also be good so that weak resonances are observed. This requirement leads to a fundamental difficulty however. All the theory of this section has been confined to levels of one class of good quantum numbers. In the neutron resonance case the only good quantum numbers that are expected are those of total angular momentum and parity.

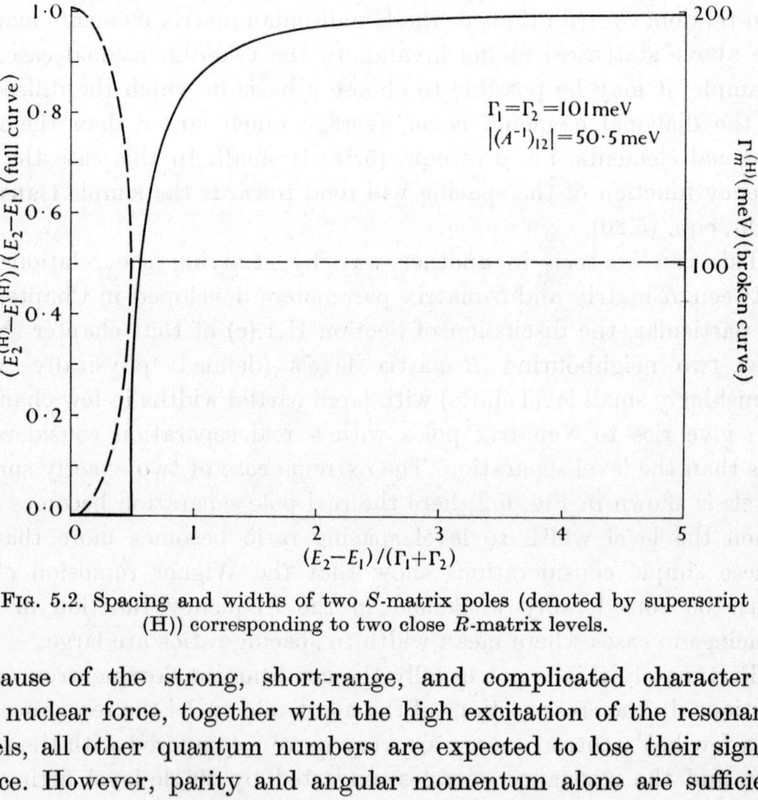

FIG. 5.2. Spacing and widths of two S-matrix poles (denoted by superscript (H)) corresponding to two close R-matrix levels.

Because of the strong, short-range, and complicated character of the nuclear force, together with the high excitation of the resonance levels, all other quantum numbers are expected to lose their significance. However, parity and angular momentum alone are sufficient to introduce complications. For this reason, the resonance data of even-target nuclei are chosen for comparison with the Wigner surmise. The s-wave resonances of these nuclei have angular momentum $J = \frac{1}{2}$ and have even parity. Instrumental sensitivity sufficient to detect the very weak s-wave resonances will, in general, also be sufficient to detect some of the p-wave resonances. These are of two different classes having angular momentum $J = \frac{1}{2}$, 3/2 and odd parity. Levels of a different class will belong to a different sub-space of the basis and their eigenvalues will be determined from the diagonalization of a distinct and independent matrix. The spacings of levels of two or more classes together will be those of two or more independent sets of eigenvalues superimposed. This problem will be treated in Section C. Here it will be sufficient to note that observation of the parities of all the levels ought to be made before the data is employed for level-spacing analysis. This is a very difficult requirement that has not been met in the best quality data available at the time of writing. The best that can be done is to make a semi-quantitative estimate of the

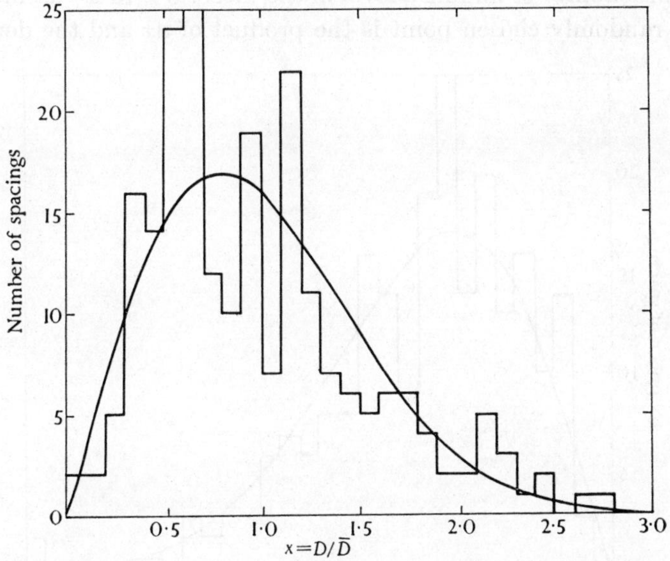

FIG. 5.3. Histogram of spacings of resonances between 0 and 3·9 keV in the cross-section of ^{232}Th compared with Wigner frequency function. (Garg *et al.* 1964)

number of very weak *s*-wave resonances that have been missed, the number of strong *p*-wave resonances that have been observed, and of the effects of these numbers, if small, on the observed level-spacing distribution.

The most extensive available data are those of Garg *et al.* (1964) on resonances in the cross-sections of ^{232}Th and ^{238}U. The histograms of the spacings deduced from these data, 223 resonances from 0 to 3·9 keV for ^{232}Th, and 227 resonances in the same energy range for ^{238}U, are shown in Figs. 5.3 and 5.4. The smooth curve shown in these diagrams is the Wigner frequency function, eqn. (5.11); the agreement with the data is apparently very good. Some quantitative tests of the same data have been made by Garrison (1964). He has calculated the second, third, and fourth moments of the spacings; they are $1{\cdot}29 \pm 0{\cdot}05$, $1{\cdot}96 \pm 0{\cdot}15$, and $3{\cdot}1 \pm 0{\cdot}5$, respectively, for ^{232}Th. These are to be compared with the values 1·273, 1·91, and 3·24, calculated from the Wigner distribution, and with the values 1·28, 1·93, and 3·29 calculated from the results of diagonalizing 10,000 order-10 matrices with random Gaussian elements (Porter 1963). The agreement is good.

B. THE NEAREST LEVEL TO A RANDOM POINT

The probability of finding a level in the interval x to $x+\mathrm{d}x$ measured from a randomly chosen point is the product of $\mathrm{d}x$ and the density of

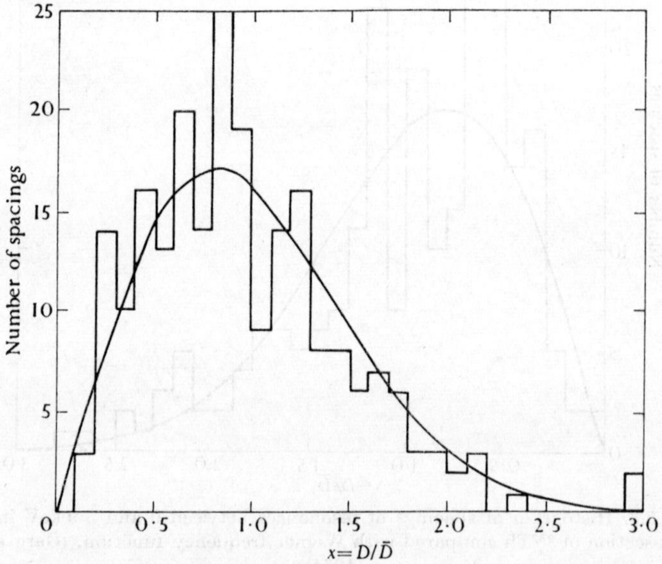

Fig. 5.4. Histogram of spacings of resonances between 0 and 4 keV in the cross-section of ^{238}U compared with Wigner frequency function (Garg *et al.* 1964).

levels $1/\bar{x}$. The probability of there being no level in the interval 0 to x is $\int_x^\infty p(x')\,\mathrm{d}x'$ where $p(x)$ is the frequency function of spacings between consecutive levels. Consequently, the probability $g(x)\mathrm{d}x$ of finding the first level in the interval x to $x+\mathrm{d}x$ measured from a random point is

$$g(x)\mathrm{d}x = \frac{\mathrm{d}x}{\bar{x}}\int_x^\infty p(x')\,\mathrm{d}x'. \tag{5.21}$$

Application of this to the Wigner distribution, eqn. (5.11), gives

$$g(x)\mathrm{d}x = \frac{\mathrm{d}x}{\bar{x}}\exp\left(-\frac{\pi x^2}{4\bar{x}^2}\right). \tag{5.22}$$

There have been surmises in the literature from time to time that there is a peculiar significance in the position of the lowest neutron resonance of a cross-section. In particular it has been supposed that this level lies particularly close to the neutron threshold (Inglis 1962). This can be tested with eqn. (5.22). Mean level spacings that have been established from the data of several resonances in the cross-sections of even-target nuclei are listed in column 4 of Table 5.2. In column 5 the position of the lowest resonance is noted, and the ratio of the two

TABLE 5.2

The energies of the lowest observed resonances in the cross-sections of even nuclei, and ratios with respect to the mean resonance spacing

Target nucleus	Observed mean resonance spacing $\bar{D} = \bar{D}(\frac{1}{2}^+)$ (eV)	Energy of lowest resonance E_R (eV)	Reference	Ratio $E_R/\bar{D}(\frac{1}{2}^+)$
$^{76}_{34}$Se	$(1{\cdot}2\pm0{\cdot}3)\times10^3$	376	Coté *et al.* (1964*c*)	$0{\cdot}31\pm0{\cdot}08$
$^{80}_{34}$Se	$(1{\cdot}7\pm0{\cdot}6)\times10^3$	$2{\cdot}0\times10^3$	Leblanc *et al.* (1959)	$1{\cdot}2\pm0{\cdot}2$
$^{90}_{40}$Zr	$(4{\cdot}5\pm1{\cdot}6)\times10^3$	$3{\cdot}8\times10^3$	Julien *et al.* (1962*a*)	$0{\cdot}84\pm0{\cdot}22$
$^{92}_{40}$Zr	$(1.2\pm0{\cdot}4)\times10^3$	$1{\cdot}86\times10^3$	Moskaler *et al.* (1964)	$1{\cdot}5\pm0{\cdot}3$
$^{94}_{40}$Zr	$(2{\cdot}4\pm0{\cdot}9)\times10^3$	$2{\cdot}27\times10^3$	Moskaler *et al.* (1964)	$0{\cdot}9\pm0{\cdot}4$
$^{114}_{50}$Sn	150 ± 60	277	Fuketa *et al.* (1963)	$1{\cdot}9\pm0{\cdot}6$
$^{116}_{50}$Sn	180 ± 50	111	Fuketa *et al.* (1963)	$0{\cdot}62\pm0{\cdot}2$
$^{118}_{50}$Sn	180 ± 50	45·8	Fuketa *et al.* (1963)	$0{\cdot}25\pm0{\cdot}08$
$^{120}_{50}$Sn	200 ± 70	365	Fuketa *et al.* (1963)	$1{\cdot}8\pm0{\cdot}6$
$^{122}_{50}$Sn	400 ± 200	107	Fuketa *et al.* (1963)	$0{\cdot}27\pm0{\cdot}13$
$^{124}_{50}$Sn	400 ± 200	61·95	Fuketa *et al.* (1963)	$0{\cdot}15\pm{\cdot}07$
$^{162}_{66}$Dy	130 ± 50	5·44	Hughes *et al.* (1959)	$0{\cdot}042\pm0{\cdot}015$
$^{182}_{74}$W	55 ± 18	4·14	Landon (1955)	$0{\cdot}075\pm0{\cdot}025$
$^{198}_{80}$Hg	99 ± 30	23·0	Levin and Hughes (1956)	$0{\cdot}23\pm0{\cdot}07$
$^{200}_{80}$Hg	$(2{\cdot}2\pm0{\cdot}7)\times10^3$	$1{\cdot}325\times10^3$	Carpenter and Bollinger (1960)	$0{\cdot}60\pm0{\cdot}20$
$^{232}_{90}$Th	$17{\cdot}5\pm0{\cdot}7$	22·1	Levin and Hughes (1956)	$1{\cdot}26\pm0{\cdot}05$
$^{232}_{92}$U	$7{\cdot}6\pm1{\cdot}5$	5·99	James (1964)	$0{\cdot}79\pm0{\cdot}15$
$^{234}_{92}$U	13 ± 2	5·20	Harvey and Hughes (1958)	$0{\cdot}40\pm0{\cdot}07$
$^{236}_{92}$U	17 ± 3	5·49	Harvey and Hughes (1958)	$0{\cdot}32\pm0{\cdot}05$
$^{238}_{92}$U	$17{\cdot}7\pm0{\cdot}7$	6·67	Lynn and Pattenden (1956)	$0{\cdot}38\pm0{\cdot}01$
$^{240}_{94}$Pu	18 ± 7	1·053	Coté *et al.* (1959)	$0{\cdot}06\pm0{\cdot}02$
$^{244}_{96}$Cm	13 ± 3	7·73	Coté *et al.* (1964*a*)	$0{\cdot}60\pm0{\cdot}15$

TABLE 5.3

Lowest observed resonances of both spins in the cross-sections of odd-mass nuclei and their ratios with respect to the mean resonance spacing

Target nucleus	I^π	Compound nucleus spin, J^π	Observed mean resonance spacing $\bar{D}$ (eV)	Inferred spacing $\bar{D}(J^\pi)$ (eV)	Energy of lowest resonance with spin J^π E_R (eV)	Reference	Ratio $E_R/\bar{D}(J^\pi)$
$^{51}_{23}$V	$\frac{7}{2}-$	4−	$(3{\cdot}6\pm0{\cdot}9)\times10^3$	$(7{\cdot}2\pm1{\cdot}8)\times10^3$	$4{\cdot}17\times10^3$	Firk *et al.* (1963)	$0{\cdot}65\pm0{\cdot}13$
		3−		$(7{\cdot}2\pm1{\cdot}8)\times10^3$	$6{\cdot}89\times10^3$	Firk *et al.* (1963)	$0{\cdot}96\pm0{\cdot}2$
$^{55}_{25}$Mn	$\frac{5}{2}-$	2−	$(2{\cdot}1\pm0{\cdot}8)\times10^3$	$(4{\cdot}2\pm1{\cdot}6)\times10^3$	$0{\cdot}335\times10^3$	Coté *et al.* (1964*b*)	$0{\cdot}08\pm0{\cdot}03$
		3−		$(4{\cdot}2\pm1{\cdot}6)\times10^3$	$1{\cdot}098\times10^3$	Coté *et al.* (1964*b*)	$0{\cdot}26\pm0{\cdot}09$
$^{77}_{34}$Se	$\frac{1}{2}-$	1−	100 ± 25	133 ± 33	112	Coté *et al.* (1964*c*)	$0{\cdot}84\pm0{\cdot}20$
		0−		400 ± 100	209	Coté *et al.* (1964*c*)	$0{\cdot}52\pm0{\cdot}13$
						Julien *et al.* (1962*a*)	
$^{107}_{47}$Ag	$\frac{1}{2}-$	0−	12 ± 5	48 ± 20	16·3	Rae *et al.* (1958)	$0{\cdot}34\pm0{\cdot}14$
		1−		16 ± 7	42	Rae *et al.* (1958)	$2{\cdot}6\pm0{\cdot}9$
$^{109}_{47}$Ag	$\frac{1}{2}-$	1−	22 ± 7	29 ± 9	5·2	Rae *et al.* (1958)	$0{\cdot}18\pm0{\cdot}06$
		0−		88 ± 28	88	Rae *et al.* (1958)	$1{\cdot}0\pm0{\cdot}3$
$^{115}_{49}$In	$\frac{9}{2}+$	5+	$6{\cdot}7\pm2$	$13{\cdot}4\pm4$	1·46	Dabbs *et al.* (1955)	$0{\cdot}11\pm0{\cdot}04$
		4+		$13{\cdot}4\pm4$	3·86	Stolovy (1959)	$0{\cdot}29\pm0{\cdot}10$
$^{149}_{62}$Sm	$\frac{7}{2}-$	4−	$2{\cdot}4\pm0{\cdot}6$	$4{\cdot}8\pm1{\cdot}2$	0·096	Marshak and Sailor (1958)	$0{\cdot}020\pm0{\cdot}005$
		5−		$4{\cdot}8\pm1{\cdot}2$	6·40	Marshak and Sailor (1958)	$1{\cdot}33\pm0{\cdot}3$

$^{151}_{63}$Eu	$\frac{5}{2}(+)$	3	$0{\cdot}75 \pm 0{\cdot}15$	$1{\cdot}5 \pm 0{\cdot}3$	0·327	Stolovy (1964)	$0{\cdot}22 \pm 0{\cdot}04$
		2		$1{\cdot}5 \pm 0{\cdot}3$	3·35		$2{\cdot}2 \pm 0{\cdot}4$
$^{155}_{64}$Gd	$\frac{3}{2}-$	2−	$2{\cdot}1 \pm 0{\cdot}2$	$3{\cdot}4 \pm 0{\cdot}3$	0·0268	Stolovy (1964)	$0{\cdot}008 \pm 0{\cdot}001$
		1−		$5{\cdot}6 \pm 0{\cdot}5$	2·01	Stolovy (1964)	$0{\cdot}36 \pm 0{\cdot}04$
$^{159}_{65}$Tb	$\frac{3}{2}(+)$	2	$3{\cdot}9 \pm 0{\cdot}6$	$6{\cdot}3 \pm 1{\cdot}0$	3·34	Wang *et al.* (1964)	$0{\cdot}53 \pm 0{\cdot}09$
		1		$10{\cdot}4 \pm 1{\cdot}5$	4·98	Wang *et al.* (1964)	$0{\cdot}48 \pm 0{\cdot}08$
$^{161}_{66}$Dy	$\frac{5}{2}(+)$	3	$2{\cdot}1 \pm 0{\cdot}4$	$4{\cdot}2 \pm 0{\cdot}8$	2·72	Brunhart *et al.* (1962)	$0{\cdot}65 \pm 0{\cdot}13$
		2		$4{\cdot}2 \pm 0{\cdot}8$	3·69	Brunhart *et al.* (1962)	$0{\cdot}88 \pm 0{\cdot}17$
$^{167}_{68}$Er	$\frac{7}{2}(+)$	4	$3{\cdot}0 \pm 1{\cdot}5$	6 ± 3	0·460	Brunhart *et al.* (1962)	$0{\cdot}08 \pm 0{\cdot}04$
		3		6 ± 3	0·584	Brunhart *et al.* (1962)	$0{\cdot}10 \pm 0{\cdot}05$
$^{169}_{69}$Tm	$\frac{1}{2}+$	1+	$6 \pm 1{\cdot}5$	8 ± 2	3·9	Singh (1964)	$0{\cdot}49 \pm 0{\cdot}12$
		0+		24 ± 6	14·5	Singh (1964)	$0{\cdot}60 \pm 0{\cdot}15$
$^{177}_{72}$Hf	$\frac{7}{2}-$	3−	$2{\cdot}9 \pm 0{\cdot}7$	$5{\cdot}8 \pm 1{\cdot}4$	1·10	Ceulemans and Poortmans (1961)	$0{\cdot}19 \pm 0{\cdot}04$
		4−		$5{\cdot}8 \pm 1{\cdot}4$	2·39	Ceulemans and Poortmans (1961)	$0{\cdot}41 \pm 0{\cdot}08$
$^{181}_{73}$Ta	$\frac{7}{2}+$	3+	$4{\cdot}4 \pm 0{\cdot}4$	$8{\cdot}8 \pm 0{\cdot}8$	4·28	Evans *et al.* (1959)	$0{\cdot}49 \pm 0{\cdot}05$
		4+		$8{\cdot}8 \pm 0{\cdot}8$	10·4	Evans *et al.* (1959)	$1{\cdot}18 \pm 0{\cdot}12$
$^{183}_{74}$W	$\frac{1}{2}+$	1−	15 ± 4	20 ± 6	7·62	Waters *et al.* (1959)	$0{\cdot}38 \pm 0{\cdot}13$
		0−		60 ± 18	47·7	Firk and Moxon (1959)	$0{\cdot}80 \pm 0{\cdot}27$
$^{195}_{78}$Pt	$\frac{1}{2}-$	1−	18 ± 4	24 ± 5	11·9	Waters (1960)	$0{\cdot}50 \pm 0{\cdot}10$
		0−		72 ± 15	66·9	Julien *et al.* (1962*b*)	$0{\cdot}93 \pm 0{\cdot}19$
$^{199}_{80}$Hg	$\frac{1}{2}-$	1−	70 ± 28	94 ± 37	33·5	Landon and Rae (1957)	$0{\cdot}36 \pm 0{\cdot}13$
		0−		282 ± 110	128	Bird *et al.* (1959)	$0{\cdot}45 \pm 0{\cdot}16$
$^{209}_{83}$Bi	$\frac{9}{2}-$	5−	$(1{\cdot}0 \pm 0{\cdot}3) \times 10^4$	$(2{\cdot}0 \pm 0{\cdot}6) \times 10^4$	784	Lynn *et al.* (1958)	$0{\cdot}039 \pm 0{\cdot}007$
		4−		$(2{\cdot}0 \pm 0{\cdot}6) \times 10^4$	$2{\cdot}23 \times 10^3$	Lynn *et al.* (1958)	$0{\cdot}11 \pm 0{\cdot}02$

quantities is given in column 6. The distribution of this ratio is shown in Fig. 5.5 and compared with the distribution function

$$G(y) = \int_{y}^{\infty} dy' e^{-\pi y'^2/4} = \text{erfc}\left(\frac{\pi^{\frac{1}{2}}y}{2}\right) \tag{5.23}$$

derived from eqn. (5.22); there is very good agreement.

Equation (5.23) may also be applied to data from odd-mass and odd nuclei provided that the lowest resonance of both angular momenta

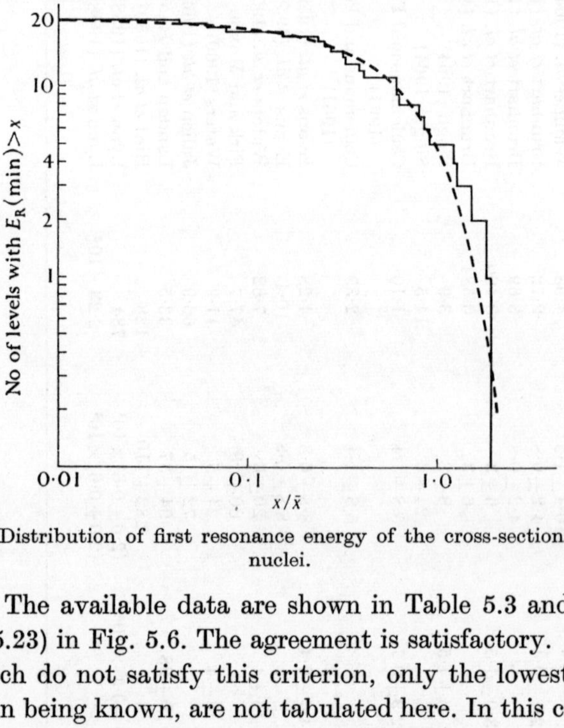

FIG. 5.5. Distribution of first resonance energy of the cross-sections of even nuclei.

are known. The available data are shown in Table 5.3 and compared with eqn. (5.23) in Fig. 5.6. The agreement is satisfactory.

Data which do not satisfy this criterion, only the lowest resonance of either spin being known, are not tabulated here. In this case the distribution function for the energy E_R of the lowest resonance is

$$G(E_R) = \text{erfc}\left(\frac{\pi^{\frac{1}{2}}E_R}{\bar{D}(I+\frac{1}{2})}\right) . \text{erfc}\left(\frac{\pi^{\frac{1}{2}}E_R}{\bar{D}(I-\frac{1}{2})}\right). \tag{5.24}$$

This is compared with the data in Fig. 5.7, the assumption being made that $\bar{D}(I+\frac{1}{2}) = \bar{D}(I-\frac{1}{2})$.

Again the agreement is satisfactory. This strongly suggests that zero neutron energy, the neutron-separation energy of the compound nucleus, is indeed a random point with respect to the nuclear level structure. The agreement can also be taken to be a test of the Wigner frequency function, eqn. (5.11).

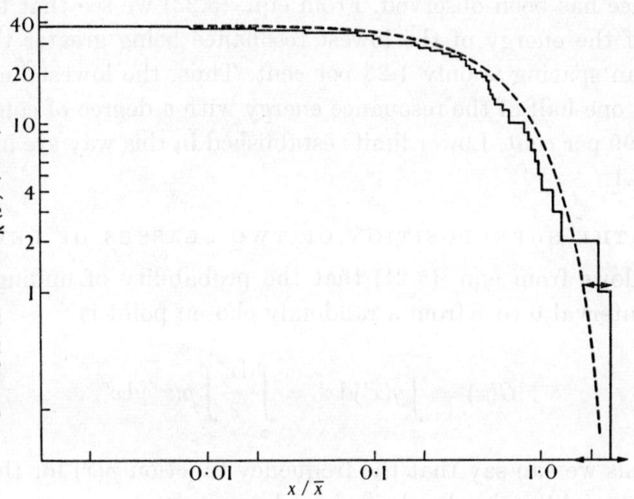

FIG. 5.6. Distribution of first resonance energies of both angular momenta in cross-sections of odd-mass nuclei.

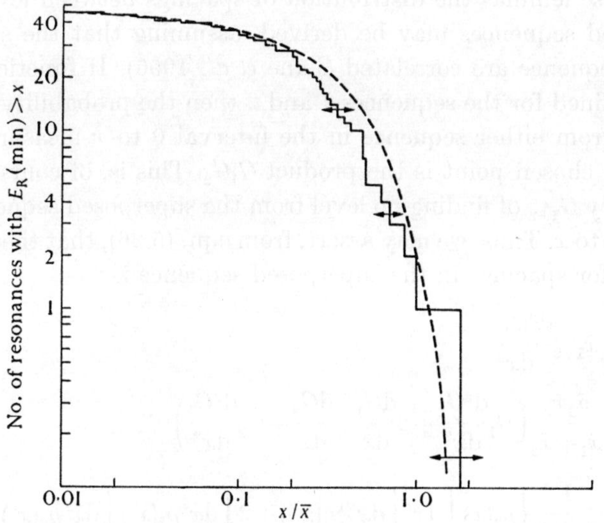

FIG. 5.7. Distribution of first resonance energy of either angular momentum in cross-sections of odd-mass nuclei. The arrows indicate uncertainties.

We have also used eqn. (5.23) to establish lower limits for the mean resonance spacing in many cross-sections in which only the lowest resonance has been observed. From eqn. (5.23) we see that the probability of the energy of the lowest resonance being greater than twice the mean spacing is only 1·23 per cent. Thus, the lowest limit on the mean is one-half of the resonance energy with a degree of confidence of almost 99 per cent. Lower limits established in this way are included in Table 4.1.

C. THE SUPERPOSITION OF TWO CLASSES OF LEVELS

It follows from eqn. (5.21) that the probability of finding no level in the interval 0 to x from a randomly chosen point is

$$G(x) = \int_x^\infty g(x')\,\mathrm{d}x' = \int_x^\infty \frac{\mathrm{d}x'}{\bar{x}} \int_{x'}^\infty p(x'')\,\mathrm{d}x''. \tag{5.25}$$

From this we can say that the frequency function $p(x)$ for the spacing between neighbouring levels is given by

$$p(x) = \bar{x}\frac{\mathrm{d}^2G}{\mathrm{d}x^2}. \tag{5.26}$$

From these lemmas the distribution of spacings between levels of two superposed sequences may be derived, assuming that the spacings of neither sequence are correlated (Lane *et al.* 1956). If functions G_1 and G_2 are defined for the sequences 1 and 2 then the probability of finding no level from either sequence in the interval 0 to x measured from a randomly chosen point is the product G_1G_2. This is, of course, just the probability G_{1+2} of finding no level from the superposed sequence in the interval 0 to x. Thus, we may assert, from eqn. (5.26), that the frequency function for spacings in the superposed sequence is

$$p_{1+2}(x) = \bar{x}_{1+2}\frac{\mathrm{d}^2G_{1+2}}{\mathrm{d}x^2} \tag{5.27a}$$

$$= \frac{\bar{x}_1\bar{x}_2}{\bar{x}_1+\bar{x}_2}\left(G_1\frac{\mathrm{d}^2G_2}{\mathrm{d}x^2}+2\frac{\mathrm{d}G_1}{\mathrm{d}x}\cdot\frac{\mathrm{d}G_2}{\mathrm{d}x}+G_2\frac{\mathrm{d}^2G_1}{\mathrm{d}x^2}\right) \tag{5.27b}$$

$$= \frac{1}{\bar{x}_1+\bar{x}_2}\left\{p_2(x)\int_x^\infty \mathrm{d}x'\int_{x'}^\infty \mathrm{d}x''\,p_1(x'')+2\int_x^\infty \mathrm{d}x'\,p_1(x')\int_x^\infty \mathrm{d}x'\,p_2(x')\right.$$

$$\left.+p_1(x)\int_x^\infty \mathrm{d}x'\int_{x'}^\infty \mathrm{d}x''\,p_2(x'')\right\}. \tag{5.27c}$$

If the Wigner distribution is assumed for the spacings of the two classes separately then the frequency function of the spacings of the superposed sequence is

$$p_{1+2}(x) = \frac{1}{\bar{x}_1+\bar{x}_2}\left[\frac{\pi x\bar{x}_1}{2\bar{x}_2^2}\exp\left(-\frac{\pi x^2}{4\bar{x}_2^2}\right)\left\{1-\mathrm{erf}\left(\frac{x\sqrt{\pi}}{2\bar{x}_1}\right)\right\}\right.$$
$$+2\exp\left\{-\frac{\pi x^2}{4}\left(\frac{1}{\bar{x}_1^2}+\frac{1}{\bar{x}_2^2}\right)\right\}$$
$$\left.+\frac{\pi x\bar{x}_2}{2\bar{x}_1^2}\exp\left(-\frac{\pi\bar{x}^2}{4\bar{x}_1^2}\right)\left\{1-\mathrm{erf}\left(\frac{x\sqrt{\pi}}{2\bar{x}_2}\right)\right\}\right]. \quad (5.28)$$

This function is shown in Fig. 5.8 for different ratios of the means $\bar{x}_1$ and $\bar{x}_2$. Even for the most unfavourable ratio ($\bar{x}_1 = \bar{x}_2$) there is still

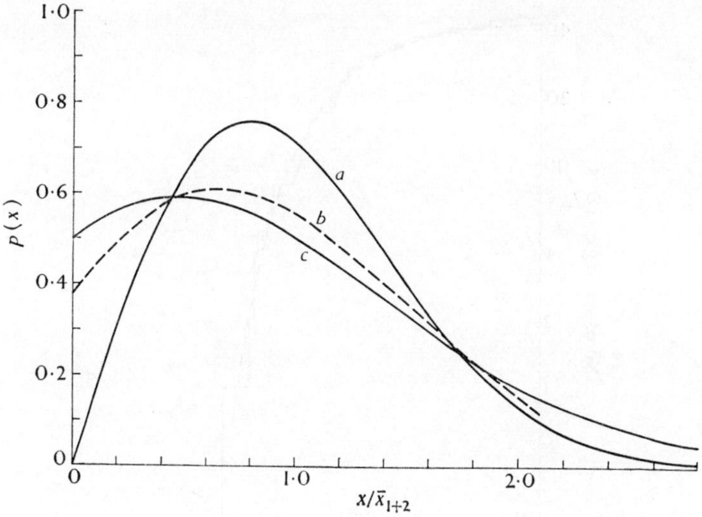

FIG. 5.8. Frequency function for spacings of two superposed sequences of levels with mean spacings in the ratio 1:1 (curve c) and 3:1 (curve b) compared with the Wigner frequency function for a single sequence (curve a).

some vestige of the level repulsion effect. The probability of small spacings occurring is so high, however, that it is expected to be very difficult to avoid a bias, owing to instrumental resolution effects, in a comparison of eqn. (5.28) with the experimental data. Thus, the experimental evidence for the Wigner surmise from target nuclei of odd mass is necessarily of limited value compared with that from even nuclei. The *s*-wave resonances of the cross-section of an odd-mass nucleus (with angular momentum *I*) correspond to the superposition of two classes of levels with angular momentum $J = I \pm \frac{1}{2}$. According to the independent-particle model of nuclear level densities the spacing of levels of angular momentum J is proportional to $(2J+1)^{-1}$. With the assumption of the correctness of this relation the distribution of the first 45 spacings from the cross-section of ^{181}Ta ($I = \frac{7}{2}$) (Evans *et al.*, Firk and Moxon 1959, Desjardins *et al.* 1960) is compared, in Fig. 5.9, with the distribution function

$$P_{1+2}(D) = \int_{D}^{\infty} p_{1+2}(D')\mathrm{d}D' \tag{5.29}$$

derived from eqn. (5.28). The same thing is done for ^{197}Au ($I = \frac{3}{2}$) in Fig. 5.10. There is good agreement in both cases.

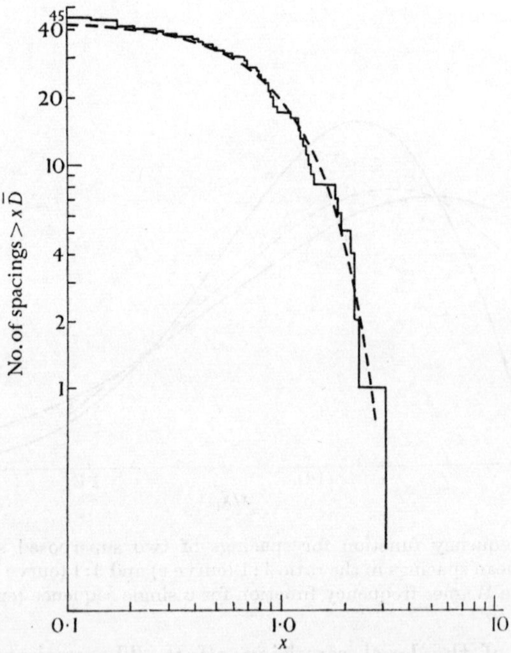

FIG. 5.9. Distribution of first 45 resonance spacings in cross-section of ^{181}Ta compared with superposed Wigner distribution function.

A caution to be observed when using eqns. (5.27) and (5.28) is that the spacings of superposed sequences of levels are correlated even though the spacings of the original sequences may be uncorrelated. This is most easily seen by superposing two sequences of uniformly spaced levels (with the same spacing $\bar{x}$). Equation (5.27) gives for the frequency function of the superposed sequence a constant value from 0 to $\bar{x}$. A particular sequence, on the other hand, will contain only two values of the spacings, q and $\bar{x}-q$ occurring alternately: a large spacing is always followed by a small spacing and vice versa. If the mean spacings $\bar{x}_1$ and $\bar{x}_2$ are slightly different the same thing will occur, but now the two values will change over intervals of many spacings; long-range correlation is damped out but short-range correlation will

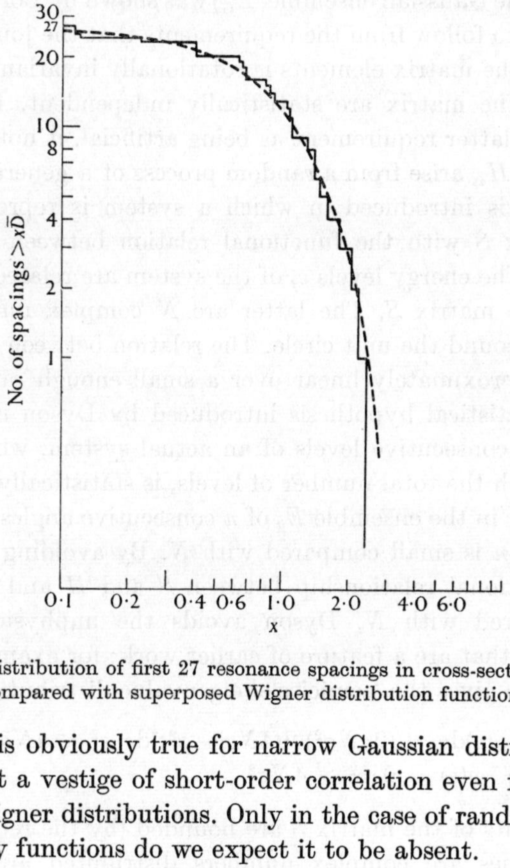

FIG. 5.10. Distribution of first 27 resonance spacings in cross-section of ^{197}Au compared with superposed Wigner distribution function.

remain. This is obviously true for narrow Gaussian distributions also and we expect a vestige of short-order correlation even for the superposition of Wigner distributions. Only in the case of random (exponential) frequency functions do we expect it to be absent.

D. CORRELATIONS AND OTHER PROPERTIES OF THE LEVEL-SPACING DISTRIBUTION

1. Classification of ensembles

The whole subject of the level-spacing distribution has been placed on an elegantly formal plane by Dyson and his collaborators. This work, together with the pioneering work of Wigner and the analytical manipulations of Mehta and Gaudin already referred to, have made the subject a distinctive branch of mathematical physics in its own right. We cannot hope, in the space available here, to give more than a summary of the results obtained in this field.

The basic statistical hypotheses underlying the level spacing distribution have been reconsidered by Dyson (1962*a*). The statistical ensemble of matrices introduced by Wigner (1951) and represented by eqn. (5.17) (the Gaussian ensemble, E_G) was shown by Porter and Rosenzweig (1960) to follow from the requirements that the joint distribution function for the matrix elements is rotationally invariant and that the elements of the matrix are statistically independent. Dyson (1962*a*) criticizes the latter requirement as being artificial, it not being reasonable that the H_{ij} arise from a random process of a general kind. A new ensemble E_β is introduced in which a system is represented by an $N \times N$ matrix S with the functional relation between S and H left unspecified. The energy levels ε_j of the system are related to the eigenvalues of the matrix S. The latter are N complex numbers $\exp i\theta_j$ distributed around the unit circle. The relation between the ε_j and the θ_j will be approximately linear over a small enough range of angles. The basic statistical hypothesis introduced by Dyson is that the behaviour of n consecutive levels of an actual system, where n is small compared with the total number of levels, is statistically equivalent to the behaviour in the ensemble E_β of n consecutive angles θ_j on the unit circle, where n is small compared with N. By avoiding the use of an explicit functional relationship between S and H and by keeping n small compared with N, Dyson avoids the unphysical eigenvalue distributions that are a feature of earlier work; for example, the Gaussian ensemble gives the 'semicircle' eigenvalue distribution

$$p(\varepsilon)\mathrm{d}\varepsilon = (2\pi N\sigma^2)^{-1}(4N\sigma^2-\varepsilon^2)^{\frac{1}{2}}\mathrm{d}\varepsilon,\ \varepsilon^2 < 4N\sigma^2$$
$$p(\varepsilon) = 0,\ \varepsilon^2 > 4N\sigma^2. \tag{5.30}$$

The elements of the matrix S are bounded (by the requirement that the eigenvalues are complex numbers distributed around the unit circle). It is therefore sensible to require that the ensemble E_β contain all possible S with equal probability. This is in distinction to the use of the Hamiltonian matrix to define an ensemble of systems, for in that case one cannot define uniform probability of the matrix elements over an infinite range; an arbitrary limit of their magnitudes, such as given by eqn. (5.17), is essential.

The ensemble E_β is termed the orthogonal ensemble E_1 when the matrices S are symmetric unitary matrices. The physical reason for this choice of S is that it implies either invariance of the systems under time inversion and under space rotations, or invariance under time inversion of systems containing an even number of half-integer spin particles. Other choices of the matrices S have been considered by Dyson (1962*a*). One is the choice of unitary self-dual quaternion matrices. The ensemble of such matrices is called the symplectic ensemble E_4. It is appropriate to systems that have time-inversion invariance, no rotation invariance, and an odd number of half-spin particles. The choice of arbitrary Hermitian matrices is appropriate to systems without time-inversion invariance; the ensemble of such matrices is the unitary ensemble E_2. Particular examples of these cases have been cited by Kahn and Porter (1963). The orthogonal ensemble is appropriate to the case of neutron resonances or of highly excited atomic levels. The unitary ensemble has its example in a system in an external magnetic field; this must be of the order of 10^{11} gauss to split nuclear levels by 1 eV or of the order of 10^{8} gauss to split atomic levels by the same amount. An example of the symplectic ensemble is the case of an atom subjected to an external multipole field in a crystal. Dyson (1962*d*) has further shown that the most general kind of matrix ensemble reduces to a direct product of independent irreducible ensembles each of which belongs to one of these three types.

The joint distribution function of the eigenvalues in the ensemble E_β is denoted by $Q_{N\beta}(\theta_1, \ldots, \theta_N)\mathrm{d}\theta_1 \ldots \mathrm{d}\theta_N$ where $\beta = 1$, 2, or 4. The probability for finding eigenvalues $\exp(\mathrm{i}\varphi_j)$ of S with angles φ_j in the intervals $(\theta_j, \theta_j+\mathrm{d}\theta_j)$ is

$$Q_{N\beta}(\theta_1, \ldots, \theta_N) = C_{N\beta}\prod_{i<j}|\mathrm{e}^{\mathrm{i}\theta_i}-\mathrm{e}^{\mathrm{i}\theta_j}|^\beta. \tag{5.31}$$

Equation (5.31) corresponds to the Wishart distribution (eqn. (5.13)) for the joint eigenvalue distribution of the Gaussian ensemble (eqn. (5.17)). Generalizations of eqn. (5.31) have been discussed by Fox and Kahn (1964). The generalized joint distribution function is of the form

$$P_N(x_1, \ldots, x_N) = f(x_1, \ldots, x_N)\prod_{i<j}|x_i-x_j|^\beta \tag{5.32a}$$

in which $f(x_1, \ldots, x_N)$ is a product $\prod_i\{g_i(x_i)\}^2$.

The choices
$$\{g(x)\}^2 = \exp(-x^2), \tag{5.32b}$$
$$= (1-x)^\mu(1+x)^\nu,\ \mu, \nu > -1;\ |x| \leqslant 1, \tag{5.32c}$$
$$= x^\alpha \mathrm{e}^{-x}, \tag{5.32d}$$
$$= 1 \tag{5.32e}$$

are labelled the Gaussian, Jacobi, Laguerre, and circular ensembles, respectively. In this terminology the Wishart distribution (eqn. (5.13)) is known as the joint eigenvalue distribution of the Gaussian orthogonal ensemble while the ensembles that Dyson has studied, leading to eqn. (5.31), are known as the circular orthogonal, the circular unitary, and the circular symplectic ensembles for $\beta = 1, 2, 4$ respectively. Dyson (1962*a*) gives an argument for understanding the different powers of β that appear in eqn. (5.31). The dimension of the space containing the ensemble E_1 is $\frac{1}{2}(N^2+N)$ while the dimension of the subspace containing matrices with two equal eigenvalues is $\{\frac{1}{2}(N^2+N)-2\}$. The difference in dimension is 2, giving a factor linear in the eigenvalue difference Δ. Similarly, for the ensemble E_2 the equivalent dimensions are (N^2) and (N^2-3), giving a factor Δ^2, while, for the ensemble E_4, the two dimensions are $(2N^2-N)$ and $(2N^2-N-5)$, giving a factor of Δ^4.

2. Electrostatic analogue

An interesting and useful analogue of eqn. (5.31) is derived from electrostatics (Dyson 1962*a*). The analogue is of N unit charges free to move on an infinitely thin circular wire, the positions of the charges being given by the angular variables $\theta_1, \ldots, \theta_N$. The function $Q_{N\beta}$ of eqn. (5.31) is the Boltzmann distribution of the variables θ of this constrained Coulomb gas at a temperature T given by $1/\beta$. Dyson has calculated the partition function by group-theoretical methods and, from the resulting study of the thermodynamics of the system, has been able to find the form of the level-spacing distribution for large values of the spacing (Dyson 1962*b*). For the orthogonal ensemble it is

$$p(D)\mathrm{d}D \sim AD^{17/8}\exp\left\{-\left(\frac{\pi D}{4\bar{D}}\right)^2 - \frac{\pi D}{4\bar{D}}\right\}; \tag{5.33}$$

for the unitary ensemble,

$$p(D)\mathrm{d}D \sim AD^2\exp\left\{-\tfrac{1}{2}\left(\frac{\pi D}{2\bar{D}}\right)^2\right\}; \tag{5.34}$$

and for the symplectic ensemble

$$p(D)\mathrm{d}D \sim AD^{17/8}\exp\left\{-\left(\frac{\pi D}{2\bar{D}}\right)^2 + \left(\frac{\pi D}{2\bar{D}}\right)\right\}. \tag{5.35}$$

The constants A in these relations are undetermined. One of the attractive features of the electrostatic analogue is, as Dyson remarks, that it reveals the phrase 'repulsion of energy levels' to be an exact physical description of the spacing distribution.

3. Long-range correlation

Important correlation properties of the level-spacing distribution have been obtained from the joint eigenvalue frequency function, for the orthogonal ensemble, $\beta = 1$. By the use of the analytical methods due to Mehta (1960) and Gaudin (1961) the n-level correlation functions may be calculated (Dyson 1962*c*). These functions represent the probability of finding a level in each of the intervals $[\theta_1, \theta_1+\mathrm{d}\theta_1], \ldots, [\theta_n, \theta_n+\mathrm{d}\theta_n]$ and may be written

$$R_n(\theta_1, \ldots, \theta_n) = [N!/(N-n)!]\int \ldots \int_0^{2\pi} P_N(\theta_1, \ldots, \theta_N)\, \mathrm{d}\theta_{n+1}\mathrm{d}\theta_{n+2} \ldots \mathrm{d}\theta_N. \tag{5.36}$$

The one-level function is just the level density $N/2\pi$. The two-level correlation function has been shown to be, in the limit $N \to \infty$,

$$R_2(x_1, x_2) = 1-\{S(r)\}^2-\left\{\int_r^\infty S(t)\mathrm{d}t\right\}\frac{\mathrm{d}S(r)}{\mathrm{d}r}, \tag{5.37}$$

where the new variables, $x_j = (N/2\pi)\theta_j$, are those appropriate to a mean spacing $\bar{D} = 1$, the variable $r = |x_1-x_2|$ and the function $S(r) = \sin(\pi r)/\pi r$.

From the two-level correlation function some useful statistics have been calculated (Dyson and Mehta 1963). The calculations are for the essentially practical case of a series of energy levels $E_j = (N\bar{D}/2\pi)\theta_j$, $j = 1, \ldots, n$, found in an interval of energy $[-L, L]$; the integer n is assumed to be large but still very much smaller than N. The first statistic, W_1, is useful for obtaining the mean-level spacing $\bar{D}$; it is simply the number of levels in the interval $[-L, L]$. The theoretical estimates of the mean $\langle W_1\rangle$ and the variance $V_1 = \langle(W_1-\langle W_1\rangle)^2\rangle$ of this statistic are

$$\langle W_1\rangle = (2L/\bar{D}), \tag{5.38a}$$

$$V_1 = \frac{2}{\pi^2}\left\{\ln(2\pi n)+1+\gamma-\frac{\pi^2}{8}\right\}, \tag{5.38b}$$

where $\gamma = 0{\cdot}5772$ is Euler's constant. This expression for the variance of W_1 immediately shows how strong are the correlation properties of level spacings. The corresponding formula for the variance of W_1 calculated from the Wigner conjecture, eqn. (5.11), with the assumption of statistical independence of the level spacings is

$$V_{\text{ind}} = 0{\cdot}273n. \tag{5.39}$$

For the case $n = 100$, $V_1 = 1{\cdot}4$ whereas $V_{\text{ind}} = 27{\cdot}3$, a difference of a factor of almost 20. Such a strong correlation inevitably follows from properties, demonstrated by Dyson (1962*c*), of long-range order, or 'crystalline structure', in the two-level correlation function.

A still better linear statistic for determining the mean-level spacing can be obtained by demanding that the computed function is smooth in the interval $[-L,\ L]$. The optimum statistic has been shown by Dyson and Mehta to be

$$W_2 = \sum_{j=1}^{n}\{1-(E_j/L)^2\}^{\frac{1}{2}} \tag{5.40}$$

for which $\langle W_2\rangle = \pi L/2\bar{D}$ and $V_2 = \frac{1}{2}$. The generalization of these statistics to the superposition of m independent-level sequences leads to results for the variances

$$V_1 = \frac{2m}{\pi^2}\left\{\ln(2\pi n)+1+\gamma-\frac{\pi^2}{8}\right\}+\frac{2}{\pi^2}\sum_{\mu=1}^{m}\ln f_\mu, \tag{5.41a}$$

$$V_2 = m/2, \tag{5.41b}$$

where the f_μ are the weightings of the individual sequences, $f_\mu = \bar{D}/\bar{D}_\mu$, $\sum_\mu f_\mu = 1$. These results show that a rare series in the superposed system contributes as much to the variance as a dense one.

4. Short-range correlations

The correlations indicated by these statistics for long range also exist at short range. This is shown by numerical computations, due to Porter (1963), of the n'th order spacing distributions, defined as the distributions of spacings of a pair of levels separated by exactly n other levels of the sequence. The calculations were carried out by diagonalization of random, real, symmetric matrices (Gaussian orthogonal ensemble) of order 10. The variances of the lowest order spacings are given in Table 5.4. The corresponding variances calculated for an independent distribution of the Wigner form are presented for comparison. Even for the 1st and 2nd order spacing distributions there is clear evidence of a departure of the variance from proportionality to

TABLE 5.4

Variances of the low-order spacing distributions from (1) diagonalization of Gaussian orthogonal matrices, (2) independent selection of nearest spacings from a Wigner distribution, compared with the experimental data from the cross-section of ^{232}Th. Also shown is the variance of the number of levels in an energy interval of length $(n+1)\bar{D}$, extrapolated from the long-range formula of Dyson and Mehta (1963)

2nd moment about mean	No. of levels in spacing, n 0	1	2	3	4	5	6
(1) From diagonalization of Gaussian orthogonal matrices $\times (1/\bar{D}^2)$	0·28	0·42	0·50	0·6	0·7	0·7	0·7
(2) From ind. Wigner distribution $\times (1/\bar{D}^2)$	0·27	0·55	0·82	1·09	1·36	1·64	1·91
(3) Of number of levels in interval of length $(n+1)\bar{D}$	0·44	0·58	0·66	0·72	0·77	0·80	0·83
(4) Exptl data from ^{232}Th (Garg *et al.* 1964)	0·29± 0·05	0·39± ·08	0·45± ·12	0·53± ·15	0·6± ·2	0·6± ·2	0·6± ·3

$(n+1)$. The moments calculated by Garrison (1964) from the cross-section data on ^{232}Th (Garg *et al.* 1964) are also shown in Table 5.4 and clearly agree much more closely with the fuller theory than they do with the idea of independently distributed spacings. The variance in the number of levels expected in an interval of length $(n+1)\bar{D}$, computed from eqn. (5.38b), is shown as a point of interest. This is expected to approximate to the variances in the top row of the table as n becomes large. The convergence in the two quantities is quite noticeable.

5. 'Staircase' statistics

Another class of statistics is derived from the so-called 'staircase' plots of number of levels as a function of energy, which often appear in the experimental literature as a criterion for determining mean-level spacings. A typical diagram of this kind, based on the data shown in Table 1.1 for the cross-section of ^{109}Ag, is shown in Fig. 5.11. In an observed energy interval $[-L, L]$ centred about some arbitrary energy taken as origin, $N(E)$ is defined as the number of levels between E and zero for positive energy, and as the number of levels between $-E$ and zero for negative energy. A function $y = AE+B$ can be found

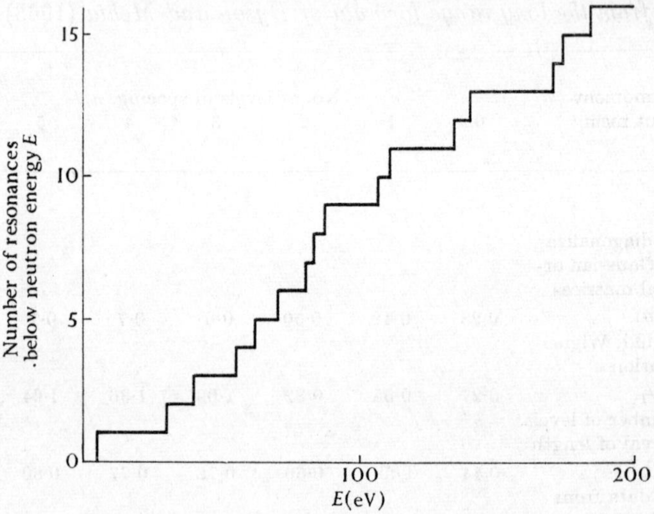

FIG. 5.11. A typical 'staircase' diagram of level density for the cross-section of ^{109}Ag.

to give an approximate overall fit to $N(E)$, the criterion for the best fit being the least squares condition. This gives a quantity Δ defined by

$$\Delta = \operatorname*{Min}_{A,B}\left\{\frac{1}{2L}\int_{-L}^{L}\{N(E)-AE-B\}^2\mathrm{d}E\right\}. \quad (5.42)$$

This quantity may be modified by applying constraints to the function. The most usual constraint on the 'staircase' plot is that y should pass through $N(-L)$ at $E = -L$. With this constraint the expression for the modified quantity Δ' is

$$\Delta' = \frac{1}{2L}\int_{-L}^{L}\{n'(E)\}^2\mathrm{d}E-\frac{3}{16L^4}\left\{\int_{-L}^{L}n'(E)(E+L)\mathrm{d}E\right\}^2, \quad (5.43a)$$

where

$$n'(E) = N(E)-N(-L)-(E+L)/D. \quad (5.43b)$$

With no constraint

$$\Delta = \frac{1}{2L}\int\limits_{-L}^{L}\{n(E)\}^2\mathrm{d}E - \frac{3}{4L^4}\left\{\int\limits_{-L}^{L} n(E)E\,\mathrm{d}E\right\}^2 - \frac{1}{4L^2}\int\limits_{-L}^{L} n(E)\,\mathrm{d}E, \tag{5.44}$$

where $n(E) = N(E) - E/\bar{D}$. Another quantity, Δ'', may be defined with the constraint that the straight line passes through the centre of the energy range of interest.

The mean values and variances of the first two of these quantities are

$$\langle\Delta'\rangle = \frac{5}{4\pi^2}\left\{\ln(2\pi n) + \gamma - \frac{\pi^2}{8} - \frac{21}{20}\right\}$$

$$= \frac{5}{4\pi^2}\{\ln(n) + 0{\cdot}1313\}, \tag{5.45}$$

$$V_{\Delta'} = \frac{1}{8\pi^4}\{\ln(n)\}^2, \tag{5.46}$$

$$\langle\Delta\rangle = \frac{1}{\pi^2}\left\{\ln(2\pi n) + \gamma - \frac{\pi^2}{8} - \frac{5}{4}\right\}$$

$$= \frac{1}{\pi^2}\{\ln(n) - 0{\cdot}0687\}, \tag{5.47}$$

$$V_{\Delta} = \frac{1}{\pi^4}\left(\frac{4\pi^2}{45} + \frac{7}{24}\right) = \frac{1{\cdot}1690}{\pi^4}. \tag{5.48}$$

For comparison the value of $\langle\Delta\rangle$ for a random series is $(1/15)n$. For a multiple series of m superposed independent sequences

$$\langle\Delta\rangle = \frac{m}{\pi^2}\{\ln(n) - 0{\cdot}0687\}, \tag{5.49}$$

$$V_{\Delta} = 1{\cdot}1690m^2/\pi^4. \tag{5.50}$$

Dyson and Mehta also calculate an 'energy' statistic, Q, which is related to the energy of the analogous two-dimensional Coulomb gas at temperature $T = 1$; it is sensitive to short-range correlations.

The intention behind the introduction of these statistics is that of testing the theoretical model, either for the basic statistical hypotheses or for hidden quantum numbers in the neutron resonance sequences. The main difficulty in comparing the data with the statistics lies in the quality of data required. The quality demanded is high because of the strong correlations that the theory reveals. The omission of only a few levels in the observation of a long sequence could be enough to cause a very large discrepancy between the observed value of a statistic and its theoretical value. Correspondingly the observation of a few unwanted levels (e.g. p-wave resonances) in a sequence (of s-wave resonances) could have the same effect. Comparisons of theory and data presented by Dyson and Mehta are shown in Table 5.5. There are clear

TABLE 5.5

'Staircase' and other statistics from theory and data

Nucleus		^{238}U	^{232}Th	^{181}Ta
Levels		57 (0–1 keV)	154 (1–4 keV)	68 (0–344 eV)
Data references		Garg *et al.* (1964*a*) Firk *et al.* (1963*a*)	Garg *et al.* (1964*a*)	Desjardins *et al.* (1960)
Statistic				
Δ''	obs.	1·778	3·265	3·411
	th.	0·84±0·58	1·04±0·72	1·53±1·24
Δ'	obs.	1·299	8·717	1·443
	th.	0·53±0·15	0·66±0·18	0·93±0·31
Δ	obs.	1·278	3·123	1·437
	th.	0·40±0·11	0·50±0·11	0·87±0·22
Q	obs.	14·62	61·17	74·1
	th.	18·2±3·9	52·4±6·4	51·4±8·6

discrepancies even though the data used are some of the best available. At the present time it would seem to be a more expedient policy to assume that the theory is correct and to use the statistics derived therefrom to test the quality of data. Only after extremely careful measurements should it be necessary to doubt the theory or to search for hidden quantum numbers, if discrepancies still persist.

6. Applications of the unitary and symplectic ensembles

At this point it is still not apparent why the unitary and symplectic ensembles have been introduced into the discussion apart from their very fundamental role discovered by Dyson (1962*a*, *d*). There is a connexion, however, between the spacing distributions derived from these ensembles and the higher-order spacing distributions appropriate to the orthogonal ensemble. One relation, conjectured by Dyson (1962*c*) and proved by Gunson (1962), is the following; if an eigenvalue series is constructed by superimposing two independent eigenvalue series, each of order N, taken from the orthogonal ensemble, and then by picking out alternate eigenvalues from the mixed series,

TABLE 5.6

Spacing frequency and distribution functions of eigenvalues from the unitary ensemble of infinite order. Computed by Kahn (1963)

$x = \pi D/2\bar{D}$	$p(D/\bar{D})$	$F(D/\bar{D})$	$x = \pi D/2\bar{D}$	$p(D/\bar{D})$	$F(D/\bar{D})$
0·0	0	0	1·6	0·883	0·5505
0·1	0·016	0·0006	1·8	0·789	0·6584
0·2	0·052	0·0023	2·0	0·661	0·7515
0·3	0·114	0·0074	2·2	0·520	0·8269
0·4	0·197	0·0172	2·4	0·387	0·8845
0·5	0·292	0·0327	2·6	0·272	0·9262
0·6	0·397	0·0546	2·8	0·182	0·9548
0·7	0·504	0·0832	3·0	0·115	0·9735
0·8	0·608	0·1187	3·2	0·070	0·9851
0·9	0·704	0·1604	3·4	0·040	0·9918
1·0	0·791	0·2081	3·6	0·022	0·9959
1·2	0·898	0·3161	3·8	0·012	0·9980
1·4	0·943	0·4336	4·0	0·006	0·9990

then the distribution of spacings in this new series is identical to the distribution of spacings of an eigenvalue series of order N taken from the unitary ensemble. We can test this relation against the spacing distribution of next-nearest neighbour resonances in the cross-sections of odd-mass nuclei such as ^{181}Ta and ^{197}Au.

The frequency function of spacings from the Gaussian unitary ensemble has been derived explicitly by Kahn and Porter (1963) for matrices of order 2

$$p(D) = \frac{32}{\pi^2}\frac{D^2}{\bar{D}^3}\exp\left(-\frac{4D^2}{\pi\bar{D}^2}\right) \tag{5.51}$$

and of order 3. It has also been computed analytically for the unitary ensemble of infinite order by Kahn (1963). These results and the associated distribution function for $x = D/\bar{D}$,

$$F(x) = \int_0^x p(x')\mathrm{d}x', \tag{5.52}$$

are given in Table 5.6. It is compared with the distribution of next-nearest neighbour spacings in the data of ^{181}Ta and ^{197}Au (Desjardins *et al.* 1960) in Figs. 5.12 and 5.13, where good agreement is found, and with the frequency histogram for ^{75}As (Garg *et al.* 1964*b*) in Fig. 5.14.

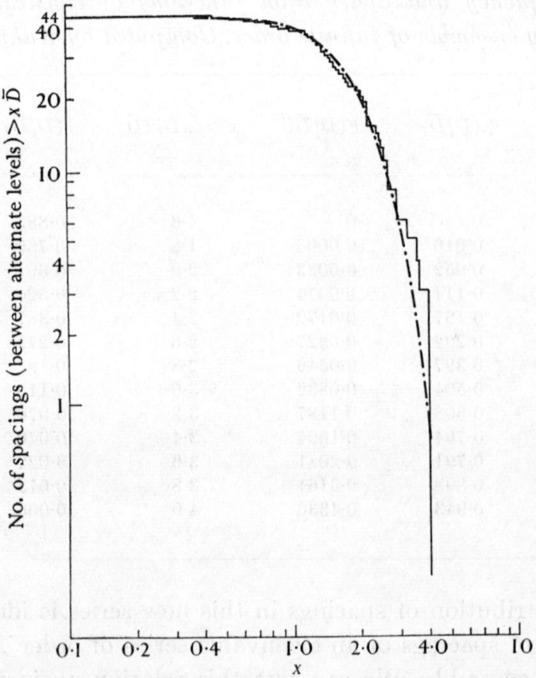

FIG. 5.12. Distribution of spacings between alternate resonances in cross-section of ^{181}Ta compared with distribution function of spacings of eigenvalues from a unitary ensemble.

The symplectic ensemble is related to the orthogonal ensemble through the following theorem due to Mehta and Dyson (1963). The probability distribution of a set of N alternate eigenvalues of a matrix in the orthogonal ensemble of order $2N$ is identical with the probability distribution of the set of all eigenvalues of a matrix in the symplectic ensemble of order N. The frequency function of spacings from the

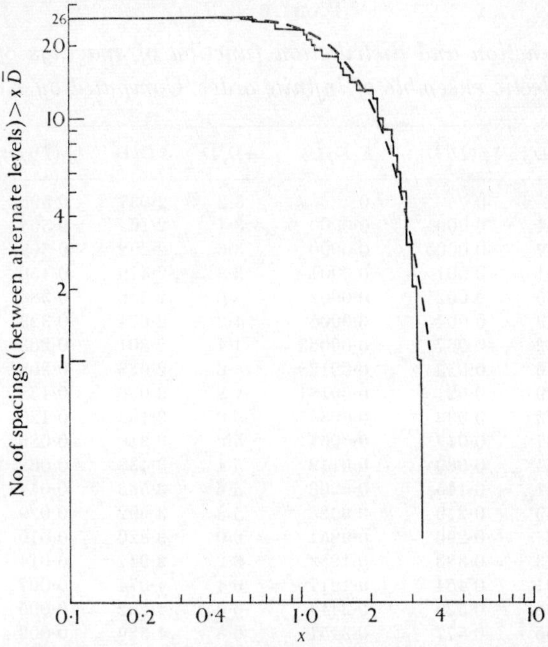

FIG. 5.13. Distribution of spacings between alternate resonances in cross-section of ^{197}Au compared with the distribution function from the unitary ensemble.

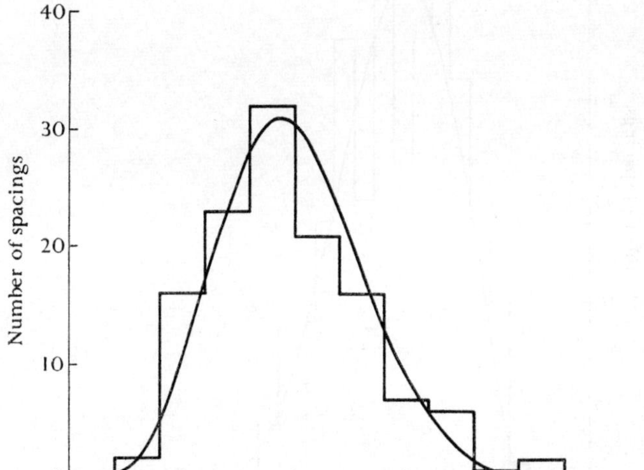

FIG. 5.14. Histogram of spacings between alternate resonances in cross-section of ^{75}As compared with frequency function of spacings of eigenvalues from the unitary ensemble (after Garg *et al.* 1964*b*).

TABLE 5.7

Frequency function and distribution function of spacings of eigenvalues from symplectic ensemble of infinite order. Computed by Kahn (1963)

$\pi D/\bar{D}$	$2D/\bar{D}$	$\frac{1}{2}p(D/\bar{D})$	$F(D/\bar{D})$	$\pi D/\bar{D}$	$2D/\bar{D}$	$\frac{1}{2}p(D/\bar{D})$	$F(D/\bar{D})$
0	0	0	0	3·2	2·037	0·596	0·5457
0·1	0·064	0·000	0·0000	3·4	2·164	0·564	0·6198
0·2	0·127	0·0000	0·0000	3·6	2·292	0·509	0·6882
0·3	0·191	0·001	0·0001	3·8	2·419	0·450	0·7499
0·4	0·255	0·002	0·0002	4·0	2·546	0·386	0·8038
0·5	0·318	0·004	0·0005	4·2	2·674	0·323	0·8490
0·6	0·382	0·007	0·00063	4·4	2·801	0·263	0·8864
0·7	0·446	0·013	0·00128	4·6	2·928	0·208	0·9164
0·8	0·509	0·021	0·00181	4·8	3·056	0·158	0·9398
0·9	0·573	0·033	0·00367	5·0	3·183	0·120	0·9577
1·0	0·637	0·047	0·00641	5·2	3·310	0·086	0·9710
1·2	0·764	0·089	0·0149	5·4	3·438	0·062	0·9803
1·4	0·891	0·145	0·0296	5·6	3·565	0·044	0·9870
1·6	1·019	0·216	0·0525	5·8	3·692	0·029	0·9915
1·8	1·46	0·296	0·0851	6·0	3·820	0·019	0·9946
2·0	1·273	0·383	0·1283	6·2	3·947	0·014	0·9967
2·2	1·401	0·454	0·1817	6·4	4·074	0·007	0·9979
2·4	1·528	0·529	0·2444	6·6	4·202	0·005	0·9988
2·6	1·655	0·577	0·3151	6·8	4·329	0·003	0·9994
2·8	1·782	0·605	0·3907	7·0	4·456	0·002	0·9996
3·0	1·910	0·613	0·4685				

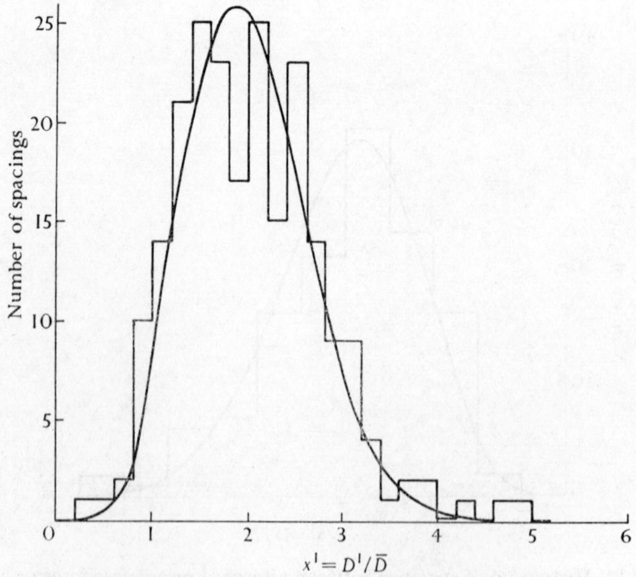

FIG. 5.15. Histogram of spacings between alternate resonances in cross-section of ^{232}Th compared with frequency function of spacings of eigenvalues associated with the symplectic ensemble (after Garg *et al.* 1964*a*).

symplectic ensemble has been computed by Kahn (1963) and is given in Table 5.7 together with its distribution function. A frequency histogram of the spacings of alternate resonances in the cross-section of ^{232}Th (Garg *et al.* 1964*a*) is shown in Fig. 5.15; yet again there is remarkable agreement with the theory.

VI

NEUTRON ELASTIC SCATTERING

A. FORMAL ASPECTS

1. Sum rules

ALTHOUGH elastic scattering is the only particle reaction that may occur in the single-particle model, it is only one of many in that of the compound nucleus. This was the reason for the introduction of the channel concept into nuclear reaction theory as described in Chapter II. For each channel c and level λ there appears ultimately in the expressions for the cross-sections a partial width $\Gamma_{\lambda(c)}$ composed of a penetration factor due to any potential energy in the channel (such as centrifugal or Coulomb barriers; see eqns. (2.9) and 2.10)) and a reduced width $\gamma^2_{\lambda(c)}$ related to the nuclear eigenfunction value projected at the channel boundary (eqn. 2.20a).

A connexion between the reduced width amplitudes $\gamma_{\lambda(c)}$ and single-particle wave-functions can be made. The basic functions X_λ of Chapter II Section C.3 may be expanded in terms of a complete set of states χ_{cp} of the form

$$\chi_{\mathrm{cp}} = \varphi_{\mathrm{c}} u_{\mathrm{p}}(r_{\mathrm{c}}) \tag{6.1}$$

where the $u_{\mathrm{p}}(r_{\mathrm{c}})$ are the radial wave-functions of a set of single-particle states defined for the particles of the channel in some real potential field, and the φ_{c} are channel-surface functions of the kind defined in eqn. (2.17). The $u_{\mathrm{p}}(r_{\mathrm{c}})$ must have the same boundary condition as the basic functions X_λ in the channel c. The expansion is

$$X_\lambda = \sum_{\mathrm{cp}} C^\lambda_{\mathrm{cp}} \chi_{\mathrm{cp}}. \tag{6.2}$$

This needs a little more definition. If it is to be taken as a fractional parentage type of expansion (Lane and Wilkinson 1955) then φ_{c} will be antisymmetrized among its identical particles, while the argument of u_{p} will refer to one labelled particle. If the particle in the channel is a nucleon, of which there are N of similar type in the total system, then the channel may be subdivided into N parts in each of which the nucleon is labelled. Application of the expansion to the reduced width amplitude (eqn. 2.20a) yields an expression for the reduced width amplitude for one such subdivision. Multiplication by N to give the reduced width amplitude irrespective of particle labelling yields

$$\gamma_{\lambda(c)} = N^{\frac{1}{2}}\left(\frac{\hbar^2}{2M_c a_c}\right)^{\frac{1}{2}} \sum_p C^{\lambda}_{cp} u_p(a_c). \tag{6.3}$$

Now, because of the incomplete anti-symmetrization of the χ_{cp}, the fractional parentage coefficients do not fulfil the relationship

$$\sum_{\lambda} C^{\lambda *}_{cp} C^{\lambda}_{c'p'} = \delta_{cp,c'p'}. \tag{6.4}$$

On the other hand the relation

$$\sum_{cp} C^{\lambda *}_{cp} C^{\lambda'}_{cp} = \delta_{\lambda\lambda'} \tag{6.5}$$

is valid. This allows us to write

$$\sum_c \gamma^2_{\lambda(c)} = N \sum_{cp} C^{\lambda^2}_{cp}\left(\frac{\hbar^2}{2M_c a_c}\right) u^2_p(a_c). \tag{6.6}$$

We may take for the values of $\hbar^2 u^2_p(a_c)/(2M_c a_c)$ the values already noted for a square potential well of radius a_c and boundary condition $B_c = -l_c$ (eqn. 3.10). This gives an approximate sum rule, first noted by Teichmann and Wigner (1952),

$$\sum_c \gamma^2_{\lambda(c)} = N\overline{\left(\frac{\hbar^2}{M_c a^2_c}\right)}. \tag{6.7}$$

An alternative approach is to use a set of χ_{cp} that is completely anti-symmetrized. Although the expansion

$$\chi_{cp} = \sum_{\lambda} C^{\lambda *}_{cp} X_{\lambda} \tag{6.8}$$

is now valid, the expansion of eqn. (6.2) is not (Lane and Thomas 1958). This is because the χ_{cp} are not orthonormal (since the single-particle state labelled by p may also occur in the description of φ_c). At this point we must appeal to the shell model. Our knowledge of nuclear structure implied by the shell model tells us that the highly excited single-particle states involved in nuclear scattering are present to only a very small degree in the low-lying states of residual nuclei. This fact leads to approximate orthonormality of the χ_{cp} and approximate validity of the expansion (6.2) in terms of these anti-symmetrized functions. Both of the relations (6.4) and (6.5) for the expansion coefficients are approximately valid. The reduced-width amplitude derived from the new expansion is

$$\gamma_{\lambda(c)} = \left(\frac{\hbar^2}{2M_c a_c}\right)^{\frac{1}{2}} \sum_p C^{\lambda}_{cp} u_p(a_c). \tag{6.9}$$

The reduced width is

$$\gamma^2_{\lambda(c)} = \frac{\hbar^2}{2M_c a_c} \cdot \left\{\sum_p C^{\lambda}_{cp} u_p(a_c)\right\}^2. \tag{6.10}$$

Because of eqn. (6.5) it is apparent that an approximate upper limit to the reduced width is $\hbar^2/(M_c a_c{}^2)$ (using eqn. (3.10)). This is the Wigner limit (also derived by Teichmann and Wigner 1952): it is related to the sum rule of eqn. (6.7). If the sum in eqn. (6.7) is limited to the low-lying states of the residual nuclei then the factor of N in the sum rule must be dropped.

A closer estimate of the order of magnitude of the reduced widths may be obtained from eqn. (6.10) by using eqn. (6.4). It is assumed that the $C^{\lambda 2}_{cp}$ are evenly distributed over an energy range W. The average value of one of the coefficients $C^{\lambda 2}_{cp}$ will be $\bar{D}/W$ where $\bar{D}$ is the average spacing of the level λ in the range W. If it is further assumed that W is approximately the difference in energy between two single-particle states, then $W \approx p\hbar^2\pi^2/(M_c a_c^2)$, according to eqn. (3.6), for s-wave states of a square well. The resulting average value of the reduced width is

$$\overline{\gamma^2_{\lambda(c)}} \approx \frac{\hbar^2}{M_c a_c^2} \cdot \frac{\bar{D}}{W} = \frac{\bar{D}}{p\pi^2} = \frac{\bar{D}}{\pi K a_c} \tag{6.11}$$

where K is the wave number of the single-particle state. If W is greater than the single-particle difference then more than one single-particle state will contribute coefficients of appreciable size to the sum in eqn. (6.10), and eqn. (6.11) will still hold roughly. The ratio of average reduced width to level spacing is known as the strength function and is of central importance in neutron reaction theory. The above estimate of its value (due to Teichmann and Wigner 1952) is probably valid when the single-particle states are mixed very thoroughly into the resonance states X_λ; if the mixing is appreciable over a range equivalent to the single-particle spacing, or more, the physical situation is described as strong coupling. The subject of the neutron strength function (by which is usually implied the strength function for the neutron channel in which the residual nucleus is in its ground state) is treated in much more detail in the following sections.

2. Average cross-sections and strength functions

(a) *R-matrix expressions*

Because the strength function is a statistical property of the internal nuclear eigenfunctions one would expect to find it related to average cross-sections, and this is shown to be so in this section.

For the relatively low neutron bombarding energies, which are the subject of this book, and most of the non-fissile target nuclei (the exceptions are possibly a few of the light nuclei like ^{6}Li and ^{10}B) the elastic scattering and total cross-sections may be calculated by the reduced R-matrix method of Chapter II, Section E.2. All of the reaction channels, being narrow radiative capture channels, may be eliminated in order to derive the diagonal neutron element of the collision matrix. This element is often called the collision function and the modified, retained element of the R-matrix is correspondingly called the R-function. Equation (2.47) now reduces to a simple algebraic relation between the collision function and the R-function. For s-wave neutrons it may be simplified even further, for the boundary condition may be adjusted to make the shift factor, $\hat{S}_n$, zero:

$$U_{nn} = e^{-2i\rho} \cdot \frac{1+i\rho R_{nn}}{1-i\rho R_{nn}} \tag{6.12}$$

It is worth noting (Thomas 1955) that the R-function is simply related to the logarithmic derivative, of the entrance-channel wave-function at the nuclear surface, that was introduced by Feshbach *et al.* (1947):

$$f_n(J) = R_{nn}^{-1}(J)+B_n. \tag{6.13}$$

Formulae for average neutron cross-sections may be obtained directly from the reduced R-matrix theory (Thomas 1955). The average total cross-section is obviously related to the average collision function (by averaging eqn. (2.43)):

$$\bar{\sigma}_T = 2\pi\lambda\!\!\!^{-2}\sum_{l}\sum_{s=|I-\frac{1}{2}|}^{I+\frac{1}{2}}\sum_{J=|l-s|}^{l+s} g_J(1-\mathrm{Re}\,\bar{U}_{nn}(J)). \tag{6.14}$$

It may be shown that the poles of the collision function are in the negative half of the complex energy plane. A closed contour integration of the collision function confined to the real axis and the positive half of the complex energy plane is therefore zero. Hence, it is possible (by the theory of contour integration) to replace an integration of U along the real energy axis by an integration along the complex energy $E+\mathrm{i}I$ (I positive and constant), if it is assumed (plausibly) that the two vertical components of the rectangular contour cancel. If I is large compared to the mean level spacing but small compared to intervals over which gross changes of the level properties occur, the R-function, and hence the U-function, are constant with respect to E along the contour $E+\mathrm{i}I$. Hence, it is possible to write for the average of the collision function over many levels

$$\bar{U}_{\mathrm{nn}}(E) = U_{\mathrm{nn}}(E+\mathrm{i}I) = \mathrm{e}^{-2\mathrm{i}\phi_{\mathrm{n}}} \cdot \frac{1-\hat{L}_{\mathrm{n}}^{*}R(E+\mathrm{i}I)}{1-\hat{L}_{\mathrm{n}}R(E+\mathrm{i}I)} \tag{6.15a}$$

$$R(E+\mathrm{i}I) = \sum_{\lambda} \frac{\gamma_{\lambda(\mathrm{n})}^{2}}{E_{\lambda}-E-\mathrm{i}(\Gamma_{\lambda}^{\mathrm{e}}/2+I)} \tag{6.15b}$$

$$= R^{\mathrm{Re}}(E)+\mathrm{i}\pi s(E). \tag{6.15c}$$

Of the two functions introduced here $R^{\mathrm{Re}}(E)$ is the overall effect of very distant levels and is usually denoted by R^{∞}:

$$R^{\infty} = R^{\mathrm{Re}}(E) = \int \mathrm{d}E_{\lambda}\rho(E_{\lambda})\gamma_{(\mathrm{n})}^{2}(E_{\lambda})\frac{(E_{\lambda}-E)}{(E_{\lambda}^{2}-E)^{2}+(\Gamma_{\lambda}^{\mathrm{e}}/2+I)^{2}} \tag{6.16}$$

where $\gamma_{(\mathrm{n})}^{2}(E_{\lambda})$ expresses the behaviour of the average reduced neutron width as a function of the level energy. The other function $s(E)$ derives from the local levels (over an energy interval of the order of I):

$$s(E) = \frac{1}{\pi}\int \mathrm{d}E_{\lambda}\gamma_{(\mathrm{n})}^{2}(E_{\lambda})\frac{\rho(E_{\lambda})(\Gamma_{\lambda}^{\mathrm{e}}/2+I)}{(E_{\lambda}-E)^{2}+(\Gamma_{\lambda}^{\mathrm{e}}/2+I)^{2}} = \frac{\overline{\gamma_{(\mathrm{n})}^{2}(E)}}{\bar{D}(E)}. \tag{6.17}$$

It is a measure of the strength of the poles of the R-function: this is the origin of the term 'strength function'.

With the use of eqn. (6.15c) for R the average collision function can be written in the form

$$\bar{U}_{\mathrm{nn}}(E) = \sqrt{\left\{\frac{(1-\pi Ps)^{2}+P^{2}R^{\infty 2}}{(1+\pi Ps)^{2}+P^{2}R^{\infty 2}}\right\}} \times \\ \times \exp\left[\mathrm{i}\left\{\mathrm{atan}\left(\frac{PR^{\infty}}{1-\pi Ps}\right)+\mathrm{atan}\left(\frac{PR^{\infty}}{1+\pi Ps}\right)-2\phi_{\mathrm{n}}\right\}\right]. \tag{6.18}$$

At this stage it is worth recalling that, in order to have physical content in the definitions of the strength function and distant level parameter, the eigenlevels are to be defined with open channel radii close to the nuclear force radius and with boundary conditions that allow the eigenlevels to coincide with the resonance energies. At low neutron energies (for practical purposes, energies less than a few keV) a good approximation to the s-wave component of the average total cross-section is (Lane and Lynn 1957a)

$$\bar{\sigma}_{\mathrm{T}}(l=0) = 4\pi^2\lambda\!\!\!^{-2}\rho s + 4\pi a^2\{(1-R^\infty)^2 - \pi^2 s^2\}. \tag{6.19}$$

The first term on the right-hand side is just the mean value, over many resonances, of the average of the resonance term of the single-level cross-section formula (eqns. 2.66 and 2.65). The term $4\pi a^2(1-R^\infty)^2$ is the potential scattering cross-section term occurring in the same formula. The remaining term of eqn. (6.19), $-4\pi a^2 . \pi^2 s^2$, has been shown to be the result of many-level interference (Lynn 1963a). In the detailed cross-section formula for a system of uniformly spaced levels with uniform reduced widths, the many-level interference term is almost independent of energy. In this sense it can be taken as part of the potential scattering cross-section.

(b) S-matrix expressions

The diagonal S-matrix element has the form (see eqn. 2.112)

$$S_{\mathrm{nn}} = U_{\mathrm{nn}} - \delta_{\mathrm{nn}}$$

$$= \mathscr{P}_{\mathrm{n}}^2\left\{Q_{\mathrm{nn}} - \mathrm{i}\sum_m \frac{G^2_{m(\mathrm{n})}\exp(2\mathrm{i}\xi_{m(\mathrm{n})})}{E-E_m+\frac{1}{2}\mathrm{i}\Gamma_m} \cdot \frac{1}{|\mathscr{P}^2_{m\mathrm{n}}|}\right\} \tag{6.20}$$

From this the average collision function is found to be

$$\bar{U}_{\mathrm{nn}} = \delta_{\mathrm{nn}} + \mathscr{P}^2_{\mathrm{n}} Q_{\mathrm{nn}} - \frac{\overline{\pi G^2_{m(\mathrm{n})}\cos 2\xi_{m(\mathrm{n})}}}{\bar{D}} - \frac{\overline{\mathrm{i}\pi G^2_{m(\mathrm{n})}\sin 2\xi_{m(\mathrm{n})}}}{\bar{D}}. \tag{6.21}$$

As in Section H.2 of Chapter II the application of unitarity to the background function together with the assumption that it is diagonal reveals that the term $\delta_{\mathrm{nn}} + \mathscr{P}^2_{\mathrm{n}} Q_{\mathrm{nn}}$ has modulus unity. If its phase angle is ϕ, say, then $\bar{U}_{\mathrm{nn}}$ can be rewritten

$$\bar{U}_{\mathrm{nn}} = e^{\mathrm{i}(\phi+\phi')}\sqrt{\left\{1 - \frac{2\pi\overline{G^2_{m(\mathrm{n})}\cos 2\xi_{m(\mathrm{n})}}\cos\phi}{\bar{D}} - \frac{2\pi\overline{G^2_{m(\mathrm{n})}\sin 2\xi_{m(\mathrm{n})}}\sin\phi}{\bar{D}} + \right.}$$

$$\left. + \frac{\pi^2\left(\overline{G^2_{m(\mathrm{n})}\cos 2\xi_{m(\mathrm{n})}}\right)^2}{\bar{D}^2} + \frac{\pi^2\left(\overline{G^2_{m(\mathrm{n})}\sin 2\xi_{m(\mathrm{n})}}\right)^2}{\bar{D}^2}\right\} \tag{6.22}$$

where ϕ' is the phase angle due to the remaining part of $\bar{U}_{nn}$. Now if interference amongst the resonance terms of the S-matrix can be ignored it can be shown by imposition of the unitarity condition that $2\xi_{m(n)} = \phi$ and the collision function reduces to

$$\bar{U}_{nn} \approx e^{i(\phi+\phi')} \sqrt{\left(1 - \frac{2\pi \overline{G^2_{m(n)}}}{\bar{D}} + \frac{\pi^2 \overline{G^2_{m(n)}}^2}{\bar{D}^2}\right)}$$

$$= e^{i(\phi+\phi')}\left(1 - \frac{\pi \overline{G^2_{m(n)}}}{\bar{D}}\right) \tag{6.23}$$

Neglect of resonance interference can be justified, however, only when $\Gamma \ll D$, and this condition is therefore essential for the validity of eqn. (6.23). If resonance interference becomes dominant then the unitarity correlation expressed in eqn. (2.136) suggests that the term $\overline{G^2_{m(n)} \sin 2\xi_{m(n)}}$ in eqn. (6.22) is negligible. It then becomes clear that eqn. (6.23) expresses a lower limit for $|\bar{U}_{nn}|$, i.e.

$$\frac{\pi \overline{G^2_{m(n)}}}{\bar{D}} > 1 - |\bar{U}_{nn}|. \tag{6.24}$$

The right-hand side of inequality (6.24) gives a lower limit for the strength function as it may be defined in the S-matrix theory.

(c) *Physical interpretation of the average collision function*

Some other functions of the average collision function have been introduced to aid the qualitative discussion of theoretical models of neutron scattering (Feshbach *et al.* 1954). The function

$$\sigma_{(se)} = (2l+1)\pi\lambda^2 |1 - \bar{U}_{nn}|^2 \tag{6.25}$$

is known as the shape elastic scattering cross-section for the partial wave of angular momentum l; the function

$$\sigma_{(ce)} = (2l+1)\pi\lambda^2 (\overline{|U_{nn}|^2} - |\bar{U}_{nn}|^2) \tag{6.26}$$

is called the *compound elastic scattering cross-section*. In statistical terminology the cross-section $\sigma_{(ce)}$ has simply the form of a variance, i.e. the mean square dispersion of the function $(2l+1)^{\frac{1}{2}}\pi^{\frac{1}{2}}\lambda|1 - U_{nn}|$ about its average value. Physically, this appears to correspond to a measure of the fluctuations of the collision function due to resonances, so $\sigma_{(ce)}$ is identified as the average elastic scattering cross-section due to the resonances and $\sigma_{(se)}$ is identified as the potential scattering cross-section. The sum of the shape and compound elastic scattering cross-sections is the average elastic scattering cross-section

$$\bar{\sigma}_{\text{n}} = (2l+1)\pi\lambda\!\!\!^{-2}\overline{|1-U_{\text{nn}}|^2}. \tag{6.27}$$

The average reaction cross-section is

$$\bar{\sigma}_{\text{r}} = (2l+1)\pi\lambda\!\!\!^{-2}(1-\overline{|U_{\text{nn}}|^2}). \tag{6.28}$$

The sum of $\bar{\sigma}_{\text{r}}$ and $\sigma_{(\text{ce})}$ is written simply in terms of the average collision function

$$\sigma_{(\text{c})} = \sigma_{(\text{ce})}+\bar{\sigma}_{\text{r}} = (2l+1)\pi\lambda\!\!\!^{-2}(1-|\bar{U}_{\text{nn}}|^2). \tag{6.29}$$

In view of the interpretation of $\sigma_{(\text{ce})}$ as the average resonance elastic scattering cross-section it is clear that $\sigma_{(\text{c})}$ is to be interpreted as the average cross-section over resonances alone, i.e. the compound nucleus formation cross-section. This interpretation of $\sigma_{(\text{c})}$ is valid to first order with respect to quantities of the kind P, Ps, and PR^{∞}; this is revealed by an expansion of eqn. (6.29) in terms of these quantities to second order. At low neutron energies, therefore, the average compound nucleus formation cross-section is

$$\sigma_{(\text{c})} = 4\pi^2\lambda\!\!\!^{-2}\rho s. \tag{6.30}$$

This should be compared with eqn. (4.3) for the strength of an individual resonance; it is clearly the average over many resonances of that expression. So long as the quantity $\pi\rho s$ is very small the shape elastic scattering cross-section for s-waves $\sigma_{(\text{se})}$ may be shown to be approximately equal to the potential scattering cross-section (Feshbach *et al.* 1954)

$$\sigma_{(\text{se})} = 4\pi a^2(1-R^{\infty})^2. \tag{6.31}$$

These interpretations of eqns. (6.25) and (6.29) have been used considerably in the literature for calculating the potential scattering cross-section and the strength function from the average collision functions of phenomenological models. The subsequent discussion of this chapter is based on eqns. (6.15) to (6.18) but the above interpretations have nevertheless been presented for their illustrative value.

B. THE STATISTICAL DISTRIBUTION OF REDUCED NEUTRON WIDTHS

1. Theoretical form of the distribution function

The earliest systematic measurements of neutron resonance strengths (eqn. 4.3) showed that neutron widths fluctuate strongly amongst resonances with the same total angular momentum and parity. The fluctuations must be attributed to the reduced width factor in the neutron width expression because the penetration factor varies smoothly with energy.

Qualitative ideas about the nature of the fluctuations of the reduced widths may be gained from eqn. (6.9) for the reduced width amplitude (Teichmann and Wigner 1952). The expansion coefficients, $C^{\lambda}_{\mathrm{cp}}$, which occur in that formula are small (much less than unity) for any nuclear reaction picture which is in the spirit of the compound nucleus theory. It would also be expected that they are random in sign for different levels λ. A possible assumption about their statistical distribution is that their real and imaginary parts have zero means in Gaussian distributions with equal variance. The reduced widths would then have an exponential frequency function (Scott 1954)

$$p(\gamma^2_{(\mathrm{n})})\mathrm{d}\gamma^2_{(\mathrm{n})} = (1/\overline{\gamma^2_{(\mathrm{n})}})\exp(-\gamma^2_{(\mathrm{n})}/\overline{\gamma^2_{(\mathrm{n})}})\mathrm{d}\gamma^2_{(\mathrm{n})}. \tag{6.32}$$

The expansion coefficients should be assumed to be real, however, for it has been shown that the reduced width amplitudes are real (Wigner and Eisenbud 1947). The Gaussian assumption for the distribution of the real $C^{\lambda}_{\mathrm{cp}}$, and hence for the reduced width amplitudes, leads to the following frequency function for the reduced widths (Brink 1955):

$$p(\gamma_{(\mathrm{n})})\mathrm{d}\gamma_{(\mathrm{n})} = \frac{1}{\sqrt{(2\pi\overline{\gamma^2_{(\mathrm{n})}})}}\exp\left(-\frac{\gamma^2_{(\mathrm{n})}}{2\overline{\gamma^2_{(\mathrm{n})}}}\right)\mathrm{d}\gamma_{(\mathrm{n})}; \tag{6.33a}$$

$$\therefore \quad p(\gamma^2_{(\mathrm{n})})\mathrm{d}\gamma^2_{(\mathrm{n})} = \frac{1}{\sqrt{(2\gamma^2_{(\mathrm{n})}\pi\overline{\gamma^2_{(\mathrm{n})}})}}\exp\left(-\frac{\gamma^2_{(\mathrm{n})}}{2\overline{\gamma^2_{(\mathrm{n})}}}\right)\mathrm{d}\gamma^2_{(\mathrm{n})}. \tag{6.33b}$$

It is interesting to note that an extreme strong-coupling model (see below) will give a Gaussian distribution for the reduced width amplitudes on the assumptions only of random sign and statistical independence of the expansion coefficients; if there are many equally significant terms in the sum over single-particle states p in eqn. (6.9), the Gaussian result follows from the central limit theorem of statistics.

Another argument for the plausibility of eqns. (6.33) is based on the overlap integral (eqn. (2.20a)) for the reduced width amplitude (Porter and Thomas 1956). The integral can be approximated by the sum over many cells of configuration space. The linear dimension of a cell should be taken to be of the order of π times a nucleon wavelength (π/K). If the linear dimension is much less than this, the values of the integrand within neighbouring cells will be approximately equal and the concept of statistical independence of the quantities in the cells cannot be applied. With this criterion for the dimension, the number of cells is very large, of the order of $(KR/\pi)^{3A}$. The compound nucleus theory would suggest that significant contributions to the integral will come from a considerable fraction of these cells. It is certainly to be expected that positive and negative values for the integrand will be equally likely. The Gaussian distribution, with zero mean, again follows for the integral by applying the central limit theorem.

The subject has been pursued through the study of random matrices and their eigenvectors. Suppose that a suitable basis is chosen for the matrix representation of dynamical variables; the eigenvectors of the basis are denoted by φ. In this representation an eigenfunction ψ that is a solution of the Schrödinger equation for the system with Hamiltonian H may be written

$$\psi_\lambda = \sum_\mu c_{\lambda\mu}\varphi_\mu \tag{6.34}$$

and the matrix representation of the Hamiltonian has the form

$$H_{\nu\mu} = \int \mathrm{d}\tau\varphi_\nu^* H\varphi_\mu. \tag{6.35}$$

In this matrix representation the Schrödinger equation is

$$\mathbf{Hc}_\lambda = E_\lambda \mathbf{c}_\lambda. \tag{6.36}$$

This general scheme can be applied immediately to the expansion of wave-functions X_λ of the resonance states in terms of the product functions χ_{cp} of the channel functions φ_c and the single-particle states u_p (eqn. 6.2). The same statistical assumptions about the elements of $\mathbf{H}$ that are used for studying the eigenvalue spacing distribution (Chapter V) may be used here to study the statistical distribution of a particular element (for channel n, say), of the eigenvector column matrix $\mathbf{c}_\lambda$, (for a level λ', say). If the elements of $\mathbf{H}$ are randomly and independently chosen from a normal distribution (eqn. 5.17) it can be shown (Porter and Rosenzweig 1960) that the frequency function of this eigenvector component over all the ensembles of N levels has the form

$$p_N(c_{\lambda'})\mathrm{d}c_{\lambda'} = \frac{\Gamma(N/2)}{\sqrt{\pi}\,.\,\Gamma\{(N-1)/2\}}(1-c_{\lambda'}^2)^{(N-3)/2}\mathrm{d}c_{\lambda'}, \tag{6.37a}$$

where N is the order of the Hamiltonian matrix.

The mean value of $c_{\lambda'}$ is zero and the variance is

$$\overline{c_{\lambda'}^2} = 1/N. \tag{6.37b}$$

For large N eqn. (6.37a) tends to the limiting form

$$p_N(c_{\lambda'})\mathrm{d}c_{\lambda'} \xrightarrow[N\to\infty]{} \{2\pi(1/N)\}^{-\frac{1}{2}}\exp(-c_{\lambda'}^2 N/2)\mathrm{d}c_{\lambda'}. \tag{6.37c}$$

This is sufficient to establish the zero mean Gaussian law for the reduced width amplitude given by eqn. (6.9) whether there are one, few or many significant terms in the sum; the only requirement is that there should be available a large number of channels with significant and uncorrelated reduced widths.

The statistical model from which eqns. (6.37) follow is appropriate to the R-matrix formalism, as described in Section A of Chapter V, and is not necessarily applicable to the partial widths of S-matrix theory. For non-fissile nuclei and low neutron energies the difference between the two sets of parameters is rather academic, because the resonances are so narrow, and the penetration factors of R-matrix theory have the same energy dependence as the threshold factors of S-matrix theory.

2. Analysis of the experimental data

The simplest way of testing a theoretical frequency function against the experimental data is the visual one of plotting a histogram of the

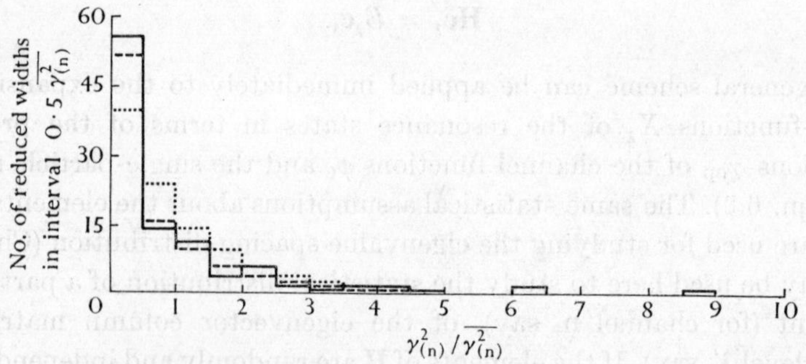

FIG. 6.1. Histogram of reduced neutron widths of cross-section of ^{238}U (full line) compared with those expected from the Porter–Thomas distribution (dashed line) and the exponential distribution (dotted line).

data and comparing it with either the proposed frequency function or, better, a histogram calculated from it. This was the method first used by Harvey *et al.* (1955) and Hughes and Harvey (1955) in studying about 150 reduced neutron widths from the cross-sections of 15 nuclei.

A histogram of much more recent data on 100 widths from the cross section of ^{238}U (Firk *et al.* 1963) is shown in Fig. 6.1 in comparison with histograms calculated from the Porter–Thomas distribution (eqn. (6.33b)) and the exponential distribution (eqn. (6.32)). It is obvious that the former distribution is in much better agreement with the data. Garrison (1964) has combined the best available data on the reduced neutron widths of the cross-sections of even-target nuclei (144 widths) and drawn their histogram on logarithmic scales (Fig.

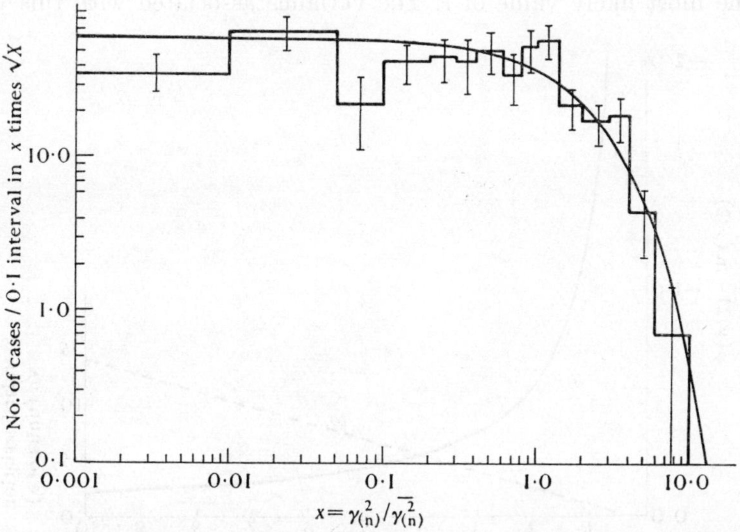

FIG. 6.2. Histogram of reduced neutron widths compiled from cross-section data on even-target nuclei (after Garrison 1964).

6.2). It is again obvious that the Porter–Thomas distribution is a good representation of the data.

Convincing as Figs. 6.1 and 6.2 are, it is desirable to have a quantitative test of the theory. Several different tests could be devised but only one method has had much application. This is the maximum likelihood method (see e.g. Kendall 1946), and the details of its application to the reduced neutron width distribution were worked out by Porter and Thomas (1956). It is first remarked that the Porter–Thomas frequency function and the exponential frequency function are special cases (with $\nu = 1$ and $\nu = 2$ respectively) of the 'chi-squared' frequency function with ν degrees of freedom,

$$p_\nu(x)\mathrm{d}x = \Gamma(\nu/2)^{-1}(\nu/2\bar{x})^{\nu/2}x^{(\nu-2)/2}\mathrm{e}^{-\nu x/2\bar{x}}\mathrm{d}x. \tag{6.38}$$

The aim of the analysis is to establish the value of ν that gives the best fit of this function to the data, together with some estimate of the error. The likelihood function $L(\nu)$ is defined as the product of the frequencies of each datum x_i calculated by substitution of x_i in the frequency function $p_\nu(x)$:

$$L(\nu) = \prod_i p_\nu(x_i). \tag{6.39}$$

The value of ν that maximizes $L(\nu)$ (or, equivalently, its logarithm) is the most likely value of ν. The variance associated with this value

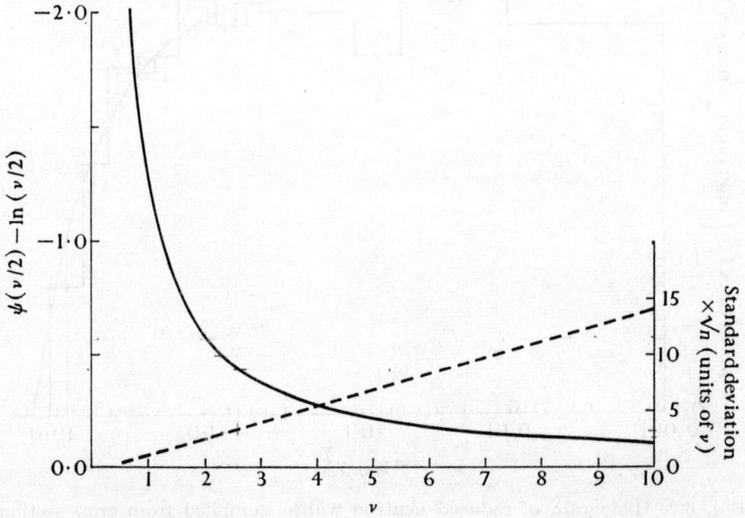

Fig. 6.3. The maximum likelihood function, $\psi(\nu/2)-\ln(\nu/2)$, for chi-squared distribution functions, and the standard deviation of the estimated value of ν.

is the negative inverse of the second derivative of $\ln L(\nu)$. For the chi-squared family the most likely value of ν is given by

$$\frac{1}{n}\sum_{i=1}^{n} \ln x_i - \ln\bar{x} = \psi(\nu/2) - \ln(\nu/2), \tag{6.40}$$

where $\psi(y)$ is the logarithmic derivative of the gamma function $\Gamma(y)$. The transcendental function forming the right-hand side of eqn. (6.40) is shown in Fig. 6.3 with the standard deviation on the estimate of ν. The evaluation of the left-hand side of eqn. (6.40) from the data at once leads to the best value of ν and its standard deviation by use of Fig. 6.3.

It is very straightforward to apply this method to accurate data which are selected without bias from a distribution of which the mean value is known. These criteria do not always apply to neutron width data. There are experimental errors, often quite large, associated with the measurement of the widths. Instrumental resolution and finite counting times usually set a bias against the selection of very weak resonances. The mean value of the reduced neutron width of a particular cross-section is not known *a priori* but must be calculated from the data themselves with consequent statistical uncertainty. The main effect of the first and last of these data imperfections is to increase the variance associated with the determination of ν. The instrumental bias, however, will cause a bias in the determination of ν unless it is taken into account. The method of doing this is to use a modification of the frequency function, eqn. (6.38), which incorporates the instrumental effect into the distribution. The simplest modification of this kind is to set $p_\nu(x) = 0$ for values of x less than a measurable lower limit and to use eqn. (6.38) with an adjusted normalization constant for values of x above this limit. More sophisticated measures can be devised if required.

The result of Porter and Thomas' analysis, which used the data of 148 reduced neutron widths from the cross-sections of 15 nuclei, was $\nu = 1{\cdot}02 \pm 0{\cdot}13$. This result implies that the Porter–Thomas frequency function ($\nu = 1$) is a perfectly acceptable representation of the data while the exponential distribution ($\nu = 2$) is not. Later analyses of more recent data of better quality have usually concentrated on data from the cross-section of a single nucleus. Thus, the maximum likelihood analysis of 100 neutron widths from the cross-section of ^{238}U gave $\nu = 1{\cdot}02 \pm 0{\cdot}12$ (Firk *et al.* 1963). Instrumental bias was believed to be small enough to be ignored in this work. All the neutron-width data available up to about 1963 have been reanalysed by Garrison (1964). They are found to be perfectly consistent with a Porter–Thomas distribution. The best set of data, consisting of 416 reduced widths from the cross-sections of ^{127}I (Garg *et al.* 1965), ^{181}Ta and ^{197}Au (Desjardins *et al.* 1960) and ^{232}Th and ^{238}U (Firk *et al.* 1963, Garg *et al.* 1964) yielded $\nu = 1{\cdot}04 \pm 0{\cdot}10$. A χ^2 goodness-of-fit test was also applied to the comparison of the data with the Porter–Thomas distribution, which was found to be perfectly acceptable.

Garrison (1964) has also tested the data for possible correlations between the reduced widths of neighbouring levels or amongst the reduced widths of a sequence of levels; he found no evidence for such a correlation. The statistical matrix model also explains this result. Ullah (1966) has shown that the joint frequency function for the eigenvector components corresponding to a single channel and levels

$\lambda = 1, 2, \ldots n$ is

$$p_N\{(c_\lambda)\} = \frac{\Gamma(N/2)}{\Gamma(N/2-n/2)}(\pi N\overline{c_\lambda^2})^{-n/2}\left(1-\frac{\sum_{\lambda=1}^{n} c_\lambda^2}{N\overline{c_\lambda^2}}\right)^{\frac{1}{2}(N-n-2)}. \tag{6.41}$$

For large values of $N-n$ this tends to a simple product of independent Gaussian forms like eqn. (6.37c). This shows that correlations between the reduced widths for different levels vanish in this limit.

3. Consequences of the statistical fluctuation of neutron widths

(a) 'Errors' in strength function measurements

The statistical distribution of neutron widths must be considered in dealing with many problems concerned with the average properties of neutron cross-sections. The immediate problem of this kind is the determination of the neutron strength function from resonance parameter data. Suppose that a sequence of N resonances of the cross-section of a nucleus have been well-resolved and their neutron widths measured; the integer N may be of the order of 100 (e.g. ^{238}U) or as low as 2 or 3. The statistical frequency function $p_N(y)$ of the sum y of N reduced neutron widths is straightforwardly calculated from the independent Porter–Thomas frequency function for a single width. It is

$$p_N(y) = \Gamma(N/2)^{-1}(1/2\bar{x})^{N/2}y^{(N-2)/2}e^{-y/2\bar{x}}. \tag{6.42}$$

This is just the chi-squared function of eqn. (6.38) with N degrees of freedom and with the mean $\bar{y}$ equal to $N\bar{x}$. With increasing N, eqn. (6.42) tends (as one would expect from the central limit theorem) to a Gaussian form with mean value $N\bar{x}$ and dispersion $\sigma^2 = 2N\bar{x}^2$. The variance of the sum y calculated from eqn. (6.42) is var $y = 2N\bar{x}^2$. Thus the statistical error associated with the determination of the mean reduced neutron width from a limited sequence of levels is never negligible and is often very large. The discussion of Chapter V shows that the contribution to the strength function of the statistical error from the determination of the mean level spacing will be much smaller, in fact almost negligible. Another source of error in the strength function determination is the missing of weak resonances in the sequence; the number of levels N is then incorrectly estimated and so are the mean values of width and spacing. However these errors in the means exactly compensate on taking their ratio, provided that the reduced widths of the missed levels would add a negligible amount to the sum of the widths. Experimental errors in the determination of the individual reduced widths are usually negligible in comparison with their fundamental fluctuations.

(b) *Average partial cross-sections*

It is often required to make calculations of average neutron partial cross-sections from strength function information. The average partial cross-section $\langle\sigma_{ab}\rangle$ over a single resonance λ is

$$\langle\sigma_{ab}\rangle = 2\pi^2\lambda\!\!\!^{-2} g_J \frac{\Gamma_{\lambda(a)}}{D}\cdot\frac{\Gamma_{\lambda(b)}/D}{\Gamma_{\lambda(T)}/D} = \frac{2\pi^2\lambda\!\!\!^{-2} g_J}{D}\cdot\frac{\Gamma_{\lambda(a)}\Gamma_{\lambda(b)}}{\Gamma_{\lambda(T)}}. \tag{6.43}$$

The average cross-section over many levels is

$$\bar{\sigma}_{ab} = 2\pi^2\lambda\!\!\!^{-2} g_J \frac{1}{\bar{D}}\overline{\left(\frac{\Gamma_{(a)}\Gamma_{(b)}}{\Gamma_{(T)}}\right)}. \tag{6.44}$$

The result of averaging over $\Gamma_{(a)}\Gamma_{(b)}/\Gamma_{(T)}$ depends on the statistical distributions of the partial widths as well as on their mean values. It is usually written in the form

$$\overline{\left(\frac{\Gamma_{(a)}\Gamma_{(b)}}{\Gamma_{(T)}}\right)} = \frac{\overline{\Gamma}_{(a)}\overline{\Gamma}_{(b)}}{\overline{\Gamma}_{(T)}}\mathscr{S}, \tag{6.45}$$

the function $\mathscr{S}$ depending on the ratios of the means of the partial widths and on the nature of the frequency functions (Lane and Lynn 1957*b*); it is, of course, unity if all the partial widths are uniformly constant from level to level. In the low energy neutron spectroscopy of non-fissile nuclei only two average partial cross-sections are of general importance, the elastic scattering cross-section σ_n, for which eqn. (6.45) gives the resonance contribution, and the total radiative capture cross-section $\bar{\sigma}_{(\gamma T)}$. The total width $\Gamma_{(T)}$ is just the sum of the neutron width $\Gamma_{(n)}$ and the total radiation width $\Gamma_{(\gamma T)}$, which, for heavy nuclei, usually fluctuates very little. In the former case the $\mathscr{S}$-function (often known as the fluctuation function) is

$$\mathscr{S}_n^{(1)} = (r+1)\int\limits_0^\infty dx p(x)\frac{(x/\bar{x})^2}{r+(x/\bar{x})} = (1+r)\left\{1-r+r\left(\frac{\pi r}{2}\right)^{1/2} e^{r/2}\operatorname{erfc}\left(\sqrt{\frac{r}{2}}\right)\right\} \tag{6.46}$$

where $r = \Gamma_{(\gamma T)}/\overline{\Gamma}_{(n)}$, and is shown in Fig. 6.4. In the radiative capture case the $\mathscr{S}$-function is (Lane and Lynn 1957*b*)

$$\mathscr{S}_{\gamma}^{(1)} = (r+1)\int_0^\infty dx p(x)\frac{(x/\bar{x})}{r+(x/\bar{x})} = (1+r)\left\{1-\left(\frac{\pi r}{2}\right)^{1/2} e^{r/2}\operatorname{erfc}\left(\sqrt{\frac{r}{2}}\right)\right\} \tag{6.47}$$

(see Fig. 6.5). The partial radiative capture cross-section for a single transition is also covered by this expression when the partial radiation width is a very small fraction of the total radiation width. The departures of $\mathscr{S}_{\text{n}}$ and $\mathscr{S}_{\lambda}$ from unity can be appreciable. Notice that the average resonance scattering cross-section that is given by eqns. (6.45) and

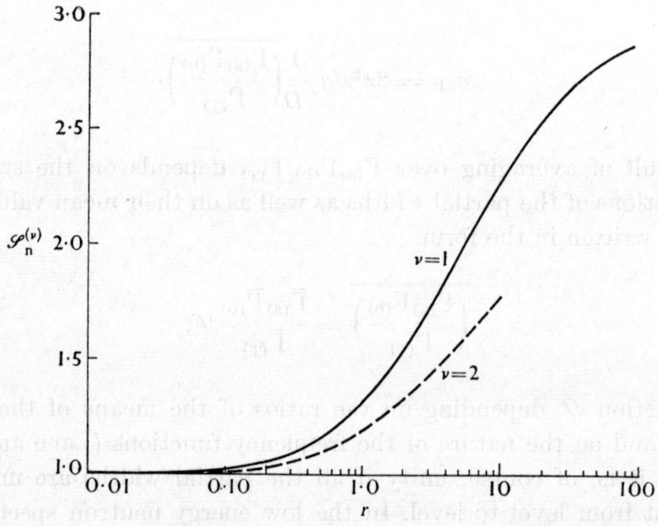

FIG. 6.4. The statistical modification factor $\mathscr{S}_{\text{n}}^{(\nu)}$ for average elastic scattering cross-sections.

(6.46) may differ from the compound elastic scattering $\sigma_{(\text{ce})} = 4\pi^2\lambda\!\!\!^{-2}\rho s.$ $(\overline{\Gamma}_{(\text{n})}/\overline{\Gamma}_{(\text{T})})$ evaluated from the single-level collision function using eqn. (6.26) (Feshbach *et al.* 1954) by a factor of 2 or more.

Sometimes the situation occurs in which the compound nucleus with specified angular momentum and parity J^{π} is formed from particles, a, through two channels with the same mean partial width. The two channels may, for instance, be labelled with different values of the channel spin s. It is not known whether the partial reduced widths are statistically independent or not, but if it is assumed that they are independent their sum will have an exponential frequency function (according to eqn. (6.42)). The averaging factors $\mathscr{S}$ of eqn. (6.45) (with $\Gamma_{(a)}$ expressing the sum of the partial widths) are, for elastic scattering,

$$\mathscr{S}_{\mathrm{n}}^{(2)} = 1-r^2\{1+(1+r)e^r\mathrm{Ei}(r)\} \tag{6.48}$$

(the lower curve of Fig. 6.4) and, for radiative capture (Lane and Lynn 1957*b*)

$$\mathscr{S}_{\gamma}^{(2)} = (1+r)\{1-re^r\mathrm{Ei}(r)\} \tag{6.49}$$

which is the upper curve of Fig. 6.5.

At higher neutron energies inelastic scattering channels may be open. For this case and, as we shall see, for the case of slow neutron

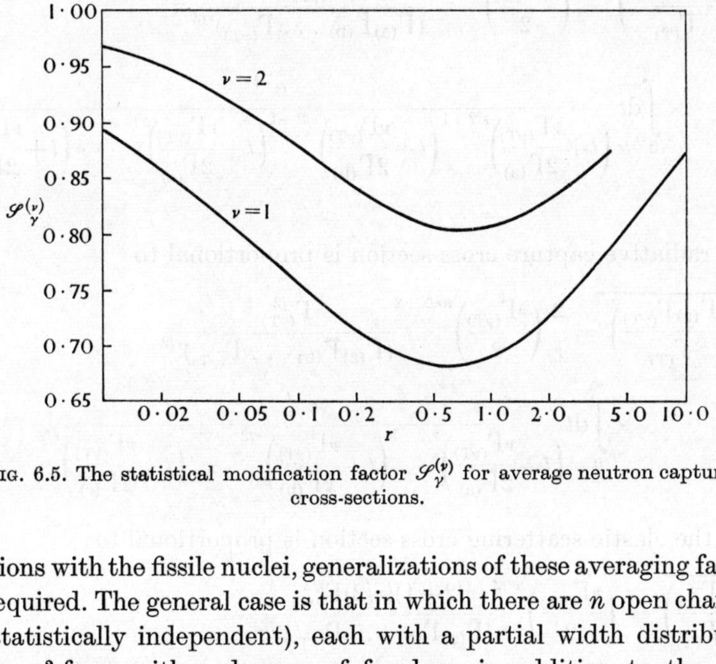

FIG. 6.5. The statistical modification factor $\mathscr{S}_{\gamma}^{(\nu)}$ for average neutron capture cross-sections.

reactions with the fissile nuclei, generalizations of these averaging factors are required. The general case is that in which there are n open channels (all statistically independent), each with a partial width distribution of the χ^2-form with ν degrees of freedom, in addition to the large number of radiation channels characterized by an (assumed) constant radiation width. The average cross-section over many resonances is proportional to the factor

$$\overline{\left(\frac{\Gamma_{(a)}\Gamma_{(b)}}{\Gamma_{(T)}}\right)} = \int \ldots \int \mathrm{d}a\mathrm{d}b \ldots \mathrm{d}s p(a)p(b) \ldots p(s)\frac{ab}{a+b+\ldots+s}, \tag{6.50}$$

where we have used the notation $a \equiv \Gamma_{(a)}$ etc., for convenience, and we shall also use $z \equiv \Gamma_{(T)}$. There does not seem to be an analytic form for this integral in the general case, but Dresner (1957) showed that it could be reduced to a single integral that can be calculated numerically. The device is to substitute for $1/(a+b+\ldots+s) = 1/z$ the integral form $\int_0^\infty dt \exp(-zt)$. If s indicates the radiation width $\Gamma_{(\gamma T)}$ the frequency function $p(s)$ is simply the δ-function, $\delta(s-\bar{s})$. All the other frequency functions have the χ^2-form, eqn. (6.38). It is now straightforward to show that eqn. (6.50) can be reduced to the form, for a general particle reaction,

$$\overline{\left(\frac{\Gamma_{(a)}\Gamma_{(b)}}{\Gamma_{(T)}}\right)} = \left(\frac{\nu\Gamma_{(\gamma T)}}{2}\right)^{n\nu/2+2} \frac{\Gamma_{(\gamma T)}^{\nu/2-1}}{(\bar{\Gamma}_{(a)}\bar{\Gamma}_{(b)}\ldots\Gamma_{(\gamma T)})^{\nu/2}} \times$$

$$\times \int_0^\infty dt \frac{e^{-t}}{\left(t+\dfrac{\nu\Gamma_{(\gamma T)}}{2\bar{\Gamma}_{(a)}}\right)^{\nu/2+1}\left(t+\dfrac{\nu\Gamma_{(\gamma T)}}{2\bar{\Gamma}_{(b)}}\right)^{\nu/2+1}\left(t+\dfrac{\nu\Gamma_{(\gamma T)}}{2\bar{\Gamma}_{(c)}}\right)^{\nu/2}\cdots\left(t+\dfrac{\nu\Gamma_{(\gamma T)}}{2\bar{\Gamma}_{(r)}}\right)^{\nu/2}} \tag{6.51}$$

The radiative capture cross-section is proportional to

$$\overline{\left(\frac{\Gamma_{(a)}\Gamma_{(\gamma T)}}{\Gamma_{(T)}}\right)} = \frac{2}{\nu}\left(\frac{\nu\Gamma_{(\gamma T)}}{2}\right)^{n\nu/2+2} \frac{\Gamma_{(\gamma T)}^{\nu/2-1}}{(\bar{\Gamma}_{(a)}\bar{\Gamma}_{(b)}\ldots\Gamma_{(\gamma T)})^{\nu/2}}$$

$$\times \int_0^\infty dt \frac{e^{-t}}{\left(t+\dfrac{\nu\Gamma_{(\gamma T)}}{2\bar{\Gamma}_{(a)}}\right)^{\nu/2+1}\left(t+\dfrac{\nu\Gamma_{(\gamma T)}}{2\bar{\Gamma}_{(b)}}\right)^{\nu/2}\cdots\left(t+\dfrac{\nu\Gamma_{(\gamma T)}}{2\bar{\Gamma}_{(r)}}\right)^{\nu/2}} \tag{6.52}$$

and the elastic scattering cross-section is proportional to

$$\overline{\left(\frac{\Gamma_{(a)}^2}{\Gamma_{(T)}}\right)} = \left(\frac{\nu\Gamma_{(\gamma T)}}{2}\right)^{n\nu/2} \frac{(\nu/2+1)(\nu/2)\Gamma_{(\gamma T)}^{\nu/2+1}}{(\bar{\Gamma}_{(a)}\bar{\Gamma}_{(b)}\ldots\Gamma_{(\gamma T)})^{\nu/2}}$$

$$\times \int_0^\infty dt \frac{e^{-t}}{\left(t+\dfrac{\nu\Gamma_{(\gamma T)}}{2\bar{\Gamma}_{(a)}}\right)^{\nu/2+2}\left(t+\dfrac{\nu\Gamma_{(\gamma T)}}{2\bar{\Gamma}_{(b)}}\right)^{\nu/2}\cdots\left(t+\dfrac{\nu\Gamma_{(\gamma T)}}{2\bar{\Gamma}_{(r)}}\right)^{\nu/2}} \tag{6.53}$$

(c) *Fluctuations in average cross-sections*

The total cross-section does not depend on the fluctuations of the partial widths; this is clear from the total cross-section analogues of eqns. (6.43) and (6.44) or, more generally, from Thomas' (1955) derivation of the average total cross-section. However, if the average total cross-section is measured over a limited energy range W containing only a moderate number of resonances (this limited value is termed an interval cross-section), then this measurement is expected to fluctuate from the true mean that may be measured over a much larger range (Egelstaff 1958). If the resonances are narrow compared with their spacing, the variance of the contribution to the interval cross-section from several resonances of a given spin and parity class is given by (Lane and Lynn 1957*a*)

$$\frac{\operatorname{var}\int\limits_W\left(\sigma_{\mathrm{T}}(J^{\pi})\mathrm{d}E\right)}{\left\langle\int\limits_W \sigma_{\mathrm{T}}(J^{\pi})\mathrm{d}E\right\rangle^2} = \frac{\operatorname{var}\left(\sum\limits_{\lambda \text{ in } W}\gamma^2_{\lambda J\pi(\mathrm{n})}\right)}{\left\langle\sum\limits_{\lambda \text{ in } W}\gamma^2_{\lambda J\pi(\mathrm{n})}\right\rangle^2} \tag{6.54a}$$

$$= \frac{1}{W/\bar{D}(J^{\pi})}\left\{\frac{\operatorname{var}(\gamma^2_{\lambda J\pi(\mathrm{n})})}{\overline{\gamma^2_{\lambda J\pi(\mathrm{n})}}^2} + \frac{\operatorname{var} D(J^{\pi})}{\bar{D}(J^{\pi})^2}\right\}, \tag{6.54b}$$

assuming independence of the distributions. The numerical value of this result is $2{\cdot}27\ \bar{D}(J^{\pi})/W$ if the Porter–Thomas and Wigner distributions are employed. While the independence assumption appears to be true for the reduced widths, there is strong theoretical evidence against this assumption for the level spacings (see Chapter V, Section D). For large values of $W/\bar{D}(J^{\pi})$ the theory of Dyson and Mehta (1963) gives $0{\cdot}44+0{\cdot}203\ln n$(eqn. (5.38b)) for the variance of the number of levels in W. The variance of the interval cross-section becomes

$$\frac{\operatorname{var}\left(\int\limits_W \sigma_{\mathrm{T}}(J^{\pi})\mathrm{d}E\right)}{\left\langle\int\limits_W \sigma_{\mathrm{T}}(J^{\pi})\mathrm{d}E\right\rangle^2} = \frac{1}{W/\bar{D}(J^{\pi})}\left\{\frac{\operatorname{var}(\gamma^2_{\lambda J\pi(\mathrm{n})})}{\overline{\gamma^2_{\lambda J\pi(\mathrm{n})}}^2} + \frac{\bar{D}(J^{\pi})}{W}\left(0{\cdot}44 + 0{\cdot}203\ln\frac{W}{\bar{D}}\right)\right\}, \tag{6.55}$$

which is very nearly two for large values of $W/\bar{D}(J^{\pi})$. Analysis of some data by Egelstaff (1958) yields values that fluctuate about $1{\cdot}7\ \bar{D}(J^{\pi})/W$ but with rather large errors. It is not clear that the discrepancies are significant. Similar fluctuations in interval cross-sections are expected for the partial cross-sections (Lane and Lynn 1957*a*, Egelstaff 1958) and for functions of the total cross-section (such as neutron transmission).

C. AVERAGE PROPERTIES OF ELASTIC SCATTERING

1. Strong absorption

In the light of the compound-nucleus theory the most natural assumption to make about the average wave-function for a nuclear reaction is that the wave in the incident channel is rapidly attenuated inside the nuclear boundary. There will be essentially no outgoing wave in this channel inside the nucleus if there is a large number of exit channels available, so the crude form of wave-function for the channel just within the nuclear boundary will be (Feshbach *et al.* 1947)

$$\psi(r) \sim \exp(-\mathrm{i}Kr) \tag{6.56}$$

where K is the average wave-number of a nucleon within the nuclear well. The corresponding logarithmic derivative at the nuclear surface is

$$\bar{f} = -\mathrm{i}Ka. \tag{6.57}$$

If the boundary condition is set at zero, the R-function is (by eqn. (6.13))

$$\bar{R} = \mathrm{i}/(Ka) \tag{6.58a}$$

giving

$$R^{\infty} = \mathrm{Re}\bar{R} = 0, \tag{6.58b}$$

$$s = \mathrm{Im}\bar{R}/\pi = 1/(\pi Ka). \tag{6.58c}$$

This result may also be derived for the discrete resonance situation by the following argument (Blatt and Weisskopf 1952). Consider a system with uniformly-spaced levels with eigenvalues $E_n = E_0 + nD$. The classical behaviour of the system at time t is obtained by superposing a large number of eigenfunctions and is represented by the wave-function

$$\psi(t) = \sum_{n=1}^{N} a_n \varphi_n \exp(-\mathrm{i}E_n t/\hbar) = \exp\left(-\frac{\mathrm{i}E_0 t}{\hbar}\right) \sum_{n=1}^{N} a_n \varphi_n \exp\left(-\frac{\mathrm{i}nDt}{\hbar}\right) \tag{6.59}$$

where the φ_n give the spatial dependence. Clearly, the period of motion of the wave-function is

$$P = 2\pi\hbar/D. \tag{6.60}$$

Thus, the classical configuration which occurs just after a particle has entered the nucleus will be repeated after a period of time of the order of P. The incident particle is now in a position to be transmitted across the nuclear boundary (re-emitted) and the probability that this will occur is given by the degree of matching of the internal and external nuclear wave-numbers, $T = 4Kk/(K+k)^2$. If the incident channel is the only one open, the lifetime, τ, of the nuclear state is of the order of P/T and the width $\Gamma_{(n)} \approx \hbar/\tau \approx 2kKD/\pi(K+k)^2$. Removal of the penetration factor $2ka$ yields eqn. (6.58c) for the strength function at low neutron energies ($k \ll K$).

Equation (6.58c) for the strength function agrees with eqn. (6.11) which is derived from the assumption that the coupling of nucleon motions through their residual forces is sufficiently strong that the single-particle states are distributed among the nuclear levels in an interval that is at least as great as the single-particle level spacing. Equation (6.58c) must be considered more carefully however. The strength function $s(E_\lambda)$ is not defined for excitation energies less than zero. It would seem natural to set it to zero in that energy range, particularly in view of our knowledge of nuclear structure; the shell model would suggest that the ground state of a compound nucleus should have a very small reduced width for the entrance neutron channel. If the strength function is defined by eqn. (6.58c) for positive excitation energy and is zero for negative excitation, application of the Stieltjes transform method gives the result (Thomas 1955) that

$$R^\infty = \mathrm{Re}\bar{R} = \frac{1}{\pi Ka} \ln\left\{\frac{(E+V)^{\frac{1}{2}}+(V-E_{\mathrm{th,n}})^{\frac{1}{2}}}{(E+V)^{\frac{1}{2}}-(V-E_{\mathrm{th,n}})^{\frac{1}{2}}}\right\} \tag{6.61}$$

where $E_{\mathrm{th,n}}$ is the nucleon separation energy. This theory implies that the surface wave-function includes a damping coefficient K' of the same order of magnitude as K:

$$\psi \sim \mathrm{e}^{(K'-\mathrm{i}K)r}. \tag{6.62}$$

This is more consistent physically with the initial assumption of the strong-absorption model.

If the potential well depth $-V$ is of the order of 45 MeV, then eqn. (6.61) gives $R^\infty \approx 0{\cdot}08$ at the neutron separation energy of a heavy nucleus. This implies that the potential scattering cross-section of the strong-absorption model is about 16 per cent less than that of an impenetrable hard sphere with the same radius. For light nuclei the difference is up to a factor of 2 larger.

2. The complex-potential model

(a) *Phenomenological ideas*

The introduction of a wave-function of the form (6.62) with complex wave-number leads naturally to the idea of using a complex potential to obtain the average value of the collision function. In the strong-absorption model described above the absorption length that appears in the wave-function is of the same order of magnitude as the wavelength. For all but the lightest nuclei a nucleon entering the nucleus will be absorbed with near certainty. The notion of absorption is to be interpreted as the collision of the incident nucleon with nucleons of the target to lead to the formation of the compound nucleus. The compound nucleus will subsequently decay, of course, one of the exit channels for this decay being the process of compound elastic scattering.

In the complex-potential model the possibility of a much longer absorption length is generally considered. An entering nucleon may simply be refracted by the potential. The spirit of the compound-nucleus hypothesis is still embodied by this model, for there is a probability (though less than unity) that the nucleon is absorbed, i.e. that a nucleon-nucleon collision occurs. The possibility now exists that one or both nucleons escape (if their energy is high enough) without further collisions (absorption). This may be termed *direct reaction*. Further collisions lead through the stages that may be described as a compound system to the thoroughly mixed system that may be described as a compound nucleus (Weisskopf 1956). However, for *low*-energy neutron reactions the initial process of absorption must lead to compound nucleus formation, there being insufficient energy for either nucleon to escape.

The complex-potential model was first applied to the analysis of low-energy neutron data by Feshbach *et al.* (1954). A square potential well was studied. The essential results of the square complex potential can be derived from the results of Chapter III, Section A for a real square well. If the imaginary component of the potential has the constant value, $-W_0$, at values of the radial coordinate less than or equal to the well radius a, and zero elsewhere, the R-function has its real well form but with the complex argument $E+\mathrm{i}W_0$:

$$R(E) = \sum_{\mathrm{p}} \frac{\gamma_{\mathrm{p}}^2}{E_{\mathrm{p}}-E-\mathrm{i}W_0} \tag{6.63a}$$

$$= \sum_{\mathrm{p}} \frac{\hbar^2/Ma^2}{E_{\mathrm{p}}-E-\mathrm{i}W_0}, \tag{6.63b}$$

using the square well expression, eqn. (3.10), for the reduced widths. According to eqns. (2.69) and (6.15)–(6.17) the potential scattering length is modified by the function

$$R^{\infty} = \mathrm{Re}R = \sum_{\mathrm{p}} \frac{(E_{\mathrm{p}}-E)\gamma_{\mathrm{p}}^{2}}{(E_{\mathrm{p}}-E)^{2}+(W_{0})^{2}} \tag{6.64}$$

and the strength function is given by

$$s = \frac{\mathrm{Im}R}{\pi} = \frac{W_{0}}{\pi}\sum_{\mathrm{p}} \frac{\gamma_{\mathrm{p}}^{2}}{(E_{\mathrm{p}}-E)^{2}+(W_{0})^{2}}. \tag{6.65}$$

If W_0 is appreciably less than the single-particle level spacing, structure, as illustrated in Fig. 6.6, is to be expected in both the potential scattering cross-section and the strength function. The structure exists for these quantities whether plotted as a function of energy or of radius (or, equivalently, mass number). In the case of very low-energy neutron reactions it is the mass number dependence that is of interest. A giant resonance will occur in the strength function whenever the appropriate single-particle state of the real component of the potential well occurs at zero energy.

(b) Comparison with data

The s-wave strength function of a square complex potential with radius constant, $r_0 = 1{\cdot}45$ fm and real depth, $V_0 = -42$ MeV has maxima at mass numbers $A \approx 13$ ($2s_{\frac{1}{2}}$ single-particle state) $A \approx 60$ ($3s_{\frac{1}{2}}$) and $A \approx 155$ ($4s_{\frac{1}{2}}$) (Feshbach *et al.* 1954). Qualitative agreement

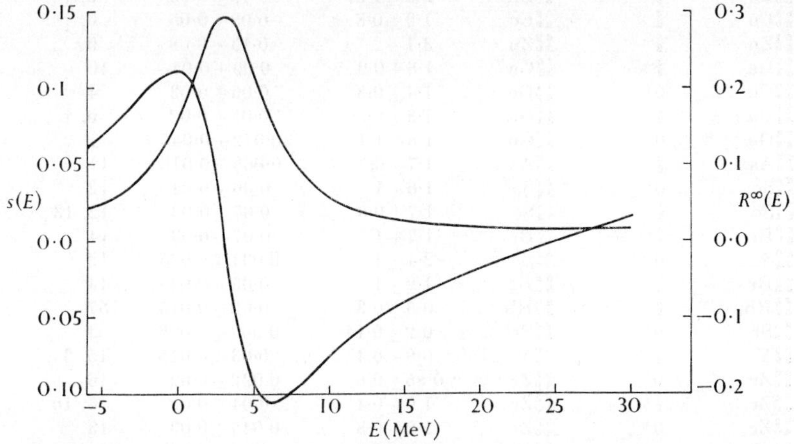

FIG. 6.6. The energy variation of strength function, s, and the distant level R-function, R^{∞}, for the square complex-potential well model (schematic).

TABLE 6.1

Compilation of neutron strength-function data

Target nucleus	I^π	Compound nucleus	$\Gamma^0_{(n)}/D$ ($\times 10^4$)	s (assuming r_0 = 1·35 fm)	References and remarks
$^{39}_{19}$K	$\frac{3}{2}+$	$^{40}_{19}$K	$0{\cdot}78\pm0{\cdot}3$	$0{\cdot}038\pm0{\cdot}015$	1
$^{40}_{20}$Ca	0+	$^{41}_{20}$Ca	$2{\cdot}8\pm1{\cdot}1$	$0{\cdot}14\pm0{\cdot}05$	2
$^{43}_{20}$Ca	$\frac{7}{2}-$	$^{44}_{20}$Ca	$1{\cdot}4\pm0{\cdot}7$	$0{\cdot}07\pm0{\cdot}03$	49
$^{44}_{20}$Ca	0+	$^{45}_{20}$Ca	$1{\cdot}7\pm1{\cdot}2$	$0{\cdot}08\pm0{\cdot}05$	3
$^{45}_{21}$Sc	$\frac{7}{2}$	$^{46}_{21}$Sc	$6\pm2{\cdot}5$	$0{\cdot}28\pm0{\cdot}11$	4
$^{46}_{22}$Ti	0+	$^{47}_{22}$Ti	$2{\cdot}7\pm1{\cdot}0$	$0{\cdot}13\pm0{\cdot}05$	2
$^{47}_{22}$Ti	$\frac{5}{2}-$	$^{48}_{22}$Ti	$2{\cdot}6\pm0{\cdot}9$	$0{\cdot}13\pm0{\cdot}04$	49
$^{48}_{22}$Ti	0+	$^{49}_{22}$Ti	$3{\cdot}7\pm1{\cdot}3$	$0{\cdot}17\pm0{\cdot}06$	2
$^{49}_{22}$Ti	$\frac{7}{2}-$	$^{50}_{22}$Ti	$2{\cdot}7\pm1{\cdot}4$	$0{\cdot}13\pm0{\cdot}07$	49
$^{50}_{22}$Ti	0+	$^{51}_{22}$Ti	$1{\cdot}9\pm1{\cdot}5$	$0{\cdot}09\pm0{\cdot}07$	2
$^{50}_{24}$Cr	0+	$^{51}_{24}$Cr	$4{\cdot}8\pm3{\cdot}2$	$0{\cdot}22\pm0{\cdot}15$	3
$^{51}_{23}$V	$\frac{7}{2}-$	$^{52}_{23}$V	$10{\cdot}7\pm2{\cdot}6$	$0{\cdot}48\pm0{\cdot}20$	5
$^{52}_{24}$Cr	0+	$^{53}_{24}$Cr	$2{\cdot}5\pm1{\cdot}0$	$0{\cdot}11\pm0{\cdot}04$	2
$^{53}_{24}$Cr	$\frac{3}{2}-$	$^{54}_{24}$Cr	14 ± 8	$0{\cdot}98\pm0{\cdot}56$	6, †
$^{54}_{24}$Cr	0+	$^{55}_{24}$Cr	$0{\cdot}8\pm0{\cdot}6$	$0{\cdot}04\pm0{\cdot}03$	3
$^{54}_{26}$Fe	0+	$^{55}_{26}$Fe	$5{\cdot}2\pm1{\cdot}5$	$0{\cdot}23\pm0{\cdot}07$	2
$^{55}_{25}$Mn	$\frac{5}{2}-$	$^{56}_{25}$Mn	$4{\cdot}1\pm0{\cdot}9$	$0{\cdot}18\pm0{\cdot}04$	7, 50
$^{56}_{26}$Fe	0+	$^{57}_{26}$Fe	$1{\cdot}6\pm0{\cdot}5$	$0{\cdot}07\pm0{\cdot}02$	2
$^{57}_{26}$Fe	$\frac{1}{2}-$	$^{58}_{26}$Fe	$3{\cdot}7\pm2{\cdot}6$	$0{\cdot}16\pm0{\cdot}1$	49
$^{58}_{28}$Ni	0+	$^{59}_{28}$Ni	$3{\cdot}6\pm1{\cdot}8$	$0{\cdot}16\pm0{\cdot}08$	3
$^{59}_{27}$Co	$\frac{7}{2}-$	$^{60}_{27}$Co	$2{\cdot}8\pm0{\cdot}7$	$0{\cdot}12\pm0{\cdot}03$	50
$^{60}_{28}$Ni	0+	$^{61}_{28}$Ni	$3{\cdot}0\pm1{\cdot}6$	$0{\cdot}13\pm0{\cdot}07$	3
$^{61}_{28}$Ni	$\frac{3}{2}-$	$^{62}_{28}$Ni	$2{\cdot}5\pm0{\cdot}9$	$0{\cdot}11\pm0{\cdot}04$	49
$^{63}_{29}$Cu	$\frac{3}{2}-$	$^{64}_{29}$Cu	$1{\cdot}9\pm0{\cdot}8$	$0{\cdot}08\pm0{\cdot}02$	4
$^{64}_{30}$Zn	0+	$^{65}_{30}$Zn	$2{\cdot}3\pm1{\cdot}0$	$0{\cdot}10\pm0{\cdot}05$	6, †
$^{65}_{29}$Cu	$\frac{3}{2}-$	$^{66}_{29}$Cu	$1{\cdot}9\pm0{\cdot}8$	$0{\cdot}08\pm0{\cdot}05$	6, †
$^{67}_{30}$Zn	$\frac{5}{2}-$	$^{68}_{30}$Zn	$3{\cdot}1\pm2$	$0{\cdot}13\pm0{\cdot}08$	9
$^{69}_{31}$Ga	$\frac{3}{2}-$	$^{70}_{31}$Ga	$1{\cdot}8\pm0{\cdot}9$	$0{\cdot}09\pm0{\cdot}04$	10
$^{70}_{32}$Ge	0+	$^{71}_{32}$Ge	$1{\cdot}4\pm0{\cdot}8$	$0{\cdot}06\pm0{\cdot}03$	4
$^{71}_{31}$Ga	$\frac{3}{2}-$	$^{72}_{31}$Ga	$1{\cdot}3\pm0{\cdot}5$	$0{\cdot}05\pm0{\cdot}02$	6, †
$^{72}_{32}$Ge	0+	$^{73}_{32}$Ge	$1{\cdot}8\pm1{\cdot}1$	$0{\cdot}072\pm0{\cdot}045$	4
$^{75}_{33}$As	$\frac{3}{2}-$	$^{76}_{33}$As	$1{\cdot}7\pm0{\cdot}3$	$0{\cdot}068\pm0{\cdot}012$	11
$^{76}_{34}$Se	0+	$^{77}_{34}$Se	$1{\cdot}6\pm1$	$0{\cdot}06\pm0{\cdot}04$	12
$^{77}_{34}$Se	$\frac{1}{2}-$	$^{78}_{34}$Se	$1{\cdot}7\pm0{\cdot}8$	$0{\cdot}07\pm0{\cdot}03$	12, 13
$^{79}_{35}$Br	$\frac{3}{2}-$	$^{80}_{35}$Br	$1{\cdot}7\pm1$	$0{\cdot}07\pm0{\cdot}03$	14
$^{80}_{34}$Se	0+	$^{81}_{34}$Se	$2{\cdot}4\pm1$	$0{\cdot}094\pm0{\cdot}055$	12
$^{81}_{35}$Br	$\frac{3}{2}-$	$^{82}_{35}$Br	$1{\cdot}2\pm1$	$0{\cdot}05\pm0{\cdot}04$	14
$^{85}_{37}$Rb	$\frac{5}{2}-$	$^{86}_{37}$Rb	$0{\cdot}5\pm0{\cdot}3$	$0{\cdot}02\pm0{\cdot}015$	57
$^{88}_{38}$Sr	0+	$^{89}_{38}$Sr	$0{\cdot}2\pm0{\cdot}14$	$0{\cdot}008\pm0{\cdot}006$	3
$^{89}_{39}$Y	$\frac{1}{2}-$	$^{90}_{39}$Y	$0{\cdot}8\pm0{\cdot}4$	$0{\cdot}03\pm0{\cdot}015$	15, 3
$^{90}_{50}$Zr	0+	$^{91}_{40}$Zr	$0{\cdot}85\pm0{\cdot}6$	$0{\cdot}032\pm0{\cdot}02$	16
$^{91}_{40}$Zr	$\frac{5}{2}+$	$^{92}_{40}$Zr	$1{\cdot}0\pm0{\cdot}4$	$0{\cdot}04\pm0{\cdot}02$	16, 16
$^{92}_{40}$Zr	0+	$^{93}_{40}$Zr	$1{\cdot}2\pm0{\cdot}8$	$0{\cdot}045\pm0{\cdot}03$	13
$^{92}_{42}$Mo	0+	$^{93}_{42}$Mo	$1{\cdot}6\pm1{\cdot}0$	$0{\cdot}06\pm0{\cdot}04$	54
$^{93}_{41}$Nb	$\frac{9}{2}+$	$^{94}_{41}$Nb	$0{\cdot}36\pm0{\cdot}06$	$0{\cdot}012\pm0{\cdot}002$	48
$^{94}_{40}$Zr	0+	$^{95}_{40}$Zr	$1{\cdot}1\pm0{\cdot}8$	$0{\cdot}04\pm0{\cdot}03$	16

TABLE 6.1 (cont.)

Compilation of neutron strength-function data

Target nucleus	I^{π}	Compound nucleus	$\Gamma^0_{(n)}/D$ ($\times 10^4$)	s (assuming r_0 = 1·35 fm)	References and remarks
$^{95}_{42}$Mo	$\frac{5}{2}$+	$^{96}_{42}$Mo	0·4±0·14	0·015±0·004	19
$^{96}_{40}$Zr	0+	$^{97}_{40}$Zr	0·9±0·6	0·034±0·022	16
$^{97}_{42}$Mo	$\frac{5}{2}$+	$^{98}_{42}$Mo	0·26±0·09	0·0095±0·0032	19
$^{99}_{43}$Tc	$\frac{9}{2}$+	$^{100}_{43}$Tc	0·45±0·2	0·016±0·007	20
$^{101}_{44}$Ru	$\frac{5}{2}$+	$^{102}_{44}$Ru	0·41±0·17	0·015±0·006	21
$^{103}_{45}$Rh	$\frac{1}{2}$−	$^{104}_{45}$Rh	0·5±0·2	0·018±0·008	22
$^{105}_{46}$Pd	$\frac{5}{2}$+	$^{106}_{46}$Pd	0·32±0·17	0·011±0·006	23
$^{107}_{47}$Ag	$\frac{1}{2}$−	$^{108}_{47}$Ag	0·42±0·09	0·015±0·003	19, 53
$^{109}_{47}$Ag	$\frac{1}{2}$−	$^{110}_{47}$Ag	0·8±0·2	0·029±0·007	24, 25, 53
$^{111}_{48}$Cd	$\frac{1}{2}$+	$^{112}_{48}$Cd	0·44±0·15	0·015±0·005	19
$^{112}_{48}$Cd	0+	$^{113}_{48}$Cd	0·45±0·23	0·015±0·007	59
$^{113}_{48}$Cd	$\frac{1}{2}$+	$^{114}_{48}$Cd	0·6±0·3	0·02±0·01	59
$^{113}_{49}$In	$\frac{9}{2}$+	$^{114}_{49}$In	0·6±0·1	0·021±0·008	19
$^{112}_{50}$Sn	0+	$^{113}_{50}$Sn	0·5±0·2	0·017±0·007	26
$^{114}_{48}$Cd	0+	$^{115}_{48}$Cd	1·3±0·7	0·043±0·02	59
$^{114}_{50}$Sn	0+	$^{115}_{50}$Sn	0·7±0·3	0·024±0·010	26
$^{115}_{49}$In	$\frac{9}{2}$+	$^{116}_{49}$In	0·31±0·06	0·011±0·002	19
$^{115}_{50}$Sn	$\frac{1}{2}$+	$^{116}_{50}$Sn	0·3±0·2	0·010±0·007	26
$^{116}_{50}$Sn	0+	$^{117}_{50}$Sn	0·37±0·15	0·013±0·003	26
$^{117}_{50}$Sn	$\frac{1}{2}$+	$^{118}_{50}$Sn	0·19±0·05	0·0065±0·0016	26
$^{118}_{50}$Sn	0+	$^{119}_{50}$Sn	0·32±0·12	0·011±0·003	26
$^{119}_{50}$Sn	$\frac{1}{2}$+	$^{120}_{50}$Sn	0·08±0·03	0·0027±0·0010	26
$^{120}_{50}$Sn	0+	$^{121}_{50}$Sn	0·09±0·04	0·0030±0·0013	26
$^{121}_{50}$Sb	$\frac{5}{2}$+	$^{122}_{51}$Sb	0·45±0·12	0·015±0·004	19
$^{122}_{50}$Sn	0+	$^{123}_{50}$Sn	0·2±0·1	0·007±0·004	26
$^{123}_{51}$Sb	$\frac{7}{2}$+	$^{124}_{51}$Sb	0·6±0·2	0·020±0·007	19
$^{123}_{52}$Te	$\frac{1}{2}$+	$^{124}_{52}$Te	1·4±0·9	0·048±0·030	27
$^{124}_{50}$Sn	0+	$^{125}_{50}$Sn	0·2±0·15	0·007±0·005	60
$^{125}_{52}$Te	$\frac{1}{2}$+	$^{126}_{52}$Te	0·4±0·25	0·14±0·09	27
$^{127}_{53}$I	$\frac{5}{2}$+	$^{128}_{53}$I	0·69±0·08	0·023±0·003	48
$^{129}_{53}$I	$\frac{7}{2}$+	$^{130}_{53}$I	0·4±0·25	0·013±0·008	28
$^{130}_{52}$Te	0+	$^{131}_{52}$Te	0·8±0·4	0·027±0·013	3
$^{133}_{55}$Cs	$\frac{7}{2}$+	$^{134}_{55}$Cs	0·7±0·1	0·022±0·003	48
$^{135}_{56}$Ba	$\frac{3}{2}$+	$^{136}_{56}$Ba	1·1±0·3	0·036±0·009	19
$^{138}_{56}$Ba	0+	$^{139}_{56}$Ba	1·8±0·6	0·059±0·020	3
$^{140}_{58}$Ce	0+	$^{141}_{58}$Ce	1·0±0·4	0·033±0·008	29
$^{141}_{59}$Pr	$\frac{5}{2}$+	$^{142}_{59}$Pr	2·5±0·5	0·083±0·017	30, 51
$^{142}_{58}$Ce	0+	$^{143}_{58}$Ce	1·2±0·5	0·039±0·009	29
$^{143}_{60}$Nd	$\frac{7}{2}$−	$^{144}_{60}$Nd	3·7±0·6	0·12±0·002	19
$^{145}_{60}$Nd	$\frac{7}{2}$−	$^{146}_{60}$Nd	3·3±1·5	0·11±0·005	19
$^{147}_{61}$Pm	$\frac{7}{2}$(+)	$^{148}_{61}$Pm	3·4±1·7	0·11±0·006	32
$^{147}_{62}$Sm	$\frac{7}{2}$−	$^{148}_{62}$Sm	4·3±1·3	0·14±0·004	19
$^{149}_{62}$Sm	$\frac{7}{2}$−	$^{150}_{62}$Sm	3·2±0·5	0·10±0·002	19
$^{151}_{62}$Sm	($\frac{7}{2}$−)	$^{152}_{62}$Sm	2·7±1·7	0·090±0·06	31
$^{151}_{63}$Eu	$\frac{5}{2}$(+)	$^{152}_{63}$Eu	2·7±0·5	0·090±0·02	19
$^{153}_{63}$Eu	$\frac{5}{2}$(+)	$^{154}_{63}$Eu	2·7±0·6	0·085±0·020	19

TABLE 6.1 (cont.)

Compilation of neutron strength-function data

Target nucleus	I^π	Compound nucleus	$\Gamma^0_{(n)}/D$ ($\times 10^4$)	s (assuming r_0 = 1·35 fm)	References and remarks
$^{155}_{64}$Gd	$\frac{3}{2}^-$	$^{156}_{64}$Gd	2·4±0·2	0·076±0·006	52, ‡
$^{157}_{64}$Gd	$\frac{3}{2}^-$	$^{158}_{64}$Gd	2·16±0·15	0·066±0·005	52, ‡
$^{159}_{65}$Tb	$\frac{3}{2}^{(+)}$	$^{160}_{65}$Tb	0·9±0·2	0·028±0·006	32
$^{161}_{66}$Dy	$\frac{5}{2}^{(+)}$	$^{162}_{66}$Dy	1·85±0·15	0·057±0·005	52, ‡
$^{62}_{66}$Dy	0^+	$^{163}_{66}$Dy	2·0±0·5	0·061±0·015	52, ‡
$^{163}_{66}$Dy	$\frac{5}{2}^{(+)}$	$^{164}_{66}$Dy	1·8±0·3	0·054±0·009	52, ‡
$^{165}_{67}$Ho	$\frac{7}{2}^{(-)}$	$^{166}_{67}$Ho	2·5±0·4	0·077±0·012	19
$^{167}_{68}$Er	$\frac{7}{2}^{(+)}$	$^{168}_{68}$Er	1·6±0·4	0·05±0·01	19
$^{169}_{69}$Tm	$\frac{1}{2}^+$	$^{170}_{69}$Tm	1·5±0·3	0·046±0·003	34
$^{171}_{70}$Yb	$\frac{1}{2}^-$	$^{172}_{70}$Yb	1·1±0·4	0·035±0·013	56
$^{173}_{70}$Yb	$\frac{5}{2}^-$	$^{174}_{70}$Yb	1·7±0·2	0·052±0·006	52, ‡
$^{175}_{71}$Lu	$\frac{7}{2}^+$	$^{176}_{71}$Lu	1·7±0·2	0·054±0·006	19
$^{176}_{71}$Lu	$7^{(-)}$	$^{177}_{71}$Lu	1·9±0·6	0·06±0·02	31
$^{177}_{72}$Hf	$\frac{7}{2}^-$	$^{178}_{72}$Hf	2·2±0·4	0·07±0·01	19
$^{179}_{72}$Hf	$\frac{9}{2}^+$	$^{180}_{72}$Hf	1·3±0·3	0·04±0·01	19
$^{181}_{73}$Ta	$\frac{7}{2}^+$	$^{182}_{73}$Ta	1·8±0·3	0·055±0·009	25
$^{182}_{74}$W	0^+	$^{183}_{74}$Ta	2·0±1·0	0·06±0·03	35
$^{183}_{74}$W	$\frac{1}{2}^-$	$^{184}_{74}$W	2·9±1·4	0·09±0·05	36
$^{185}_{75}$Re	$\frac{5}{2}^+$	$^{186}_{75}$Re	2·1±0·2	0·062±0·006	23
$^{187}_{75}$Re	$\frac{5}{2}^+$	$^{188}_{75}$Re	0·6±0·3	0·018±0·009	23
$^{191}_{77}$Ir	$\frac{3}{2}^+$	$^{192}_{77}$Ir	1·9±0·7	0·06±0·02	37
$^{193}_{77}$Ir	$\frac{3}{2}^+$	$^{194}_{77}$Ir	1·5±0·5	0·04±0·01	37
$^{195}_{78}$Pt	$\frac{1}{2}^-$	$^{196}_{78}$Pt	2·2±0·7	0·06±0·02	15
$^{197}_{79}$Au	$\frac{3}{2}^+$	$^{198}_{79}$Au	1·5±0·3	0·04±0·01	25
$^{198}_{80}$Hg	0^+	$^{199}_{80}$Hg	1·5±0·9	0·04±0·03	38
$^{199}_{80}$Hg	$\frac{1}{2}^-$	$^{200}_{80}$Hg	2·0±1·4	0·06±0·04	38
$^{200}_{80}$Hg	0^+	$^{201}_{80}$Hg	1·5±1·1	0·04±0·03	38
$^{201}_{80}$Hg	$\frac{3}{2}^-$	$^{202}_{80}$Hg	1·5±0·8	0·04±0·02	38
$^{207}_{82}$Pb	$\frac{1}{2}^-$	$^{208}_{82}$Pb	0·25±0·18	0·007±0·005	3
$^{209}_{83}$Bi	$\frac{9}{2}^-$	$^{210}_{83}$Bi	0·57±0·17	0·016±0·005	39
$^{230}_{90}$Th	0^+	$^{231}_{90}$Th	0·74±0·3	0·021±0·01	58
$^{231}_{91}$Pa	$\frac{3}{2}^-$	$^{232}_{91}$Pa	0·8±0·2	0·022±0·006	40
$^{232}_{90}$Th	0^+	$^{233}_{90}$Th	0·69±0·07	0·019±0·002	41
$^{232}_{92}$U	0^+	$^{233}_{92}$U	1·0±0·5	0·03±0·01	42
$^{234}_{92}$U	0^+	$^{235}_{92}$U	1·2±0·3	0·03±0·01	43
$^{236}_{92}$U	0^+	$^{237}_{92}$U	1·3±0·3	0·04±0·01	43
$^{237}_{93}$Np	$\frac{5}{2}^+$	$^{238}_{93}$Np	1·9±0·4	0·047±0·01	44
$^{238}_{92}$U	0^+	$^{239}_{92}$U	1·0±0·17	0·027±0·005	45, 46
$^{240}_{94}$Pu	0^+	$^{241}_{94}$Pu	0·93±0·25	0·025±0·006	61
$^{242}_{94}$Pu	0^+	$^{243}_{94}$Pu	0·95±0·4	0·026±0·01	55
$^{243}_{95}$Am	$\frac{5}{2}^-$	$^{244}_{95}$Am	0·84±0·35	0·023±0·009	47

Remarks

† From transmission 'area' methods, with poor resolution.

‡ From average cross-sections.

TABLE 6.1 (cont.)

Compilation of neutron strength-function data

References

1. Marshak and Newson (1957)
2. Bowman *et al.* (1962)
3. Bilpuch *et al.* (1961)
4. Miller *et al.* (1959)
5. Firk *et al.* (1963)
6. Coté *et al.* (1958)
7. Coté *et al.* (1964*b*)
8. Morgenstern *et al.* (1964)
9. Dahlberg and Bollinger (1956)
10. Julien *et al.* (1964)
11. Garg *et al.* (1964*b*)
12' Coté *et al.* (1964*c*)
13. Julien *et al.* (1962*a*)
14. Leblanc *et al.* (1959)
15. Julien *et al.* (1962*b*)
16. Moskalev *et al.* (1964)
17. Saplakoglu *et al.* (1958)
18. Jackson (1963)
19. Hughes *et al.* (1958)
20. Slaughter *et al.* (1958)
21. Bolotin and Chrien (1963)
22. Ribon *et al.* (1962)
23. Hughes *et al.* (1959)
24. Rae *et al.* (1958)
25. Desjardins *et al.* (1960)
26. Fuketa *et al.* (1963)
27. Bolotin and Chrien (1960)
28. Harvey *et al.* (1958*a*)
29. Newson *et al.* (1959)
30. Corge *et al.* (1961)
31. Harvey *et al.* (1958*b*)
32. Wang *et al.* (1964)
33. Zimmerman (1957)
34. Singh (1964)
35. Waters *et al.* (1959)
36. Firk and Moxon (1959)
37. Bolotin and Chrien (1959)
38. Carpenter and Bollinger (1960)
39. Nichols *et al.* (1959)
40. Patterson and Harvey (1962)
41. Garg *et al.* (1964*a*)
42. James (1964)
43. Harvey and Hughes (1958)
44. Slaughter *et al.* (1961)
45. Firk *et al.* (1963*c*)
46. Rosen *et al.* (1960)
47. Coté *et al.* (1958)
48. Garg *et al.* (1965)
49. Wagner *et al.* (1965)
50. Morgenstern *et al.* (1965*b*)
51. Rainwater *et al.* (1965)
52. Chrien and Mughabghab (1965)
53. Pattenden (1965*a*)
54. Pevzner *et al.* (1963)
55. Auchampaugh *et al.* (1966)
56. Wang *et al.* (1966)
57. Iliescu *et al.* (1965)
58. Kalebin *et al.* (1966)
59. Adamchuk *et al.* (1966*a*)
60. Adamchuk *et al.* (1966*b*)
61. Asghar *et al.* (1966*b*)

of the slow neutron data was found in the initial studies of the complex-potential theory (Carter *et al.* 1954) with a value of the imaginary component $W_0 \approx 3{\cdot}4$ MeV. The *s*-wave neutron strength function data that are available at the present time are listed in Table 6.1. Two points are to be noted. One is that the quantity referred to as the strength function in the experimental literature is denoted by $\overline{\Gamma}{}^0_{(n)}/\bar{D}$ and is equal to $2k_1as$ where k_1 is the neutron wave-number at 1 eV. The other point is that for odd-mass target nuclei the angular momenta of the *s*-wave resonances have generally not been identified and the product of the spin weighting factor g_J and the neutron width is the result of the measurement. In consequence of this the mean quantity $\overline{g_J\Gamma^0_{(n)}}$ is evaluated from the resonance data and the quantity listed as $\overline{\Gamma}{}^0_{(n)}/\bar{D}$ is really $\overline{2g_J\Gamma^0_{(n)}}/2\bar{D}$ where $\bar{D}$ is the mean spacing over all *s*-wave resonances. The uncertainty introduced by the factor g_J is much smaller than the uncertainty inherent in the statistics of the widths themselves; this was discussed in Section B.3. The uncertainties quoted in Table 6.1 are simply the square roots of the variances associated with the frequency function in eqn. (6.42). Some authors (e.g. Muradyan and Adamchuk 1965) quote the most probable value of the strength function instead of the expected value (the mean), and also define their quoted errors by the limits enclosing 68 per cent of the total probability; these are generally larger (particularly the upper limit) than the root variances and perhaps give a better idea of the uncertainty associated with the estimate. It is obvious from the table that the largest values of the strength function occur near mass numbers 50 and 150, in qualitative agreement with the model.

(c) *The wave function for scattering in the complex-potential field*

The R-function of eqn. (6.63) can be regarded as the reduced R-function (see Chapter II, Section E.2, eqn. 2.60) of a system with resonances at the eigenvalues E_{p} and with absorption widths (into many channels) equal to $2W_0$; the total widths are therefore equal to $2W_0 + 2P\gamma^2_{\mathrm{p(n)}}$. We can use these facts to calculate the reciprocal level matrix **A** for the system (eqn. 2.49 and above) and hence, from eqn. (2.53), the internal wave-function Ψ_{CP} when there is unit flux in the entrance channel. At low energies the penetration factor P will be small enough that the off-diagonal elements of matrix **A** may be neglected, and the wave-function for scattering in the complex-potential field becomes

$$\Psi_{\mathrm{CP}} = -\mathrm{i}\hbar^{\frac{1}{2}}\mathrm{e}^{-\mathrm{i}\phi}\left(\frac{P\hbar^2}{Ma}\right)^{\frac{1}{2}} \sum_{\mathrm{p}} \frac{u_{\mathrm{p}}(a)u_{\mathrm{p}}(r)}{E_{\mathrm{p}}-E-\frac{1}{2}\mathrm{i}(2W_0+2P\gamma^2_{\mathrm{p}})}. \tag{6.66}$$

3. A surface-absorption model

It has often been suggested on physical grounds that the absorptive region of the nucleus should be concentrated near the surface (e.g. Gomes 1959). Here, there would seem to be a much greater chance that a collision between nucleons would not be inhibited by the Pauli principle. The R-function of a simple complex potential with an imaginary part concentrated into a delta function at the surface has been studied by Thomas (1955). The surface absorption is in addition to the constant volume absorption and is represented by a pure imaginary delta function of strength $\mathrm{i}\alpha\hbar^2/2Ma$. By integrating the wave-function across this surface it is found that the logarithmic derivative is changed by a finite amount $-i\alpha/a$, so that the R-function outside the surface, R_+, is related to the R-function inside, R_-, by

$$R_+ = (R_-^{-1} - i\alpha)^{-1}. \tag{6.67}$$

The internal R-function is given by eqn. (6.63a). If this is substituted in eqn. (6.67) and some rearrangement is carried out we obtain

$$R_+ = \sum_p \frac{\gamma_p^2}{E_p - E + D_p(E) - i\{W_p + C_p(E)\}} \tag{6.68a}$$

where

$$D_p(E) = \alpha\left\{(E_p - E)\sum_{q\neq p}\frac{\gamma_q^2 W_0}{(E_q-E)^2+W_0^2} - W_0\sum_{q\neq p}\frac{\gamma_q^2(E_q-E)}{(E_q-E)^2+W_0^2}\right\}, \tag{6.68b}$$

$$C_p(E) = \alpha\left\{(E_p - E)\sum_{q\neq p}\frac{\gamma_q^2 (E_q-E)}{(E_q-E)^2+W_0^2} + W_0\sum_{q\neq p}\frac{\gamma_q^2 W_0}{(E_q-E)^2+W_0^2}\right\}, \tag{6.68c}$$

$$W_p = W_0 + \alpha\gamma_p^2. \tag{6.68d}$$

If the real part of the complex potential is square the reduced widths γ_p^2 are equal to $\hbar^2/(Ma^2)$ (eqn. (3.10)) and the absorption widths are $2W_p \approx (2W_0 + 2\alpha\hbar^2/Ma^2)$. If the real part has a diffuse edge the reduced widths are increased (see eqn. 3.12) and the surface contribution to the absorption width rises correspondingly. The additional terms $D_p(E)$ and $C_p(E)$ in the denominators of eqn. (6.68a) are unimportant (with values of W_0 and γ_p^2 small compared to the eigenvalue spacings) for energies E close to the eigenvalues E_p, but cause the disappearance of the surface contribution to the absorption (i.e. the strength function) between the eigenvalues. This is to be understood by the fact that at the potential edge the wave function of the scattered particle has a node at energies between the single-particle levels, and is therefore unaffected by the delta-function absorption at this point.

4. The foundations of the complex-potential model

(a) *The role of the Pauli principle*

The complex-potential model as discussed above is a purely phenomenological treatment of nuclear reactions. It is the task of nuclear theory to substantiate the model.

A semi-classical treatment makes it appear very plausible that in such a model the imaginary component is small (Lane and Wandel 1955). The classical analogue of the complex potential is the scattering of light by a partially absorptive, refracting sphere. If W and the particle energy E are small compared with the real component of the potential V_0 a simple calculation using a wave-function of the form (6.62) shows that the mean free path in the absorptive medium is approximately $\hbar v/2W$ where v is the velocity of the particle. From the success of the shell model it is apparent that the mean free path of nucleons in the lowest bound states of a nucleus is much greater than the length of a nucleon orbit, which is of the order of $2\pi a$. This gives an empirical limit on W for nucleons at energies a little above zero excitation; it must be much less than $\frac{1}{2}$ MeV (Elliott and Lane 1957). For higher excitation energies a calculation has been made of the mean free path of nucleons in 'infinite nuclear matter' as represented by a Fermi gas. In a classical system the mean free path would be simply the product of the reciprocals of the density ρ of particles in the matter and of the mean cross-section of a pair of nucleons $\langle\sigma\rangle$. This result is greatly increased if the Pauli principle is taken into account; collisions that would result in one or both of the particles occupying an already occupied state are no longer allowed. The value of W thus calculated varies from about 2 MeV at an incident nucleon energy of zero through 6 MeV at 10 MeV neutron energy to about 10 MeV maximum (Lane and Wandel 1955).

(b) *Intermediate coupling and the average wave-function*

In the single-particle model of nuclear reactions the resonance level eigenfunctions X_λ contain only one term in the expansion eqn. (6.2), namely, the one corresponding to the product of the channel state φ_c and the single-particle state $u_p(r)$. The coefficient C^λ_{cp} has the value unity for this term and all other coefficients are zero. In the opposite model, the statistical model, which is the extreme version of Bohr's compound-nucleus hypothesis, there are a large number of terms in the expansion of the wave function X_λ; the coefficients C^λ_{cp} that correspond to basis functions χ_{cp} far removed in energy from E_λ are assumed to be small but of the same order of magnitude as those of states that are close in energy. In other words, the single-particle states are assumed to be dissolved, by the residual nuclear forces, among the compound-nucleus states over an energy interval that is at least as great as the single-particle level spacing. This dissolution of the basis states φ_{cp} introduces the possibility of inelastic scattering by the resonance states X_λ.

It was proposed by Lane *et al.* (1955) that an intermediate situation is possible, the mixing effect of residual forces on the independent-particle states in the average potential field of the nucleons being neither so weak as to cause virtually no mixing nor so strong as to make a statistical description valid. This is the intermediate-coupling assumption whereby the coefficients C^{λ}_{cp} are appreciable in magnitude for states λ close to the energy E_{cp} of the basis states but are small elsewhere, as illustrated in Fig. 6.7. The reduced widths are related to the C^{λ}_{cp} by eqn. (6.10) and, if it is assumed that C^{λ}_{cp} have random signs for different c and p, this simplifies to

$$\gamma^2_{\lambda(\text{c})} = \left(\frac{\hbar^2}{2M_{\text{c}}a_{\text{c}}}\right)\sum_{\text{p}} C^{\lambda 2}_{\text{cp}} u_{\text{p}}(a_{\text{c}}). \tag{6.69}$$

The schematic behaviour of the reduced widths is shown in Fig. 6.7. It is expected that the mixing of independent-particle states will be limited to a small energy interval which depends on the strength of the residual nucleon interactions. Thus, the coefficients $C^{\lambda 2}_{\text{cp}}$ are expected to be roughly proportional to the level spacing $\bar{D}$, and the strength function $s_{\text{c}} = \overline{\gamma^2_{(\text{c})}}/\bar{D}$ consequently shows the giant resonance behaviour illustrated in Fig. 6.7.

The average wave-function of the compound system may be studied using the expected behaviour of the C^{λ}_{cp} on the intermediate coupling assumption. We shall confine this study to low neutron energies at which the off-diagonal elements of the level matrix **A** may be neglected. The internal wave-function of the system with unit flux in the entrance channel c is (from eqn. (2.53))

$$\Psi^{\prime(\text{c})} = \text{i}\hbar^{\frac{1}{2}}\text{e}^{-\text{i}\phi_{\text{c}}}\sum_{\lambda}\frac{(2P_{\text{c}})^{\frac{1}{2}}\gamma_{\lambda(\text{c})}X_{\lambda}}{E_{\lambda}-E-\frac{1}{2}\text{i}\Gamma_{\lambda(\text{T})}} \tag{6.70}$$

The projection of this upon the entrance-channel function φ_{c} is, from eqn. (6.2),

$$\psi_{\text{c}} = \int_{\mathscr{S}} \text{d}\mathscr{S}\,\Psi^{\prime(\text{c})}\varphi^*_{\text{c}} = \text{i}\hbar^{\frac{1}{2}}\text{e}^{-\text{i}\phi_{\text{c}}}\sum_{\text{p}}\sum_{\lambda}\frac{(2P_{\text{c}})^{\frac{1}{2}}\gamma_{\lambda(\text{c})}C^{\lambda}_{(\text{cp})}u_{\text{p}}(r_{\text{c}})}{E_{\lambda}-E-\frac{1}{2}\text{i}\Gamma_{\lambda(\text{T})}} \tag{6.71}$$

where the surface integral is calculated at an arbitrary target-projectile radius within the channel boundary a_{c}. Substitution of eqn. (6.9) for $\gamma_{\lambda(\text{c})}$ gives

$$\psi_{\text{c}} = \text{i}\hbar^{\frac{1}{2}}\left(\frac{\hbar^2 P_{\text{c}}}{M_{\text{c}}a_{\text{c}}}\right)^{\frac{1}{2}}\text{e}^{-\text{i}\phi_{\text{c}}}\sum_{\text{p}} u_{\text{p}}(a_{\text{c}})u_{\text{p}}(r_{\text{c}})\sum_{\lambda}\frac{C^{\lambda 2}_{\text{cp}}}{E_{\lambda}-E-\frac{1}{2}\text{i}\Gamma_{\lambda(\text{T})}} \tag{6.72}$$

On average, the part of ψ_c with the phase of $ie^{-i\phi_c}$ (the imaginary part in the limit $\phi_c \to 0$) vanishes for local levels λ but not for far-away levels. An explicit evaluation of the limiting imaginary part of eqn. (6.72) may be made if a form is assumed for the average behaviour of $\overline{C^{\lambda 2}_{cp}}$. It seems rather reasonable to assume a Lorentzian expression for $\overline{C^{\lambda 2}_{cp}}/\bar{D}_\lambda$:

$$\frac{\overline{C^{\lambda 2}_{cp}}}{\bar{D}_\lambda} = \frac{1}{\pi} \cdot \frac{W_p}{(E_{cp}-E_\lambda)^2+W_p^2}. \tag{6.73}$$

By contour integration, i $\mathrm{Im}(e^{i\phi_c}\psi_c)$ and hence ψ_c, if contributions of local levels are neglected, becomes

$$i\ \mathrm{Im}(e^{i\phi_c}\psi_c) \approx i\hbar^{\frac{1}{2}}\left(\frac{\hbar^2 P_c}{M_c a_c}\right)^{\frac{1}{2}} \sum_p \frac{(E_p-E)}{(E_p-E)^2+(W_p)^2} u_p(a_c)u_p(r_c). \tag{6.74}$$

The average of ψ_c over an interval of energy containing many local levels λ may also be evaluated by contour integration. First, the average of the resonance terms over the local energy interval is calculated giving

$$\overline{\sum_\lambda \frac{C^{\lambda 2}_{cp}}{E_\lambda - E - \frac{1}{2}i\Gamma_{\lambda(T)}}} = \sum_\lambda \frac{\overline{C^{\lambda 2}_{cp}}}{E_\lambda - E - \frac{1}{2}i(\Gamma_{\lambda(T)}+2I)} \tag{6.75}$$

where I is large compared with the level spacing $\bar{D}$ but small compared with W_p. The sum over λ is then replaced by an integral, which is evaluated by contour integration after substituting eqn. (6.73) for $\overline{C^{\lambda 2}_{cp}}$, with the result

$$\psi_c = i\hbar^{\frac{1}{2}}\left(\frac{\hbar^2 P_c}{M_c a_c}\right)^{\frac{1}{2}} e^{-i\phi_c} \sum_p \frac{u_p(a_c)u_p(r_c)}{E_p-E+iW_p}. \tag{6.76}$$

The right-hand side of this expression is just eqn. (6.66) for the wave function Ψ_{CP} for scattering by a square complex-potential well (with $W_p = W_0 + P\gamma_p^2$), showing that the average of the projected wave ψ_c of the actual nuclear scattering can be represented by the complex-potential model provided that the coefficients of expansion of the compound-nucleus wave-function have the average behaviour assumed in eqn. (6.73). Furthermore, the imaginary part of $e^{i\phi_c}\psi_c$, neglecting local level fluctuations, is equal to the imaginary part of the average of $e^{i\phi_c}\psi_c$ showing that $\mathrm{Im}(e^{i\phi_c}\psi_c)$ represents the effect of distant levels at energy E. The real part of $e^{i\phi_c}\psi_c$ on the other hand, i.e. Re $(e^{i\phi_c}\Psi_{CP})$

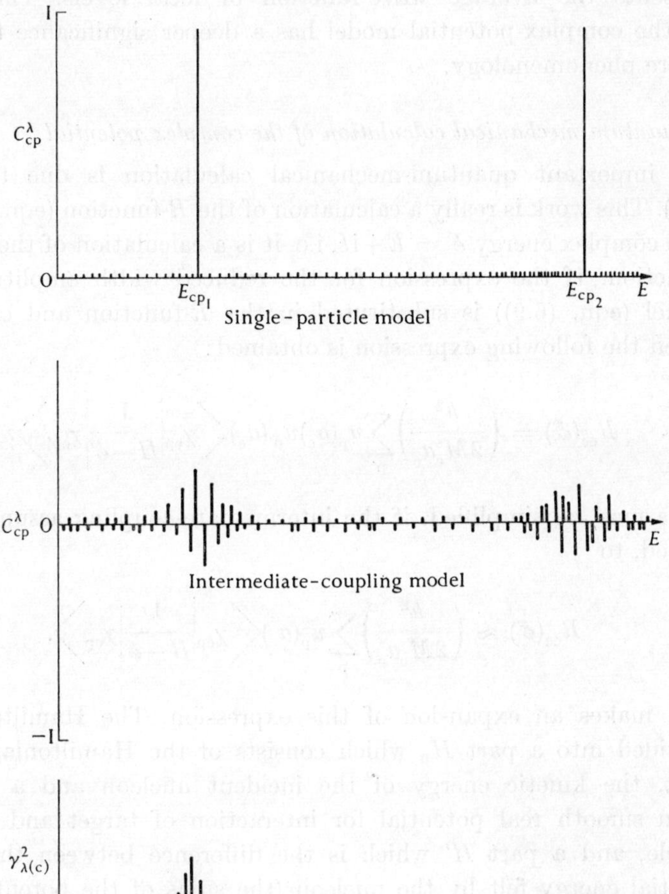

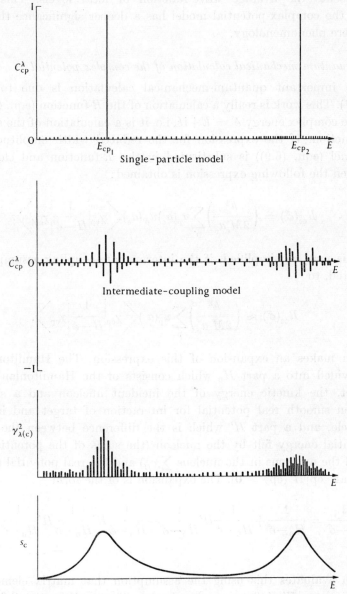

FIG. 6.7. Diagram of the expansion coefficients of the internal eigenfunctions X_λ for a single channel c. The top part is for a single-particle model, the lengths of the vertical lines indicating the size of the expansion coefficients; the very short vertical lines therein are meant to indicate zero coefficients. In the lower part of the figure it is shown how the expansion coefficients for the intermediate-coupling model give the reduced widths of the compound states λ and hence the strength function.

represents the average wave-function of local levels. This shows that the complex-potential model has a deeper significance than one of mere phenomenology.

(c) *Quantum mechanical calculation of the complex potential*

An important quantum-mechanical calculation is due to Bloch (1957). This work is really a calculation of the R-function (eqn. (6.15b)) at the complex energy $\mathscr{E} = E+\mathrm{i}I$, i.e. it is a calculation of the average R-function. If the expression for the reduced width amplitude of a channel (eqn. (6.9)) is substituted in the R-function and closure is applied the following expression is obtained:

$$R_{\mathrm{cc}}(\mathscr{E}) = \left(\frac{\hbar^2}{2M_{\mathrm{c}}a_{\mathrm{c}}}\right)\sum_{\mathrm{p}'} u_{\mathrm{p}}(a_{\mathrm{c}})u_{\mathrm{p}'}(a_{\mathrm{c}})\left\langle \chi_{\mathrm{cp}}\left|\frac{1}{H-\mathscr{E}}\right|\chi_{\mathrm{cp}'}\right\rangle. \tag{6.77}$$

This may be simplified, if the intermediate-coupling assumption is adopted, to

$$R_{\mathrm{cc}}(\mathscr{E}) \approx \left(\frac{\hbar^2}{2M_{\mathrm{c}}a_{\mathrm{c}}}\right)\sum_{\mathrm{p}} u_{\mathrm{p}}^2(a_{\mathrm{c}})\left\langle \chi_{\mathrm{cp}}\left|\frac{1}{H-\mathscr{E}}\right|\chi_{\mathrm{cp}}\right\rangle. \tag{6.78}$$

Bloch makes an expansion of this expression. The Hamiltonian H is divided into a part H_0 which consists of the Hamiltonian of the target, the kinetic energy of the incident nucleon and a suitably chosen smooth real potential for interaction of target and incident particle, and a part H' which is the difference between the actual potential energy felt by the nucleon (the sums of the potentials due to all the nucleons in the nucleus $\sum_i v_{ij}$) and the real potential (chosen so that $\langle \mathrm{cp}|H'|\mathrm{cp}\rangle = 0$). The expansion is of the form

$$\frac{1}{H-\mathscr{E}} = \frac{1}{H_0-\mathscr{E}}+\frac{1}{H_0-\mathscr{E}}H'\frac{1}{H_0-\mathscr{E}}+\frac{1}{H_0-\mathscr{E}}H'\frac{1}{H_0-\mathscr{E}}H'\frac{1}{H_0-\mathscr{E}}+\ldots \tag{6.79}$$

Bloch evaluates this using the assumption that matrix elements of the type $\langle \mathrm{cp}|H'|\mathrm{c'p'}\rangle$ are random in sign. The result for the R-function is

$$R_{\mathrm{cc}}(\mathscr{E}) \approx \sum_{\mathrm{p}} \frac{(a_{\mathrm{c}}/2)u_{\mathrm{p}}^2(a_{\mathrm{c}})(\hbar^2/M_{\mathrm{c}}a_{\mathrm{c}}^2)}{E_{\mathrm{cp}}+\Delta_{\mathrm{cp}}(E)-\mathscr{E}-\mathrm{i}W_{\mathrm{cp}}(E)} \tag{6.80a}$$

where the quantity Δ_{cp} has the form, in the limit of Im $\mathscr{E} \to 0$,

$$\Delta_{\mathrm{cp}}(E) \approx \mathrm{Pr}\int \frac{|\langle \mathrm{cp}|H'|\mathrm{c'p'}\rangle|^2}{E - E_{\mathrm{c'p'}}} \rho_{\mathrm{c'p'}}(E_{\mathrm{c'p'}})dE_{\mathrm{c'p'}} \tag{6.80b}$$

and W_{cp} is

$$W_{\mathrm{cp}}(E) = \pi\rho_{\mathrm{c'p'}}(E)|\langle \mathrm{cp}|H'|\mathrm{c'p'}\rangle|^2_E \tag{6.80c}$$

where $\rho_{\mathrm{c'p'}}(E)$ is the density of channel-particle states other than cp at energy E.

Provided that $W_{\mathrm{cp}}(E)$ of eqn. (6.80c) is not too sensitive to p and that $\Delta_{\mathrm{cp}}(E)$ is not strongly dependent on E it is plausible that it should be possible to find a potential with the eigenvalues $E = E'_{\mathrm{p}} + E_{\mathrm{c}} + \Delta_{\mathrm{cp}} = E_{\mathrm{pc}} + \Delta_{\mathrm{cp}}$ where the E'_{p} are the eigenvalues for the original real potential V. It is shown by Bloch that the real part of the required potential is

$$V_{\mathrm{c}} = \left\langle \mathrm{cp}\left|\sum_j v_{ij}\right|\mathrm{cp}\right\rangle + \int dE_{\mathrm{c'p'}}\rho_{\mathrm{c'p'}}(E_{\mathrm{c'p'}}) \frac{\left|\left\langle \mathrm{cp}\left|\sum_j v_{ij}\right|\mathrm{c'p'}\right\rangle\right|^2}{E - E_{\mathrm{c'p'}}}. \tag{6.81}$$

Arguments for the mild and smooth dependence of V_{c} and W_{cp} on energy are given by Brown (1959).

Equation (6.80a) is very similar in form to eqn. (6.63a) if the identifications $E = \mathscr{E}$, $E_{\mathrm{p}} = E_{\mathrm{cp}} + \Delta_{\mathrm{cp}}(E)$ and $W_0 = W_{\mathrm{cp}}(E)$ are made. This suggests the validity of using a complex-potential model to calculate the average collision functions and its associated cross-sections given in eqns. (6.14), (6.25), and (6.29). Of course, eqn. (6.80a) is only valid in the region of each single-particle level E_{cp} because of the cancellation of cross terms $\mathrm{p} \neq \mathrm{p'}$ in the approximations leading to it, and only then if the W_{cp} are small compared with the single-particle level spacings. The last condition is demanded by the assumed giant-resonance behaviour, in the large, of the coefficients $C^{\lambda 2}_{\mathrm{cp}}$ around the energies E_{cp}; this leads to the same behaviour in the reduced widths and in the strength function, and peaking in the strength function of a complex potential depends on the smallness of W_0 (eqn. (6.65)).

Some evaluations of eqn. (6.80c) have been made for a Fermi gas. The results are very similar to those of the 'semi-classical' calculation for W (Cini and Fubini 1955). Two further refinements of the theory have opposite effects (Elliott and Lane 1957). If the real part of the potential is velocity-dependent the value of W is decreased. The expected velocity-dependence would cause a reduction by a factor of 20. On the other hand if the temperature of the Fermi gas is greater than zero the Pauli principle is not so effective in forbidding collisions and W is raised. This would apply if the residual nucleus in the channel were in an excited state. The results of the various calculations and the analysis of experimental data all justify the assumption made in the theory that W is small compared with V for low and intermediate nucleon energies, or, more fundamentally, that the intermediate coupling assumption of Lane *et al.* (1956) is correct.

Equation (6.63a) is an accurate representation of the R-function for a complex potential well only if the imaginary part is constant to the radius at which R is evaluated. However, it is an approximation to the R-function in the neighbourhood of the single-particle levels for other forms of the imaginary part; this is demonstrated by eqn. (6.68a) for the extreme surface-coupling model of Section C.3. We may assume from this that the approximation (6.80a) does not imply that W_{cp} has to be radially constant. The radial form of W may be inferred by evaluating R_{cc} of eqn. (6.80) as a function of radius. It is apparent that

$$W_{\mathrm{cp}}(r) = \pi\rho_{\mathrm{c'p'}}(E)\overline{|\langle \mathrm{cp}|H'|\mathrm{c'p'}\rangle_{\mathscr{S}}|_{\mathrm{E}}^{2}} \tag{6.82}$$

where the subscript $\mathscr{S}$ indicates evaluation of the matrix element over the channel surface at r_{c}. The matrix element of eqn. (6.80c) implies integration over the radial parameter r_{c} as far as the channel surface. The effect of the radial dependence of W on the strength function has been found by Porter (1955) to be approximated by

$$s = \frac{M}{2\pi^2\hbar^2\alpha}\int \mathrm{d}r\,W(r)|u(r)|^2 \tag{6.83}$$

where $u(r)$ is the particle wave-function in the complex potential.

D. REFINEMENTS OF THE COMPLEX-POTENTIAL MODEL

1. Radial form of the potential

(a) *General discussion*

The availability of a theoretical foundation for the complex-potential model and the promising results of its application to the analysis of experimental data have stimulated much work on the extension and refinement of the model. The most obvious improvement on the square complex potential is the modification of its edge, as discussed in Chapter III for a real potential, so that the potential changes rather gradually to zero.

A form for this surface diffuseness that can be treated analytically for s-wave neutrons has been discussed by Fiedeldey and Frahn (1962):

$$\begin{aligned} V(r) &= V_0\{1-\rho_1(r)\},\ r \leqslant a_0 \\ &= 0,\ r > a_0 \end{aligned} \tag{6.84a}$$

$$\begin{aligned} W(r) &= -W_1\{1-\rho_1(r)\}-W_2\rho_1(r),\ r \leqslant a_0 \\ &= -W_2\rho_2(r),\ r > a_0 \end{aligned} \tag{6.84b}$$

where $\rho_n(r) = [\cosh\{(a_0-r)/d_n\}]^{-2}$. The radius of the well at half the central value of the potential $V(0)$ is $a = a_0 - d_1 \cosh^{-1}\sqrt{2} = a_0 - 0{\cdot}8814\, d_1$. This potential will describe surface as well as volume absorption, through the term in W_2, and its shape can be made similar to the Woods–Saxon potential, which is commonly used in numerical complex well analyses. It is interesting to note that the centre of the surface absorption term lies outside the nuclear radius a as proposed in the theory of Gomes (1959) by about the correct order of magnitude. The diffuseness coefficient d_1 is related to the equivalent quantity d of the Eckart potential (eqn. (3.11)) by the numerical formula $d_1 = 2{\cdot}949\, d$. One would expect d_1 to lie between 1 and 2 fm therefore. Setting d_1 equal to zero gives the complex square well. Increasing d_1 to between 1 and 2 fm has the following effects, at low neutron energies, on the size resonance in the s-wave neutron strength function. The peaks of the strength function are shifted to lower mass numbers. The strength function curve as a whole is raised considerably. The widths of the peaks in the strength function also increase. The average value of the potential scattering cross-section is raised and the separation of the pair of extrema in R^∞ associated with each strength function peak is increased.

Some of these effects can be inferred from the approximate expression (eqn. (6.63a)) for the R-function of the complex potential. The reduced widths γ_p^2 of the single-particle states increase as the boundary of the well is softened: there is less reflection of the wave at the edge (see eqn. (3.12)). According to eqn. (6.65) this accounts for the general increase in the strength function. For low neutron energy a size resonance occurs when the potential well has a radius at which an eigenvalue E_p occurs at zero energy. The radial dependence of such an eigenvalue depends on the diffuseness of the well edge. In a square well the bound eigenvalue approaches zero energy sharply as the well radius is decreased but in a diffuse well this approach is much more gradual. It follows that in the diffuse well the eigenvalue lies close to zero energy over a much greater range of mass numbers and the width of the size resonance is correspondingly increased. The greater binding of the single-particle state in the diffuse well also accounts for the lower mass numbers at which the strength-function peaks occur.

(b) Numerical computations

These features have also been noted in numerical computations. Such computations have played an important part in analysis of neutron strength-function data, so a word might be said here about the technique of making them. The solution of the Schrödinger equation for relative motion in a central potential $\mathscr{V}(r)$ is separable into a spherical harmonic $Y_m^{(l)}(\theta, \phi)$ and a part $R(r)$ depending on the radius coordinate r. The second order differential equation for the radial wave-function $\psi(r)$ $(=rR(r))$ is

$$-\frac{\hbar^2}{2M}\frac{d^2\psi}{dr^2}+\left\{\mathscr{V}(r)+\frac{\hbar^2 l(l+1)}{2Mr^2}\right\}\psi = E\psi \tag{6.85}$$

where M is the reduced mass of the relative motion. Usually, the nature of the potential energy is that it is constant (and strongly negative) for small values of the radius, rises gradually through the surface region and becomes asymptotically zero for large values of the radius. In the constant central part the solutions of eqn. (6.85) are the products of ρ with the spherical Bessel and Neumann function $j_l(\rho)$ and $n_l(\rho)$ the complex argument ρ being

$$\rho = \rho_1+\mathrm{i}\rho_2 = r\sqrt{\left\{\frac{2M}{\hbar^2}(E-\mathscr{V}(0))\right\}}. \tag{6.86}$$

We shall denote the coefficient of r in this equation by $\mathscr{K}$. The physical requirements demand that the solution of eqn. (6.85) shall be regular at $r = 0$ giving $\rho j_0(\rho)$ as the required solution at small r. For the s-wave case this is just

$$\rho j_0(\rho) = \cosh\rho_2\sin\rho_1+\mathrm{i}\sinh\rho_2\cos\rho_1 \tag{6.87}$$

with the derivative (with respect to r)

$$(\rho j_0(\rho))' = \frac{(\rho_2-\mathrm{i}\rho_1)}{r}\sinh\rho_2\sin\rho_1+\frac{(\rho_1+\mathrm{i}\rho_2)}{r}\cosh\rho_2\cos\rho_1. \tag{6.88}$$

For p-waves the solution is

$$\rho j_1(\rho) = \frac{1}{2\mathrm{i}}\{e^{\mathrm{i}\rho}-e^{-\mathrm{i}\rho}+\mathrm{i}\rho(e^{\mathrm{i}\rho}+e^{-\mathrm{i}\rho})\}. \tag{6.89}$$

For higher values of l the solutions are calculated from the Bessel function recurrence relations

$$j_l(\rho) = \frac{2l-1}{\rho} j_{l-1}(\rho) - j_{l-2}(\rho) \tag{6.90}$$

and the derivatives from the relation

$$\frac{\mathrm{d}j_l}{\mathrm{d}r} = \frac{\mathscr{K}}{2l+1}\{l j_{l-1}(\rho) - (l+1) j_{l+1}(\rho)\}. \tag{6.91}$$

These solutions and derivatives at some small (but non-zero) value of r provide the starting point for step-by-step numerical integration of eqn. (6.85) by a standard technique such as the Runge–Kutte method (see, e.g., Margenau and Murphy 1948). For this purpose eqn. (6.85) must be broken into its real and imaginary parts. Let us write

$$\psi(r) = v(r) + \mathrm{i}w(r) \text{ and } \mathscr{V}(r) = V(r) - \mathrm{i}W(r).$$

Then eqn. 6.85 becomes

$$\frac{\mathrm{d}^2 v}{\mathrm{d}r^2} + \frac{2M}{\hbar^2}\{E - V(r)\}v - \frac{2M}{\hbar^2} W(r) w - \frac{l(l+1)v}{r^2} = 0, \tag{6.92a}$$

$$\frac{\mathrm{d}^2 w}{\mathrm{d}r^2} + \frac{2M}{\hbar^2}\{E - V(r)\}w + \frac{2M}{\hbar^2} W(r) v - \frac{l(l+1)w}{r^2} = 0. \tag{6.92b}$$

The integration of these equations proceeds to some value of r (r' say) within the asymptotic region and the solution there must be matched to the general form of superposed incoming and outgoing waves $I_l - U_l O_l$, and this matching determines the collision function U_l:

$$U_l = \frac{\psi'(r') I_l - \psi(r') I_l'}{\psi'(r') O_l - \psi(r') O_l'}. \tag{6.93}$$

The R-function of the model (and hence the average R-function of the actual problem) may be found from this by using eqn. (6.15a). If in particular $\hat{S}_l (= \mathrm{Re}\,\hat{L}_l)$ is assumed to be zero (the physical assumption) we find

$$R_l = \frac{U_l - \exp(-2\mathrm{i}\phi_l)}{\mathrm{i}P_l\{U_l + \exp(-2\mathrm{i}\phi_l)\}}. \tag{6.94}$$

The real and imaginary parts of this are just the distant level parameter (which modifies the potential scattering term) and the strength function, respectively, of eqns. (6.16) and (6.17). The quantities of interest for direct comparison with the data are $P_l R_l^\infty$ and $P_l s_l$.

The usual form of well employed in numerical investigations of the optical model is the complex generalization of the Eckart potential (eqn. 3.11); it is usually called the Woods–Saxon (1954) potential. Volume absorption in this potential is usually represented by an imaginary component with the same radial dependence as the real part, and surface absorption by an imaginary Gaussian term centred (usually) at the well radius a. The parameters for the Eckart potential that were found by Ross *et al.* (1956) (see below eqn. (3.22)) imply that the $3s$ and $4s$ single-particle levels should reach zero energy at mass numbers 60 and 170 respectively (see Fig. 3.3). These are only slightly higher than the observed positions of the strength-function maxima. This confirms that the potential required to give the properties of occupied shell-model states offers also a reasonable description of low-energy neutron scattering.

Vogt (1962) has analysed the neutron strength-function data in an attempt to determine independently the value of d to be used in the Woods–Saxon potential. In this analysis the problem is simplified by assuming the imaginary component of the potential to be square. Numerical calculations indicate that the differences in phase shift between this potential and the correct Woods–Saxon form are small provided that W is small compared to V. The R-function for the well has the approximate form of eqn. (6.63a) with the reduced widths γ_p^2 given by eqn. (3.12). If the strength function, eqn. (6.65), derived from eqn. (6.63a), is integrated over a single giant resonance the result is (for small W_0)

$$\int \mathrm{d}E s(E) \approx \gamma_\mathrm{p}^2 = \frac{\hbar^2}{Ma^2}(1+6{\cdot}7d^2), \tag{6.95}$$

where d is in fm. Vogt has numerically integrated the neutron strength-function data for the $4s$ giant resonance (from mass number 95, $Ka = 3\pi$ to mass number 230, $Ka = 4\pi$) with a suitable weighting factor to remove the dependence on nuclear radius, and has compared the result with eqn. (6.95) to obtain a value of $d = 0{\cdot}31 \pm 0{\cdot}06$ fm. The result will probably not be affected by collective couplings (see Section D.2). It could be affected by the radial dependence of the imaginary component. Vogt has checked this numerically using a Gaussian form for W, the peak being centred at a, having a width of 1 fm and a peak value of 9·5 MeV. The result for the diffuseness parameter is not changed appreciably. A much more important defect of the method is that it ignores the possible variation of the imaginary component with mass number (see Section D.6).

The most careful recent attempt at fitting the strength function data with the spherical potential is due to Moldauer (1963). His fit over the data from $A = 40$ to 140 is shown in Fig. 6.8. In the real part of the

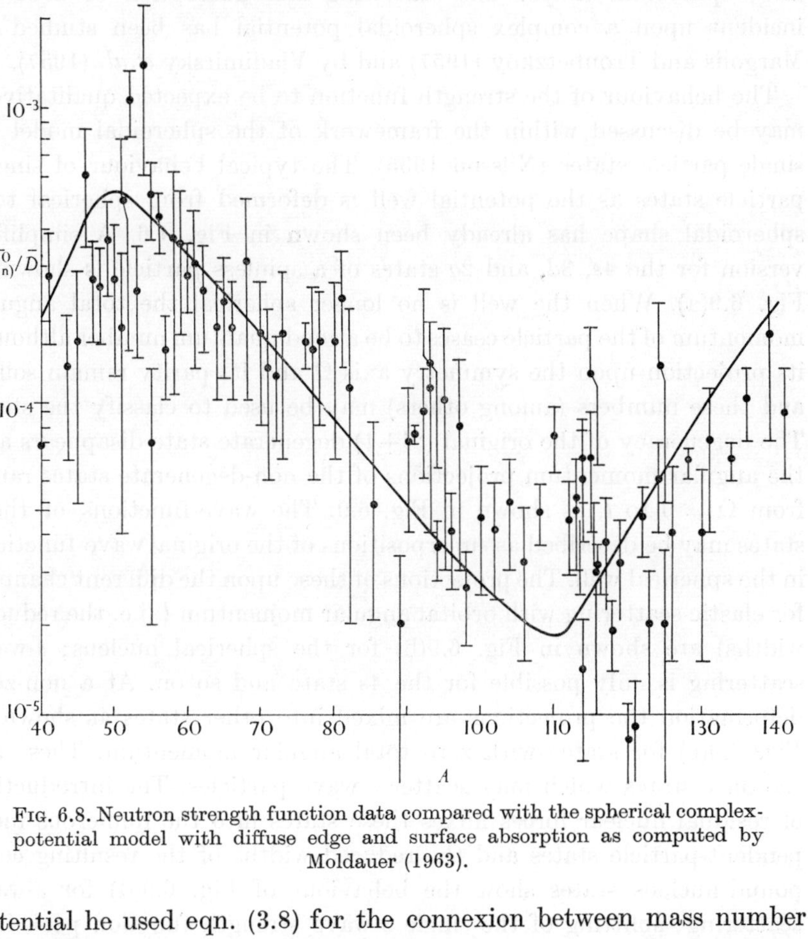

FIG. 6.8. Neutron strength function data compared with the spherical complex-potential model with diffuse edge and surface absorption as computed by Moldauer (1963).

potential he used eqn. (3.8) for the connexion between mass number and radius, with $r_0 = 1{\cdot}16$ fm and $b = 0{\cdot}6$ fm; this is equivalent to $r_0 \approx 1{\cdot}3$ fm in eqn. (3.7), over this mass number range. The well depth was $V_0 = -46$ MeV and the diffuseness parameter $d = 0{\cdot}62$ fm. The imaginary component of the potential was a Gaussian surface term of width dispersion 0·35 fm, magnitude $W_0 = 14$ MeV and centred 0·5 fm outside the potential radius.

2. Deformation from sphericity

Another necessary improvement in the shape of the model is to include the possibility of the target not being truly spherical. It is well known, mainly from studies of the quadrupole moments of the ground states, that nuclei in the mass number ranges 150 to 190 and above 224 are permanently deformed. They are generally assumed to have spheroidal shape. The scattering and absorption of neutrons incident upon a complex spheroidal potential has been studied by Margolis and Troubetzkoy (1957) and by Vladimirsky *et al.* (1957).

The behaviour of the strength function to be expected qualitatively may be discussed within the framework of the spheroidal model for single-particle states (Nilsson 1955). The typical behaviour of single-particle states as the potential well is deformed from spherical to a spheroidal shape has already been shown in Fig. 4.6. A simplified version for the $4s$, $3d$, and $2g$ states of a spinless particle is shown in Fig. 6.9(a). When the well is no longer spherical the total angular momentum of the particle ceases to be a good quantum number although its projection upon the symmetry axis Ω and its parity remain sound and these numbers (among others) may be used to classify the state. The degeneracy of the original $(2l+1)$ degenerate state disappears and the angular momentum projections of the non-degenerate states range from $\Omega = 0$ to l, as shown in Fig. 6.9. The wave-functions of these states may be described as superpositions of the original wave-functions in the spherical well. The projections of these upon the different channels for elastic scattering with orbital angular momentum l (i.e. the reduced widths) are shown in Fig. 6.9(b) for the spherical nucleus; s-wave scattering is only possible for the $4s$ state and so on. At a non-zero deformation the projections are mixed into other states as shown in Fig. 6.9(c) for states with zero total angular momentum. These are the only states which may scatter s-wave particles. The introduction of residual nuclear forces mixes these states into the numerous independent-particle states and the reduced widths of the resulting compound-nucleus states show the behaviour of Fig. 6.9(d) for s-wave scattering; splitting of the single s-wave strength function peak into two or more components is to be expected.

A useful expansion for a surface differing not too greatly from spherical is the following:

$$a(\theta, \phi) = a_0\left\{1+\sum_{\lambda\geqslant 2}^{\infty}\sum_{\mu=-\lambda}^{\lambda}\alpha_{\lambda\mu}Y_{\mu}^{(\lambda)}(\theta, \phi)\right\} \tag{6.96}$$

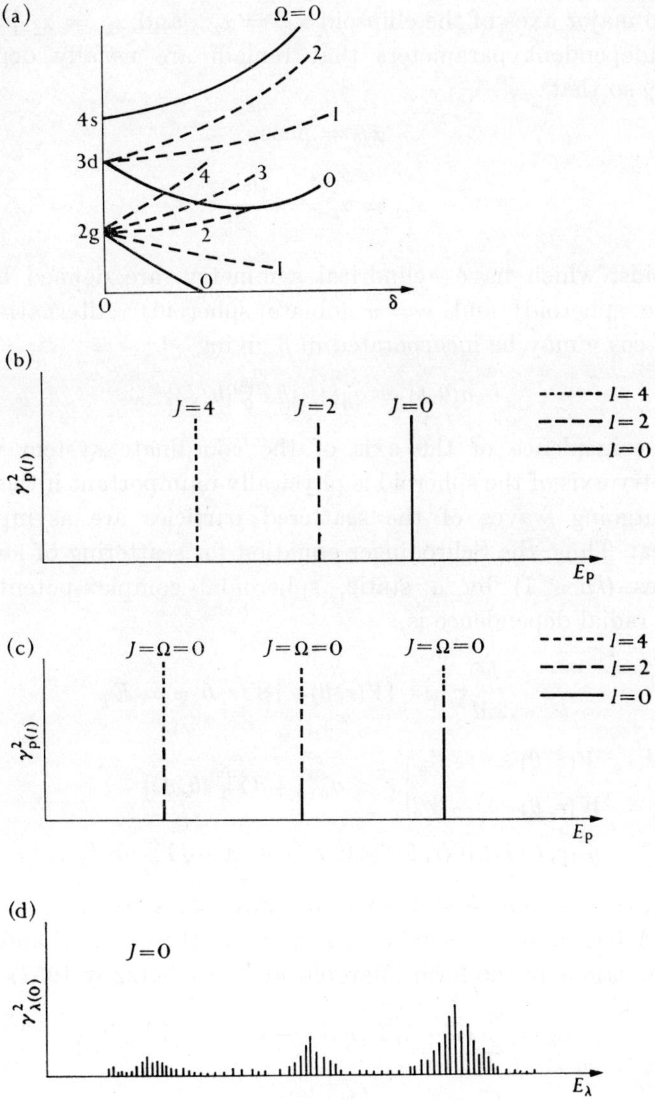

FIG. 6.9. Effect of nuclear deformation on dissolution of single-particle states amongst compound states.

where the $Y_{\mu}^{(\lambda)}$ are spherical harmonics and the $\alpha_{\lambda\mu}$ are expansion coefficients. If the surface is an ellipsoid the expansion is limited to the terms in $\lambda = 2$ and if, further, the polar and azimuthal angles θ and ϕ refer to major axes of the ellipsoid $\alpha_{22} = \alpha_{2-2}$ and $\alpha_{21} = \alpha_{2-1} = 0$. The two independent parameters that remain are usually denoted by β and γ so that

$$\alpha_{20} = \beta\cos\gamma, \tag{6.97a}$$

$$\alpha_{22} = \alpha_{2-2} = \frac{\beta\sin\gamma}{2^{\frac{1}{2}}}. \tag{6.97b}$$

Spheroids, which have cylindrical symmetry, are defined by $\gamma = 0$ (prolate spheroid) and $\gamma = \pi$ (oblate spheroid). Alternatively, the sign of cos γ may be incorporated in β giving

$$a(\theta,\phi) = a_0\{1+\beta Y_0^{(2)}(\theta, \phi)\}. \tag{6.98}$$

The coincidence of the axis of the coordinate system with the symmetry axis of the spheroid is physically unimportant if the incident and outgoing waves of the scattered particles are asymptotically spherical. Thus, the Schrödinger equation for scattering of low-energy particles ($ka \ll 1$) by a static, spheroidal complex-potential with square radial dependence is

$$-\frac{\hbar^2}{2M}\nabla^2\psi+\{V(r, \theta)+iW(r, \theta\}\psi = E\psi \tag{6.99}$$

$$\left.\begin{aligned} V(r, \theta) &= -V_0 \\ W(r, \theta) &= -W_0 \end{aligned}\right\}, r < a_0\{1+\beta Y_0^{(2)}(\theta, \phi)\}$$

$$V(r, \theta) = W(r, \theta) = 0,\ r > a_0\{1+\beta Y_0^{(2)}(\theta, \phi)\}.$$

This wave equation is not separable into parts referring to r and θ alone. A technique for solving it is to write the external and internal wave-functions in the form (Margolis and Troubetzkoy 1957)

$$\psi_e = \sum_l (2l+1)^{\frac{1}{2}} i^l \{I_l(kr) - U_l O_l(kr)\}\, Y_0^{(l)}(\theta, \phi) \tag{6.100a}$$

$$\psi_i = \sum_l A_l j_l(Kr) Y_0^{(l)}(\theta,\phi) \tag{6.100b}$$

where the I_l and O_l are the ingoing and outgoing free waves of eqn. (2.6), k and K are the wave numbers outside and inside the well respectively.

The functions ψ_e and ψ_i and their radial derivatives must be equated at the edge of the well, $a = a_0(1+\beta Y_0^{(2)}(\theta,\phi))$ in order to determine the scattering coefficients U_l. Because the Schrödinger equation, eqn. (6.99), is invariant with respect to reflections through the origin (parity conservation) only terms of a single parity need be included in these equations, i.e. the sums over l need contain only the even ($l = 0, 2, 4, \ldots$) or odd ($l = 1, 3, 5, \ldots$) sequences. Since the model is used for studying low-energy scattering only the even l sequence is important. The equations are solved in practice by cutting off the l sums beyond a given high value $l = L$ (for example, $L = 8$). The $L/2$ roots, $\cos\theta_i = \mu_i$, of the Legendre polynomical $P_L(\mu)$ are substituted in turn into the equations to give L simultaneous linear equations from which the A_l and U_l may be found, and from the latter the strength function may be determined (eqn. (6.15)). The effect of the deformation is, as we expected, to split a single strength-function resonance of a spherical well into two major components. The splitting of these components increases with increasing deformation while minor structure also appears. Such a splitting is qualitatively confirmed by the results of neutron resonance studies in the mass number region $A = 150$ to $A = 180$.

3. Coupling to collective modes of the target

At a deeper level it must be recognized that a deformed nucleus is not simply to be represented by a static potential well but that it also has dynamic collective properties associated with it. Thus, in the bombardment of a spheroidal object by particles it is apparent that the target may be set into rotation. The coupling of the target to its rotational modes has to be considered in calculating the scattering. A similar statement is true if a spherical target has any collective modes which may be excited. The typical situation here is that the target may execute a quadrupole vibration about its mean spherical shape.

The Hamiltonian of the target-nucleon system consists of three parts: the Hamiltonian of the collective motion of the target, the kinetic energy of the bombarding nucleon and the potential energy of this nucleon in the field of the target. The last part can be expressed as the sum of a mean central potential and potential energy terms that depend on the collective coordinates of the target. If the latter are ignored, the eigenfunctions of the Hamiltonian are essentially simple products between the wave-function of the nucleon in the central potential and the collective wave-function of the target. It is probably simplest to think of these eigenstates as the discrete states that would be obtained by imposition of the R-matrix boundary condition. For spinless target and projectile, neighbouring states of total angular momentum $J = 0$ would be of the types $[u_{ns}, \chi_{0+}]^{J=0}$ (the s-wave single-particle state, with principal quantum number n, coupled to the lowest

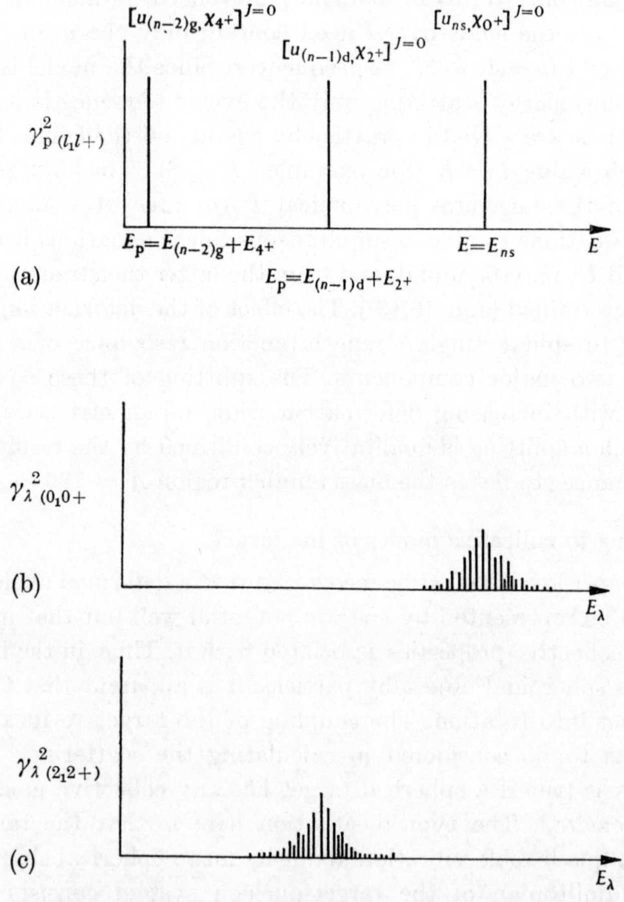

FIG. 6.10. Reduced widths for single-particle states coupled to collective states of the target (a) and after the resulting dissolution amongst compound states in the absence of the coupling term between single-particle and collective motion in the Hamiltonian; reduced widths for s-wave elastic scattering (b); and d-wave inelastic scattering to the 2^+ state (c).

collective state, the ground state, of spin and parity $0+$), $[u_{(n-1)d}, \chi_{2+}]^{J=0}$, $[u_{(n-2)g}, \chi_{4+}]^{J=0}$, and so on. The reduced widths γ_p^2 of these states can be obtained by suitable application of eqn. (2.20a) and are shown schematically in Fig. 6.10(a). According to the interpretation of Lane *et al.* (1955) these states are dissolved among the actual resonance levels as illustrated in Fig. 6.10(b) and (c). The reduced widths shown in Fig. 6.10(b) correspond to s-wave particles in the channel leaving the residual nucleus in the ground state 0^+ and those in Fig. 6.10(c) to d-wave particles leaving the nucleus in the collective 2^+ state.

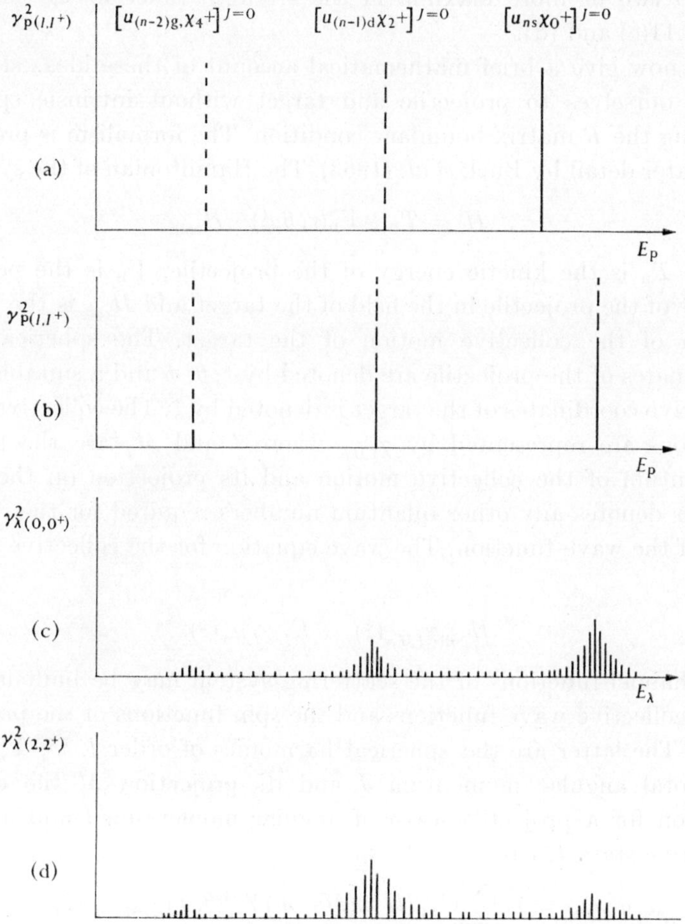

FIG. 6.11. Reduced widths for single-particle states coupled to collective target states (a), after their mixing and shifting due to the coupling term in the Hamiltonian (b), and dissolution amongst the compound states ((c) and (d)).

For each channel there is a single giant resonance in the strength function corresponding to each principal quantum number.

On including the potential energy terms that depend on the collective coordinates we require new eigenfunctions. An expansion of these in terms of the product functions is suitable. The introduction of the extra potential terms causes the 'repulsion' of the closest levels of the basis system as illustrated in Figs. 6.11(a) and (b) and the product functions are mixed as the reduced width values on this figure show. The dissolution of these states among the resonance levels now gives rise to two or more maxima in the strength functions as shown in Fig. 6.11(c) and (d).

We now give a brief mathematical account of these ideas still confining ourselves to projectile and target without intrinsic spin but relaxing the R-matrix boundary condition. The formalism is presented in greater detail by Buck *et al.* (1963). The Hamiltonian of the system is

$$H = T_{\mathrm{n}}+V_{\mathrm{n}}(r, \theta,\phi)+H_{\mathrm{coll}} \tag{6.101}$$

where T_{n} is the kinetic energy of the projectile, V_{n} is the potential energy of the projectile in the field of the target and H_{coll} is the Hamiltonian of the collective motion of the target. The spherical polar coordinates of the projectile are denoted by r, θ, ϕ and a suitable set of collective coordinates of the target is denoted by ξ. The collective wave-functions are represented by $\chi_{IM_I\nu}$ where I and M_I are the angular momentum of the collective motion and its projection on the z-axis while ν denotes any other quantum numbers required for the description of the wave-function. The wave equation for the collective motion is just

$$H_{\mathrm{coll}}\chi_{IM_I\nu}(\xi) = E_{I\nu}\chi_{IM_I\nu}(\xi). \tag{6.102}$$

The channel functions of the scattering system may be built up from these collective wave-functions and the spin functions of the projectile wave. The latter are the spherical harmonics of order l, m, $Y_m^{(l)}(\theta,\phi)$. For total angular momentum J and its projection M the channel function for a projectile wave of angular momentum l and a target collective state I, ν is

$$\varphi_{\nu lIJM} = r^{-1}\sum_m C_{JM}(lI:mM-m)Y_m^{(l)}(\theta,\phi)\chi_{IM-m\nu}(\xi) \tag{6.103}$$

where the $C_{JM}(lI;mM-m)$ are the Clebsch–Gordan coefficients. The channel functions and radial wave-functions, $u_{lI\nu}^J(r)$, for the target in state $I\nu$, are combined to obtain the complete wave-functions for given J and M:

$$\psi_{JM} = \sum_{l'I'\nu'} u_{l'I'\nu'}^J(r)\varphi_{\nu'l'I'JM}(\theta,\phi,\xi). \tag{6.104}$$

This satisfies the Schrödinger equation $H\psi_{JM} = E\psi_{JM}$. The radial wave-function for the target ground state has the usual form of ingoing and outgoing wave and for the other target states is simply an outgoing wave. It is the object of the calculation to find the coefficients of the outgoing waves. A general form of expansion for the potential energy V_{n} in terms of spherical tensors is available (Buck *et al.* 1963) but we prefer to confine ourselves to a more specialized expansion in spherical harmonics:

$$V(r, \theta, \phi, \xi) = v_0(r, \xi) + \sum_{\lambda \geqslant 2} \sum_{\mu=-\lambda}^{\lambda} v_{\lambda\mu}(r, \xi) Y_{\mu}^{(\lambda)}(\theta, \phi). \qquad (6.105)$$

This expansion is substituted in the Hamiltonian operator (eqn. (6.101)) of the Schrödinger equation, from which a set of coupled differential equations for the radial wave-functions is obtained by use of the orthogonality relations of the channel functions. The coupled equations have the form

$$\frac{\mathrm{d}^2 u^J_{l'I'v'}}{\mathrm{d}r^2} + \left[\frac{2M}{\hbar^2}\{E - E_{\mathrm{coll},\,I'v'} - V^{00}_{v'v'}(r)\} - \frac{l'(l'+1)}{r^2}\right] u^J_{l'I'v''}$$
$$-\frac{2M}{\hbar^2} \sum_{v'' \neq v'} V^{00}_{v'v''}(r) u^J_{l'I'v''} + \frac{2M}{\hbar^2} \sum_{\lambda \geqslant 2} \sum_{\mu} \sum_{l''I''v''} \langle l''I''; J | Y^{(\lambda)}_{\mu} | l'I'; J \rangle$$
$$\times V^{\lambda\mu}_{v'v''}(r) u^J_{l''I''v''} = 0, \qquad (6.106)$$

where $V^{\lambda\mu}_{v'v''}(r) = \langle v' | v_{\lambda\mu}(r, \xi) | v'' \rangle$. To be manipulated, these equations must be reduced by consideration of the physics of special cases.

(a) Permanently-deformed rotating nuclei

If the collective motion is pure rotation of a body with fixed shape the collective wave-function need only be characterized by its angular momentum quantum number I. The collective coordinates ξ are specified by the single parameter β which defines the eccentricity of the spheroid (see eqn. (6.97a)). For an even nucleus with zero-spin ground state the energy of the collective motion is (see eqn. 4.93 in Chapter IV, Section C.3)

$$E_{\mathrm{coll},\,I} = I(I+1)\hbar^2/2\mathscr{I} \qquad (6.107)$$

where $\mathscr{I}$ is the moment of inertia about an axis perpendicular to the axis of symmetry. The 'central potential' term $V^{00}_{v'v''}(r)$ is $v_0(r)$ in the expansion (6.105) and there are no other terms of the form $V^{00}_{v'v''}(r)$. The remaining coupling terms of eqn. (6.106) may be simplified by observing that, in terms of polar angles θ', ϕ' measured about its symmetry axis, a spheroid is defined by eqn. (6.98). The corresponding expansion of the potential energy $V_{\mathrm{n}}(r, \xi)$ includes only the $\mu = 0$ terms of eqn. (6.105). Typical forms of the coefficients $v_{\lambda}(r)$ for a square potential and a trapezoidal potential are shown in Fig. 6.12 due to

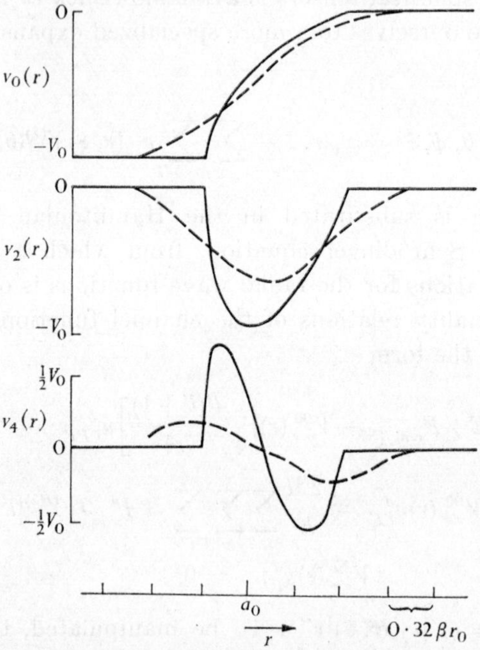

FIG. 6.12. Potential energy perturbations in a trapezoidal complex potential well due to rotational motion (after Chase *et al.* 1958).

Chase *et al.* (1958). The trapezoidal potential is defined by

$$V(r) = (V_0 - \mathrm{i}W_0) \times \begin{bmatrix} 1, & r \leqslant a - \frac{1}{2}\Delta \\ -\{(r-a)/\Delta\} + \frac{1}{2}, & a - \frac{1}{2}\Delta \leqslant r \leqslant a + \frac{1}{2}\Delta \\ 0, & a + \frac{1}{2}\Delta \leqslant r. \end{bmatrix} \tag{6.108}$$

In Fig. 6.12 the value of Δ was chosen to be $0{\cdot}95\ \beta a_0$. The coefficient of the main coupling terms in $v_2(r)$ is (Chase *et al.* 1958)

$$\langle l''I''; J|\, Y_0^{(2)}(\theta', \phi')\,|l'I'; J\rangle = \frac{1}{(4\pi)^{\frac{1}{2}}} W(I''l''I'l'; J2)$$
$$\times (2I''+1)^{\frac{1}{2}}(2l''+1)^{\frac{1}{2}} C_{I'0}(2I''00) C_{l'0}(2l''00) \tag{6.109}$$

which employs the W coefficient of Racah (1942) (tabulated by Rotenberg *et al.* 1959).

For s-wave scattering ($J = 0$) this coefficient has non-zero values for $l' = I'$, $l'' = I''$, l'' lying between $|l'-2|$ and $l'+2$, and I'' lying between $|I'-2|$ and $I'+2$.

Equations (6.106) have been numerically integrated for a trapezoidal potential with the limitation of neglect of the terms in $\lambda = 4$ (Chase *et al.* 1958). The parameters used were $V_0 = -44$ MeV, $W_0 = 2{\cdot}2$ MeV, $r_0 = 1{\cdot}35$ fm, $\Delta = 2{\cdot}75$ fm. Values of β were obtained from the

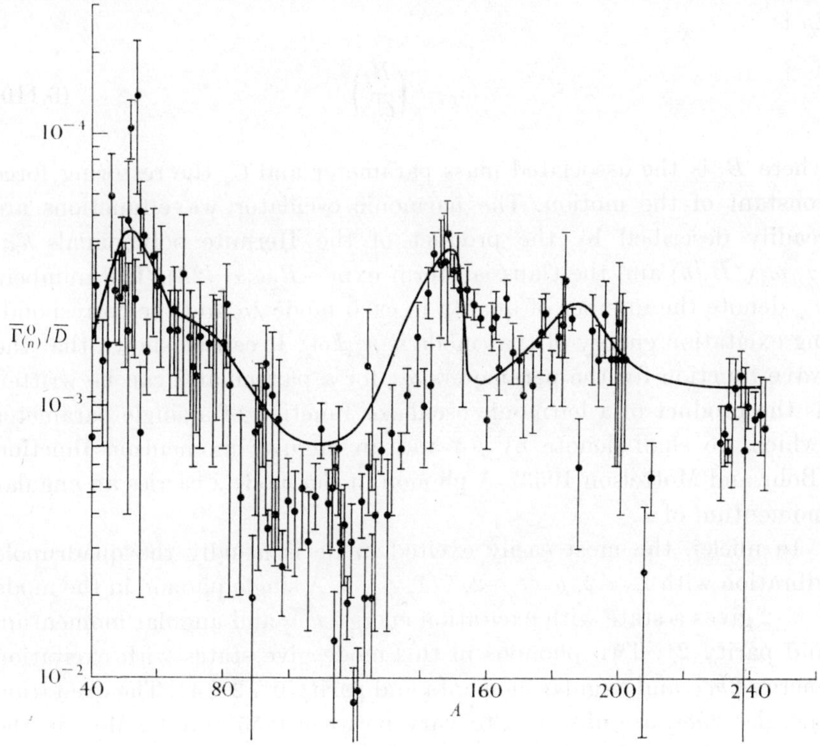

FIG. 6.13. Data on the s-wave neutron strength function compared with the model (solid curve) of a diffuse complex potential coupled to vibrational and rotational motion.

measured intrinsic quadrupole moments of nuclear ground states. The result of the calculation is that the single 4s giant resonance of the s-wave neutron strength-function at mass number 160 is replaced by roughly equal peaks at mass numbers 145 and 180. That this result agrees rather well with the experimental data can be seen from Fig. 6.13.

(b) Vibrating spherical nuclei

Surface vibrations have been discussed in Chapter IV, Section C.1. The collective parameters employed for the description of a surface vibration are the coefficients $\alpha_{\lambda\mu}$ which occur in the expansion of the radius of the surface about its 'mean' value a_0 in eqn. (6.96). With the assumption that the restoring force is directly proportional to the $\alpha_{\lambda\mu}$ the wave-functions for the $\alpha_{\lambda\mu}$ are the harmonic oscillator wave-functions, and the frequency of vibration associated with each mode $\lambda\mu$ is

$$\omega_\lambda = \left(\frac{B_\lambda}{C_\lambda}\right)^{\frac{1}{2}} \tag{6.110}$$

where B_λ is the associated mass parameter and C_λ the restoring force constant of the motion. The harmonic oscillator wave-functions are readily described by the product of the Hermite polynomials $h_{n_{\lambda\mu}}$ $(\alpha_{\lambda\mu}\omega_\lambda\sqrt{B_\lambda/\hbar})$ and the Gaussian term $\exp(-B_\lambda\omega_\lambda\alpha^2_{\lambda\mu}/2\hbar)$. The numbers $n_{\lambda\mu}$ denote the number of quanta in each mode $\lambda\mu$ and the corresponding excitation energy of that mode is $n_{\lambda\mu}\hbar\omega_\lambda$. It can be shown that the wave-function for the parameters $\alpha_{\lambda\mu}$ for a particular λ can be written as the product of a harmonic oscillator function of a single parameter (which we shall denote by β_λ) and an angular momentum function (Bohr and Mottelson 1953). A phonon in the mode λ carries an angular momentum of λ.

In nuclei, the most easily excited mode is usually the quadrupole vibration with $\lambda = 2$, $\mu = -2, -1, \ldots 2$. A single phonon in the mode $\lambda = 2$ gives a state with excitation energy $\hbar\omega_2$ and angular momentum and parity 2^+. Two phonons in this mode give states with excitation energy $2\hbar\omega_2$ and angular momenta and parity 0^+, 2^+, 4^+. The excitation energies $2\hbar\omega_2$ are observed to vary between 0·55 and 1·2 MeV in the mass number region $A \approx 44$ to $A \approx 86$.

If we confine our discussion to vibrational modes with cylindrical symmetry we require the expansion

$$a(\theta,\phi') = a_0\left\{1+\sum_{\lambda\geqslant 2}\beta_\lambda Y_0^{(\lambda)}(\theta',\phi')\right\} \tag{6.111}$$

with the polar angles measured about the symmetry axis. For small values of the deformation parameters β_λ the Woods–Saxon potential readily lends itself to a Taylor expansion to yield the terms $v_\lambda(r, \xi)$ of eqn. (6.105). To first order

$$v_0(r,\xi) = \frac{(V_0 - \mathrm{i}W_0)}{1+\exp\{(r-a_0)/d\}}, \tag{6.112a}$$

$$v_\lambda(r,\xi) = \frac{(V_0 - \mathrm{i}W_0)\exp\{(r-a_0)/d\}}{[1+\exp\{(r-a_0)/d\}]^2}\cdot\frac{a_0\beta_\lambda}{d}. \tag{6.112b}$$

This expansion is valid if $a_0\beta_\lambda/d$ is much less than unity, which excludes its application to the permanently deformed nuclei for which β_2 usually lies between 0·2 and 0·4. It is useful for studying the vibrations

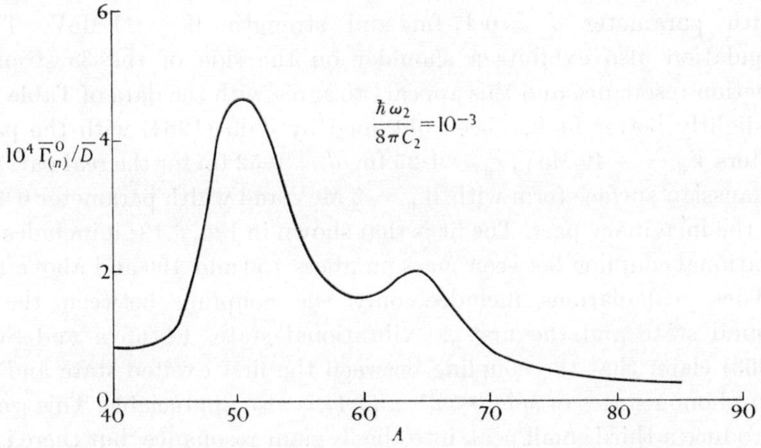

FIG. 6.14. The s-wave neutron strength function in the region of the square well 3s-single-neutron state, split by vibrational coupling (after Margolis 1962).

of spherical nuclei however. Using eqns. (6.112) and the properties of the Hermite functions we obtain for the matrix elements $\langle n_\lambda|v_\lambda|m_\lambda\rangle$:

$$\langle n_\lambda|v_0|m_\lambda\rangle = \delta_{n_\lambda m_\lambda} v_0(r) \tag{6.113a}$$

$$\langle m_\lambda|v_\lambda|n_\lambda\rangle = \langle n_\lambda|v_\lambda|m_\lambda\rangle = \left\{\frac{(n_\lambda+1)!}{n_\lambda!}\right\}^{\frac{1}{2}}\left(\frac{\hbar}{2B_\lambda\omega_\lambda}\right)^{\frac{1}{2}}\delta_{m_\lambda,n_\lambda+1}$$

$$\times\frac{(V_0-\mathrm{i}W_0)\exp\{(r-a_0)/d\}}{[1+\exp\{(r-a_0)/d\}]^2}\cdot\frac{a_0}{d}. \tag{6.113b}$$

In other words a particular component of the wave-function (eqn. (6.104)) can only excite virtual transitions in which one 'phonon' is created or destroyed. The remaining factor of the matrix element, the spin part, is given by eqn. (6.109) for the case $\lambda = 2$ (quadrupole vibrations).

Numerical studies have been made of the scattering of neutrons by a spherical complex potential with quadrupole oscillations. Margolis (1963) used a square well. The result of his calculation for the s-wave strength function is shown in Fig. 6.14 for the region of the 3s giant resonance. The parameters he used in the calculation approximately reproduce the observed spacings in the low-lying vibrational spectra of nuclei in this region as well as the surface energy term of the Weizsacker mass formula. The curve indicates that a shoulder should be found on the high mass-number side of the strength-function resonance. Buck and Perey (1962) used a Woods–Saxon form with parameters $V_0 = -48$ MeV, $r_0 = 1{\cdot}27$ fm, $d = 0{\cdot}65$ fm, $\lambda = 21{\cdot}5$. Surface absorption was employed; the form was the radial derivative of eqn. (3.11), width parameter $d' = 0{\cdot}47$ fm and strength $W = 11$ MeV. Their calculation also exhibits a shoulder on the side of the 3s strength function resonance and this appears to agree with the data of Table 6.1. A slightly better fit has been obtained by Jain (1964) with the parameters $V_0 = -49$ MeV, $r_0 = 1{\cdot}25$ fm, $d = 0{\cdot}52$ fm for the real part and a Gaussian surface term with $W_0 = 6$ MeV and width parameter 0·4 fm for the imaginary part. The fit is that shown in Fig. 6.13; it includes the rotational coupling between mass numbers 150 and 190 and above 220.

These calculations included only the coupling between the 0^+ ground state and the first 2^+ vibrational state. Furuoya and Sugie (1963) claim that the coupling between the first excited state and the two-phonon states of spin 0^+, 2^+, and 4^+ is also appreciable. This would introduce a third small peak into the 3s giant resonance, but there is no evidence for it in the data.

Margolis (1962) has also studied the coupling of a square potential to octupole vibrations ($\lambda = 3$). In this case single-particle states of odd parity are connected with those of even parity; the energy separation of these states is large and the coupling is correspondingly weak. The high energy of octupole vibrations in nuclei, about 3 MeV (Lane and Pendlebury 1959), also weakens the effect, according to eqn. (6.113b). The octupole vibration is not, therefore, expected to play an important role in determining the average properties of neutron elastic scattering.

(c) *The effect of spin-orbit splitting and target spin*

The discussion so far has been for the scattering of spinless particles. Consideration of the neutron spin introduces an important complication. The single-particle states of higher angular momentum, with which the s-state is coupled through the collective excitation of the target, are split by spin-orbit coupling. According to Fig. 3.3, the d-state, which is the most important coupled state for rotations and quadrupole vibrations, and which, in the absence of spin-orbit coupling and diffuseness, lies below the s-state, is split into a $d_{3/2}$ state lying above the s-state and a $d_{5/2}$ state lying just below. One would expect, therefore, that there would be three main subsidiary peaks in the structure of each giant resonance in the s-wave strength function instead of the two calculated by Chase *et al.* and apparently observed. The data for the $4s$ giant resonance actually does show a suggestion of a third peak (at $A \approx 165$) but is not at all conclusive. The possibility exists that for strongly deformed nuclei the third peak would occur in the mass number range above $A \approx 190$ where in fact the target nuclei are nearly spherical and the effect is subdued.

Even more complication, but of a less important nature, is introduced with the consideration of targets with non-zero spin, I. Resonances of two angular momenta, $J = I-\frac{1}{2}$ and $J = I+\frac{1}{2}$, can be excited by s-wave neutrons. The two angular momenta are coupled in different proportions to the $d_{3/2}$ and $d_{5/2}$ states through the collective effects. This would introduce an angular momentum dependence into the s-wave strength function (Firk *et al.* 1963a). In the quadrupole vibration case the spin of the target is also coupled to the phonon through a dipole interaction (de-Shalit 1961), complicating still further the analysis of the effect. Some evidence of angular momentum dependence of the s-wave strength function has been observed in a few cases, namely, $^{75}As+n$ (Garg *et al.* 1964, Julien *et al.* 1964), $^{59}Co+n$ (Morgenstern *et al.* 1964), $^{77}Se+n$ (Julien *et al.* 1962*b*), $^{69}Ga+n$ (Julien *et al.* 1964), and of the potential scattering cross-section in one case, $^{51}V+n$ (Firk *et al.* 1963*a*), but it is not clear that it is due to the effects described above (see Section D.6).

4. Potential scattering

The resonances in the neutron cross-section are superimposed on, and interfere with, a very slowly varying background scattering cross-section known as potential scattering. This term appears in eqn. (2.69), for example. In low energy s-wave neutron bombardment it has the simple form $4\pi a^2 (1-R^\infty)^2$, showing that it depends on the form of the complex potential through the sum, in the R-function, over far-away levels. This quantity, R^∞, is directly related to the strength function, discussed in the previous sections, by eqn. (6.16) which may be written

$$R^\infty = \int dE_\lambda \frac{s(E_\lambda)(E_\lambda - E)}{(E_\lambda - E)^2 + (\frac{1}{2}\Gamma_{\lambda(\mathrm{T})} + I)^2}. \tag{6.114}$$

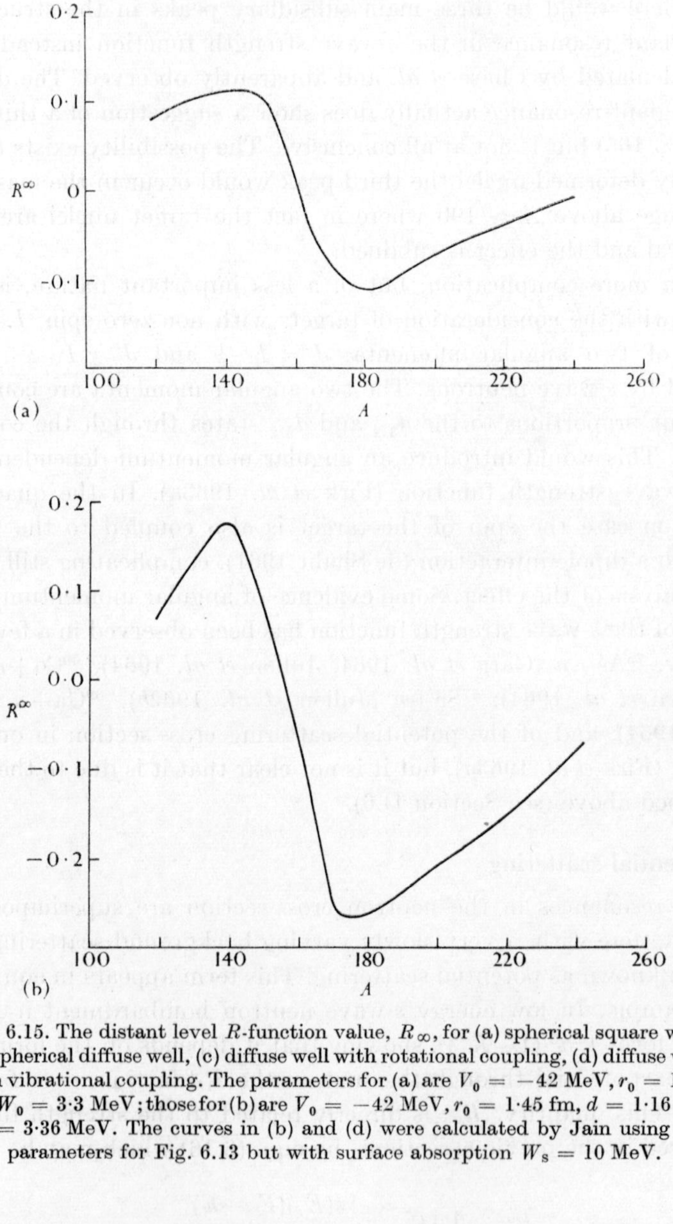

FIG. 6.15. The distant level R-function value, R_∞, for (a) spherical square well, (b) spherical diffuse well, (c) diffuse well with rotational coupling, (d) diffuse well with vibrational coupling. The parameters for (a) are $V_0 = -42$ MeV, $r_0 = 1{\cdot}45$ fm, $W_0 = 3{\cdot}3$ MeV; those for (b) are $V_0 = -42$ MeV, $r_0 = 1{\cdot}45$ fm, $d = 1{\cdot}16$ fm, $W_0 = 3{\cdot}36$ MeV. The curves in (b) and (d) were calculated by Jain using the parameters for Fig. 6.13 but with surface absorption $W_S = 10$ MeV.

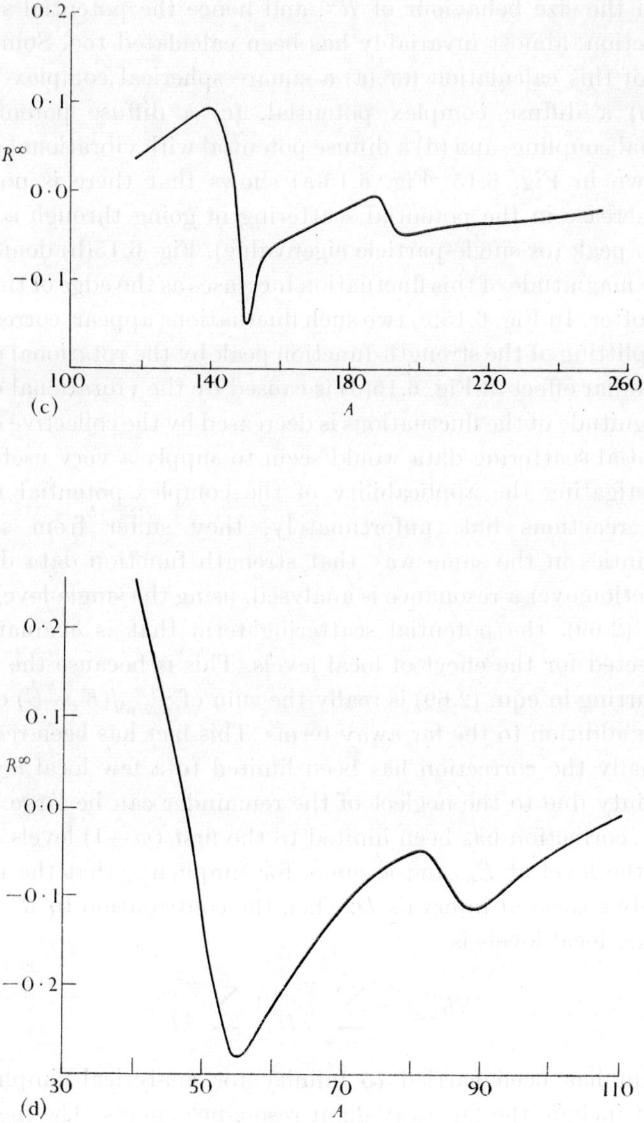

FIG. 6.15. (*Continued*)

The typical behaviour of R^{∞} through a giant resonance in the strength function is illustrated in Fig. 6.6.

In complex-potential model calculations of the neutron strength function the size behaviour of R^{∞}, and hence the potential scattering cross-section, almost invariably has been calculated too. Some typical results of this calculation for (a) a square spherical complex-potential well, (b) a diffuse complex potential, (c) a diffuse potential with rotational coupling, and (d) a diffuse potential with vibrational coupling, are shown in Fig. 6.15. Fig. 6.15(a) shows that there is normally a sharp increase in the potential scattering in going through a strength function peak (or single-particle eigenvalue). Fig. 6.15(b) demonstrates that the magnitude of this fluctuation increases as the edge of the well becomes softer. In Fig. 6.15(c) two such fluctuations appear, corresponding to the splitting of the strength-function peak by the rotational coupling, and a similar effect in Fig. 6.15(d) is caused by the vibrational coupling. The magnitude of the fluctuations is decreased by the collective coupling.

Potential scattering data would seem to supply a very useful means of investigating the applicability of the complex-potential model to nuclear reactions but, unfortunately, they suffer from statistical uncertainties in the same way that strength function data do. If the cross-section over a resonance is analysed, using the single-level formula of eqn. (2.69), the potential scattering term that is evaluated must be corrected for the effect of local levels. This is because the quantity R^{∞} occurring in eqn. (2.69) is really the sum of $\gamma^2_{\lambda(\mathrm{n})}/(E_{\lambda}-E)$ over local levels in addition to the far-away terms. This fact has been recognized, but usually the correction has been limited to a few local levels. The uncertainty due to the neglect of the remainder can be large. Suppose that the correction has been limited to the first $(m-1)$ levels on either side of the level at E_0, and assume, for simplicity, that the levels are uniformly spaced at intervals D. Then the contribution to R^{∞} from the remaining local levels is

$$\Delta R^{\infty}_{\mathrm{loc}} = \sum_{\lambda=-m}^{-\infty} \frac{\gamma^2_{\lambda(\mathrm{n})}}{\lambda D} + \sum_{\lambda=m}^{\infty} \frac{\gamma^2_{\lambda(\mathrm{n})}}{\lambda D}. \tag{6.115}$$

This sum has been carried to infinity for analytical simplicity but does not include the far-away giant resonance effects. The mean value of $\Delta R^{\infty 2}_{\mathrm{loc}}$ is zero and its mean square value is

$$\overline{\Delta R^{\infty 2}_{\mathrm{loc}}} = 2s^2 \sum_{\lambda=m}^{\infty} \frac{\overline{(\gamma^2_{\lambda(\mathrm{n})}/\overline{\gamma^2_{\lambda(\mathrm{n})}})^2}}{\lambda^2}. \tag{6.116}$$

The second moment of the reduced widths is three, according to the Porter–Thomas distribution (eqn. (6.33b)), giving

$$\overline{\Delta R_{\text{loc}}^{\infty 2}} = 6s^2\left(\frac{\pi^2}{6} - \sum_{\lambda=1}^{m-1}\frac{1}{\lambda^2}\right). \tag{6.117}$$

The square root of $\overline{\Delta R_{\text{loc}}^{\infty 2}}/s^2$ is plotted against m in Fig. 6.16; the significance of $\overline{\Delta R_{\text{loc}}^{\infty 2}}$ is that it is the variance in the expected value of the potential scattering length, $\alpha_{\text{n(pot)}} = \surd\{\sigma_{\text{n(pot)}}/4\pi a^2\}$, due to the inherent statistical uncertainties in the resonance properties, and it

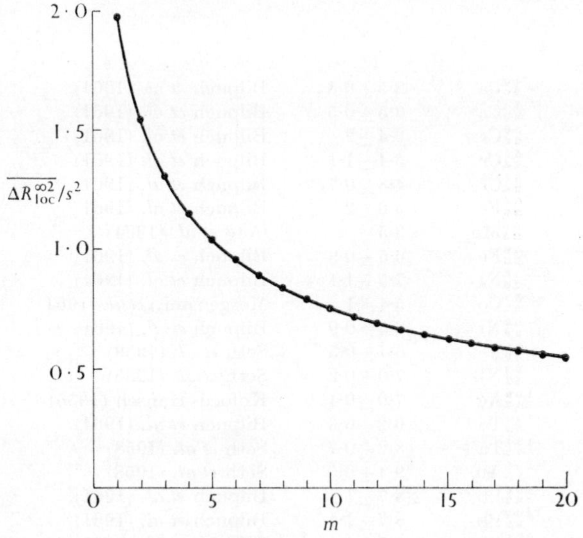

FIG. 6.16. Expected variance in determination of R^∞ from cross-section analysis over a region of $2m-1$ resonances.

can be seen that it can be large, in practice, when the strength function is large.

Potential scattering data are compiled in Table 6.2. Most data are from detailed total cross-section measurements and the error described above has been incorporated into the errors quoted by the authors. A few data are from average transmission measurements in the kilovolt region. The data are plotted as a function of mass number in Fig. 6.17. The full curve is from a spherical complex potential with $r_0 \approx 1{\cdot}3$ fm and other parameters, due to Moldauer (1963), given at the end of Section D.2a. The broken curve is from a complex-potential model with vibrational and rotational coupling; the parameters are due to

Jain (1964) and are given in Section D.2 with the exception of r_0 which, here, is 1·35 fm.

The last value of the radius parameter suggests that the various fits to the strength function data that we have discussed ought to be

TABLE 6.2

Potential scattering for low-energy neutrons compiled from resonance data and from average cross-section data

Target	α_n(pot) (10^{-13} cm)	Reference
$^{40}_{20}$Ca	3·5±0·8	Bilpuch *et al.* (1961)
$^{44}_{20}$Ca	3·5±0·5	Bilpuch *et al.* (1961)
$^{50}_{24}$Cr	6·4±2	Bilpuch *et al.* (1961)
$^{52}_{24}$Cr	5·4±1·1	Bilpuch *et al.* (1961)
$^{54}_{24}$Cr	4·8±0·7	Bilpuch *et al.* (1961)
$^{54}_{26}$Fe	5·6±2	Bilpuch *et al.* (1961)
$^{56}_{25}$Mn	≈3·5	Coté *et al.* (1964)
$^{56}_{26}$Fe	6·5±0·9	Bilpuch *et al.* (1961)
$^{58}_{28}$Ni	7·5±1·1	Bilpuch *et al.* (1961)
$^{59}_{27}$Co	5·4±1	Morgenstern *et al.* (1964)
$^{60}_{28}$Ni	6·5±0·9	Bilpuch *et al.* (1961)
$^{89}_{39}$Y	6·7±0·3	Seth *et al.* (1958)
$^{93}_{41}$Nb	7·0±0·2	Seth *et al.* (1958)
$^{109}_{47}$Ag	7·0±0·4	Kofoed–Hansen (1955)
$^{130}_{52}$Te	6·2±0·3	Bilpuch *et al.* (1961)
$^{181}_{73}$Ta	8·2±0·7	Seth *et al.* (1958)
$^{197}_{79}$Au	9·4±0·5	Seth *et al.* (1958)
$^{206}_{82}$Pb	8·7±1·1	Bilpuch *et al.* (1961)
$^{207}_{82}$Pb	8·7±1·1	Bilpuch *et al.* (1961)
$^{208}_{82}$Pb	8·7±1·1	Bilpuch *et al.* (1961)
$^{209}_{83}$Bi	9·1±0·3	Firk *et al.* (1963*b*)
$^{232}_{90}$Th	9·6±·15	Uttley and Lynn (1966)
$^{235}_{92}$U	9·65±·05	Uttley (1965)
$^{238}_{92}$U	9·2±·15	Lynn (1963)

reformulated with a higher value of r_0. Further consideration implies, indeed, that r_0 should be 5–10 per cent higher than the value 1·35 fm. This is for the same reason that the potential scattering cross-section is lower than the value $4\pi a^2$ in the strong-absorption model (Section C.1); the strength function has to be cut off at energies below the ground state of the compound nucleus and consequently there is no (negative) contribution to R^∞ from states below this level (they are already occupied). No provision is made in the complex-potential model for such a cut-off. If r_0 is increased in this way the other parameters of the complex potential have to be transformed according to eqn. (3.23).

5. Isotopic spin independence

Lane (1962) has proposed the addition of an isotopic spin dependence to the complex potential to explain a prominent and systematic feature

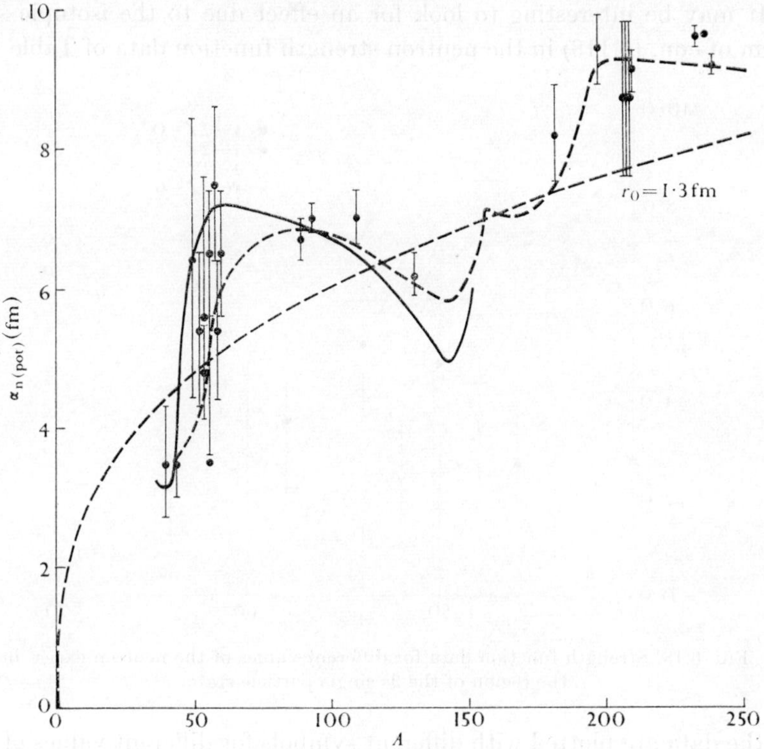

FIG. 6.17. Potential scattering length data and comparison with models. The full curve is calculated from a spherical complex potential (Moldauer 1963). The broken curve is for a complex potential with vibrational and rotational coupling, calculated by Jain (1964).

of (p,n) reactions. The additional term results from the straightforward calculation of the potential energy as a sum over two-body potentials, with Heisenberg exchange components, averaged over a Fermi gas. If $\boldsymbol{\tau}$ and $\mathbf{T}$ denote the isotopic spins of an incident nucleon and target nucleus of mass A, the potential energy has the form

$$V = V_0 + (\boldsymbol{\tau} \,.\, \mathbf{T})V_1/A \tag{6.118}$$

where V_0 and V_1 are independent of isotopic spin. This term has particularly interesting implications for incident protons, but for neutrons it gives rise to the mean potential

$$V_n = V_0 + \tfrac{1}{4}\{(N-Z)/A\}V_1, \qquad (6.119)$$

for the total isotopic spin of the compound system will have the single value $\tfrac{1}{2}(N-Z)+\tfrac{1}{2}$.

It may be interesting to look for an effect due to the isotopic spin term of eqn. (6.118) in the neutron strength function data of Table 6.1.

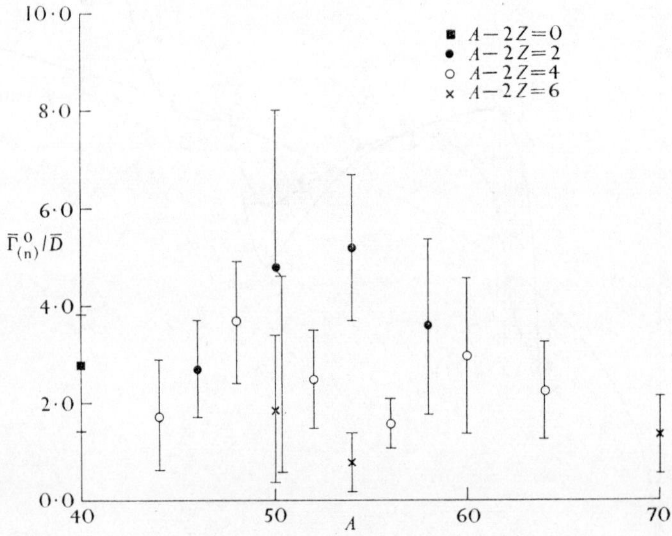

FIG. 6.18. Strength function data for different values of the neutron excess in the region of the 3*s* single-particle state.

If the data are plotted with different symbols for different values of the neutron excess the isotopic spin term should reveal itself as a mass-number in the giant resonance for changing neutron excess. This is done in Fig. 6.18; the data are so disappointingly sparse and inaccurate that no trend emerges.

6. Spin-spin coupling

A potential energy term dependent upon the coupling between the spin of the incident nucleon and the spin of the target would be quite analogous to the isotopic spin term discussed in the last section; a possible source would be the existence of Bartlett spin-exchange forces in the nucleon-nucleon interaction. If it were of the same order of magnitude as the isotopic spin term it would be considerably easier to find evidence for it in neutron cross-section data. This is because we should have to look, not for evidence of small changes in the potential due to changing N and Z over a sequence of target nuclei, but rather for the much larger changes in the cross-sections of the same target nucleus for the different angular momenta J.

If it is assumed that the spin-coupling term has the same form as eqn. (6.118), explicitly,

$$\delta V = (\mathbf{i}\,.\,\mathbf{I})V_2/A \tag{6.120}$$

we find that the potential for s-wave states of angular momentum J is

$$V = V_0+0{\cdot}5\{J(J+1)-I(I+1)-\mathrm{i}(\mathrm{i}+1)\}V_2/A. \tag{6.121}$$

The extra term is zero for even targets. For odd or odd-mass targets it has the form $0{\cdot}5\,IV_2/A$ for angular momentum $J = I+\frac{1}{2}$ and $-0{\cdot}5$ $(I+1)$ V_2/A for angular momentum $J = I-\frac{1}{2}$. The difference for the two J values formed from high-spin targets could be appreciable; the $s_{1/2}$ single-particle levels would appear at zero neutron energy at different mass numbers, and considerably different values of strength functions and potential scattering lengths could occur in the giant resonance regions.

Unfortunately, relevant data are again very sparse. The angular momenta of only a few resonances in the cross-section of any one nucleus have been measured and the statistical errors in the strength functions, inherent in drawing a small sample from a Porter–Thomas distribution, are large. The strength functions are shown in Table 6.3, with the number of resonances in the sample shown in brackets. In some cases there are considerable differences between the two values, exceeding even the quoted square-root variance. These require rather more careful consideration to decide their significance.

Let us consider y and z as the two observables or samples divided by their population means. The joint frequency function of y and z is simply the product of their individual frequency functions s and t

$$p(y,z)\mathrm{d}y\,\mathrm{d}z = s(y)t(z)\mathrm{d}y\,\mathrm{d}z. \tag{6.122}$$

From this their joint distribution function may be calculated for the probability of y being greater than a and z being less than y/b (i.e. y/z being greater than some value b)

$$P(a,b) = \int\limits_a^\infty \mathrm{d}y\, s(y) \int\limits_0^{y/b} \mathrm{d}z\, t(z). \tag{6.123a}$$

TABLE 6.3

s-wave neutron strength-functions of odd-mass targets for both values of total angular momentum

Target nucleus	I^π	$s(I-\frac{1}{2})$	$s(I+\frac{1}{2})$	Reference	$P(O, b)$	$N+M$	$P(O, b)$
^{51}V	$\frac{7}{2}-$	9·5 ± 3·5	11·6 ± 4·6	Firk *et al.* (1963*a*)			
^{59}Co	$\frac{7}{2}-$	6·7 ± 3·3(5)	3·3 ± 1·4(8)	Morgenstern *et al.* (1965)	0·18		
^{69}Ga	$\frac{3}{2}-$	<0·4(0)	1·8 ± 0·9(7)	Julien *et al.* (1964)		12	0·1
^{63}Cu	$\frac{3}{2}-$	1·56 ± 1·0(4)	2·6 ± 1·3(8)	Julien *et al.* (1964)	0·26	13	0·26
^{65}Cu	$\frac{3}{2}-$	1·0 ± 0·7(3)	1·7 ± 1·0(6)	Julien *et al.* (1964)	0·27	12	0·27
^{75}As	$\frac{3}{2}-$	1·0 ± 0·3(12)	2·5 ± 0·6(15)	Julien *et al.* (1964)	0·058	50	0·018
^{77}Se	$\frac{1}{2}-$	3·6 ± 3·0(3)	0·36 ± 0·2(6)	Julien *et al.* (1962*b*)	0·01		
^{107}Ag	$\frac{1}{2}-$	1·0 ± 1·0(2)	3·4 ± 2(6)	Asghar (1964)	0·19		
^{109}Ag	$\frac{1}{2}-$	0·36 ± 0·34(3)	0·85 ± 0·4(10)	Asghar (1964)	0·2		
^{169}Tm	$\frac{1}{2}+$	1·59 ± 0·6(5)	1·31 ± 0·4(9)	Singh (1964)	0·38		
^{195}Pt	$\frac{1}{2}-$	2·3 ± 1·5(6)	1·9 ± 0·8(13)	Julien *et al.* (1962*b*)	0·37		
^{197}Au	$\frac{3}{2}+$	1·2 ± 0·3(12)	2·4 ± 0·6(26)	Julien *et al.* (1966)	0·10	64	0·01

Numbers in brackets following entries in third and fourth columns give number of resonances actually assigned the spin quoted. The probability estimate in column 6 is based on these numbers. Column 7 gives the number of resonances actually observed in the same energy interval as the earlier entries. The resonances without spin assignments are usually weak, and, if measured, might not be expected to affect the ratio of the strength functions quoted in columns 3 and 4. The probability in column 8 is based on this assumption (and the $2J+1$ level density rule).

The probability, then, of y/z being greater than b is just $P(0, b)$. If the sample y (or z) is composed of M (or N) items drawn from a Porter–Thomas distribution the frequency function s (or t) will have the form of

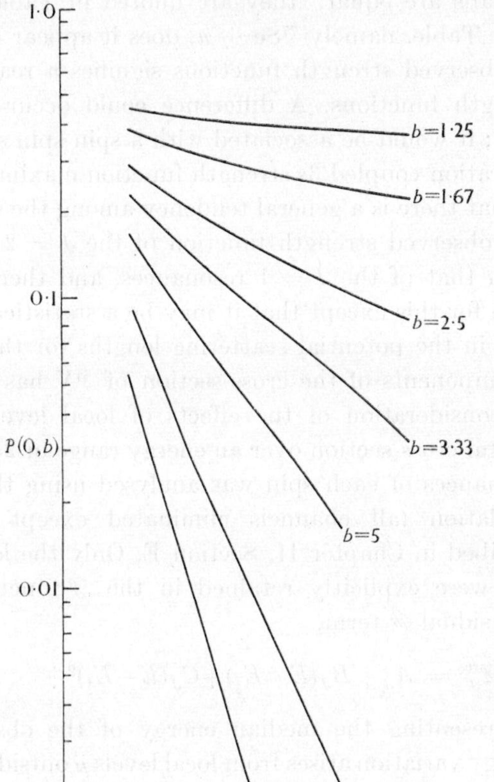

FIG. 6.19. Probability of measuring a ratio, b or greater, for two local strength function values, each determined by a measurement of N resonances, if the true strength functions are equal.

eqn. (6.42). If M and N are even for both samples the calculation of $P(0, b)$ is straightforward; the result is

$$P(0, b) = 1-\{(Mb)^M/(M-1)!\}\sum_{k=0}^{N-1} \frac{N^k}{k!} \frac{(k+M-1)!}{(N+Mb)^{k+M}}, \tag{6.123b}$$

and in Fig. 6.19 we show some results when N and M are equal with simple interpolation between even values of N.

Fig. 6.19 and similar calculations for unequal N and M are used to estimate the probability, $P(0, b)$, that the observed sample strength functions bear their observed ratio, or a greater value, when the true population means are equal; they are quoted in Table 6.3. In only one case of the Table, namely ^{77}Se + n, does it appear likely that the difference in observed strength functions signifies a real difference in the true strength functions. A difference could occur in this mass-number region; it would be associated with a spin-spin splitting of the subsidiary vibration-coupled $3s$ strength function maximum. However, it does seem that there is a general tendency among the spin 3/2 target nuclei for the observed strength function of the $J = 2$ resonances to be higher than that of the $J = 1$ resonances, and there seems to be no explanation for this except that it may be a statistical freak.

A difference in the potential scattering lengths for the two angular momentum components of the cross-section of ^{51}V has been inferred after careful consideration of the effects of local levels (Firk *et al.* 1963*a*). The total cross-section over an energy range of 25 keV containing three resonances of each spin was analysed using the reduced R-matrix formulation (all channels eliminated except the entrance channel) described in Chapter II, Section E. Only the levels observed in this range were explicitly retained in the $\mathscr{R}$-function sum over levels, but a residual $\mathscr{R}$ term,

$$\mathscr{R}_J^{\text{res}} = A_J + B_J(E - E_{\frac{1}{2}}) + C_J(E - E_{\frac{1}{2}})^2 + \dots \tag{6.124a}$$

(with $E_{1/2}$ representing the median energy of the observations), in which the energy variation arises from local levels μ outside the observed range, i.e.

$$A_J = R_J^{\infty} + \sum_{\mu(J)} \frac{\gamma^2_{\mu(\text{n})}}{E_\mu - E_{1/2}}, \tag{6.124b}$$

$$B_J = \sum_{\mu(J)} \frac{\gamma^2_{\mu(\text{n})}}{(E_\mu - E_{1/2})^2}, \tag{6.124c}$$

$$C_J = \sum_{\mu(J)} \frac{\gamma^2_{\mu(\text{n})}}{(E_\mu - E_{1/2})^3}, \text{ etc.,} \tag{6.124d}$$

was also included in the analysis. The fitting process provided estimates of the coefficients of the leading terms in the expansion of $\mathscr{R}^{\text{res}}$, as well as parameters for the explicitly included levels, and from these it is possible to make estimates of the limits on R^∞ for each spin. The potential scattering length of the system in angular momentum state $J = 3$ was found to about 7·5 fm, and for $J = 4$ was 5 fm or less. No significant difference was found in the strength-function values but this is not inconsistent with the scattering length observation if we assume, as seems very likely from the high strength function, that the

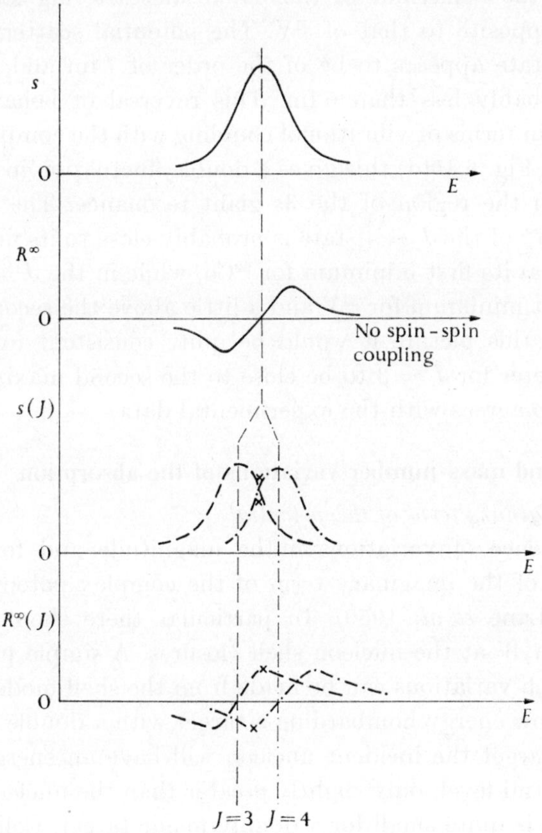

FIG. 6.20. Effect on strength functions and distant level R-functions, for levels of different total angular momenta, that might be caused by a spin-spin coupling term in the complex potential.

^{52}V neutron separation energy is straddled by the main component of the 3s giant resonance. A small splitting of the resonance due to the spin coupling would cause little difference in the strength functions, situated in a slowly varying maximum region, but a considerable difference in the potential scattering, which is in a region of maximum change (see Fig. 6.20). The magnitude of the potential scattering difference indicates that V_2 is of the order of 10 to 20 times W.

A similar analysis of the cross-section of ^{55}Mn (Coté *et al.* 1964*b*) indicates that the potential scattering length of the $J = 3$ component is less than about 4 fm, but the presence of a strong, close, bound level prevents information from being obtained for the other spin. A multi-level analysis of the data of Garg *et al.* (1965) on the cross-section of ^{59}Co shows that the behaviour of the potential scattering lengths of this nucleus is opposite to that of ^{51}V. The potential scattering length in the $J = 4$ state appears to be of the order of 7 fm and in the $J = 3$ state is probably less than 5 fm. This reversal of behaviour can be understood in terms of vibrational coupling with the complex potential. As shown in Fig. 6.15(d) this gives a double fluctuation in the potential scattering in the region of the 3*s* giant resonance. The distant level parameter R^{∞} of the $J = 4$ state is probably close to its first maximum for ^{51}V and at its first minimum for ^{59}Co, while in the $J = 3$ state it is near the first minimum for ^{51}V and a little above the second maximum for ^{59}Co. In this picture it would be quite consistent for the distant level parameter for $J = 3$ to be close to the second maximum at ^{55}Mn and this also agrees with the experimental data.

7. Energy and mass-number variations of the absorption

(*a*) *The imaginary term of the potential*

The existence of variations in the magnitude and form of radial dependence of the imaginary term of the complex potential has been suggested (Lane *et al.* 1959). In particular there should be marked variations in W at the nucleon shell closures. A simple physical argument for such variations can be made from the shell model. Consider a nucleon of low energy bombarding a target with a double shell closure. Inside the target the incident nucleon will have an energy, measured from the Fermi level, only slightly greater than the nucleon separation energy; this is quite small for a doubly magic target. Collisions within the target will only be allowed if both nucleons can occupy final states which lie above the shell gaps. It is obvious that if the shell gaps are greater than half the nucleon separation energy, the Pauli principle forbids collisions of the incident nucleon with the target nucleons and there is no absorption of the former; the imaginary component of the well is zero. Even if the shell gaps are not so great, or if there is only a single shell closure (neutron or proton), it seems likely that the mean free path of the incident nucleon will be increased as a result of the Pauli principle.

This result is embodied in the quantum-mechanical expression, eqn.

(6.82), for W (Bloch 1957). The operator $H' = (\sum_j v_{ij} - V)$ acts between pairs of particles. The matrix elements $\langle c'p'|H'|cp\rangle_{\mathscr{S}}$ are therefore zero except when the states $\chi_{c,p,}$ contain components of two-particle, one-hole states, the state χ_{cp} being a one-particle state relative to the ground state φ_c as the 'vacuum state'. These states must also have the same total angular momentum and parity as the initial target-nucleon system (Sugie 1960). The imaginary term W_{cp} is therefore proportional to the density, at the excitation energy due to the bombarding nucleon, of two-particle, one-hole states in the real potential with the same angular momentum and parity as the initial system.

The density of such states depends strongly on energy. The general behaviour of the overall density of two-particle, one-hole states is given by a formula due to Ericson (1960):

$$\rho(U;\, 2 \text{ part}, 1 \text{ hole}) = \tfrac{1}{4}\rho_s^3 U^2. \tag{6.125}$$

This leads to the quadratic dependence of W on energy observed in the result of the calculation by Lane and Wandel (1955) using the Fermi gas model of the nucleus. Equation (6.125) does not take account of shell effects, and the insertion of a 'shell-breaking' energy in a formula of this type would greatly reduce the density of states, and hence the value of W, at low and moderate excitation energies. Thus, we expect the imaginary part of the potential to be generally low in the regions of mass number 90 (closure of the $1g_{9/2}$ neutron shell), 120 (closure of the $1g_{9/2}$ proton shell), 138 (closure of the $1h_{11/2}$ neutron shell) and particularly small in the region of $A = 208$ (closure of both the $1h_{11/2}$ proton shell and the $3p_{1/2}$ neutron shell). We see from Fig. 3.3 that the shell gaps at lower mass numbers than 90 are not nearly so prominent, so we do not expect such strong variations in W in these regions.

More detailed considerations include the effect of parity conservation (which is much more restrictive than angular momentum conservation). At mass number 90 most of the two-particle, one-hole states leave the neutron shell intact. From Fig. 3.3 we see that the incident neutron may be placed in the $2d_{5/2}$, the $3s_{1/2}$, the $1g_{7/2}$, or $2d_{3/2}$ level in order of increasing energy. A proton may be taken from the $2p_{1/2}$, $1f_{5/2}$ or $2p_{3/2}$ level and placed in the $1g_{9/2}$ level. The net parity of any of these states, relative to the ground state of the target is odd. We expect, therefore, that the imaginary component of the potential will be larger for incident p-waves than for s-waves, and it will already be moderately small for p-waves because of the shell gap. The radial form of W (p-waves) comes from the collision of a p neutron with a p or f

proton to give a g proton. Because the major part of the $1g_{9/2}$ wave-function is near the nuclear radius, W should be predominantly surface peaked. The very small value of W for s-waves comes mainly from taking a neutron from the $1g_{9/2}$ shell and putting it and the incident neutron in the $2d_{5/2}$ state. This also should be surface-peaked. The combined effect of the low value of the imaginary potential and its surface peaking in a region about midway between the $3s$ and $4s$ giant resonances should cause abnormally low values of the strength

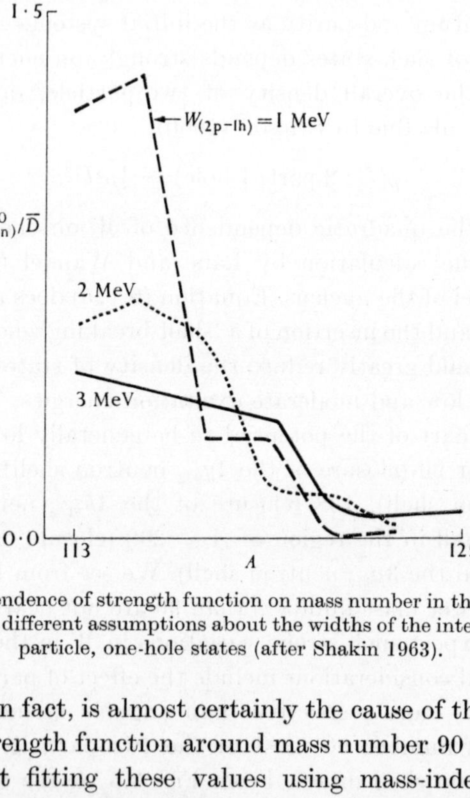

FIG. 6.21. Dependence of strength function on mass number in the region of the tin isotopes for different assumptions about the widths of the intermediate two-particle, one-hole states (after Shakin 1963).

function. This, in fact, is almost certainly the cause of the observed low values of the strength function around mass number 90 (see Table 6.1). All attempts at fitting these values using mass-independent parameters of the complex potential have failed when it has been demanded that the other mass-number regions are fitted simultaneously.

At mass number 120 the proton shell must remain unbroken in most of the states. Neutrons are placed in the $2d_{3/2}$ or $1h_{11/2}$ states, leaving a hole in the $2d_{3/2}$, $3s_{1/2}$ or $1g_{7/2}$ state. Both parities are present among the resulting two-particle, one-hole states so both values of W are expected to be moderately small and W (s-wave) to have an appreciable volume component. Explicit calculations have been made by

Shakin (1963) of the strength functions of the tin isotopes. The results are shown in Fig. 6.21. In the three curves the averaging of the matrix element $|\langle \mathrm{cp}|H'|\mathrm{c'p'}\rangle|^2$ has been made over an energy interval of width $W_{2\mathrm{p}-1\mathrm{h}}$. The physical reason for this is that the core states c′ of the residual nucleus are not true independent-particle states. In particular, the two-particle, one-hole states are spread or dissolved into the core-particle states c′p′. The spreading function can be assumed to be Lorentzian in form with half-width $W_{2\mathrm{p}-1\mathrm{h}}$, or, as in Shakin's calculation, uniform over a limited energy interval. The spreading width $W_{2\mathrm{p}-1\mathrm{h}}$ is governed by the mixing of the two-particle, one-hole states with three-particle, two-hole states and also back into the single-particle state cp, the expression for this width being of the same form as eqn. (6.80c). Comparison of Fig. 6.21 with the strength function data of Fuketa *et al.* (1963) indicates best agreement of the data with Shakin's results for $W_{2\mathrm{p}-1\mathrm{h}} = 3$ MeV and reasonable agreement for $W_{2\mathrm{p}-1\mathrm{h}} = 1$ MeV and 2 MeV. The marked decrease in the strength function with mass number indicates the strong effect of the energy gap above the $1h_{11/2}$ neutron shell.

At mass number 138, the incident neutron is placed in the $2f_{7/2}$, $1h_{9/2}$ or $3p_{3/2}$ shell, a proton in the $1g_{7/2}$, $3s_{1/2}$, $2d_{3/2}$ or $1h_{11/2}$ shell, leaving a hole in the $2d_{5/2}$ sub-shell. Most of these states are of odd parity, giving a moderately small W for p-waves and a smaller value for s-waves. The effect on the s-wave strength function is rather indeterminate, for this mass number is not very far from the expected position of the $4s$ giant resonance; if it coincided with the giant resonance the strength function would be enhanced by the small value of W and between the giant resonances it would be diminished (as at mass number 90). The strength function in this intermediate situation is probably not much affected either way. There is no evidence of an effect in the data of Table 6.1.

At mass number 208 both the 82-proton shell and the 126-neutron shells are closed. The imaginary potential is expected to be very small for both p-waves and s-waves, but particularly so for s-waves. The few available data in this region confirm that the strength function is small.

(*b*) *Doorway states*

The two-particle, one-hole states have been called doorway states because they provide the mechanism that allows the single-particle system to pass to the true compound nucleus states. The possibility exists that these states are directly observable as intermediate structure in the strength function; the condition for this is that their spreading widths W_{2p-1h} are smaller than their spacings. In this case the imaginary potential W_{cp} will fluctuate with energy, peaks occurring at the energies of the two-particle, one-hole states where the core-particle states c′p′ contain the maximum admixture of two-particle, one-hole components. The size of the peaks will be governed by the matrix element (as in eqn. (6.80c)) for combining the two-particle, one-hole state with the single-particle state; it has been shown by Feshbach *et al.* (1966) that this can fluctuate considerably in a manner reminiscent of the Porter–Thomas distribution. The structure in the strength function, of course, will depend on the position of the single-particle state as well as on the behaviour of W. From eqn. (6.125) the spacing of the 2p-1h states is estimated to be of the order of 100 keV (for a single angular momentum and parity) in a typical non-shell nucleus. The damping-width W_{2p-1h} has been calculated for ^{208}Pb (Feshbach *et al.* 1964). It is of the order of 100 keV. Estimates of W_{2p-1h} may also be based on the quadratic energy dependence of W. The average energy of a particle (above the Fermi level) in the doorway state will be about one-half of the energy of a slow bombarding particle. This suggests that W_{2p-1h} may be of the order of one-half of W. Fits to strength function data have usually employed values of W of about 3 MeV. These considerations suggest that intermediate structure should not be observable except near the shell closures.

For the latter case there seems to be one rather well-established example in neutron reaction data (Farrell *et al.* 1965). The cross-section of ^{208}Pb has resonances spaced at roughly 50-keV intervals in the energy range up to 2 MeV. The total angular momentum and parity of most of these has been established (Fowler 1966) and very few are found to be *s*-wave resonances ($J^{\pi} = 1/2^{+}$). One of these few is the resonance at 500 keV with a neutron width of 58 keV. This resonance is assumed to be a nearly pure two-particle, one-hole state for, as we have already seen, the doubly magic nature of ^{208}Pb will hardly permit these states to be excited at such a low excitation energy (4·4 MeV), let alone more complicated states. The *s*-wave resonances in the cross-section of ^{206}Pb are much denser ($\approx$20 MeV^{-1}). Their interesting feature is that the strongest resonances seem to be clustered around the same neutron energy as that of the resonance in the ^{208}Pb cross-section. This is best shown by the diagram of Farrell *et al.* (Fig. 6.22); this is a cumulative histogram (as a function of neutron energy) of the reduced neutron widths of the resonances of the ^{206}Pb cross-section compared with the same thing for the one resonance of the ^{208}Pb cross-section. The summed strength of the former appears to be asymptotically approaching the single strength of the latter. The interpretation of this phenomenon is that the doorway state responsible for the group of resonances in the cross-section of ^{206}Pb is very similar to the two-particle, one-hole state in ^{209}Pb. In the two nuclei therefore, W_{cp} in this energy region (and E_{cp}) are very nearly the same, but in ^{209}Pb the strength function is concentrated on the one state while in ^{207}Pb the same strength is distributed over many, more complicated, states. The configuration of the two-particle, one-hole state is assumed to be that of a

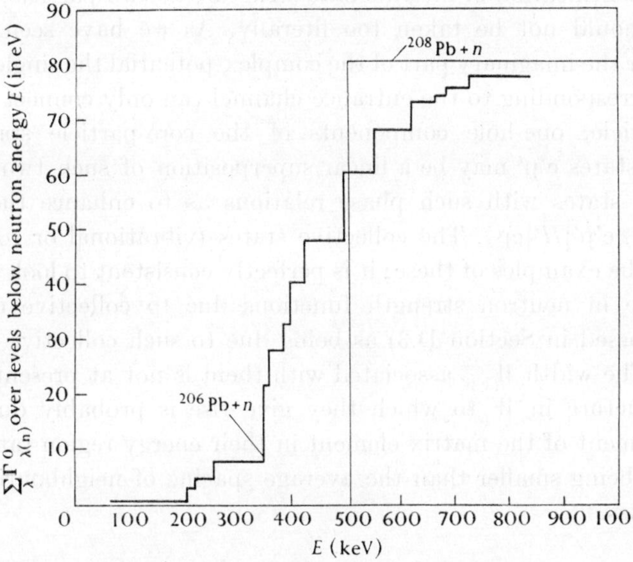

FIG. 6.22. Cumulative histogram of reduced neutron widths in region of a possible doorway state in ^{207}Pb, compared with an assumed two-particle, one-hole state in ^{209}Pb (after Farrell *et al.* 1965).

single proton lifted from the 82-proton shell leaving a hole, and a single neutron outside the 126-neutron shell. In the ^{207}Pb instance there are, in addition, two $p_{1/2}$ holes in the neutron shell, but these play an inert role, being also present in the single-particle state cp. The rather surprising feature of the experimental data is that the 2p−1h state occurs at very nearly the same *neutron* energy in the two compound nuclei, even though this is to be expected in the most naive application of the independent-particle model. While the width of the doorway state in ^{209}Pb is very small and cannot be deduced from the data, in ^{207}Pb it can be deduced from the cumulative histogram of Fig. 6.22. In a Lorentz line, half of the integrated area lies between the limits of one half-width on either side of the resonance energy. Applied to Fig. 6.22 this gives $W_{2p-1h} \approx 150$ keV for the doorway state of ^{207}Pb; this is in order of magnitude agreement with the estimate of Feshbach *et al.*

There seems to be no other well-substantiated evidence for doorway structure in neutron spectroscopy data. The differences in neutron strength functions for different spin values, the evidence for which was discussed in Section D.6, may be a manifestation of the effect, but in this case we would not expect the systematically higher value for the higher spin that seems to be observed.

The identification of intermediate structure as two-particle, one-hole states should not be taken too literally. As we have seen, in eqn. (6.82) for the imaginary part of the complex-potential the single-particle state corresponding to the entrance channel can only connect with the two-particle, one-hole components of the core-particle states c′p′. Certain states c′p′ may be a linear superposition of such two-particle, one-hole states with such phase relations as to enhance the matrix element $\langle c'p'|H'|cp\rangle$. The collective states (vibrational or rotational) seem to be examples of these; it is perfectly consistent to look upon the structure in neutron strength functions due to collective couplings (as discussed in Section D.3) as being due to such collective doorway states. The width $W_{c'p'}$ associated with them is not at present known. The structure in W to which they give rise is probably due to the enhancement of the matrix element in their energy region rather than to $W_{c'p'}$ being smaller than the average spacing of neighbouring doorway states.

8. *p*-wave neutron strength functions

Very few individual *p*-wave resonances have been positively identified. Occasionally a *p*-wave resonance has a sufficiently large neutron width that it may be identified by the absence of interference between resonance and potential scattering. Usually the identification rests upon the study of the capture γ-ray spectum of the resonance; a transition that would be $M1$ or $E2$ for an *s*-wave resonance, and therefore weak, may appear as an intense $E1$ γ-ray for a *p*-wave resonance. The number of resonances that have been identified is much too small to give *p*-wave strength functions with any precision except for the cross-section of ^{93}Nb (Jackson 1963) and for a few nuclei with very low level densities where resonance measurements have been extended to hundreds of keV. Other data on *p*-wave strength functions have been obtained by statistical analysis of resonance neutron widths or by analysis of average cross-sections over the energy range 1 keV to about 50 keV. If the neutron widths of a sequence of resonances have been measured by careful and sensitive methods many of the p-wave resonances will have been included in the measurement as well as virtually all the s-wave resonances. A histogram of the distribution of the 'reduced' widths (the s-wave penetration factor having been removed from all the widths) is a superposition of two Porter–Thomas distributions with different mean values. The histogram can often be analysed to give the mean values and hence an estimate of the p-wave strength function.

At this point it is necessary to specify more closely the definition of the p-wave strength function. In the resonance measurements described above it is really the quantity $g_J\Gamma_{(n)}$ that is measured. To obtain $\Gamma_{(n)}$ the approximation $g_J = 0{\cdot}5$ is applied. After removing the usual $2(2l+1)$ factor for the number of channel spin and angular momentum components the strength function obtained from the statistical analysis of the resonance data is defined as

$$s(l) = \frac{2}{2(2l+1)} \sum_{s=|I-\frac{1}{2}|}^{I+\frac{1}{2}} \sum_{J=|l-s|}^{l+s} g_J s(J,l). \qquad (6.126)$$

This is also the quantity obtained from average total cross-section data. The angular momentum weighting would not be relevant if the strength function were independent of J. It was conjectured in Section D.6 that the coupling of nucleon and target spins may cause dependence of the s-wave strength function on the total angular momentum. Evidence for the angular momentum dependence of the p-wave strength function is much stronger than conjecture; it arises from the strong nucleon spin-orbit coupling that is basic to the nuclear shell model. The form of the dependence is obtained by recoupling the component spins of a channel wave-function. The usual basis used in nuclear reaction theory in defining a channel is to couple the spins of the pair of particles to give the channel spin s; this is then coupled to the orbital angular momentum l to give the total angular momentum J. The spin-orbit channel functions are defined by coupling the spin of the bombarding nucleon i to the orbital angular momentum l to give total nucleon angular momentum j; this is coupled to the target angular momentum I to give the total J. The relation between the two sets of channel functions is

$$\varphi_{\alpha\{(I,i)s,l\}}(J) = \sum_j (-)^{I+i+l+J}\{(2j+1)(2s+1)\}^{\frac{1}{2}} \times W(IiJl;\, sj)\varphi_{\alpha\{(l,i)j,I\}}(J). \qquad (6.127)$$

Expansions of the type eqn. (6.2) allow us to write down a similar relation between the corresponding reduced width amplitudes and hence (using the random sign assumption for the coefficients C^{λ}_{cp}) for the reduced widths and strength functions:

$$s_{\alpha\{(I,i)s,l\}}(J) = \sum_{j=|l-\frac{1}{2}|}^{l+\frac{1}{2}} (2j+1)(2s+1)W^2(IiJl\,;\,sj)\times s_{\alpha\{(l,i)j,I\}}. \tag{6.128}$$

This relation may be substituted in the usual expressions for average cross-sections. Thus, the total cross-section becomes

$$\bar{\sigma}_{\text{T}}(l=1) = 2\pi^2\lambda\!\!\!^{-2}\sum_J g_{(J)} \sum_{s=|I-\frac{1}{2}|}^{I+\frac{1}{2}} 2P_1 s_{\alpha\{(I,i)s,l\}}(J)$$
$$= 2\pi^2\lambda\!\!\!^{-2}P_1\{2s_{(j=\frac{1}{2},l=1)}+4s_{(j=\frac{3}{2},l=1)}\}, \tag{6.129}$$

irrespective of I, on the assumption that the strength function depends solely on l and j. The weighting of the strength functions in eqn. (6.129) is just that which appears in complex potential calculations of the p-wave strength function. This is not generally true of the average partial cross-sections (Margolis 1963). For example, the average capture cross-section of an even nucleus is

$$\bar{\sigma}_{\gamma\text{T}}(l=1) = 2\pi^2\lambda\!\!\!^{-2}P_1\Bigg[2s_{\{n(l=1,i)j=\frac{1}{2},0\}}(J=\tfrac{1}{2})\cdot\frac{\bar{\Gamma}_{(\gamma\text{T})}(J=\frac{1}{2})}{\bar{\Gamma}_{(\text{T})}(J=\frac{1}{2})}\mathscr{S}^{(1)}_{\gamma}(J=\tfrac{1}{2})$$
$$+4s_{\{n(l=1,i)j=\frac{3}{2},0\}}(J=\tfrac{3}{2})\cdot\frac{\bar{\Gamma}_{(\gamma\text{T})}(J=\frac{3}{2})}{\bar{\Gamma}_{(\text{T})}(J=\frac{3}{2})}\mathscr{S}^{(1)}_{\gamma}(J=\tfrac{3}{2})\Bigg]. \tag{6.130}$$

The different weighting of the j components is not even constant with energy.

Because of these considerations and others described in Chapter VII, Section H, we must reject, for quantitative purposes, all the p-wave strength function data that have been extracted to date by analysis of average capture cross-sections in the kilovolt region. These have all employed implicitly the simplifying assumption that the p-wave strength function is independent of J.

The capture results of Gibbons *et al.* (1961) and Popov and Fenin (1962) do give qualitative indication, however, of a maximum in the p-wave strength function around mass number 100 where Fig. 3.3 shows that the $3p_{3/2}$ state is at zero energy. The splitting of the $3p$ giant resonance that might be expected from the spin-orbit splitting of the single particle states, illustrated in Fig. 3.3, has been shown by Krueger and Margolis (1961) to be insufficient to be observable against the large absorption width due to the imaginary part of the potential.

The few remaining data, from total cross-section measurements of

TABLE 6.4

Compilation of p-wave strength functions from analyses of neutron resonance and average transmission data

Target nucleus	I^{π}	Compound nucleus	$\bar{\Gamma}^{(1)}_{(n)}/\bar{D}$ (units of 10^{-4} eV$^{\frac{1}{2}}$)	Reference
$^{88}_{38}$Sr	0^{+}	$^{89}_{38}$Sr	$1{\cdot}2 \pm 0{\cdot}5$	Bilpuch *et al.* (1961)
$^{93}_{41}$Nb	$\frac{9}{2}^{+}$	$^{94}_{41}$Nb	$4{\cdot}6 \pm 1{\cdot}0$	Saplakoglu *et al.* (1958) Jackson (1963) Le Poittevin *et al.* (1965) Garg *et al.* (1965), Uttley *et al.* (1966)
$^{98}_{42}$Mo	0^{+}	$^{99}_{42}$Mo	$6{\cdot}8 \pm 0{\cdot}5$	Uttley *et al.* (1966)
$^{100}_{42}$Mo	0^{+}	$^{101}_{42}$Mo	$4{\cdot}6 \pm 0{\cdot}5$	Uttley *et al.* (1966)
$^{103}_{45}$Rh	$\frac{1}{2}^{-}$	$^{104}_{45}$Rh	$5{\cdot}1 \pm 0{\cdot}5$	Uttley *et al.* (1966)
$_{47}$Ag	$\frac{1}{2}$		$(1{\cdot}7 \pm 0{\cdot}8)$	Desjardins *et al.* (1960)
$^{207}_{82}$Pb	$\frac{1}{2}^{-}$	$^{208}_{82}$Pb	$0{\cdot}17 \pm 0{\cdot}15$	Bilpuch *et al.* (1961)
$^{208}_{82}$Pb	0^{+}	$^{209}_{82}$Pb	$0{\cdot}32 \pm 0{\cdot}15$	Bilpuch *et al.* (1961)
$^{232}_{90}$Th	0^{+}	$^{233}_{90}$Th	$1{\cdot}8 \pm 0{\cdot}2$	Lynn (1963*a*), Uttley *et al.* (1966)
$^{235}_{92}$U	$\frac{7}{2}^{-}$	$^{236}_{92}$U	$1{\cdot}75 \pm 0{\cdot}25$	Uttley *et al.* (1966)
$^{238}_{92}$U	0^{+}	$^{239}_{92}$U	$2{\cdot}4 \pm 0{\cdot}3$	Lynn (1963*a*), Uttley *et al.* (1966)
$^{239}_{94}$Pu	$\frac{1}{2}^{+}$	$^{240}_{94}$Pu	$2{\cdot}5 \pm 0{\cdot}5$	Uttley (1964)

various kinds, are listed in Table 6.4. In this, and in Fig. 6.23, the quantity $\bar{\Gamma}^{(1)}_{(n)}/\bar{D}$ rather than s_1, is shown. The normalized reduced width $\Gamma^{(1)}_{(n)}$ for a p-wave resonance at energy E_{R} is defined by

$$\Gamma^{(1)}_{(n)} = \frac{\Gamma_{R(n)}}{(ka)^2\sqrt{(E_R)}}, \qquad (6.131)$$

in which $\Gamma_{R(n)}$ and E_R are normally expressed in eV.

The results are all in general agreement with the spherical complex-potential model with typical parameters found for explaining s-wave data. More elaborate models have been used for calculating p-wave strength functions, notably that of Buck and Perey (1962), which includes vibrational and rotational coupling as well as spin-orbit coupling. Their curve, using the parameters of Section D.3, is shown in Fig. 6.23. It shows one large general maximum in the region of $A \approx 100$, where the nuclei are spherical, but there is much structure in the permanently deformed region about $A \approx 240$. The results quoted in Table 6.4 for this region seem to confirm their model.

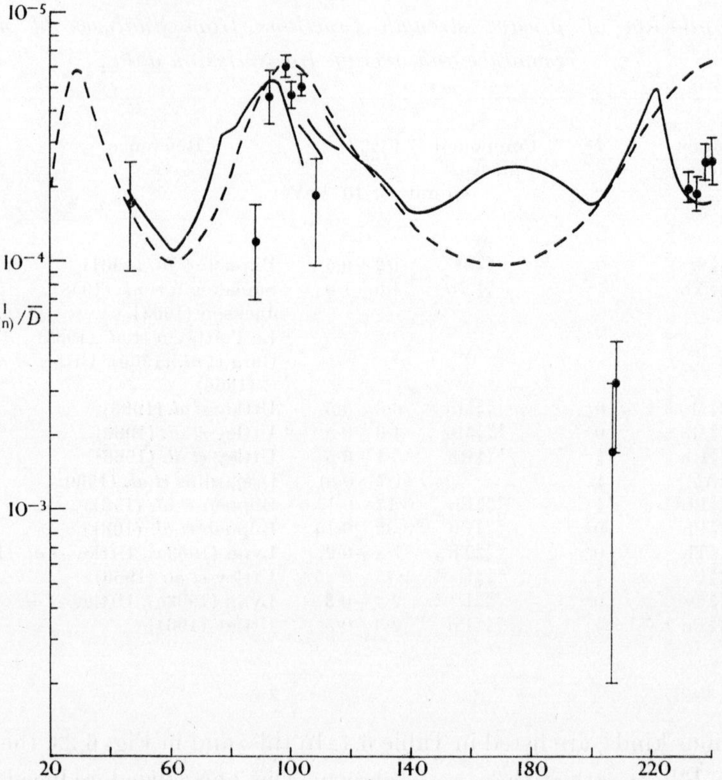

FIG. 6.23. p-wave strength function data and complex-potential model with vibrational, rotational, and spin-orbit coupling (Buck and Perey 1962); this is the full curve in the diagram. The parameters employed for it are those quoted in Section D.3(b) with the spin-orbit coupling parameter $\lambda = 21{\cdot}5$ (see eqn. (3.22)). The broken curve in the diagram is a typical result from a spherical complex potential with no collective coupling.

VII

RADIATIVE CAPTURE

A. DATA

THE principal slow neutron reaction, occurring at a measurable rate in the neutron bombardment of almost every nucleus, is the absorption of the neutron to form the next heaviest isotope accompanied by the emission of electromagnetic radiation which carries off the excitation

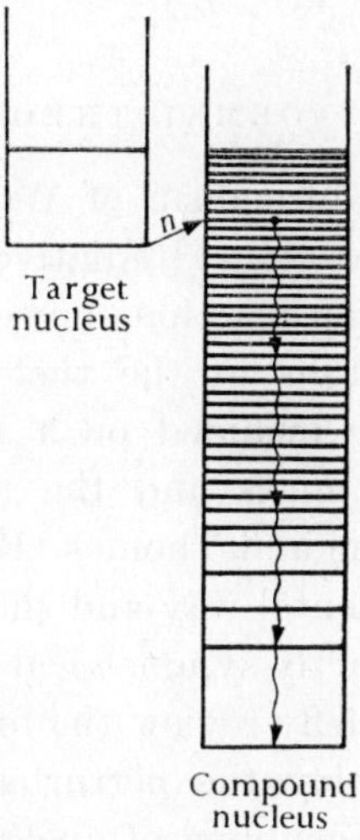

FIG. 7.1. Schematic diagram of neutron capture followed by a cascade of gamma radiation.

energy (equal to the neutron separation energy plus the kinetic energy of the bombarding particle). The excitation energy is seldom carried off in a single step (transition to the ground state). It is more usual for a transition to occur to an intermediate state (see Fig. 7.1); this is known as the primary transition. The remaining energy is carried off in one or more steps (secondary, tertiary, etc. transitions), the entire sequence being known as the cascade.

The strength of the primary transition from a resonance state, λ, to a given final state, μ, is governed by the partial radiation width $\Gamma_{\lambda(\gamma\mu)}$ of the resonance for that transition. The strength of the entire neutron-capture process for the resonance, λ, is given by the total radiation width, $\Gamma_{\lambda(\gamma T)}$ which is the sum of the partial widths $\Gamma_{\lambda(\gamma\mu)}$ over all the final states μ lying below the resonance state in energy. The available data on slow-neutron reactions largely comprise values of the total radiation widths measured for a large range of nuclei from intermediate to heavy masses, and in many cases for a number of resonances. In addition, there are some data on partial radiation widths for high-energy primary transitions and, at thermal neutron energies, many capture γ-ray spectra are known, usually with good enough resolution to separate many of the high-energy lines. These spectra are complicated, of course, by the presence of γ-rays corresponding to the secondary and higher order transitions. We now proceed to consider the theoretical analysis of such data.

B. FORMAL THEORY

The original dispersion formalism of Wigner and Eisenbud (1947) referred only to particle reactions. Radiative capture is such an important feature of slow neutron reactions however that it is necessary to include reference to photons in the theory. Many authors simply assumed that it could be included on a par with the particles by referring to radiation channels and the reduced width amplitudes associated with them. Lane and Thomas (1958) first included photons in the theory in a fundamental way and showed that their occurrence in the formalism is not exactly symmetrical with the particle channels, although nearly so. We briefly review the formal aspects here.

Lane and Thomas employ the perturbation approach to electromagnetic phenomena, the coupling of nucleons to the electromagnetic field being small, and they consider processes in which one photon at most exists in the system at a given time. The usual perturbation theory expression (see e.g. Heitler 1954) for the transition probability between an initial state Ψ and final state Φ, with emission of a photon into a solid angle element $d\Omega$, is

$$T = \frac{2\pi}{\hbar}|\langle\Psi|H^{(1)}(\mathscr{A})|\Phi\rangle|^2 d\rho \tag{7.1}$$

where $H^{(1)}(\mathscr{A})$ is the electromagnetic perturbation operator (written in terms of the vector potential $\mathscr{A}$) and $\mathrm{d}\rho$ is the density of photon states with direction vector within the solid angle element $\mathrm{d}\Omega$ in a large volume V surrounding the source. This is equal to the square modulus $|U_{c\gamma}|^2$ of the collision matrix element if $\Psi = \Psi^{(c)}$, the internal wave-function of the system with unit incoming flux in channel c, eqn. (2.53). The result obtained for the collision matrix elements involving photons, γ, is

$$U_{c\gamma} = ie^{i\phi_c}e^{i\phi_\gamma}\sum_{\lambda\mu} A_{\lambda\mu}\Gamma^{\frac{1}{2}}_{\mu(c)}\Gamma^{\frac{1}{2}}_{\lambda(\gamma)} \tag{7.2}$$

which is formally similar to the particle collision-matrix elements, eqn. (2.48). It is important for the study of slow neutron reactions, for which radiative capture cross-sections can be greater than the particle cross-sections, that the effects of damping are properly included in the derivation of eqn. (7.2). Lane and Thomas (1958) show that this is so if the level width quantities $\Gamma_{\lambda\mu} = \sum_c \Gamma^{\frac{1}{2}}_{\lambda(c)}\Gamma^{\frac{1}{2}}_{\mu(c)}$ entering the reciprocal level matrix **A** formally include the photon channels γ as well as the particle channels c. The product of the photon width amplitude and phase factor occurring in eqn. (7.2) is

$$e^{i\phi_\gamma}\Gamma^{\frac{1}{2}}_{\lambda(\gamma)} = \left(\frac{2\pi d\rho}{\hbar}\right)^{\frac{1}{2}}\hbar^{\frac{1}{2}}\int d\tau X^*_\lambda H^{(1)}(\mathscr{A})\Phi. \tag{7.3}$$

To obtain the partial width irrespective of the angle of emission this is to be integrated over the complete solid angle.

So far it appears that the inclusion of photons in the theory occurs exactly as for particles. In the practical use of the R-matrix theory this is not so, however, for the states X_λ are defined only for the internal region of configuration space, delineated by the channel radii a_c, whereas it is clear that there ought also to be a contribution to the photon width amplitudes from the external region. Formally, this difficulty may be overcome by setting the channel radii at infinity but the price paid for this is that the eigenstates X_λ have no physical significance in the sense of bearing a one-to-one correspondence with the resonances. For the R-matrix to be physically useful it is necessary that the open channel radii be placed as little outside the nuclear force field as possible. With this condition it is possible to investigate the structure of the collision matrix further.

The wave-function in the external region may be divided into three parts. One is the wave-function in the channel of the incident particle; it is (cf. eqn. 2.34)

$$\Psi^{(c)}_{\text{ext}} = \mathscr{I}_c - U_{cc}\mathscr{O}_c. \tag{7.4}$$

The second part consists of the wave functions in the remaining open-channels, c^+

$$\sum_{c^+\neq c}\Psi^{(c^+)}_{\text{ext}} = \sum_{c^+\neq c} -U_{c^+c}\mathscr{O}_{c^+}. \tag{7.5}$$

The third part consists of the closed channels, c^-, of other particles:

$$\sum_{c^-}\Psi^{(c^-)}_{ext} = \sum_{c^-} -i\hbar^{\frac{1}{2}}\sum_{\lambda\mu} A_{\lambda\mu}\Gamma^{\frac{1}{2}}_{\mu(c)}\varphi_{c^-}\int_{\mathscr{S}_{c^-}} X_{\lambda}\varphi^*_{c^-}\,d\mathscr{S}$$

$$\times\,\mathscr{O}_{c^-}(r_{c^-})/\mathscr{O}_{c^-}(a_{c^-}) \qquad (7.6a)$$

$$= \sum_{c^-} -i\hbar^{\frac{1}{2}}\sum_{\lambda\mu} A_{\lambda\mu}\Gamma^{\frac{1}{2}}_{\mu(c)}\left(\frac{2M_{c^-}a_{c^-}}{\hbar^2}\right)^{\frac{1}{2}}\gamma_{\lambda(c^-)}\frac{\mathscr{O}_{c^-}(r_{c^-})}{\mathscr{O}_{c^-}(a_{c^-})}\varphi_{c^-} \qquad (7.6b)$$

where $\mathscr{O}_{c^-}$ is the 'exponentially decaying' outgoing wave-function in channel c^- analogous to the outgoing wave-functions in the open channels. The surface $\mathscr{S}_{c^-}$ in configuration space is specified by the condition $r_{c^-} = a_{c^-}$. The contribution of these external regions to the right-hand side of eqn. (7.1) are:

$$\int \Psi^{(c)}_{ext}H^{(1)}(\mathscr{A})\Phi\,d\tau = \int (\mathscr{I}_c - U_{cc}\mathscr{O}_{cc})H^{(1)}\Phi\,d\tau$$

$$= \int \left\{\mathscr{I}_c - e^{-2i\phi_c}\left(1+i\sum_{\lambda\mu}\Gamma^{\frac{1}{2}}_{\mu(c)}A_{\lambda\mu}\Gamma^{\frac{1}{2}}_{\lambda(c)}\right)\mathscr{O}_c\right\}H^{(1)}\Phi\,d\tau$$

$$= \int (\mathscr{I}_c - e^{-2i\phi_c}\mathscr{O}_c)H^{(1)}\Phi\,d\tau - ie^{-2i\phi_c}\sum_{\lambda\mu} A_{\lambda\mu}\Gamma^{\frac{1}{2}}_{\mu(c)}\int \Gamma^{\frac{1}{2}}_{\lambda(c)}\mathscr{O}_c H^{(1)}\Phi\,d\tau, \qquad (7.7a)$$

$$\sum_{c^+\neq c}\int \Psi^{(c^+)}_{ext}H^{(1)}\Phi\,d\tau = \sum_{c^+\neq c} -\int U_{c^+c}\mathscr{O}_{c^+}H^{(1)}\Phi\,d\tau$$

$$= \sum_{c\neq c} -ie^{-i\phi_c}e^{-i\phi_c}\sum_{\lambda\mu} A_{\lambda\mu}\Gamma^{\frac{1}{2}}_{\mu(c)}\int \Gamma^{\frac{1}{2}}_{\lambda(c^+)}\mathscr{O}_{c^+}H^{(1)}\Phi\,d\tau \qquad (7.7b)$$

$$\sum_{c^-}\int \Psi^{(c^-)}_{ext}H^{(1)}\Phi\,d\tau =$$

$$\sum_{c^-} -i\hbar^{\frac{1}{2}}\left(\frac{2M_{c^-}a_{c^-}}{\hbar^2}\right)^{\frac{1}{2}}\sum_{\lambda\mu} A_{\lambda\mu}\Gamma^{\frac{1}{2}}_{\mu(c)}\int \gamma_{\lambda(c^-)}\varphi_{c^-}\frac{\mathscr{O}_{c^-}(r_{c^-})}{\mathscr{O}_{c^-}(a_{c^-})}H^{(1)}\Phi\,d\tau. \qquad (7.7c)$$

It is now apparent that $U_{c\gamma}$ can be put into the form

$$U_{c\gamma} = ie^{-i\phi_c}e^{-i\phi_\gamma}\sum_{\lambda\mu} A_{\lambda\mu}\Gamma^{\frac{1}{2}}_{\mu(c)}\Gamma^{\frac{1}{2}}_{\lambda(\gamma)} + \left(\frac{2\pi d\rho}{\hbar}\right)^{\frac{1}{2}}\int_{r_c=a_c}^{\infty} (\mathscr{I}_c - e^{-2i\phi_c}\mathscr{O}_c)H^{(1)}\Phi\,d\tau_c \qquad (7.8a)$$

where

$$e^{-i\phi_\gamma}\Gamma^{\frac{1}{2}}_{\lambda(\gamma)} = -(2\pi d\rho)^{\frac{1}{2}}\left\{\int X_\lambda^* H^{(1)}\Phi d\tau\right.$$

$$+\hbar^{-\frac{1}{2}}\sum_{c^+(\text{inc.c})} e^{-i\phi_{c^+}}\Gamma^{\frac{1}{2}}_{(c^+)}\int_{r_{c^+}=a_{c^+}}^{\infty} \mathcal{O}^*_{c^+} H^{(1)}\Phi d\tau_{c^+}$$

$$\left.+\sum_{c^-}\left(\frac{2M_{c^-}a_{c^-}}{\hbar^2}\right)^{\frac{1}{2}}\gamma_{\lambda(c^-)}\int_{r_{c^-}=a_{c^-}}^{\infty}\frac{\mathcal{O}_{c^-}(r_{c^-})}{\mathcal{O}_{c^-}(a_{c^-})}\varphi_{c^-}H^{(1)}\Phi d\tau_{c^-}\right\}. \tag{7.8b}$$

This shows, not only that the radiation width includes contributions from the channels (both open and closed) in the external region, but also that the capture amplitude includes a non-resonant part analogous to the potential scattering contribution to the elastic scattering amplitude. It is referred to as the hard-sphere capture amplitude (Lane and Lynn 1960*a*).

In order to simplify the succeeding equations it is worthwhile to extend the definition of the states X_λ to include their smooth continuation into the channels. We denote such extended states by X_λ^e thus

$$X_\lambda^e = X_\lambda, \text{ all } r_{c'} \leqslant a_{c'} \tag{7.9a}$$

$$= \hbar^{-\frac{1}{2}}e^{-i\phi_{c^+}}\Gamma^{\frac{1}{2}}_{(c^+)}\mathcal{O}_{c^+},\ r_{c^+}>a_{c^+},\ r_{c'\neq c^+}\leqslant a_{c'} \tag{7.9b}$$

$$= \left(\frac{2M_{c^-}a_{c^-}}{\hbar^2}\right)^{\frac{1}{2}}\gamma_{\lambda(c^-)}\frac{\mathcal{O}_{c^-}(r_{c^-})}{\mathcal{O}_{c^-}(a_{c^-})}\varphi_{c^-},\ r_{c^-}>a_{c^-},\ r_{c'\neq c^-}\leqslant a_{c'}. \tag{7.9c}$$

If the convention of choosing extremely large channel radii for the bound channels is adopted, as suggested in Chapter II, Section F, then the contribution of the third part eqn. (7.9c) is negligible.

Equations (7.1) and (7.8) are written for a vector potential which has the plane wave form

$$\mathcal{A} = c(2\pi\hbar/\omega V)^{\frac{1}{2}}\mathbf{u}\exp(-i\boldsymbol{\kappa}\,.\,\mathbf{r}), \tag{7.10}$$

where ω is the circular frequency of the wave, and $\boldsymbol{\kappa}$ is the propagation vector indicating the direction of the wave and its wave number κ. This is proportional to the energy of the γ-ray, the actual relation being $\kappa = \omega/c = \varepsilon_\gamma/\hbar c$. Finally, $\mathbf{u}$ is the polarization vector. The normalization of this plane wave corresponds to a photon density of

$$d\rho = \{\omega^2 V/(2\pi)^3\hbar c^3\}d\Omega.$$

The Hamiltonian for a system of nucleons in a potential field, V, interacting with an electromagnetic field with vector potential $\mathscr{A}$ is

$$H(\mathscr{A}) = (4AM)^{-1}\sum_{j,k}\left\{\mathbf{p}_j-\mathbf{p}_k-\frac{e_j}{c}\mathscr{A}(\mathbf{r}_j)+\frac{e_k}{c}\mathscr{A}(\mathbf{r}_k)\right\}^2 + V-\left(\frac{e\hbar}{2Mc}\right)\sum_j \mu_j(\boldsymbol{\sigma}_j\,.\,\mathbf{curl}\,\mathscr{A}_j), \qquad (7.11)$$

where the $\mathbf{p}_j$ are the momenta of the particles j, the e_j are their charges, the $\boldsymbol{\sigma}_j$ are their integral angular momenta and the μ_j are their magnetic moments in units of the nuclear magneton $(e\hbar/2Mc)$ in which M is the nucleon mass and e is the proton charge. This expression is for ordinary forces; velocity dependent forces and exchange forces are not considered here (see Sachs 1953 for a discussion of them). The term which is linear in $\mathscr{A}$ in the expansion of eqn. (7.11) is the first order perturbation operator (equivalent to the coupling with one photon in the field):

$$H^{(1)}(\mathscr{A}) = -(4AMc)^{-1}\sum_{j,k}\{(\mathbf{p}_j-\mathbf{p}_k)\,.\,(e_j\mathscr{A}_j-e_k\mathscr{A}_k) + (e_j\mathscr{A}_j-e_k\mathscr{A}_k)\,.\,(\mathbf{p}_j-\mathbf{p}_k)\} - (e\hbar/2Mc)\sum_j \mu_j(\boldsymbol{\sigma}_j\,.\,\mathbf{curl}\,\mathscr{A}_j). \qquad (7.12)$$

A vector field can be expanded in terms of the vector spherical harmonics, which form a complete set. The vector spherical harmonics (which are described more fully by Blatt and Weisskopf 1952, Appendix B) are eigenfunctions of the total angular momentum operators $\mathbf{J}^2$ and $\mathbf{J}_z$ (we call the eigenvalues $\mathscr{L}$ and $\mathscr{M}$) and are formed by coupling the spherical harmonics $Y_m^{(l)}$ to a set of vectors $\boldsymbol{\chi}$ expressed in the unit vectors $\mathbf{e}$ along the cartesian axes as

$$\chi_{\pm 1} = \mp\frac{1}{\sqrt{2}}(\mathbf{e}_x \pm i\mathbf{e}_y), \qquad (7.13a)$$

$$\chi_0 = \mathbf{e}_z. \qquad (7.13b)$$

The latter are themselves eigenfunctions of an operator, S_z, perfectly analogous to a spin operator, with eigenvalues -1, 0, $+1$. The vector spherical harmonics $\mathbf{Y}_{\mathscr{L}l1}^{\mathscr{M}}$ are thus defined by

$$\mathbf{Y}_{\mathscr{L}l1}^{\mathscr{M}}(\theta,\phi) = \sum_{m=-l}^{l}\sum_{m'=-1}^{1} C_{l1}(\mathscr{L}\mathscr{M};mm')Y_m^{(l)}(\theta,\phi)\chi_{m'}, \qquad (7.14)$$

using the usual Clebsch–Gordan coefficients. The vector spherical harmonics have the property that $\mathbf{Y}_{\mathscr{L}\mathscr{L}1}^{\mathscr{M}}$ has parity $(-)^{\mathscr{L}}$; the other vector spherical harmonics $\mathbf{Y}^{\mathscr{M}}_{\mathscr{L},\mathscr{L}\pm1,1}$ can be obtained from $\mathbf{Y}^{\mathscr{M}}_{\mathscr{L}\mathscr{L}1}$ by the **curl** operation and so have the opposite parity.

As we have stated, any vector field can be expanded in these spherical harmonics. In particular the spatial dependence of the circularly polarized plane wave-form of the vector potential has the expansion

$$\mathscr{A}(\mathbf{r}) = \frac{1}{\sqrt{2}}(\mathbf{e}_x \pm \mathrm{i}\mathbf{e}_y)\exp(\mathrm{i}\kappa z) = \pm\exp(\mathrm{i}\kappa z)\chi_{\pm1} \tag{7.15a}$$

$$= \mp\sum_{\mathscr{L}=1}^{\infty}\sum_{l=\mathscr{L}-1}^{\mathscr{L}+1} \mathrm{i}^l\sqrt{\{4\pi(2l+1)\}}C_{l1}(\mathscr{L},\pm1;0,\pm1)j_l(\kappa r)\mathbf{Y}^{\pm1}_{\mathscr{L}l1}(\theta,\phi). \tag{7.15b}$$

In general the plane wave-form of eqn. (7.15a) is not travelling in the z-direction so the general expansion involves terms $\mathbf{Y}^{\mathscr{M}}_{\mathscr{L}l1}$ with all values of $\mathscr{M}$ from $-\mathscr{L}$ to $\mathscr{L}$. The general expression for an arbitrary direction of the propagation vector with respect to the z-axis is obtained from eqn. (7.15b) by use of the rotation matrices for transforming irreducible tensor operators from one cartesian frame to another differing from the first by rotation through the Euler angles α, β, γ (see Edmonds 1960, p. 51 or Rose 1957, p. 48). The result for a wave with its propagation vector in a direction β to the z-axis (the Euler angles α and γ affect only the polarization vector) is

$$\mathscr{A}(\mathbf{r}) = \mathbf{u}_p e^{\mathrm{i}\boldsymbol{\kappa}\cdot\mathbf{r}}$$

$$= \mp\sum_{\mathscr{L}=1}^{\infty}\sum_{l=\mathscr{L}-1}^{\mathscr{L}+1} \mathrm{i}^l\sqrt{\{4\pi(2l+1)\}}C_{l1}(\mathscr{L},\pm1;0,\pm1)j_l(\kappa r).$$

$$\cdot\sum_{\mathscr{M}=-\mathscr{L}}^{\mathscr{L}} D^{\mathscr{L}}_{\mathscr{M},\pm1}(\alpha\beta\gamma)\mathbf{Y}^{\mathscr{M}}_{\mathscr{L}l1}(\theta,\phi). \tag{7.15c}$$

The rotation matrices $D^j_{m'm}$ have the explicit form

$$D^j_{m'm}(\alpha\beta\gamma) = \mathrm{e}^{-\mathrm{i}m'\alpha}d^j_{m'm}(\beta)\mathrm{e}^{-\mathrm{i}m\gamma}$$

$$d^j_{m'm}(\beta) = \{(j+m)!(j-m)!(j+m')!(j-m')!\}^{\frac{1}{2}}$$

$$\cdot\sum_n \frac{(-)^n(\cos\beta/2)^{2j+m-m'-2n}(-\sin\beta/2)^{m'-m+2n}}{(j-m'-n)!(j+m-n)!(n+m'-m)!n!} \tag{7.15d}$$

The sum in this last equation is for values of the integer n that give factorial arguments greater than or equal to zero.

Equation (7.15a) is limited to terms involving only the $\chi_{\pm1}$ of the photon basis for the following reason. In free space the magnetic field $\mathbf{H} = \mathbf{curl}\,\mathscr{A}$. By Maxwell's equations the electric field $\mathbf{E}$ is proportional to **curl H**, and from this it follows that **E** has the same spatial dependence as $\mathscr{A}$. Now it is well known that a plane electromagnetic wave can only have transverse components in the electric and magnetic fields and so the vector potential describing the wave is similarly limited.

By the substitution of an expansion of the type (7.15c) into eqn. (7.12) the required multipole expansion of the electromagnetic perturbation operator can be obtained. After substituting this into the matrix elements (eqn. (7.1)) various integral expressions involving vector operations can be found for the individual terms. Most of these we shall not need, so we do not give them here; they can be found in other works such as Blatt and Weisskopf (1952). It is desirable to say something here about the classification of these terms, however. In a typical term of order $\mathscr{L}$ in the expansion of the vector potential there are three sub-terms, one of which—the term in $\mathbf{Y}^{\mathscr{M}}_{\mathscr{L}\mathscr{L}1}$—has parity $(-)^{\mathscr{L}}$, and the other two, $\mathbf{Y}^{\mathscr{M}}_{\mathscr{L}\mathscr{L}\pm1,1}$ have parity $-(-)^{\mathscr{L}}$. Now let us notice the effect of the first of these on the parity of the perturbation operator. In the first part of this operator the vector potential occurs in the scalar product with a momentum vector (which has odd parity). The component of $H^{(1)}$ that we are considering has parity $-(-)^{\mathscr{L}}$. The same is true of the second term in $H^{(1)}$ because the **curl** operation reverses the parity of the vector potential, and the axial vector $\boldsymbol{\sigma}$ has even parity. By the same kind of argument the part of $H^{(1)}$ due to the components $\mathbf{Y}^{\mathscr{M}}_{\mathscr{L}\mathscr{L}\pm1,1}$ in $\mathscr{A}$ has parity $(-)^{\mathscr{L}}$. Since the magnetic vector **H** is just **curl** $\mathscr{A}$, and the components in $H^{(1)}$ due to these specific components of $\mathscr{A}$ have parity opposite to them, the parity of the perturbation operator component is just that of the magnetic vector component. In order to have a non-zero matrix element for a specific component of the perturbation operator the difference in parity between the initial and final states must be the same as that of this component. The terms in $H^{(1)}$ with multipolarity $\mathscr{L}\mathscr{M}$ are thus divided into groups for which the magnetic vector has parity $(-)^{\mathscr{L}}$ (these are called electric multiple operators since it is found that they arise principally from the terms involving the charges) and groups with the opposite parity (called magnetic multipole operators—the contribution to these comes mainly from the magnetic moments). The various components of the electromagnetic perturbation operator are proportional to irreducible tensor operators denoted by $\mathscr{H}^{(\mathscr{L})}_{\mathrm{T}\mathscr{M}}$ where the subscript T denotes the parity, electric or magnetic in type. Thus the partial radiation width for a photon channel with multipolarity $\mathscr{L}\mathscr{M}$ (in which the photon carries $\mathscr{L}$

units of angular momentum and $\mathscr{M}$ units of angular momentum projection on the z-axis) is

$$\Gamma^{\frac{1}{2}}_{\lambda(\gamma\mathscr{L}\mathscr{M})} = \frac{(8\pi)^{\frac{1}{2}}\kappa^{\mathscr{L}+\frac{1}{2}}(\mathscr{L}+1)^{\frac{1}{2}}}{\mathscr{L}^{\frac{1}{2}}(2\mathscr{L}+1)!!}\langle X^{\mathrm{e}}_{\lambda JM}|\mathscr{H}^{(\mathscr{L})}_{\mathrm{T}\mathscr{M}}|\Phi_{J'M'}\rangle \tag{7.16}$$

for the transition from a state with angular momentum and projection J and M to a state with angular momentum and projection J' and M'.

In the M'th component of the irreducible tensor operator $\mathscr{H}^{(\mathscr{L})}_{\mathrm{T}\mathscr{M}}$ of rank $\mathscr{L}$, the general subscript T has to be specialized to either E or M denoting electric or magnetic radiation according to the parity difference $(-)^{\mathscr{L}}$ or $(-)^{\mathscr{L}+1}$, respectively, of the initial and final state. This, together with the conservation of angular momentum ($|J'-\mathscr{L}|$ to $J'+\mathscr{L}$ must encompass J) results in the selection rules for transitions between states $J^{\pi}M$ and $J'^{\pi'}M'$ shown in Table 7.1.

TABLE 7.1

Selection rules for transitions of different multipolarity

	$\mathscr{L}$	ΔJ	$\Delta\pi$
Electric dipole	1	$-1, 0, 1$ (except $J = 0 \rightarrow J' = 0$)	$-$
Electric quadrupole	2	$-2, -1, 0, 1, 2$ (except $J = 0 \rightarrow J' = 0$)	$+$
Magnetic dipole	1	$-1, 0, 1$ (except $J = 0 \rightarrow J' = 0$)	$+$

The partial radiation width of a transition of multipolarity is proportional to $\varepsilon_{\gamma}^{2\mathscr{L}+1}$ among other factors. Because of this it is common to define a reduced partial radiation width by removing this energy factor from the proper width.

The angular distribution for the radiation emitted in a transition of multipolarity $\mathscr{L}\mathscr{M}$ is obtained from the Poynting vector $(c/4\pi)(\mathbf{E}\times\mathbf{H})$ for the energy flow. In the wave zone the electric and magnetic vectors are perpendicular so the energy density is proportional to $\mathbf{E}^*.\mathbf{E}$ or $\mathbf{H}^*.\mathbf{H}$. In magnetic radiation the magnetic vector is proportional to $\mathbf{Y}^{\mathscr{M}}_{\mathscr{L}\mathscr{L}1}(\theta,\phi)$ and in electric radiation the electric vector is proportional to $\mathbf{Y}^{\mathscr{M}}_{\mathscr{L}\mathscr{L}1}(\theta,\phi)$ so in either case the angular dependence $Z(\theta,\phi)$ of the energy density is proportional to $\mathbf{Y}^{\mathscr{M}}_{\mathscr{L}\mathscr{L}1}{}^*.\,\mathbf{Y}^{\mathscr{M}}_{\mathscr{L}\mathscr{L}1}$, i.e.

$$Z(\theta,\phi) = \mathbf{Y}^{\mathscr{M}*}_{\mathscr{L}\mathscr{L}1}\cdot\mathbf{Y}^{\mathscr{M}}_{\mathscr{L}\mathscr{L}1}$$
$$= \tfrac{1}{2}\left\{1-\frac{\mathscr{M}(\mathscr{M}+1)}{\mathscr{L}(\mathscr{L}+1)}\right\}|Y^{(\mathscr{L})}_{\mathscr{M}+1}|^2+\tfrac{1}{2}\left\{1-\frac{\mathscr{M}(\mathscr{M}-1)}{\mathscr{L}(\mathscr{L}+1)}\right\}|Y^{(\mathscr{L})}_{\mathscr{M}-1}|^2$$
$$+\frac{\mathscr{M}^2}{\mathscr{L}(\mathscr{L}+1)}|Y^{(\mathscr{L})}_{\mathscr{M}}|^2. \tag{7.17}$$

Since this result implies that electric and magnetic type transitions cannot be distinguished by a measurement of the angular distribution of the radiation, it is necessary to use the polarization of the radiation to make this distinction.

It has been shown by Blatt and Weisskopf (1952) that magnetic radiation is weaker than electric radiation of the same multipolarity by a factor of the order of v/c where v is the velocity of the nucleon causing the transition. Numerically, this factor is of the order of 1/10 for slow neutron capture transitions. It has also been shown by them that electric multipole transitions are very roughly proportional to $(\omega a/c)^{2\mathscr{L}}$. This implies that for typical transitions that occur in slow neutron capture, e.g. of energy 3 MeV in a nucleus of radius $a = 7\times10^{-13}$ cm, an electric quadrupole transition is about 100 times slower than an electric dipole transition. For this reason it only appears necessary to consider electric and magnetic dipole transitions at the present stage in the study of resonance neutron capture, because gamma-ray detectors with high-energy resolution are not sufficiently efficient nor neutron sources sufficiently intense to permit investigation of very weak transitions.

For electric and magnetic dipole transitions the operators $\mathscr{H}^{\mathscr{L}}_{\mathrm{T}\mathscr{M}}$ have the following forms in the long wavelength approximation ($\kappa a \ll 1$; this is sufficiently satisfied if the energy of the radiation is less than about 10 MeV):

$$\mathscr{H}^{(1)}_{\mathrm{E}\mathscr{M}} = \sum_k e_k r_k Y^{(1)}_{\mathscr{M}}(\theta_k,\phi_k) \tag{7.18a}$$

$$\mathscr{H}^{(1)}_{\mathrm{M}\mathscr{M}} = \frac{e\hbar}{2Mc}\left(\frac{3}{4\pi}\right)^{\frac{1}{2}}\sum_k (L_{k\mathscr{M}}+\mu_k\sigma_{k\mathscr{M}}) \tag{7.18b}$$

where the $L_{k\mathscr{M}}$ and $\sigma_{k\mathscr{M}}$ are the spherical components of the orbital angular momentum and intrinsic spin vectors respectively (see e.g. Edmonds 1957); thus

$$L_{k\pm1} = \frac{1}{\sqrt{2}}(L_x\pm \mathrm{i}L_y) \tag{7.19a}$$

$$L_{k0} = L_z. \tag{7.19b}$$

In experiments involving unpolarized particles the radiation width is required for transitions from a state $X^{\mathrm{e}}_{\lambda J}$, averaged over all values of M from $-J$ to J, to a state Φ with angular momentum J', summed over all values of M' from $-J'$ to J' irrespective of the polarization $\mathscr{M}$ of the photon; this is given by

$$\Gamma_{\lambda(\gamma\mathscr{L})} = \frac{\sum\limits_{MM'\mathscr{M}} \Gamma_{\lambda(\gamma\mathscr{L}\mathscr{M})}}{2J+1} \tag{7.20a}$$

$$= \frac{8\pi\kappa^{2\mathscr{L}+1}(\mathscr{L}+1)|\langle X^{\mathrm{e}}_{\lambda J}||\mathscr{H}^{(\mathscr{L})}_{\mathrm{T}}||\Phi_{J'}\rangle|^2}{\mathscr{L}\{(2\mathscr{L}+1)!!\}^2(2J+1)} \tag{7.20b}$$

(see Edmonds 1959, p. 76). The reduced matrix element introduced in this equation is defined in the usual way by

$$\langle X^{\mathrm{e}}_{\lambda J}||\mathscr{H}^{(\mathscr{L})}_{\mathrm{T}}||\Phi_{J'}\rangle = (2\mathscr{L}+1)^{\frac{1}{2}} \sum_{MM'} C_{J'\mathscr{L}}(JM;M'\mathscr{M})\langle X_{\lambda JM}|\mathscr{H}^{(\mathscr{L})}_{\mathrm{T}\mathscr{M}}|\Phi_{J'M'}\rangle, \tag{7.21}$$

the $C_{J'\mathscr{L}}(JM;M'\mathscr{M})$ being the Clebsch–Gordan coefficients for the coupling of two angular momentum vectors with quantum numbers $J'M'$ and $\mathscr{L}\mathscr{M}$ to give a resultant angular momentum state JM.

The hard-sphere component of the capture amplitude given in eqn. (7.8a) can be similarly expressed in multipole components of the type

$$|U^{\mathrm{HS}}_{\mathrm{c}\gamma(\mathscr{L})}|^2 = \frac{8\pi(\mathscr{L}+1)}{\mathscr{L}\{(2\mathscr{L}+1)!!\}^2}\frac{\kappa^{2\mathscr{L}+1}}{\hbar}\frac{|\langle \mathscr{I}_{\mathrm{c}J} - \mathrm{e}^{-2\mathrm{i}\phi_{\mathrm{c}}}\mathscr{O}_{\mathrm{c}J}||\mathscr{H}^{(\mathscr{L})}_{\mathrm{T}}||\Phi_{J'}\rangle|^2}{(2J+1)} \tag{7.22}$$

where the integral over r_{c} involved in the matrix elements has the lower limit a_{c}.

C. STATISTICAL PROPERTIES OF RADIATION WIDTHS

1. Theoretical views

The partial radiative capture amplitude of eqn. (7.8b) is normally a highly complicated but essentially real quantity; it is expected, therefore, that the statistical distribution of this amplitude over the levels λ will, by the central limit theorem, be normal with zero mean. It follows that the statistical distribution of the partial radiative widths is expected to have the Porter–Thomas form that applies to the distribution of reduced neutron widths (eqn. (6.33b)).

The essential reality of the capture amplitude depends on the smallness of the phase shifts ϕ_c. For medium and heavy nuclei at relatively low neutron bombarding energies all these phase shifts are sufficiently small that they can be ignored. At higher bombarding energies (in the MeV region) their effect needs investigation; so long as the channel contributions to the capture amplitude are appreciable their effect would be to change the width distribution towards an exponential form.

The complication of the capture amplitude resides principally in the eigenfunction X_λ. Suppose that an extremely simple form is assumed for the final-state wave function, Φ: for example, that it is a simple product of a single-particle wave function $u_p(r)\chi^J_\mu\psi_0$ corresponding to a neutron in a p-state and a wave function ψ_0 corresponding to the zero spin ground state of the residual nucleus. The single p-wave neutron moves in the field of this core. The function χ^J_μ carries the angular momentum properties of the neutron, coupling to a total angular momentum of J_μ. The functions χ^J_μ and ψ_0 may be combined into a single-channel function φ_c so that the final state may be written

$$\Phi_{J\mu} = u_p(r)\varphi_{c\mu}^{\;J}. \tag{7.23}$$

Suppose, for definiteness, that $J_\mu = \frac{1}{2}$. If the state X_λ corresponds to an s-wave resonance it will carry angular momentum $J = \frac{1}{2}$ and parity opposite to that of Φ_μ, allowing an electric dipole transition between the two states. The expansion, eqn. (6.2), for X_λ now permits the simplification of the expression for the capture amplitude, eqn. (7.8b) to

$$\Gamma^{\frac{1}{2}}_{\lambda(\gamma\mu)} = \left(\frac{16\pi}{9}\right)^{\frac{1}{2}} \kappa^{\frac{3}{2}} \sum_{c'p'} C^\lambda_{c'p'} \frac{\langle u_{p'}\varphi_{c'}^{\;J}||\mathscr{H}^{(1)}_{\mathrm{E}}||u_p\varphi^J_{c\mu}\rangle}{(2J+1)^{\frac{1}{2}}}. \tag{7.24}$$

The operator $\mathscr{H}^{(1)}_{\mathrm{E}}$ is a single-particle operator (see eqn. (7.18a)). Thus

$$\Gamma^{\frac{1}{2}}_{\lambda(\gamma\mu)} = \left(\frac{16\pi}{9}\right)^{\frac{1}{2}} \kappa^{\frac{3}{2}} \sum_{cp'} C^\lambda_{cp'} \frac{\langle u_{p'}\chi^{J\pi_{p'}}||\mathscr{H}^{(1)}_{\mathrm{E}}||u_p\chi^{J\pi_p}\rangle}{(2J+1)^{\frac{1}{2}}}$$

$$+\sum_{c'p} C^\lambda_{c'p} \frac{\langle \psi_{c'}||\mathscr{H}^{(1)}_{\mathrm{E}}||\psi_0\rangle}{(2J+1)^{\frac{1}{2}}}. \tag{7.25}$$

It may be argued plausibly (Lane 1959) that contributions to the amplitude from the 'core transitions' (second term on the right-hand side of eqn. (7.25)) are negligible. Also, the only member of the first term on the right-hand side of eqn. (7.25) that does not vanish is that with p′ = s, where s denotes a single-particle s-state, so that the capture amplitude in this instance is essentially the product of a single-particle matrix element and the coefficient $C^{\lambda}_{\mathrm{cs}}$. The latter is linearly related to the reduced width amplitude for neutron emission to the ground state (eqn. (6.3)). In consequence, the partial widths for the transition to state μ are governed by the same statistics as the reduced neutron widths. In fact, in this example, these partial radiation widths and the reduced elastic neutron widths are fully correlated.

If the final state is more complicated than we have assumed above there will be many non-zero contributions to an expression of the type in eqn. (7.25). If the coefficients $C^{\lambda}_{\mathrm{c'p'}}$ occurring in that expression are normally and independently distributed (see Chapter VI, Section B.1) then a Porter–Thomas distribution for the partial radiation widths certainly must follow. It is conceivable, of course, (though not likely) that the relevant coefficients $C^{\lambda}_{\mathrm{c'p'}}$ are anti-correlated. In such an event it is possible for the partial radiation widths to have a distribution of greater uniformity than the Porter–Thomas form (see also Rosenzweig 1963).

2. Experimental data

Measurements of partial radiation widths are extremely difficult so there are not many data available for testing the hypothesis that the distribution law is of the Porter–Thomas form. The initial measurements that revealed strong fluctuations in partial radiation widths were made by Bird (1959) on resonances in the cross-section of ^{199}Hg and Kennett *et al.* (1958) on ^{55}Mn resonances. The most complete and careful data from measurements made with scintillation detectors appear to be those published by Bollinger *et al.* (1963). In this work attention was confined to high-energy electric dipole transitions from initial states with spin and parity 1^-. The final states involved in such transitions have spin and parity of either 0^+ or 2^+. In order that the spectrum be as simple as possible only even-proton, odd-neutron targets with spin and parity $\frac{1}{2}^-$ were studied. The compound nuclei are even in character and the capture γ-ray spectrum is simplified by the existence of the energy gap in the sequence of low-lying states. Four such nuclei have been studied; they are ^{77}Se, ^{183}W, ^{195}Pt, and ^{199}Hg.

The sample of data available for three transitions from eight resonances in the reaction ^{195}Pt (n, γ) ^{196}Pt is shown in Table 7.2. It was assumed that these data were three independent samples (one sample corresponding to each transition) drawn from a population with a chi-squared distribution of ν degrees of freedom (eqn. (6.38)). The statistical analysis carried out by Bollinger *et al.* was designed to determine ν by a modification of the maximum likelihood method described in Chapter VI, Section B2. In each sample each member was divided by the sample mean and the resulting collection of ratios (from all the samples) was used to determine an estimate of ν, called ν_p, by the maximum likelihood method. It is known that such an estimate obtained from a small sample is biased so the distribution of the estimator

TABLE 7.2

Intensities of high energy transitions observed in the reaction ^{195}Pt (n, γ) ^{196}Pt *to the three lowest energy states of* Pt^{196} (Bollinger *et al.* 1963)

Resonance energy (eV)	Energy of final state (keV) 0	354	686
	Relative intensities of γ-rays		
12	2355±24	214±26	39±26
19	433±8	210±10	226±12
67·4	2019±52	1782±73	97±71
112	556±25	676±40	353±44
120	1413±33	122±28	452±42
140	275±17	225±28	2495±54
151	246±28	71±37	75±41
189	703±42	115±55	943±77

was obtained by Monte Carlo techniques for various assumed values ν_a of ν. The probability that the estimator can be greater than the observed value, $\nu_p = 2{\cdot}06$, is plotted as a function of ν_a in Fig. 7.2. The best value of ν to be obtained from these data may be defined as the value of ν_a that gives a probability of 0·5, and the standard deviation limits are those values of ν_a that correspond to probabilities of 0·163 and 0·837. Thus, for ^{195}Pt (n, γ) the data give $\nu = 1{\cdot}56 \pm 0{\cdot}51$. In a similar way it was found that for ^{199}Hg (n, γ) $\nu = 1{\cdot}24 \pm 1{\cdot}22$, for ^{183}W (n, γ), $\nu = 1{\cdot}1 \pm 0{\cdot}8$, and for ^{77}Se (n, γ), $\nu = 1{\cdot}0 \pm 0{\cdot}8$. Other data (Chrien *et al.* 1962) on the ^{195}Pt (n, γ) reaction agree with the result quoted here (Bollinger *et al.* 1963).

Evidence of a more indirect nature comes from the γ-ray spectra following thermal neutron capture. In these spectra very many more high-energy transitions may be resolved than in the spectra of resonance capture. If it is assumed that the reduced partial radiation widths for these transitions have the same value when averaged over many resonances it is found that their fluctuations (compiled for 127 transitions from many nuclei) are in reasonable agreement with a Porter–Thomas distribution (Bartholomew 1962). Apart from the uncertainty in the assumption of equal mean radiative widths for the studied transitions these thermal capture data also suffer from the deficiency of not corresponding to a unique resonance. Often, the strengths of the

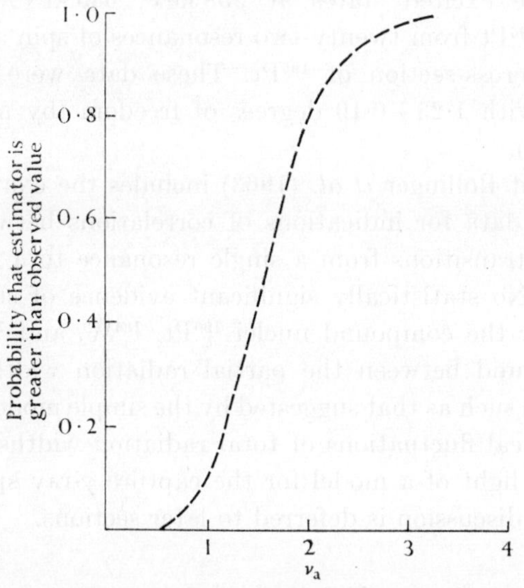

FIG. 7.2. Probability that the estimator of ν determined from three samples, each of eight members, by the maximum likelihood procedure is greater than 2·06 (the experimentally observed value). The probability is plotted as a function of ν_a the value of ν assumed for the mathematical populations from which the samples were drawn by Monte Carlo techniques (after Bollinger *et al.* 1963).

transitions are governed, not even by a weighted mean of the partial radiation widths of the nearest levels, but by a complicated interference effect. Despite their great resolution, therefore, the thermal neutron γ-ray spectra are of somewhat limited value in the study of the neutron resonance capture process.

More recently, the advent of lithium-drifted germanium semiconductor counters has provided a high resolution γ-ray detector with an efficiency sufficient to allow it to be used in neutron resonance work. Two experimental studies with this kind of detector confirm that the partial radiation width distribution is of the Porter–Thomas form. A measurement by Rae *et al.* (1966) of seventeen high-energy primary

E1 transitions from each of two resonant states with angular momentum and parity 0^- in the cross-section of ^{199}Hg, and of twenty-eight transitions from two 1^- states in the same cross-section, were analysed using the χ^2-test to fit the assumed distribution law of eqn. (6.38) to the histogram of the data. The result found was $\nu = 0{\cdot}96\ ^{+0\cdot24}_{-0\cdot17}$ this encompasses the Porter–Thomas form ($\nu = 1$). An exponential distribution ($\nu = 2$) was not compatible with the data. Jackson *et al.* (1966) studied with particular care the five transitions to the ground state and the excited states at 358 keV, 689 keV, 1143 keV, and 1404 keV of ^{196}Pt from twenty-two resonances of spin and parity 1^- in the neutron cross-section of ^{195}Pt. These data were found to fit a distribution with $1{\cdot}23 \pm 0{\cdot}19$ degrees of freedom (by maximum likelihood analysis).

The work of Bollinger *et al.* (1963) includes the examination of the experimental data for indications of correlations between the widths for radiative transitions from a single resonance to a number of low-lying states. No statistically significant evidence of such correlations was found for the compound nuclei ^{196}Pt, ^{184}W, and ^{78}Se. Nor was a correlation found between the partial radiation widths and reduced neutron width such as that suggested by the simple model of Section C.1.

The statistical fluctuations of total radiation widths must be interpreted in the light of a model for the capture γ-ray spectrum; consequently their discussion is deferred to later sections.

D. STATISTICAL MODEL OF SLOW NEUTRON CAPTURE

1. Estimates of partial radiation widths

The oldest and most commonly used model of slow neutron capture may be described as the statistical model. In its simplest form (Blatt and Weisskopf 1952) it is a straightforward extension of the single-particle model. Consider a spinless particle in an s-wave state (which, for simplicity, we take as bound) in a potential field. The radiation width for an electric dipole transition to a lower p-wave state is (from eqns. (7.20b) and (7.20a))

$$\Gamma_{\mathrm{p}(\gamma)} = \frac{16\pi\kappa^3}{9}|\langle J=0||\mathbf{Y}^{(1)}||J=1\rangle|^2\left\{\bar{e}\int_0^\infty \mathrm{d}r\, ru_0(r)u_1(r)\right\} \quad (7.26a)$$

$$= \frac{4\kappa^3}{3}\left\{\bar{e}\int_0^\infty \mathrm{d}r\, ru_0(r)u_1(r)\right\}^2, \quad (7.26b)$$

where $\bar{e}$ is the effective charge of a single particle in a system of particles; for a neutron in a nucleus it is $-Z/A$ times the proton charge, and for a proton it is N/A times its own charge. In eqn. (7.26) the intrinsic spins of the system are ignored. This is the simplest form of the single-particle model for bound states. In the statistical model it is assumed that the initial single-particle state is dissolved amongst the compound-nucleus states over an energy interval of the order of the spacing D_s of single-particle states of given orbital angular momentum (in this case, $l = 0$). The transition strength of the single-particle state is correspondingly dissolved so that the partial width of an s-wave compound-nucleus state is

$$\Gamma_{\lambda(\gamma)} = \frac{4\kappa^3}{3}\left\{\bar{e}\int_0^\infty \mathrm{d}r\, r u_0(r) u_1(r)\right\}^2 \bar{D}(l=0)/D_s \tag{7.27}$$

where $\bar{D}(l = 0)$ is the spacing of such states.

A simple rough estimate of the integral is obtained by assuming that the radial wave-functions are uniform within the nuclear radius and zero without (Blatt and Weisskopf 1952). The result is

$$\int_0^\infty \mathrm{d}r\, r u_0(r) u_1(r) \approx \frac{3a}{4} \tag{7.28}$$

and the partial radiation width from an s-wave compound-nucleus state is

$$\Gamma_{\lambda(\gamma)} \approx \frac{3}{4}\bar{e}^2\left(\frac{\varepsilon_\gamma}{\hbar c}\right)^3 a^2 \cdot \frac{\bar{D}(l=0)}{D_s} \tag{7.29}$$

for an electric dipole transition carrying energy ε_γ.

2. The γ-ray spectrum

The form of the spectrum of primary radiation from slow neutron capture is obtained by multiplying eqn. (7·29) by the level density of final states:

$$f_1(\varepsilon_\gamma)\mathrm{d}\varepsilon_\gamma = \frac{3}{4}\bar{e}^2\left(\frac{\varepsilon_\gamma}{\hbar c}\right)^3 a^2 \cdot \frac{1}{D_s}\frac{\rho(E_{\mathrm{th,n}}-\varepsilon_\gamma)}{\rho(E_{\mathrm{th,n}})}\mathrm{d}\varepsilon_\gamma. \tag{7.30}$$

In heavy nuclei the level density usually increases so strongly between the ground state and the neutron separation energy that a peak in the primary spectrum occurs at a gamma-ray energy of a few MeV. The energy of the peak is at higher energies for higher orders of multipolarity. The primary spectrum of electric dipole radiation is illustrated in Fig. 7.3 for two values of the mass number ($A = 110$ and $A = 236$) and a shell-model form of the level density law (Newton 1956; see Chapter IV, Section C.5).

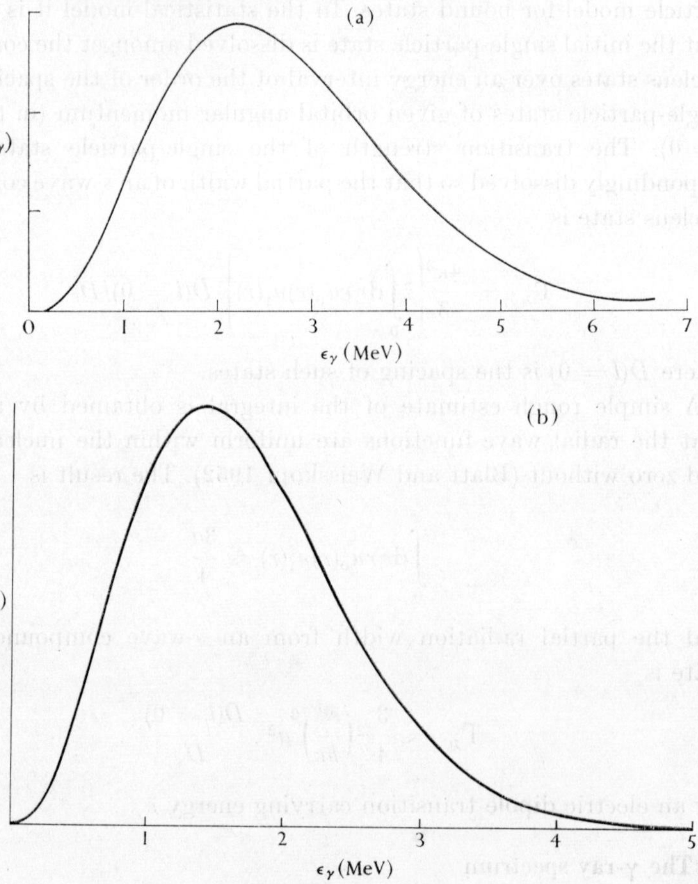

FIG. 7.3. Primary γ-ray spectrum in the statistical model for $A = 110$ (a) and $A = 236$ (b).

These spectra cannot be compared directly with the experimental material. Observed capture γ-ray spectra include secondary and higher-order transitions as well as the primary transitions. The expression in eqn. (7.30) is generalized to denote the spectrum of γ-rays from an initial state at excitation energy U

$$f(\varepsilon_\gamma, U)\mathrm{d}\varepsilon_\gamma = C(U)\,.\,\frac{3}{4}\bar{e}^2\left(\frac{\varepsilon_\gamma}{\hbar c}\right)^3 a^2\,.\,\frac{1}{D_s}\,\frac{\rho(U-\varepsilon_\gamma)}{\rho(U)}\,d\varepsilon_\gamma. \tag{7.31}$$

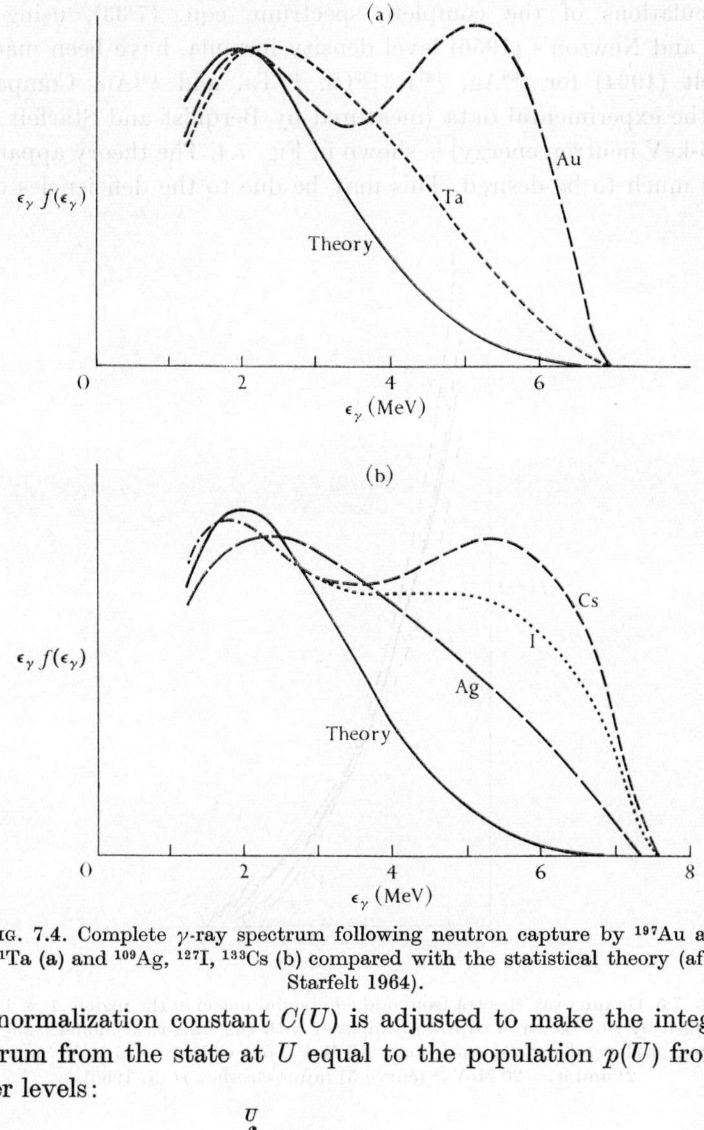

FIG. 7.4. Complete γ-ray spectrum following neutron capture by ^{197}Au and ^{181}Ta (a) and ^{109}Ag, ^{127}I, ^{133}Cs (b) compared with the statistical theory (after Starfelt 1964).

The normalization constant $C(U)$ is adjusted to make the integrated spectrum from the state at U equal to the population $p(U)$ from the higher levels:

$$\int_0^U f(\varepsilon_\gamma, U)\mathrm{d}\varepsilon_\gamma = p(U). \tag{7.32}$$

The population $p(U)$ is unity for the capturing level at $U = E_{\mathrm{th,n}}$. The complete γ-ray spectrum has the form

$$f(\varepsilon_\gamma)\mathrm{d}\varepsilon_\gamma = \mathrm{d}\varepsilon_\gamma \int_{\varepsilon_\gamma}^{E_{\mathrm{th,n}}} \mathrm{d}U \;.\; f(\varepsilon_\gamma, U). \tag{7.33}$$

Calculations of the complete spectrum, eqn. (7.33), using eqn. (7.26) and Newton's (1956) level density formula, have been made by Starfelt (1964) for ^{109}Ag, ^{127}I, ^{133}Cs, ^{181}Ta, and ^{197}Au. Comparison with the experimental data (measured by Berquist and Starfelt 1962, at 125-keV neutron energy) is shown in Fig. 7.4. The theory apparently leaves much to be desired. This may be due to the deficiencies of the

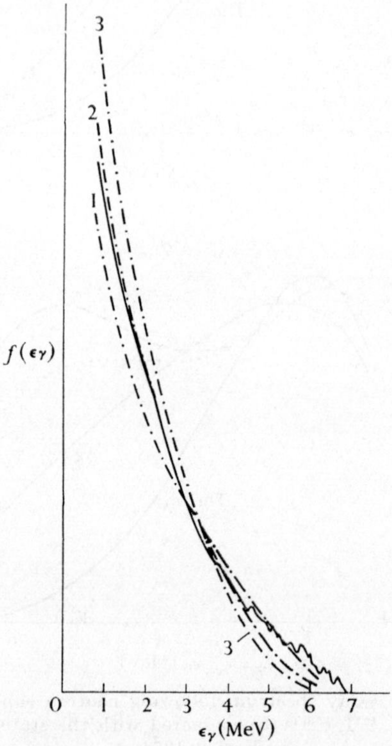

FIG. 7.5. Gamma-ray spectra from odd compound nuclei in the region $A \approx 110$ formed by slow neutron capture compared with the statistical model using a Fermi gas level-density law using $a = 10$ MeV^{-1} (curve 1), $a = 15$ MeV^{-1} (curve 2) and $a = 20$ MeV^{-1} (curve 3) (after Groshev *et al.* 1960).

level density formula employed. It was concluded in Chapter IV that there is not yet quantitative consistency between theory and data on level densities. Groshev *et al.* (1960) have recognized the deficiency in detailed knowledge of the nuclear level-density behaviour below the neutron separation energy by calculating the spectrum, using mathematical methods developed by Strutinsky *et al.* (1960), for different assumed level density laws. All the level density formulae employed had the feature of exhibiting an energy gap of 1·2 MeV above the ground state for even-compound nuclei. In addition it was assumed that transitions from levels just above the gap to the ground state were strongly inhibited. This was found necessary to give a good fit to the capture γ-ray spectrum of even nuclei but could be explained as being due to a scarcity of levels with non-zero angular momentum projection along

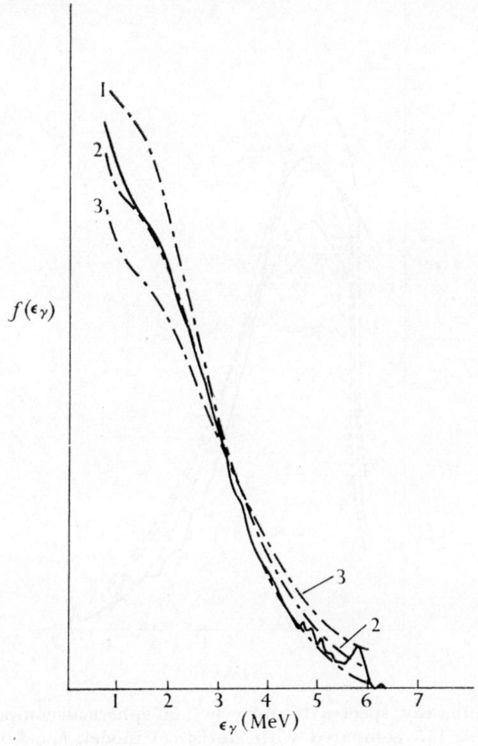

FIG. 7.6. Gamma-ray spectra from odd compound nuclei in the region $A \approx 175$ compared with the statistical model using a constant temperature level-density law with $T = 0{\cdot}7$ MeV (curve 1), $T = 0{\cdot}8$ MeV (curve 2), $T = 0{\cdot}9$ MeV (curve 3) (after Groshev *et al.* 1960).

the nuclear symmetry axis. Three classes of nuclei were examined. It was found that the spectra data on thermal neutron capture compiled by Groshev *et al.* (1959) of odd nuclei with $A \approx 110$ could be best fitted with a 'Fermi gas' formula $\rho(U) \propto \exp\{\surd(15\,\text{MeV}^{-1}U)\}$ (Fig. 7.5). The spectra of odd nuclei with $A \approx 175$ could be fitted with a constant temperature formula $\rho(U) = \exp(U/0{\cdot}8\,\text{MeV})$ (Fig. 7.6), and this was also true for even non-spherical nuclei in the same mass region (Fig. 7.7). To fit the spectrum of ^{198}Au a Fermi gas formula $\rho(U) = \exp$

$\{\sqrt{(5\,\text{MeV}^{-1}U)}\}$ had to be used. The constants in the exponents of these formulae all imply a rather lower value of the single-particle level density than would be inferred from Newton's analysis, eqn. (4.45).

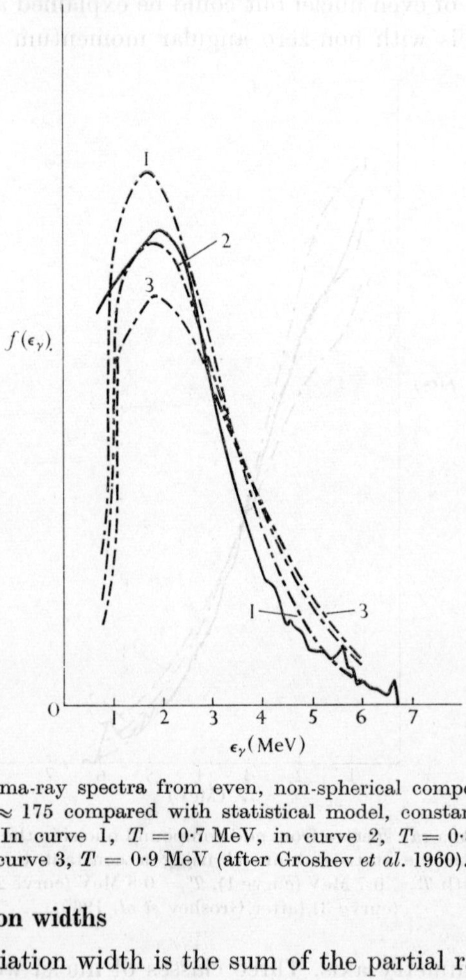

FIG. 7.7. Gamma-ray spectra from even, non-spherical compound nuclei in the region $A \approx 175$ compared with statistical model, constant temperature level density. In curve 1, $T = 0{\cdot}7$ MeV, in curve 2, $T = 0{\cdot}8$ MeV, and in curve 3, $T = 0{\cdot}9$ MeV (after Groshev *et al.* 1960).

3. Total radiation widths

The total radiation width is the sum of the partial radiation widths over all final states. For most heavy nuclei such a sum can be represented accurately by an integral:

$$\Gamma_{(\gamma T)}(J) = \sum_{\mu} \Gamma_{(\gamma\mu)}$$

$$\approx \sum_{I=|J-1|}^{J+1} \int_0^{E_{\text{th,n}}} \mathrm{d}\varepsilon\rho(E_{\text{th,n}}-\varepsilon, I)\Gamma_{(\gamma\mu)}(\varepsilon, J). \tag{7.34}$$

Some typical estimates of total radiation widths for electric dipole transitions are shown in Table 7.3. In these estimates (derived from Blatt and Weisskopf 1952) the single-particle level spacing was assumed to be 30 MeV, and the 'Fermi gas' level density law $\{\rho(U) \propto \exp \sqrt{(2\pi^2\rho_S U/3)}\}$ was used. The theoretical estimates for the electric

TABLE 7.3

Simple statistical model estimates of total radiation widths (electric dipole transitions)

A	$E_{\text{th},\text{n}}$	$\frac{2\pi^2\rho_S}{3}$(MeV^{-1})	$\Gamma_{(\gamma T)}$(meV)
28	8	1·8	11300
110	8	26	750
180	7	40	400

dipole widths are about an order of magnitude greater than the experimental values (see Table 7.4) but again the single-particle level densities employed are low. Before any significance can be claimed for these comparisons it is necessary to make better estimates of the matrix elements of eqn. (7.27). A large error in these estimates probably comes from the assumptions about the radial wave-functions in eqn. (7.28). The dipole integrals have been calculated numerically for the Eckart potential with the parameters of Ross *et al.* (1956) quoted in Chapter III, Section C. The results are shown in Table 7.5. Apart from being considerably smaller, numerically, than the values from eqn. (7.29) they also show a rather different mass-number dependence; they have the empirical form

$$\left|\int_0^\infty dr\, r u_0(r) u_1(r)\right|^2 \approx 0{\cdot}012 A^{\frac{1}{3}} \times 10^{-24}\ \text{cm}^2 \tag{7.35}$$

over the mass number range from $A = 40$ to 200. Use of eqn. (7.35) in the total radiation width brings closer agreement (to within a factor of 3) with the experimental values.

Apart from the general magnitudes of the total radiation widths of slow neutron resonances it is desirable to be able to explain the features of their mass number dependence. The radiation widths compiled from experimental data are listed in Table 7.4 and are plotted as a

Table 7.4

Average values of total radiation widths observed in low-energy neutron spectroscopy. The values are mostly for s-wave resonances but a few p-wave values have been included where they are known

Target nucleus	I^π	Compound nucleus	J^π	Neutron separation energy, $E_{\text{th, n}}$ (MeV)	$\bar{\Gamma}_{(\gamma)}$ (meV)	References and remarks
$^{23}_{11}$Na	$\frac{3}{2}^+$	$^{24}_{11}$Na	1^+	6·959	$\leqslant 320$	1; a
$^{35}_{17}$Cl	$\frac{3}{2}^+$	$^{36}_{17}$Cl	1^+	8·577	600 ± 30	2, 72; d
$^{45}_{21}$Sc	$\frac{7}{2}^-$	$^{46}_{21}$Sc	3^- or 4^-		420 ± 60	72: d
$^{51}_{23}$V	$\frac{7}{2}^-$	$^{52}_{23}$V	3^- and 4^-	7·304	~ 1500	3; b
$^{55}_{25}$Mn	$\frac{5}{2}^-$	$^{56}_{25}$Mn	2^- and 3^-	7·270	450 ± 40	4; b
$^{56}_{26}$Fe	0^+	$^{57}_{26}$Fe	$\frac{1}{2}^+$	7·641	673 ± 74	5; c
$^{59}_{27}$Co	$\frac{7}{2}^-$	$^{60}_{27}$Co	4^-	7·497	435 ± 15	6; c
$^{63}_{30}$Cu	$\frac{3}{2}^-$	$^{64}_{30}$Cu	1^- or 2^-	7·92	550 ± 65	80
$^{69}_{31}$Ga	$\frac{3}{2}^-$	$^{70}_{31}$Ga	2^-	7·71	210 ± 40	7; c
$^{71}_{31}$Ga	$\frac{3}{2}^-$	$^{72}_{31}$Ga	1^-	7·1	370	7; c
			2^-		350 ± 110	7: c
$^{74}_{34}$Se	0^+	$^{75}_{34}$Se	$\frac{1}{2}^+$	7·96	189 ± 30	8; c
$^{75}_{33}$As	$\frac{3}{2}^-$	$^{76}_{33}$As	1^-	7·33	320 ± 30	7
			2^-		≈ 300	7
$^{77}_{34}$Se	$\frac{1}{2}^-$	$^{78}_{34}$Se	1^-	10·48	500 ± 150	9
$^{79}_{35}$Br	$\frac{3}{2}^-$	$^{80}_{35}$Br	1^- and 2^-	7·88	330 ± 30	8, 71
$^{80}_{36}$Kr	0^+	$^{81}_{36}$Kr	$\frac{1}{2}^+$	7·8	400 ± 90	10; c
$^{81}_{35}$Br	$\frac{3}{2}^-$	$^{82}_{35}$Br	1^- or 2^-	7·8	350 ± 30	14; c
$^{83}_{36}$Kr	$\frac{9}{2}^+$	$^{84}_{36}$Kr	4^+ or 5^+	10·5	220 ± 60	10: c
$^{85}_{37}$Rb	$\frac{5}{2}^-$	$^{86}_{37}$Rb	2^- or 3^-	8·82	215 ± 20	76
$^{87}_{37}$Rb	$\frac{3}{2}^-$	$^{88}_{37}$Rb	1^- or 2^-	6·24	145 ± 30	76
$^{87}_{38}$Sr	$\frac{9}{2}^+$	$^{88}_{38}$Sr	4^+ or 5^+	11·14	205 ± 20	11; c
$^{91}_{40}$Zr	$\frac{5}{2}^+$	$^{92}_{40}$Zr	2^+ or 3^+	8·66	315 ± 50	12; c
			1^-, 2^-, 3^- or 4^-		290 ± 50	12, 13; c
$^{93}_{41}$Nb	$\frac{9}{2}^+$	$^{94}_{41}$Nb	4^+ and 5^+	7·20	115 ± 15	13, 14
					185 ± 10	76
			3^- to 6^-		240 ± 15	13
$^{95}_{42}$Mo	$\frac{5}{2}^+$	$^{96}_{42}$Mo	2^+ or 3^+	9·16	145 ± 15	70
$^{96}_{40}$Zr	0^+	$^{97}_{40}$Zr	$\frac{1}{2}^+$	5·6	370 ± 90	12; c
$^{97}_{42}$Mo	$\frac{5}{2}^+$	$^{98}_{42}$Mo	2^+ or 3^+	8·3	150 ± 10	70; c
$^{99}_{44}$Ru	$\frac{5}{2}^+$	$^{100}_{44}$Ru	2^+ or 3^+	9·4	280 ± 18	16; c
$^{99}_{43}$Tc	$\frac{9}{2}^+$	$^{100}_{43}$Tc	4^+ or 5^+	6·3	280 ± 20	17; c
$^{101}_{44}$Ru	$\frac{5}{2}^+$	$^{102}_{44}$Ru	2^+ and 3^+	9·2	200 ± 20	16, 71
$^{102}_{44}$Ru	0^+	$^{103}_{44}$Ru	$\frac{1}{2}^+$	9·3	290 ± 50	16; c
$^{103}_{45}$Rh	$\frac{1}{2}^-$	$^{104}_{45}$Rh	0^-	6·79	240 ± 10	18, 19
			1^-		180 ± 10	19
$^{107}_{47}$Ag	$\frac{1}{2}^-$	$^{108}_{47}$Ag	0^-	7·22	132 ± 9	20; c
			1^-		136 ± 12	20
$^{109}_{47}$Ag	$\frac{1}{2}^-$	$^{110}_{47}$Ag	0^-	6·81	136 ± 15	20,21
			1^-		137 ± 3	20

TABLE 7.4 (cont.)

Average values of total radiation widths observed in low-energy neutron spectroscopy. The values are mostly for s-wave resonances but a few p-wave values have been included where they are known

Target nucleus	I^{π}	Compound nucleus	J^{π}	Neutron separation energy, $E_{\mathrm{th,n}}$ (MeV)	$\overline{\Gamma}_{(\gamma)}$ (meV)	References and remarks
$^{110}_{48}$Cd	0^+	$^{111}_{48}$Cd	$\frac{1}{2}^+$	7·2	140 ± 70	22; c
$^{111}_{48}$Cd	$\frac{1}{2}^+$	$^{112}_{48}$Cd	0^+ or 1^+	9·48	120 ± 20	77
			1^+		104 ± 12	77
$^{113}_{48}$Cd	$\frac{1}{2}^+$	$^{114}_{48}$Cd	0^+ or 1^+	9·05	113 ± 5	23, 77
$^{113}_{49}$In	$\frac{9}{2}^+$	$^{114}_{49}$In	4^+ or 5^+	7·31	60 ± 20	15; c
$^{115}_{49}$In	$\frac{9}{2}^+$	$^{116}_{49}$In	4^+	6·62	81 ± 4	24, 25, 26; c
			5^+		72 ± 2	24, 25, 26; c
$^{121}_{51}$Sb	$\frac{5}{2}^+$	$^{122}_{51}$Sb	2^+ and 3^+	6·78	74 ± 9	11
$^{123}_{51}$Sb	$\frac{7}{2}^+$	$^{124}_{51}$Sb	3^+ or 4^+	6·46	111 ± 20	11; c
$^{123}_{52}$Te	$\frac{1}{2}^+$	$^{124}_{52}$Te	1^+	9·40	104 ± 3	27; c
$^{133}_{55}$Cs	$\frac{7}{2}^+$	$^{134}_{55}$Cs	3^+ or 4^+	6·70	115 ± 20	26; c
$^{135}_{56}$Ba	$\frac{3}{2}^+$	$^{136}_{56}$Ba	1^+ or 2^+	9·21	114 ± 10	11, 71
$^{135}_{43}$Xe	$\frac{3}{2}^+$	$^{136}_{54}$Xe	2^+	7·56	94 ± 3	28; c
$^{138}_{57}$La	$5^{(-)}$		$\frac{9}{2}^{(-)}$ or $\frac{11}{2}^{(-)}$	8·78	99 ± 6	81
$^{139}_{57}$La	$\frac{7}{2}^+$	$^{140}_{57}$La		4·99	150 ± 30	11; c
$^{141}_{59}$Pr	$\frac{5}{2}^+$	$^{142}_{59}$Pr		5·65	73 ± 7	30, 29
$^{143}_{60}$Nd	$\frac{7}{2}^-$	$^{144}_{60}$Nd	3^- or 4^-	7·81	94 ± 16	31; c
$^{145}_{60}$Nd	$\frac{7}{2}^-$	$^{146}_{60}$Nd	3^- or 4^-	7·56	51 ± 4	11, 31; c
$^{147}_{62}$Sm	$\frac{7}{2}^-$	$^{148}_{62}$Sm	3^- or 4^-	8·13	61 ± 5	33; c
$^{149}_{62}$Sm	$\frac{7}{2}^-$	$^{150}_{62}$Sm	4^-	8·0	63 ± 1	34; c
$^{151}_{63}$Eu	$\frac{5}{2}^{(+)}$	$^{152}_{63}$Eu	2	6·4	92 ± 3	35, 36; c
			3		85 ± 2	35, 36, 26
$^{152}_{62}$Sm	0^+	$^{153}_{62}$Sm	$\frac{1}{2}^+$	6·0	71 ± 10	37; c
$^{153}_{63}$Eu	$\frac{5}{2}^{(+)}$	$^{154}_{63}$Eu	3	6·3	92 ± 2	35; c
$^{155}_{64}$Gd	$\frac{3}{2}^-$	$^{156}_{64}$Gd	1^-	8·45	110 ± 1	36; c
			2^-		109 ± 1	36
$^{157}_{64}$Gd	$\frac{3}{2}^-$	$^{158}_{64}$Gd	2^-	7·92	106 ± 1	36; c
$^{159}_{65}$Tb	$\frac{3}{2}^{(+)}$	$^{160}_{65}$Tb	1	6·3	92 ± 10	38
			2		84 ± 4	38
$^{161}_{66}$Dy	$\frac{5}{2}^{(+)}$	$^{162}_{66}$Dy	2	8·18	124 ± 15	39, 40; c
			3		119 ± 10	39, 40; c
$^{162}_{66}$Dy	0^+	$^{163}_{66}$Dy	$\frac{1}{2}^+$	6·28	175 ± 45	39; c
$^{163}_{66}$Dy	$\frac{5}{2}^{(+)}$	$^{164}_{66}$Dy	2	7·63	$100{\cdot}8\pm0{\cdot}7$	79; c
$^{164}_{66}$Dy	0^+	$^{165}_{66}$Dy	$\frac{1}{2}^+$	$\sim$6	166 ± 4	41; d
$^{165}_{67}$Ho	$\frac{7}{2}^{(-)}$	$^{166}_{67}$Ho	3 and 4	6·1	60 ± 14	15
$^{169}_{69}$Tm	$\frac{1}{2}^+$	$^{170}_{69}$Tm	0^+	6·4	90 ± 3	42
			1^+		91 ± 3	42
$^{168}_{70}$Yb	0^+	$^{169}_{70}$Yb	$\frac{1}{2}^+$	7·2	70 ± 10	43
$^{175}_{71}$Lu	$\frac{7}{2}^+$	$^{176}_{71}$Lu	3^+ or 4^+	6·3	70 ± 1	79

TABLE 7.4 (cont.)

Average values of total radiation widths observed low-energy neutron spectroscopy. The values are mostly for s-wave resonances but a few p-wave values have been included where they are known

Target nucleus	I^{π}	Compound nucleus	J^{π}	Neutron separation energy, $E_{\text{th},\text{n}}$ (MeV)	$\bar{\Gamma}_{(\gamma)}$ (meV)	References and remarks
$^{176}_{71}$Lu	7(−)	$^{177}_{71}$Lu	$\frac{13}{2}$ or $\frac{15}{2}$	6·84	58·6±0·2	79
$^{177}_{72}$Hf	$\frac{7}{2}^-$	$^{178}_{72}$Hf	3^-	7·59	67±2	46, 47; c
			4^-		60±1	46, 47; c
$^{180}_{73}$Ta	⩾6^-	$^{181}_{73}$Ta		7·64	30±5	48; c
$^{181}_{73}$Ta	$\frac{7}{2}^+$	$^{182}_{73}$Ta	4^+	6·06	65±6	49; c
$^{182}_{74}$W	0^+	$^{183}_{74}$W	$\frac{1}{2}^+$	6·29	46±2	50; c
$^{183}_{74}$W	$\frac{1}{2}^-$	$^{184}_{74}$W	0^-	7·42	73±4	51
			1^-		61±5	51
$^{185}_{75}$Re	$\frac{5}{2}^+$	$^{186}_{75}$Re	2^+ or 3^+	6·23	56±1	52; c
$^{186}_{74}$W	0^+	$^{187}_{74}$W	$\frac{1}{2}^+$	5·25	45±6	51; c
$^{187}_{73}$Re	$\frac{5}{2}^+$	$^{188}_{75}$Re	2^+ or 3^+	5·95	45±1	52; c
$^{191}_{77}$Ir	$\frac{3}{2}^+$	$^{192}_{77}$Ir	1^+ or 2^+	6·15	68·9±0·9	79; c
$^{193}_{77}$Ir	$\frac{3}{2}^+$	$^{194}_{77}$Ir	1^+ or 2^+	5·96	84±1	79; c
$^{195}_{78}$Pt	$\frac{1}{2}^-$	$^{196}_{78}$Pt	0^-	7·92	104±20	53
			1^-		106±6	54
$^{197}_{79}$Au	$\frac{3}{2}^+$	$^{198}_{79}$Au	1^+	6·49	136±15	55; c
			2^+		124±3	56; c
$^{196}_{80}$Hg	0^+	$^{197}_{80}$Hg	$\frac{1}{2}^+$	6·9	221±100	57; c
$^{198}_{80}$Hg	0^+	$^{199}_{80}$Hg	$\frac{1}{2}^+$	6·68	115±6	57, 58
$^{199}_{80}$Hg	$\frac{1}{2}^-$	$^{200}_{80}$Hg	0^-	8·01	330±60	58; c
			1^-		289±10	57; c
$^{201}_{80}$Hg	$\frac{3}{2}^-$	$^{202}_{80}$Hg	1^-	7·76	509±57	57; c
			2^-		300±200	57
$^{209}_{83}$Bi	$\frac{9}{2}^-$	$^{210}_{83}$Bi	4^-	4·58	⩽44±3	59; a
$^{231}_{91}$Pa	$\frac{3}{2}^-$	$^{232}_{91}$Pa	1^- or 2^-	5·67	51±5	60
					42±2	61
$^{232}_{90}$Th	0^+	$^{233}_{90}$Th	$\frac{1}{2}^+$	5·13	23·8±1·5	69, 73
$^{234}_{92}$U	0^+	$^{235}_{92}$U	$\frac{1}{2}^+$	5·24	31±9	62; c
$^{236}_{92}$U	0^+	$^{237}_{92}$U	$\frac{1}{2}^+$	5·42	29±7	63; c
$^{237}_{93}$Np	$\frac{5}{2}^+$	$^{238}_{93}$Np	2^+ or 3^+	5·37	32±3	64; c
$^{238}_{92}$U	0^+	$^{239}_{92}$U	$\frac{1}{2}^+$	4·76	27·6±1·3	65
$^{240}_{94}$Pu	0^+	$^{241}_{44}$Pu	$\frac{1}{2}^+$	5·52	18±2	78
$^{242}_{94}$Pu	0^+	$^{245}_{94}$Pu	$\frac{1}{2}^+$	5·02	27±5	66; c
$^{243}_{95}$Am	$\frac{5}{2}^-$	$^{244}_{95}$Am	2^- or 3^-	5·15	44±3	66; c
$^{244}_{96}$Cm	0^+	$^{245}_{96}$Cm	$\frac{1}{2}^+$	5·72	37±3	68; c
$^{246}_{96}$Cm	0^+	$^{247}_{96}$Cm	$\frac{1}{2}^+$		35±5	68; c

TABLE 7.4 (cont.)

Average values of total radiation widths observed in low-energy neutron spectroscopy.

Remarks

a. From thermal capture cross-section, and properties of lowest resonance.
b. From many-level fit including thermal capture cross-section.
c. From measurements on one resonance.
d. By fitting low energy cross-section to parameters of bound level.

References

1. Lynn *et al.* (1958*a*)
2. Brugger *et al.* (1956)
3. Firk *et al.* (1963)
4. Coté *et al.* (1964*b*)
5. Moore *et al.* (1963)
6. Lynn and Moxon (1967)
7. Julien *et al.* (1964)
8. Leblanc *et al.* (1959)
9. Coté *et al.* (1964*c*)
10. Mann *et al.* (1959)
11. Stolovy and Harvey (1957)
12. Julien *et al.* (1962*a*)
13. Jackson (1963)
14. Saplakoglu *et al.* (1958)
15. Harvey *et al.* (1955)
16. Bolotin and Chrien (1963)
17. Slaughter *et al.* (1958)
18. Ribon *et al.* (1961)
19. Wang *et al.* (1963)
20. Rae *et al.* (1958)
21. Desjardins *et al.* (1960)
22. Simpson and Fluharty (1957*a*)
23. Sailor *et al.* (1954)
24. Stolovy (1959)
25. Domani and Sailor (1960)
26. Landon and Sailor (1955)
27. Foote (1954)
28. Bernstein *et al.* (1956)
29. Corge *et al.* (1961)
30. Wang *et al.* (1964)
31. Bianchi *et al.* (1963)
32. Block *et al.* (1958)
33. Hughes *et al.* (1959)
34. Marshak and Sailor (1958)
35. Domani and Patronis (1959)
36. Stolovy (1964)
37. Bernabei *et al.* (1962)
38. Wang *et al.* (1964)
39. Zimmerman (1957)
40. Brunhart *et al.* (1962)
41. Sher *et al.* (1961)
42. Singh (1964)
43. Sailor *et al.* (1954b)
44. Harvey *et al.* (1958*b*)
45. Foote *et al.* (1953)
46. Igo and Landon (1956)
47. Ceulemanns and Poortmans (1961)
48. Evans *et al.* (1955)
49. Evans *et al.* (1959)
50. Landon (1955)
51. Waters *et al.* (1959)
52. Igo (1955)
53. Julien *et al.* (1962*b*)
54. Waters (1960)
55. Desjardins *et al.* (1960)
56. Wood (1956)
57. Carpenter and Bollinger (1960)
58. Bird *et al.* (1959)
59. Lynn *et al.* (1958*b*)
60. Simpson *et al.* (1962)
61. Patterson and Harvey (1962)
62. Harvey and Hughes (1958)
63. McCallum (1957)
64. Smith *et al.* (1957)
65. Firk *et al.* (1963c)
66. Coté *et al.* (1958)
67. Egelstaff *et al.* (1958)
68. Coté *et al.* (1964*a*)
69. Asghar *et al.* (1965)
70. Huynh *et al.* (1965)
71. Kim Hi San *et al.* (1965)
72. Romanov and Shapiro (1965)
73. Haddad *et al.* (1965)
76. Iliescu *et al.* (1965)
77. Adamchuk *et al.* (1966*a*)
78. Asghar *et al.* (1966*b*)
79. Brunner and Widder (1966)
80. Julien *et al.* (1965)
81. Harvey and Slaughter (1965)

function of mass number in Fig. 7.8. The most striking features of this diagram are the strong maxima just before the closed neutron shells at mass numbers $90(N = 50)$, $138(N = 82)$, and $208(N = 126)$. These are readily explained by the simple statistical theory of this section.

Cameron (1959) has made careful estimates of total radiation widths. The form of eqn. (7.27) was used for the partial radiation widths but an

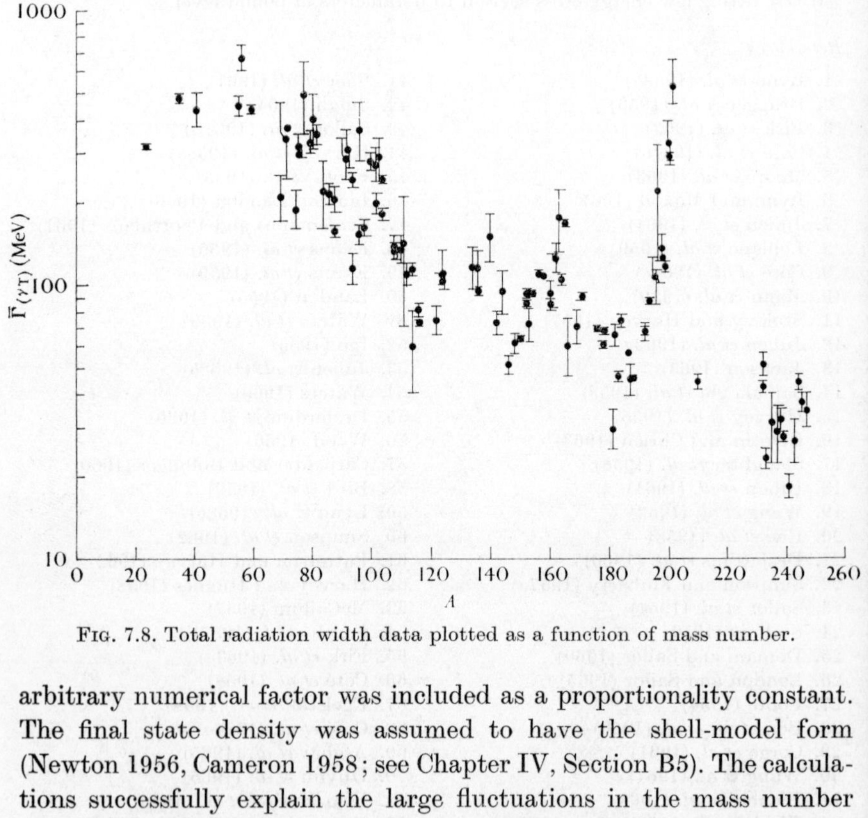

FIG. 7.8. Total radiation width data plotted as a function of mass number.

arbitrary numerical factor was included as a proportionality constant. The final state density was assumed to have the shell-model form (Newton 1956, Cameron 1958; see Chapter IV, Section B5). The calculations successfully explain the large fluctuations in the mass number dependence of total radiation widths observed for nuclei near major shell closures (Fig. 7.9). The deduced value of the proportionality constant gives Cameron's estimate of the mean partial radiation width for an electric dipole transition to a single final state

$$\bar{\Gamma}_{(\gamma\mu)}(\text{meV}) = 0{\cdot}33\times 10^{-6}\varepsilon_\gamma{}^3(\text{MeV})A^{2/3}\bar{D}(\text{eV}). \tag{7.36}$$

This is to be compared with the combination of eqns. (7.27) and (7.28),

$$\bar{\Gamma}_{(\gamma\mu)}(\text{meV}) = 2\times 10^{-6}\varepsilon_\gamma{}^3(\text{MeV})A^{2/3}\bar{D}(\text{eV}) \tag{7.37}$$

and the combination (7.27) and (7.35)

$$\bar{\Gamma}_{(\gamma\mu)}(\text{meV}) = 2{\cdot}5\times 10^{-6}\varepsilon_{\gamma}^{\ 3}(\text{MeV})A^{1/2}\bar{D}(\text{eV})\,; \tag{7.38}$$

it is rather smaller than the two theoretical estimates.

Cameron (1960) claims that the same assumptions made in his total radiation width calculations also reproduce the capture spectra well but the number of transitions to low excitation energies is overestimated. He expresses the view that the statistical model breaks down in the sense that eqn. (7.36) is an overestimate for low-energy

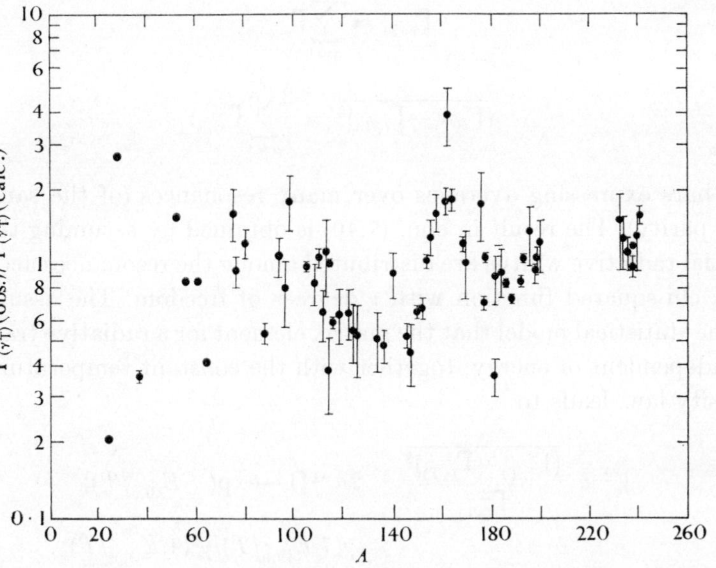

FIG. 7.9. Result of a statistical theory calculation of total radiation widths (Cameron 1959).

transitions and an underestimate of the strength of high-energy transitions. As a compensation for the deficiencies of eqn. (7.36) the level density formula employed (Cameron 1958) is clearly overestimating the density of low-lying states; this is probably due to an underestimate of the single-particle level density ρ_s and spin dispersion constant σ_M^2, as concluded in Chapter IV, Section B.5.

4. Fluctuations of total radiation widths

The knowledge that there are strong fluctuations amongst the partial radiation widths of resonances of the same angular momentum and parity for any given transition raises the question, what are the fluctuations of total radiation widths of resonances of the same class? This question can only be answered theoretically with the aid of a model such as we are discussing in this section.

The application of the statistical model of neutron capture to the fluctuations of total radiation widths was made by Porter and Thomas (1956). By using the basic theorems of statistics, that the mean and variance of a population are equal to the sums of the means and variances, respectively of the sub-populations,

$$\bar{\Gamma}_{(\gamma\mathrm{T})} = \sum_{\mu=1}^{n} \bar{\Gamma}_{(\gamma\mu)} \tag{7.39}$$

$$\overline{(\Gamma_{(\gamma\mathrm{T})}-\bar{\Gamma}_{(\gamma\mathrm{T})})^2} = \frac{2}{\nu}\sum_{\mu=1}^{n} \bar{\Gamma}^2_{(\gamma\mu)}, \tag{7.40}$$

the bars expressing averages over many resonances (of the same spin and parity). The result in eqn. (7.40) is obtained by assuming that the partial radiative widths are distributed among the resonances according to a chi-squared function with ν degrees of freedom. The assumption of the statistical model that the matrix element for a radiative transition is independent of energy, together with the constant temperature level density law, leads to

$$V^2 \equiv \frac{\overline{(\Gamma_{(\gamma\mathrm{T})}-\bar{\Gamma}_{(\gamma\mathrm{T})})^2}}{\bar{\Gamma}^2_{(\gamma\mathrm{T})}} = 2n^{-1}\{1-\exp(-E_{\mathrm{th,n}}/T)\} \times \{\gamma(7,E_{\mathrm{th,n}}/T)/\gamma^2(4,E_{\mathrm{th,n}}/T)\}, \tag{7.41}$$

where $n = \int\limits_0^{E_{\mathrm{th,n}}} \rho(E)\mathrm{d}E = CT\{\exp(E_{\mathrm{th,n}}/T)-1\}$ and $\gamma(n,\, x)$ is the incomplete gamma function of order n and argument x. The relative variance, V^2, ranges from $(2/n)\times 5{\cdot}3$, for $E_{\mathrm{th,n}}/T = 3$, through $(2/n)\times 10{\cdot}9$, for $E_{\mathrm{th,n}}/T = 6$ to $(2/n)\times 20$ for $E_{\mathrm{th,n}}/T = \infty$.

For heavy nuclei the calculated value of V^2 is very small. For example, in the compound nucleus ^{239}U the neutron separation energy, $E_{\mathrm{th,n}}$ is equal to 4·7 MeV and the nuclear temperature T taken from the analysis of Lang and Le Couteur is about 0·5 MeV. The density of odd-parity states with $J = \frac{1}{2}$ and 3/2 (those reached from even parity $J = \frac{1}{2}$ states by electric dipole radiation) at the separation energy is inferred to be $0{\cdot}17\times 10^6\ \mathrm{MeV}^{-1}$, leading to $n = 8\times 10^4$ and $V^2 = 4\times 10^{-4}$.

Experimental data on fluctuations of total radiation widths are not numerous, the experimental uncertainty in the measurements of these widths usually outweighing the fluctuations. The widths of twenty-three resonances in the cross-section of ^{232}Th (Asghar *et al.* 1965) have been analysed by a maximum likelihood method to determine the dispersion constant that appears in the normal frequency law assumed for the widths:

$$p(\Gamma_{(\gamma T)})d\Gamma_{(\gamma T)} = \frac{1}{\sigma\sqrt{(2\pi)}} e^{-(\Gamma_{(\gamma T)}-\bar{\Gamma}_{(\gamma T)})^2/2\sigma^2} d\Gamma_{(\gamma T)}. \quad (7.42)$$

The value of $V^2 = \sigma^2/\Gamma^2_{(\gamma T)}$ was found to be 7×10^{-3}. A similar value was found for the resonances of ^{238}U (Moxon 1964). Such a value of V^2 is much greater than the theoretical expectation, indicating a breakdown of the statistical model at least for the high-energy transitions; the value of V^2 for the ^{239}U data can be explained, at least qualitatively, by the strong group of four transitions with energy about 4 MeV observed with an intensity of 0·07 transitions per capture in the thermal neutron capture γ-ray spectrum of ^{238}U (Fiebiger 1962, Bartholomew and Higgs 1958).

In the lighter nuclei the much lower rate of increase with energy of the level density requires the capture γ-ray spectrum to be much harder, and, in fact, it is found that as much as half of the primary spectrum may be concentrated on only a handful of transitions to low-lying states of the compound nucleus. This implies that there should be very considerable fluctuations of the total radiation widths among the resonances of these nuclei. An example of this is the sequence of radiation widths of the first fifteen resonances in the cross-section of ^{59}Co (Moxon 1965) (see Table 1.2). The smallest width was observed for the resonance at 6·4 keV ($\Gamma_{(\gamma T)} = 0{\cdot}22 \pm 0{\cdot}05$) and the largest at 5·01 keV ($\Gamma_{(\gamma T)} = 1{\cdot}0$ eV). The value of V^2 for the sequence is 0·17 (corresponding to an effective value of ν of 12); the statistical-model estimate, using a nuclear temperature $T = 1$ MeV, is a factor of 10 less than this.

E. GIANT-RESONANCE MODEL

1. Energy dependence and magnitude of the partial radiation width

The single-particle model and the derived statistical model consider only the transitions of a single particle in the field of all the other nucleons. The next stage in the development of the theory is the introduction of the independent-particle shell model (Wilkinson 1956). It is easiest first to consider the inverse problem of absorption of radiation—the photonuclear effect. Whereas the single-particle model of an electric dipole transition may consider only the elevation of a single-valency nucleon from one state to another, in the shell model all possible elevations which satisfy the electric dipole conditions of $|j_i - j_f| = 0, 1$ and $\pi_i \pi_f = -1$ must be considered. These include elevations from occupied shells to partially occupied or unoccupied shells. The anti-symmetrization of the shell-model wave-functions implies that such transitions are cooperative in character. A transition from a state in which a subshell has occupation number n and vacancy p to a state in which the subshell occupation is reduced by one occurs with probability of $n\times$ (corresponding single-particle probability).

Wilkinson (1956) has shown that the strong transitions which occur in the shell model defined by an infinite square potential well with spin-orbit coupling are clustered in energy, providing a possible explanation of the giant resonance in the nuclear photo-absorption cross-section. An idealization of this model is provided by the infinite harmonic oscillator potential. An apparent alternative model is the collective model of a dipole vibration of the proton fluid of a nucleus against the neutron fluid (Goldhaber and Teller 1948). Brink (1957) has shown that this is equivalent to the harmonic-oscillator shell model. It is plausible and useful, therefore, to use the semi-classical results of the collective model for a description of the photonuclear giant resonance.

According to this, the photonuclear absorption cross-section has the Lorentzian form:

$$\sigma_{\gamma,\mathrm{T}} = \frac{16\pi^2}{9}\frac{3}{4\pi}\frac{1}{\hbar c}\frac{e^2\hbar^2}{2M}\frac{NZ}{A} \times \frac{1}{\Gamma_{\mathrm{G}}}\frac{(\Gamma_{\mathrm{G}} E)^2}{(E^2 - E_{\mathrm{G}}^2)^2 + (\Gamma_{\mathrm{G}} E)^2}(1+0{\cdot}8x) \tag{7.43}$$

The constant is determined by the photonuclear dipole sum rule, common to all models, for the transition probabilities to states μ from a state λ,

$$\sum_{\mu} (E_\mu - E_\lambda)|\langle X_\mu|\mathscr{H}^{(1)}_{\mathrm{E}\mathscr{M}}|\mathrm{X}_\lambda\rangle|^2 = \frac{3}{4\pi}\frac{NZ}{A}\frac{e^2\hbar^2}{2M}, \tag{7.44}$$

which is valid so long as the nuclear forces do not have exchange character. Levinger and Bethe (1950) have studied the effect of exchange forces on the sum rule and have concluded that the right-hand side of eqn. (7.44) is to be multiplied by a factor $(1+0{\cdot}8x)$ where x is the fraction of exchange force present in the nuclear force. These results lead to the following expression for the average partial width of an electric dipole transition with energy ε between the ground state $(\lambda = 0)$ and an excited state μ with total angular momentum J_μ (Brink 1955)

$$\bar{\Gamma}_{(\gamma\mu)}(\varepsilon, J_\mu) = \frac{4}{3\pi}\frac{NZ}{A}\frac{e^2}{\hbar c}\frac{(1+0{\cdot}8x)}{Mc^2}\frac{\Gamma_G\varepsilon^4}{(\varepsilon^2-E_G^2)^2+(\Gamma_G\varepsilon)^2}D(J_\mu). \tag{7.45}$$

The same result is assumed to hold, and has been demonstrated for ^{12}C in the (p, γ) reaction on ^{11}B (Gove *et al.* 1961), for electric dipole

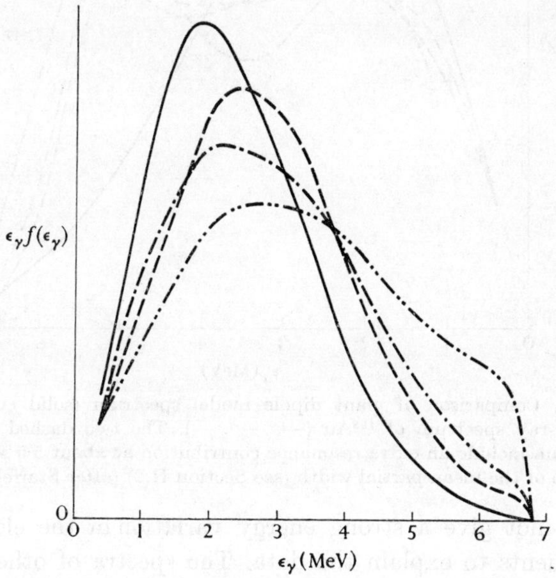

FIG. 7.10. Calculations (Starfelt 1964) of the γ-ray spectrum following neutron capture by ^{197}Au. Solid curve is a statistical theory calculation with Newton's level-density formula. Curves — — — and —.—.— are giant dipole resonance calculations with Newton's level-density law. Curve —. . —. . — is a giant dipole calculation with a constant-temperature (T = 0·7 MeV) level density law.

transitions between higher excited states. This expression has the satisfactory feature that for excitations below the neutron separation energy the higher energy transitions are enhanced, as we concluded they ought to be, following the comparison of data with the statistical model.

2. The γ-ray spectrum

Calculations of the shape of the γ-ray spectrum in this model have been made by Starfelt (1964) using eqn. (7.45) with $E_G = 13{\cdot}5$ MeV, $\Gamma_G = 3{\cdot}4$ MeV and $x = 0$. He has shown that the spectrum for ^{198}Au is displaced to higher energies compared with the statistical-model spectrum, as shown in Fig. 7.10 in which Newton's shell-model level density equation was used. Comparison with the spectrum of Au is shown in Fig. 7.11 in which it is apparent that even this giant-resonance

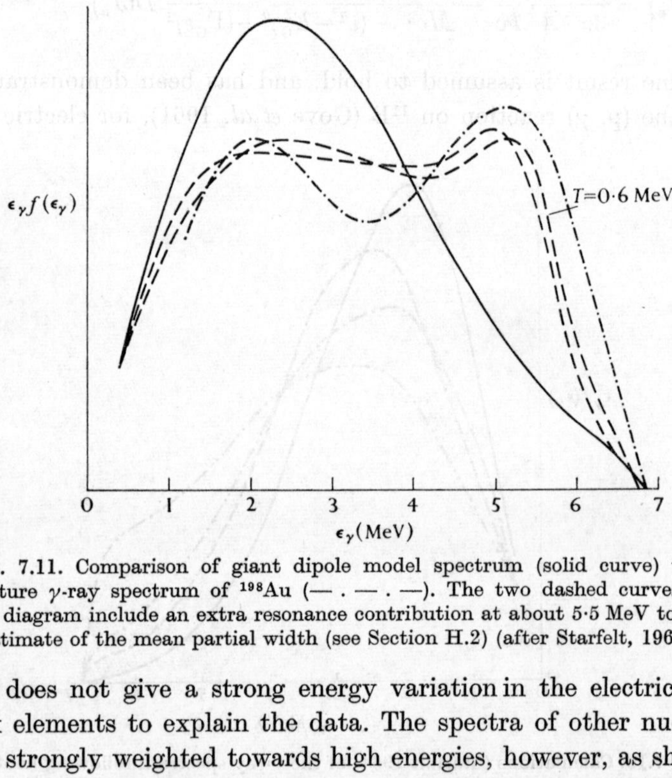

FIG. 7.11. Comparison of giant dipole model spectrum (solid curve) with capture γ-ray spectrum of ^{198}Au (— . — . —). The two dashed curves on the diagram include an extra resonance contribution at about 5·5 MeV to the estimate of the mean partial width (see Section H.2) (after Starfelt, 1964).

model does not give a strong energy variation in the electric dipole matrix elements to explain the data. The spectra of other nuclei are not so strongly weighted towards high energies, however, as shown in Fig. 7.4; it may be that the model is sufficient to explain most spectra, discrepancies in the way of strong high-energy transitions being confined to nuclei that are in the region of neutron shell closures.

3. Total radiation widths

(a) *Spin dependence*

Brink (1955) has used eqn. (7.45) for the partial radiation widths to determine resonance total radiation widths in the neutron capture process. The total radiation width is the sum over all partial widths:

$$\Gamma_{(\gamma T)}(J) = \sum_{\mu} \Gamma_{(\gamma\mu)}$$

$$\approx \sum_{I=|J-1|}^{J+1} \int_{0}^{E_{\text{th,n}}} \mathrm{d}\varepsilon \rho(E_{\text{th,n}}-\varepsilon, I)\Gamma_{(\gamma\mu)}(\varepsilon, J)$$

$$= \frac{4}{3\pi} \cdot \frac{NZ}{A} \cdot \frac{e^2}{\hbar c} \frac{(1+0{\cdot}8x)}{Mc^2} \sum_{I=|J-1|}^{J+1} \int_{0}^{\infty} \mathrm{d}\varepsilon \frac{\rho(E_{\text{th,n}}-\varepsilon, I)}{\rho(E_{\text{th,n}}, J)} \frac{\Gamma \varepsilon^4}{(\varepsilon^2 - E_{\text{G}}^2)^2 + (\Gamma_{\text{G}}\varepsilon)^2} \tag{7.46}$$

If J is greater than or equal to unity some simple conclusions may be drawn from eqn. (7.41) about the angular momentum dependence of the total radiation width. If the level density of the final states, as well as the initial state, is proportional to $(2J+1)$, as suggested by the discussions of Chapter IV, Section B.6, then the total radiation width is independent of J. This is also true if the level density is independent of J or has some other linear dependence on J. For states with no angular momentum the total radiation width is the same as for states with higher J if the level density of the initial states is proportional to $(2J+1)$, but is only one-third of this value if the level density is independent of J. States with $J = \frac{1}{2}$ also have the same radiation width as higher spin states if the $(2J+1)$ level density law is valid. If the level density is independent of J then the total radiation width of such states is only 2/3 of the value for higher spins.

The expectations based on the $(2J+1)$ level density law are largely borne out by the data on total radiation widths. Thus, in Table 7.4, there are several cases of targets with angular momentum $I = \frac{1}{2}$ where the radiation widths have been measured for resonances with angular momenta $J = 0$ and 1. In the cases of ^{107}Ag, ^{109}Ag, ^{169}Tm, ^{183}W, ^{195}Pt, and ^{199}Hg the radiation widths are almost equal to within the assessed uncertainties. Only in the case of ^{103}Rh does there appear to be a significant difference, but the ratio $\Gamma_{(\gamma T)}(J = 0)/\Gamma_{(\gamma T)}(J = 1) = 1{\cdot}3$, rather than being less than unity as would be expected if there were a deviation from the $(2J+1)$ law.

(b) *Absolute values*

Brink used the Fermi gas level-density formula with a single-particle level density $\rho_{\text{S}} = 3A/4\pi^2$ to calculate absolute values of the total radiation width. At mass number $A \approx 100$ his estimates exceed the observed values by a factor of the order of 2. Starfelt (1964) has made similar calculations of eqn. (7.46) using both the shell-model level density formula of Newton (1956) and a constant temperature formula $\rho \propto \exp(U/T)$. His calculation for gold gave $\Gamma_{(\gamma T)} = 451$ meV in the former case and $\Gamma_{(\gamma T)} = 421$ meV in the latter case for a temperature $T = 0{\cdot}7$ MeV. These results are a factor of 3 greater than the observed value of 130 meV but agreement can be obtained with a lower temperature ($T \approx 0{\cdot}6$ MeV).

F. VALENCY NUCLEON TRANSITIONS

Although the electric dipole transitions in the square-well shell model are clustered in energy, their mean energy is only about one-half of the observed giant-resonance energy (ranging from about 23 MeV for ^{16}O to 14 MeV for ^{208}Pb). It has been shown that the elevation of the giant resonance is due to the residual interaction (the 'particle-hole' interaction) between a nucleon, when it is raised from a complete shell, and the remaining nucleons in the shell (Brown and Bolsterli 1959). While some residue of this effect may occur for the 'valency' nucleons belonging to incomplete shells it is not expected to be nearly so great and consequently the valency nucleon transitions should have much lower energies than the dipole resonance energy. It can be held, then, that it is not valid to extrapolate the giant resonance form (eqn. (7.45)) to the much lower energies involved in slow neutron capture processes. At these energies irregularities in the transition strengths may occur corresponding to valency nucleon transitions. There is some direct experimental evidence on this point; although the total photonuclear yield from 8 to 20 MeV in ^{206,207,208}Pb and ^{209}Bi can be fitted well by the Lorentz form (Harvey *et al.* 1964), elastic photon-scattering measurements in the range 6 to 8 MeV show a considerable amount of structure (Axel *et al.* 1963).

The valency nucleon effect is a possible explanation of the coarse size structure observed in average total radiation widths. The observed radiation widths of Table 7.4 are plotted as a function of mass number in Fig. 7.8. The most striking features of the diagram are the large maxima at the nucleon shell closures. These are mainly due to the large neutron-separation energies at these closures; in expression (7.34) or (7.46) the level spacing of initial states effectively cancels with the level density of final states leaving the extent of the integrand as the major variable factor. However, in Fig. 7.8 it is also apparent that there is a less striking but, nevertheless, well-developed maximum in the mass number range $A \approx 160$–180 in which there is no significant change of either separation energy or level density behaviour. This and other structure (at mass number 90) are brought out more clearly in a diagram of Cameron (1959) (Fig. 7.9) which shows the ratio of observed radiation width to the calculated, statistical model width. The discrepancies between observed capture γ-ray spectra of several nuclei, particularly near neutron shell closures, and calculations based on the giant-resonance model could also be due to valency nucleon effects (Lane and Lynn 1960*b*).

The formal demonstration of these effects begins from eqn. (7.20) for the partial radiation width for a transition of multipolarity to a final state μ. Specialized to E1 radiation eqn. (7.20) becomes

$$\Gamma_{\lambda(\gamma \mathrm{E1},\mu)} = \frac{16\pi\kappa^3}{9}\frac{|\langle X_\lambda(J_\lambda)||\mathscr{H}_{\mathrm{E}}^{(1)}||X_\mu(J_\mu)\rangle|^2}{(2J_\lambda+1)}. \tag{7.47}$$

The single-particle effects are revealed in this formula by using the expansion of eqns. (6.1) and (6.2) with the channel functions (labelled by $c \equiv \alpha I_\alpha j$) defined in the spin-orbit coupling scheme; here I_α is the spin of the residual nucleus or 'core'. If core transitions are neglected (Lane 1959) the partial radiation width becomes

$$\Gamma_{\lambda(\gamma \mathrm{E1},\mu)} = \frac{16\pi\kappa^3}{9}\sum_{\alpha\mathrm{p}',\alpha\mathrm{p}''}\overline{C_{\alpha\mathrm{p}'}^{\lambda 2}C_{\alpha\mathrm{p}''}^{\mu 2}}\left|\bar{e}\int_0^\infty dr\, u_{\mathrm{p}'}(r)r\, u_{\mathrm{p}''}(r)\right|^2 \times\frac{|\langle j'I_\alpha J_\lambda||\mathbf{Y}^{(1)}||j''I_\alpha J_\mu\rangle|^2}{(2J_\lambda+1)} \tag{7.48}$$

where, in the suffices labelling the sums and coefficients, it is understood that p$'$, etc. indicate not only the radial function of the single-particle state but also that its spin-orbit angular momentum j' is coupled into the channel function. Cross terms with factors such as $C_{\alpha\mathrm{p}'}^{\lambda}$, $C_{\alpha\mathrm{p}''}^{\lambda}$ have been dropped in squaring the matrix element as a result of the assumed randomness of sign of the coefficients $C_{\alpha\mathrm{p}}^{\lambda}$ and $C_{\alpha\mathrm{p}}^{\mu}$. The same assumption gives eqn. (6.69), and the intermediate-coupling assumption allows us to invert this equation to write

$$\overline{C_{\alpha\mathrm{p}}^{\lambda 2}} = \frac{2Ma_\alpha}{\hbar^2}u_{\mathrm{p}}^{-2}(a_\alpha)\overline{\gamma_{\lambda(c)}^2} \tag{7.49}$$

for the local average of the $C_{\alpha\mathrm{p}}^{\lambda 2}$, provided that the single-particle state p (coupled to α) is the closest in energy to the levels λ. Equation (7.49) immediately allows us to relate the partial radiation width to the strength functions and level spacings of the initial and final states:

$$\Gamma_{\lambda(\gamma\mathrm{E1},\mu)} = \frac{16\pi\kappa^3}{9}\bar{D}_\lambda(J_\lambda)\sum_{\alpha p'p''} s_{\lambda c}\,.\,\overline{\gamma^2_{\mu(c'')}} \times\left|\bar{e}\int_0^\infty dr\, u_{p'}(r) r\, u_{p''}(r)\right|^2 . \frac{|\langle j' I_\alpha J_\lambda||\mathbf{Y}^{(1)}||j'' I_\alpha J_\mu\rangle|^2}{(2J_\lambda+1)} \times\left(\frac{2Ma_\alpha}{\hbar^2}\right)^2 u_{p'}^{-2}(a_\alpha) u_{p''}^{-2}(a_\alpha). \qquad (7.50)$$

where $s_{\lambda c}$ indicates the strength function for channel c in the energy region of the initial level λ.

A statistical-model expression may be derived from this equation. The strong-coupling model for the strength function $s_{\lambda c}$ is assumed for each channel c (eqn. (6.58c)), and the sum rule over all channels c (i.e. all α) is applied to the reduced widths $\gamma^2_{\mu(c)}$ (eqn. (6.7) with $N = 1$ to allow for the fact that we are only considering valency nucleons). This can be done on the assumption that the initial state λ is at least as complicated as the final state. Therefore, every component of μ has an appreciable combining component in λ. This gives, approximately,

$$\Gamma_{\lambda(\gamma\mathrm{E1},\mu)} = \frac{16\pi}{9}\frac{\varepsilon_\gamma^3}{\hbar^2c^2}\frac{\bar{e}^2}{\hbar c}\frac{1}{\pi K a}\frac{4M}{\hbar^2}\overline{u^{-4}(a)}\,\bar{D}_\lambda(J_\lambda) \times\overline{\sum_{p'}\left|\int_0^\infty dr\, u_{p'}(r) r\, u_{p''}(r)\right|^2 . \frac{|\langle j' I_\alpha J_\lambda||\mathbf{Y}^{(1)}||j'' I_\alpha J_\mu\rangle|^2}{(2J_\lambda+1)}} \qquad (7.51)$$

where the final averaged factor denotes the average of the *sum* of the squared matrix elements to a specific single-particle state p″. By the usual methods of Racah algebra (see Edmonds 1957, pp. 111 and 76) the angular part of the matrix element is found to be

$$\frac{|\langle j' I_\alpha J_\lambda||\mathbf{Y}^{(1)}||j'' I_\alpha J_\mu\rangle|^2}{(2J_\lambda+1)} = \frac{1}{4\pi}\,.\,(2J_\mu+1)(2j'+1)(2j''+1)(2l'+1) \,.\,(2l''+1)W^2(j'J_\lambda j''J_\mu; I1)W^2(l'j'l''j''; \tfrac{1}{2}1)C^2_{l'1}(l''0; 00). \qquad (7.52)$$

The radial parts of the matrix elements have been computed, by numerical integration, for neutron wave-functions in an Eckart potential with spin-orbit coupling and the parameters of Ross *et al.* (1956) listed in Chapter III, Section C. The radius of the well was adjusted in each case so that the initial single-particle state p was just bound.

The results are listed in Table 7.5. The averaging of the sums of squared matrix elements calculated from eqn. (7.52) and Table 7.5 was limited, for convenience, to states $J_\lambda = \frac{1}{2}$, $J_\mu = \frac{1}{2}, 3/2$, $J_\lambda = 3/2$, $J_\mu = \frac{1}{2}, 3/2, 5/2$ and to $I_c = 0, 1$, and 2. The result of this sampling was the semi-empirical relation

$$\overline{\sum_{p'}\left|\int_0^\infty \mathrm{d}r\, u_{p'}(r) r\, u_{p''}(r)\right|^2 \cdot \frac{|\langle J_\lambda||\mathbf{Y}^{(1)}||J_\mu\rangle|^2}{(2J_\lambda+1)}} \approx 0{\cdot}001 A^{\frac{4}{3}} \times 10^{-24}\mathrm{cm}^2. \tag{7.53}$$

Substitution into eqn. (7.51) gives

$$\bar{\Gamma}_{\lambda(\gamma\mathrm{E1},\mu)}(\mathrm{meV}) = 0{\cdot}16\times 10^{-6}\varepsilon_\gamma^3(\mathrm{MeV})A^{\frac{8}{3}}D(J_\lambda)(\text{in eV}). \tag{7.54}$$

This is remarkably close to Cameron's empirically-determined relation, eqn. (7.36), from the fitting of total radiation widths, which suggests that the structure in the radiation-width mass-number dependence and capture γ-ray spectra could be studied profitably on the basis of eqn. (7.51).

This programme has not yet been pursued numerically but some qualitative conclusions are possible. In eqn. (7.50) the product $s_{\mu\alpha p''}\bar{D}_\mu(J_\mu)$ is substituted for the mean reduced width $\gamma^2_{\mu(c'')}$ giving for the primary spectral form

$$f_1(\varepsilon_\gamma) = \bar{\Gamma}_{\lambda(\gamma\mathrm{E1},\mu)} \sum_{J_\mu=|J_\lambda-1|}^{J_\lambda+1} \rho(E_\lambda-\varepsilon_\gamma, J_\mu) = \frac{16\pi}{9}\left(\frac{\bar{e}^2}{\hbar c}\right)\left(\frac{2Ma}{\hbar^2}\right)^2$$

$$\times\, \bar{D}_\lambda(J_\lambda)n(J_\lambda)\frac{\varepsilon_\gamma^{\;3}}{(\hbar c)^2}\sum_{p'p''} u_{p'}^{-2}(a_\alpha)u_{p''}^{-2}(a_\alpha)R_{p'p''}$$

$$\sum_{I_\alpha} A_{\alpha p'p''}\int_0^{E_{\mathrm{th,n}}} \mathrm{d}\varepsilon_\alpha \rho(\varepsilon_\alpha, I_\alpha)s_{\alpha p'}(E_\lambda)s_{\alpha p''}(E_\lambda-\varepsilon_\gamma), \tag{7.55}$$

where $R_{p'p''}$ has been written for the square of the radial part of the single-particle matrix element and $A_{\alpha p'p''}$ for the square of the angular part. The integral over the states of the residual nucleus of the channel, which is used to approximate the sum over α, has been cut off at the nucleon separation energy because it is not expected that a compound-nucleus state at this excitation energy will contain any appreciable component of residual nucleus states at a higher excitation. For the same reason the strength function for the final states $s_{\alpha p''}(E_\lambda-\varepsilon_\gamma)$

TABLE 7.5

Single particle radial overlap integral, $I = \int^{\infty} dr\, u_p(r) u_q(r) r$, *calculated for an Eckart potential with spin-orbit coupling*

$A \sim 35$				$A \sim 70$				$A \sim 120$				$A \sim 200$			
p	q	ε (MeV)	I^2 (barns)	p	q	ε (MeV)	I^2 (barns)	p	q	ε (MeV)	I^2 (barns)	p	q	ε (MeV)	I^2 (barns)
				$3\,s_{1/2}$	$2\,p_{1/2}$	5·7	0·100					$4\,s_{1/2}$	$3\,p_{1/2}$	4·8	0·173
				$3\,s_{1/2}$	$2\,p_{3/2}$	7·7	0·088					$4\,s_{1/2}$	$3\,p_{3/2}$	5·9	0·163
$2\,p_{1/2}$	$2\,s_{1/2}$	10·0	0·100					$3\,p_{1/2}$	$3\,s_{1/2}$	7·2	0·195				
$2\,p_{1/2}$	$1\,d_{3/2}$	8·2	0·043					$3\,p_{1/2}$	$2\,d_{3/2}$	6·7	0·095				
$2\,p_{3/2}$	$2\,s_{1/2}$	7·7	0·108					$3\,p_{3/2}$	$3\,s_{1/2}$	6·4	0·199				
$2\,p_{3/2}$	$1\,d_{3/2}$	5·3	0·043					$3\,p_{3/2}$	$2\,d_{3/2}$	5·8	0·092				
$2\,p_{3/2}$	$1\,d_{5/2}$	11·2	0·033					$3\,p_{3/2}$	$2\,d_{5/2}$	8·3	0·098				
				$2\,d_{3/2}$	$2\,p_{1/2}$	8·5	0·175					$3\,d_{3/2}$	$3\,p_{1/2}$	6·4	0·282
				$2\,d_{3/2}$	$2\,p_{3/2}$	10·3	0·175					$3\,d_{3/2}$	$3\,p_{3/2}$	7·4	0·285
				$2\,d_{3/2}$	$1\,f_{5/2}$	9·2	0·036					$3\,d_{3/2}$	$2\,f_{5/2}$	6·9	0·095

				$2\,d_{5/2}$	$2\,p_{3/2}$	7·4	0·174					$3\,d_{5/2}$	$3\,p_{3/2}$	5·7	0·281
				$2\,d_{5/2}$	$1\,f_{5/2}$	5·3	0·034					$3\,d_{5/2}$	$2\,f_{5/2}$	5·0	0·090
				$2\,d_{5/2}$	$1\,f_{7/2}$	11·3	0·037					$3\,d_{5/2}$	$2\,f_{7/2}$	7·9	0·098
$1\,f_{5/2}$	$1\,d_{3/2}$	11·2	0·141					$2\,f_{5/2}$	$2\,d_{3/2}$	7·7	0·250				
$1\,f_{5/2}$	$1\,d_{5/2}$	16·0	0·146					$2\,f_{5/2}$	$2\,d_{5/2}$	10·1	0·255				
								$2\,f_{5/2}$	$1\,g_{7/2}$	9·4	0·036				
$1\,f_{7/2}$	$1\,d_{5/2}$	9·7	0·136					$2\,f_{7/2}$	$2\,d_{5/2}$	7·0	0·246				
								$2\,f_{7/2}$	$1\,g_{7/2}$	6·1	0·021				
								$2\,f_{7/2}$	$1\,g_{9/2}$	11·3	0·039				
				$1\,g_{7/2}$	$1\,f_{5/2}$	9·8	0·207					$2\,g_{7/2}$	$2\,f_{5/2}$	7·2	0·334
				$1\,g_{7/2}$	$1\,f_{7/2}$	8·3	0·205					$2\,g_{7/2}$	$2\,f_{7/2}$	9·8	0·349
												$2\,g_{7/2}$	$1\,h_{9/2}$	9·7	0·036
				$1\,g_{9/2}$	$1\,f_{7/2}$	8·6	0·197					$2\,g_{9/2}$	$2\,f_{7/2}$	6·4	0·327
												$2\,g_{9/2}$	$1\,h_{9/2}$	5·8	0·015
												$2\,g_{9/2}$	$1\,h_{11/2}$	11·1	0·040
								$1\,h_{9/2}$	$1\,g_{7/2}$	8·9	0·276				
								$1\,h_{9/2}$	$1\,g_{9/2}$	13·8	0·297				
				$1\,h_{11/2}$	$1\,g_{9/2}$	7·9	0·264					$2\,h_{11/2}$	$2\,g_{9/2}$	6·0	0·416
												$2\,h_{11/2}$	$1\,i_{11/2}$	5·5	0·009
												$2\,h_{11/2}$	$1\,i_{13/2}$	10·9	0·039
												$1\,i_{11/2}$	$1\,h_{9/2}$	7·8	0·026
								$1\,i_{13/2}$	$1\,h_{11/2}$	7·2	0·078				

is assumed to be zero if $\varepsilon_\gamma > E_{\text{th,n}} - \varepsilon_\alpha$. According to the intermediate-coupling assumption of Lane, Thomas, and Wigner (1955) and its experimental justification by the complex-potential analyses of neutron reaction data, the strength functions $s_{\alpha p'}(E_\lambda)$ and $s_{\alpha p''}(E_\mu)$ are expected to peak at the energies of the single-particle states p′ and p″ respectively in the fields of the residual nuclei c, i.e. at energies $E_{p'}+\varepsilon_\alpha$ and $E_{p''}+\varepsilon_\alpha$. The function $n(J_\lambda) = 1$ if $J_\lambda = 0$, 2 if $J_\lambda = \frac{1}{2}$, and 3 otherwise. To obtain qualitative conclusions about the model we make the very simple assumption that these strength functions are delta functions

$$s_{\alpha p'}(E_\lambda) = \frac{1}{D_{p'}}\left(\frac{\hbar^2}{Ma_\alpha^2}\right)\delta(E_\lambda - E_{p'} - \varepsilon_\alpha), \tag{7.56a}$$

$$s_{\alpha p''}(E_\lambda - \varepsilon_\gamma) = \frac{1}{D_{p''}}\left(\frac{\hbar^2}{Ma_\alpha^2}\right)\delta(E_\lambda - \varepsilon_\gamma - E_{p'} - \varepsilon_\alpha), \tag{7.56b}$$

where $D_{p'}$ and $D_{p''}$ are the spacings of single-particle states with the same angular momentum properties as p′ and p″ respectively.

The primary spectral form then becomes

$$f_1(\varepsilon_\gamma) = \frac{16\pi}{9}\left(\frac{\bar{e}^2}{\hbar c}\right)\left(\frac{2Ma}{\hbar^2}\right)^2 \frac{1}{(\hbar c)^2} D_\lambda(J_\lambda) n(J_\lambda)\left(\frac{\hbar^2}{Ma^2}\right)$$

$$\cdot \sum_{p'p''} \frac{u_{p'}^{-2}(a) u_{p''}^{-2}(a)}{D_{p'} D_{p''}} R_{p'p''} \cdot \sum_{I_\alpha} A_{\alpha p'p''} \delta(\varepsilon_\gamma - E_{p'} + E_{p''})(E_{p'} - E_{p''})^3$$

$$\times \rho(E_\lambda - E_{p'}, I_\alpha). \tag{7.57}$$

It is clear from Fig. 3.3 or Table 7.5 that the energy difference of single-particle states that are connected through an electric dipole transition is of the order of 5 to 7 MeV, and consequently we expect to find the bulk of the primary transition spectrum in this energy range, according to eqn. (7.57). The experimental evidence that this is indeed so lies in Starfelt's analysis of capture γ-ray spectra, which he could not fit using either the statistical model or photonuclear model of the radiation process. The use of Table 7.5 together with eqn. (7.57) suggests that the important neutron transitions for the spectrum of $^{110}_{47}\text{Ag}$ are $2f_{7/2} \rightarrow 1g_{7/2}$, $3p_{3/2} \rightarrow 3s_{1/2}$, $3p_{3/2} \rightarrow 2d_{3/2}$ with a mean energy of about 6 MeV. In $^{134}_{55}\text{Cs}$ the $1i_{13/2} \rightarrow 1h_{11/2}$ neutron transition ought to be most important; this has an energy of over 7 MeV and is an explanation of why Starfelt finds the spectrum of caesium to be harder than that of silver. Similarly in $^{182}_{73}$Ta the important neutron transitions are $1j_{15/2} \rightarrow 1i_{13/2}$, $4s_{1/2} \rightarrow 3p_{3/2}$, $3d_{5/2} \rightarrow 3p_{3/2}$, $3d_{5/2} \rightarrow 2f_{5/2}$ and $4s_{1/2} \rightarrow 3p_{1/2}$ and there is an important proton transition from $1i_{13/2} \rightarrow 1h_{11/2}$; these have a mean energy of about 5·5 MeV. In $^{198}_{79}$Au the important transitions are for neutrons, from $3d_{3/2} \rightarrow 2f_{5/2}$, $3d_{5/2} \rightarrow 2f_{5/2}$, $2g_{7/2} \rightarrow 2f_{5/2}$, $3d_{3/2} \rightarrow 3p_{1/2}$ and $4s_{1/2} \rightarrow 3p_{1/2}$ with a mean energy of over 6 MeV. Again the difference could be an explanation of the observed difference in the hardness of the spectrum. Qualitatively, eqn. (7.57) seems to be able to explain the behaviour of the total radiation width also. This will have a maximum when there are several unfilled orbitals p′ connecting with several bound orbitals p″. Examination of Fig. 3.3 shows that this will best occur about half-way through a shell filling. In particular, when A is in the region of 165 both a major neutron and proton shell are about half full and we would expect large values of the radiation width, as observed (see Fig. 7.8). Conversely, just beyond the closure of both of these shells there are no bound orbitals p′ connecting with the available states p″ and we expect the total radiation widths to be unusually low, as observed for $^{210}_{83}$Bi.

The valency-nucleon model may also provide an explanation of the differences observed between the total radiation widths of odd-parity and even-parity levels of the same compound nucleus (e.g. ^{94}Nb, Jackson 1963). According to the model the single-particle components of the initial state may be predominantly of the same parity. If the important, low-lying residual core states are also largely of one parity (which is possible, according to the independent-particle model of level densities) then the electric dipole transitions will be strongest from the compound-nucleus states with parity equal to the product of the predominant single-particle component and the predominant core parity. The model suggests that these will be the odd parity states in the region of Nb, in agreement with observation.

G. DIRECT CAPTURE

1. The statistical or strong-coupling model

In the formal theory of Section B it was shown that in the capture reaction, in contrast to particle reactions, it is not possible to express the cross-section formally in terms of resonances with physical significance alone. There remains a component of the collision matrix element known as the hard-sphere capture amplitude $U^{\mathrm{HS}}_{c\gamma}$ (Lane and Lynn 1960a). For electric dipole radiation this has the form (from

Eqs. (7.8a) and (7.22)), for partial wave of orbital angular momentum l and total angular momentum J,

$$U^{\mathrm{HS}}_{\mathrm{c}\gamma(\mathrm{E1})} = \left(\frac{16\pi}{9}\cdot\frac{\kappa^3}{\hbar}\right)^{\frac{1}{2}}\cdot\left[\frac{\mathrm{i}\bar{e}\pi^{\frac{1}{2}}}{k_{\mathrm{c}}}\int\limits_{a_{\mathrm{c}}}^{\infty}\mathrm{d}r_\alpha\{I_l(r_\alpha)-e^{-\mathrm{i}\phi_l}O_l(r_\alpha)\}r_\alpha^2 u_{\mathrm{f}}(r_\alpha).\right] \times\frac{\langle J||\mathbf{Y}^{(1)}||J_{\mathrm{f}}\rangle}{(2J+1)^{\frac{1}{2}}} \tag{7.58}$$

where the radial wave-function $u_{\mathrm{f}}(r_\alpha)$ of the final state in channel $\alpha p''$ is implicitly weighted by the reduced width amplitude of the final state in this channel. In this radial integral we are now specifying the type α of the particles in the channel because the usual label c includes the angular momentum properties which, of course, are different for the final state.

An infinite hard sphere would not, of course, have a bound state to which radiative transitions could occur in a scattering process. Thus, the importance of eqn. (7.58) lies in the fact that it is a major formal contribution to what may be called 'direct' or 'potential' capture, which is defined as the component of the capture cross-section without resonance behaviour, in a model with physical content. The remainder of the process is due to the effect of very far-away levels, in direct analogy with the contribution of these to the potential scattering cross-section. The far-away levels have the effect of producing a 'potential' scattered wave within the nucleus, whereas the local levels absorb the potential scattered wave in this region. The matrix element between the internal potential scattered wave and the final state has to be added to the 'hard-sphere' matrix element to give the amplitude of direct capture.

In the simplest version of the strong-absorption model it is assumed that the incident wave is immediately absorbed on entering the nucleus; the direct capture is obtained immediately from the hard-sphere component, eqn. (7.58). The direct electric dipole capture cross-section for s-wave neutrons at low energies is (Lane and Lynn 1960*b*)

$$\sigma_{\gamma(\mathrm{dir})} = \frac{32\pi}{3}\left(\frac{\bar{e}^2}{\hbar c}\right)\frac{\varepsilon_\gamma^3}{\hbar^2c^2}\cdot\frac{a^5}{\hbar v}\left(\frac{\gamma^2_{\mu(\alpha)}}{\hbar^2/Ma^2}\right)\frac{1}{y^4}\left(\frac{y+3}{y+1}\right)^2 \tag{7.59a}$$

$$= \frac{0{\cdot}062}{a\sqrt{E}}\left(\frac{Z}{A}\right)^2\left(\frac{\gamma^2_{\mu(\alpha)}}{\hbar^2/Ma^2}\right)y^2\left(\frac{y+3}{y+1}\right)^2 \text{ barns,} \tag{7.59b}$$

where $\gamma^2_{\mu(\alpha)}$ is the reduced width for the p-wave neutron channel of the final state μ, and $y = k_\mu a$ where k_μ is the wave-number corresponding to the binding energy E_μ of the state μ. The numerical value of the force radius a is assumed to be in units of 1 fm. For a heavy nucleus with a single-particle p-wave neutron state bound by about 5 MeV, eqn. (7.59) gives a direct capture cross-section of the order of 1/4 barn at thermal neutron energies.

The cross-sections of the anomalously strong high energy groups in the capture γ-ray spectra of the heavy nuclei with mass numbers between about 180 and 208 are usually much higher than this (Lane and Lynn 1960*b*); these strong transitions are more likely to be due to the valency-nucleon transitions in the matrix elements of resonance capture as explained in Section E. An exception is capture by ^{206}Pb, for the capture cross-section by a single transition to the ground state (a nearly pure $3p_{1/2}$ hole state) is 0·025 barns. Many intermediate nuclei with mass numbers around 60 do have cross-sections for the high energy transitions of around 1/4 barn, and these transitions could possibly be direct capture. According to eqn. (7.59) the strengths of these transitions should be proportional to the reduced widths in the final state of the channel corresponding to the residual nucleus ground state and a p-wave neutron. Many of these reduced widths are known from deuteron stripping reactions, the angular distribution of the emitted proton being used to characterize the orbit of the captured neutron as p-wave. The observation of positive correlations between the (d, p) yields to many final states of intermediate nuclei and the thermal neutron capture γ-ray yields to the same states thus provide evidence for the direct capture process at these low energies. The earliest experimental observations of this fact were made by Groshev *et al.* (1958) for nuclei such as ^{59}Co and ^{56}Fe, and a recent example is the measurement of several γ-ray transitions in thermal capture by ^{55}Mn. The correlation coefficient between the γ-ray strengths and (d, p) yields for eight final states known to be $l_{\rm n} = 1$ is given by

$$\rho = \frac{\sum_i (x_i - \bar{x})(y_i - \bar{y})}{\sum_i (x_i - \bar{x})^2 \sum_i (y_i - \bar{y})^2} \tag{7.60}$$

where x_i and y_i are the reduced gamma and (d,p) widths for the transition to the i'th final state. The observed value is 0·84, a nearly significant positive correlation (Kennett *et al.* 1966). On the other hand, Prestwich and Coté (1967) have found that a similar positive correlation exists for capture at the 1098 eV and 2355 eV resonances in the cross-section of ^{55}Mn. This indicates that the proper explanation for such correlation may be one based on the valency-nucleon model for resonance capture.

In the more sophisticated version of the strong-absorption model, the strength function is set to zero below the ground state of the compound nucleus and this allows the potential scattered wave to penetrate the interior of the nucleus slightly (see Chapter VI, Section C.1). The cross-section for direct capture is consequently increased. An estimate of the amount of increase gives a factor of about $\frac{1}{2}$ for heavy nuclei and somewhat more for lighter nuclei.

2. The intermediate-coupling model

In the intermediate-coupling model, absorption of the ingoing nucleon by collisions within the nucleus is pictured as being relatively slight and there is an appreciable proportion of 'potential' scattered wave in the interior. For Lorentzian behaviour of the coupling coefficients $C^{\lambda}_{\mathrm{cp}}$ among the independent-particle states, it was shown in Chapter VI, Section C.2 that the projection of the interior wave-function of the compound nucleus upon the extrapolated entrance-channel function is equal to the imaginary part of the model wave-function of a complex-potential well, provided that the local levels are ignored. This wave-function, $\mathrm{i}\,\mathrm{Im}(\mathrm{e}^{\mathrm{i}\phi_{\mathrm{c}}}\Psi_{\mathrm{cp}})$ of eqn. (6.66), is the part of the interior radial wave-function of the compound nucleus that describes potential scattering at non-resonant energies when there is unit incoming flux in channel c:

$$\psi(r_{\mathrm{c}}) = \mathrm{i}\hbar^{\frac{1}{2}}\mathrm{e}^{-\mathrm{i}\phi_{\mathrm{c}}}\sum_{\mathrm{p}}\frac{\Gamma^{\frac{1}{2}}_{\mathrm{p(c)}}u_{\mathrm{p}}(r_{\mathrm{c}})(E_{\mathrm{p}}-E)}{(E_{\mathrm{p}}-E)^2+(W_{\mathrm{p}}+\frac{1}{2}\Gamma_{\mathrm{p(c)}})^2}. \tag{7.61}$$

The collision function at a non-resonant energy E is obtained from the R-function by retaining only the far-away terms in the sum over levels, i.e. by setting $R = R^{\infty}$; thus

$$U^{\mathrm{p}} = \mathrm{e}^{-2\mathrm{i}\phi_{\mathrm{c}}}\frac{1+\mathrm{i}PR^{\infty}}{1-\mathrm{i}PR^{\infty}} \tag{7.62a}$$

and the complex-potential model indicates that

$$R^{\infty} = \sum_{\mathrm{p}}\frac{\gamma^2_{\mathrm{p(c)}}(E_{\mathrm{p}}-E)}{(E_{\mathrm{p}}-E)^2+(W_{\mathrm{p}}+\frac{1}{2}\Gamma_{\mathrm{p(c)}})^2} \tag{7.62b}$$

The external radial wave-function for the potential scattered wave is thus

$$\psi_{\text{ext}}(r_c) = \frac{1}{v_c^{\frac{1}{2}}}\{I_c(r_c) - U^p O_c(r_c)\} \tag{7.63}$$

for unit incoming flux in channel c. The product $e^{i\phi_c}\psi_{\text{ext}}(r_c)$ is simply the imaginary part of $e^{i\phi_c}$ times the external wave-function of the complex potential, the R-function for which is given by eqn. (6.63a). The complete wave-function describing potential scattering at a sharp energy E is now given by $ie^{-i\phi_c}\text{Im}(e^{i\phi_c}\Psi^{e}_{cp})$ (where the superscript e indicates the inclusion of the external region as we have described) multiplied into the channel function. The main purpose of the latter is to supply the dependence of the wave-function on the angular and spin variables required in an evaluation of the matrix element for the transition. For the purposes of direct capture the function for intrinsic excitation of the particles included in the channel function plays an inert role.

The collision matrix element for direct capture in the intermediate coupling situation is thus

$$U^{D}_{c\gamma(E1)}(J) = \left(\frac{16\pi}{9}\frac{\kappa^3}{\hbar}\right)^{\frac{1}{2}} \frac{\langle ie^{-i\phi_c}\text{Im}(e^{i\phi_c}\Psi^{e}_{cp})\varphi_c||\mathscr{H}^{(1)}_{E}||X_\mu\rangle}{(2J+1)^{\frac{1}{2}}}. \tag{7.64}$$

Here the operator $\mathscr{H}^{(1)}_{E}$ is specialized to the case of relative motion of the incident particle and target; in eqn. (7.18a) there is just one term k and the effective charge for an incident neutron is $-(Z/A)e$. The intrinsic excitation function in eqn. (7.64) now separates out from the final state X_μ the single-particle motion associated with the intrinsic excitation α (normally the ground states) of the target and projectile in channel c. In the E1 case this is just the single neutron p-wave state. The direct capture cross-section has been numerically computed from this formula for incident s-wave neutrons at thermal energy using a Woods–Saxon complex potential with parameters $V_0 = -42$ MeV, $a = 1{\cdot}35\ A^{1/3}$ fm, $d = 0{\cdot}58$ fm and for three values of W_0: 0·5 MeV, 3·36 MeV, and 10 MeV (Lane and Lynn 1960*b*). For $W_0 = 3{\cdot}36$ MeV the direct capture is shown in Fig. 7.12, in relation to the potential scattering cross-section and the neutron strength-function, as a function of mass number. The direct capture shows an interesting double peak associated with the maximum and minimum of the potential scattering cross-section. This may be explained by the fact that the main contribution to the radial integral of the direct capture matrix element

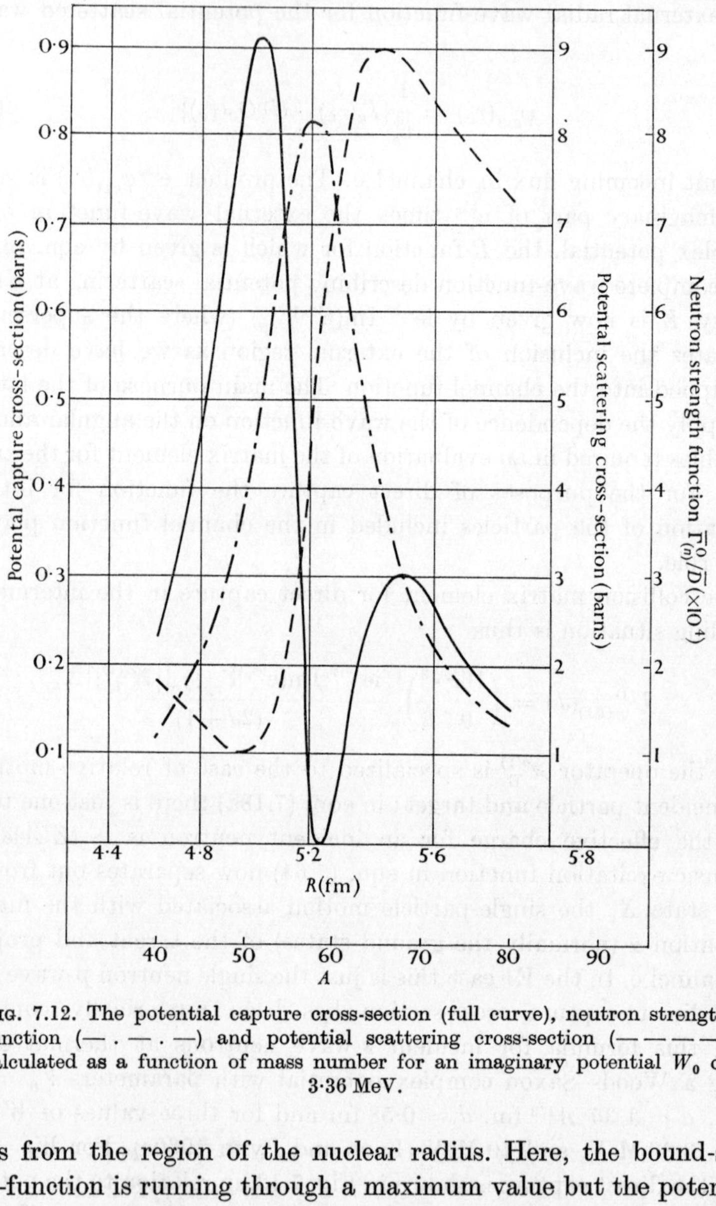

FIG. 7.12. The potential capture cross-section (full curve), neutron strength function (— . — . —) and potential scattering cross-section (— — —) calculated as a function of mass number for an imaginary potential W_0 of 3·36 MeV.

comes from the region of the nuclear radius. Here, the bound-state wave-function is running through a maximum value but the potential-scattering wave-function is close to a node. At the potential scattering minimum the node is within the nuclear radius and the integrand at the nuclear radius is therefore quite appreciable. With increasing mass number the node proceeds through the nuclear radius causing cancellation of the 'inner' and 'outer' parts of the matrix element and then reaches a point some distance outside where there is partial recovery of the matrix element. The mass number dependence of the direct capture cross-section for different values of the imaginary part of the potential is shown in Fig. 7.13. The smaller the value of W_0 the more the direct capture is enhanced in the region of the strength-function giant resonance. It is apparent that around mass number 50 the potential capture at thermal neutron energies could be about 1 barn or more,

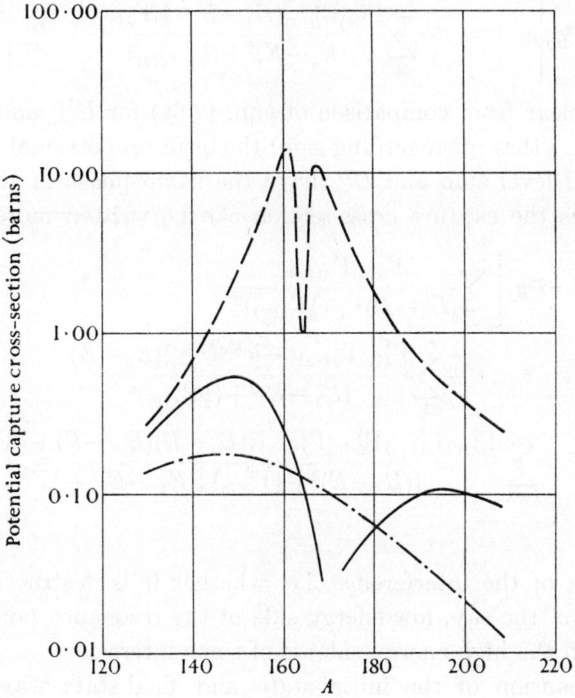

FIG. 7.13. The potential capture cross-section as a function of mass number for different values of W_0. — — — — $W_0 = 0{\cdot}5$ MeV, —.—.— $W_0 = 10$ MeV, ——— $W_0 = 3{\cdot}36$ MeV.

which is the order of magnitude of very many of the experimentally observed high-energy transitions (Lane and Lynn 1960*b*).

3. Interference between potential and resonance capture

In general, the calculation of neutron capture at a sharp neutron energy requires the full matrix element of eqn. (7.8a). We schematically divide this into local resonance terms, distant resonance terms, and the 'hard-sphere' term. We have already seen how the last two components are combined to give the non-resonant direct or potential capture amplitude. It is now clear that the addition of this to the local resonance component of the amplitude gives rise to interference between potential capture and resonance capture.

The specific form of the cross-section for primary transitions to state μ from *narrow* local resonances is (for the spin component J)

$$\sigma_{\gamma\mu} = \pi\bar{\lambda}^2 g_J |U_{c\gamma\mu}|^2$$

$$= \pi\bar{\lambda}^2 g_J \left| \mathrm{i}e^{-\mathrm{i}\phi_c} e^{-\mathrm{i}\phi_{\gamma\mu}} \sum_\lambda \frac{\Gamma^{\frac{1}{2}}_{\lambda(c)}\Gamma^{\frac{1}{2}}_{\lambda(\gamma\mu)}(E_\lambda - E + \frac{1}{2}\mathrm{i}\Gamma_{\lambda(T)})}{(E_\lambda - E)^2 + (\frac{1}{2}\Gamma_{\lambda(T)})^2} + U^{D}_{c\gamma\mu} \right|^2. \quad (7.65)$$

It is now clear from comparison of eqn. (7.64) for $U^D_{c\gamma\mu}$ and eqn. (7.8) for $e^{-\mathrm{i}\phi}{}_{\gamma}\Gamma^{\frac{1}{2}}_{\gamma(\gamma\mu)}$ that (disregarding sign) the term proportional to $(E_\lambda - E)$ in the local level sum and $U^D_{c\gamma\mu}$ have the same phase in the complex plane. Thus the capture cross-section can be written more explicitly

$$\sigma_{\gamma\mu} = \pi\bar{\lambda}^2 g_J \Bigg[\sum_\lambda \frac{\Gamma_{\lambda(c)}\Gamma_{\lambda(\gamma\mu)}}{(E_\lambda - E)^2 + (\frac{1}{2}\Gamma_{\lambda(T)})^2} + \sum_\lambda \frac{\Gamma^{\frac{1}{2}}_{\lambda(c)}\Gamma^{\frac{1}{2}}_{\lambda(\gamma\mu)}(-\mathrm{i}e^{\mathrm{i}\phi_c}U^D_{c\gamma\mu})(E_\lambda - E)}{(E_\lambda - E)^2 + (\frac{1}{2}\Gamma_{\lambda(T)})^2}$$

$$+ |U^D_{c\gamma\mu}|^2 + \sum_{\lambda \neq \lambda'} \frac{\Gamma^{\frac{1}{2}}_{\lambda(c)}\Gamma^{\frac{1}{2}}_{\lambda(\gamma\mu)}\Gamma^{\frac{1}{2}}_{\lambda'(c)}\Gamma^{\frac{1}{2}}_{\lambda'(\gamma\mu)}\{(E_\lambda - E)(E_{\lambda'} - E) + \frac{1}{4}\Gamma_{\lambda(T)}\Gamma_{\lambda'(T)}\}}{\{(E_\lambda - E)^2 + \frac{1}{4}\Gamma^2_{\lambda(T)}\}\{(E_{\lambda'} - E)^2 + \frac{1}{4}\Gamma^2_{\lambda'(T)}\}} \Bigg] \quad (7.66)$$

The sign of the interference, i.e. whether it is destructive or constructive on, the say, low-energy side of the resonance (and therefore opposite on the high-energy side) is of some interest.

The expansion of the initial-state and final-state wave-functions in the partial radiation width amplitude of eqn. (7.8) permits us to make some statements about this. The expansion adopted is that introduced at the beginning of Chapter VI (eqn. (6.2)). Using this we obtain (considering only the valency-nucleon components of the transition)

$$\Gamma^{\frac{1}{2}}_{\lambda(\gamma\mu)} = \frac{(8\pi)^{\frac{1}{2}}\kappa^{\mathscr{L}+\frac{1}{2}}(\mathscr{L}+1)^{\frac{1}{2}}}{\mathscr{L}^{\frac{1}{2}}(2\mathscr{L}+1)!!(2J+1)^{\frac{1}{2}}} \sum_{\alpha p' p''} C^{\lambda}_{\alpha p'} C^{\lambda}_{\alpha p''} \langle u_{p'}\varphi_{\alpha j'} \| \mathscr{H}^{(\mathscr{L})}_{T} \| u_{p''}\varphi_{\alpha j''} \rangle. \quad (7.67)$$

In the first place, let us consider s-wave neutron capture by an even nucleus to a pure single-particle p-wave state, i.e. $\alpha p''$ is limited to one term, the ground state of the residual nucleus and the single neutron p-wave state ($C^{\mu}_{\alpha p''} \approx \pm 1$). Then (according to the intermediate-coupling model) there is only significant coefficient $C^{\lambda}_{\alpha p''}$ in the sum in eqn. (7.67), and this coefficient is directly related to the reduced neutron-width amplitude for elastic scattering (from eqn. (6.9))

$$\gamma_{\lambda(c)} = \left(\frac{\hbar^2}{2Ma_{\alpha}}\right)^{\frac{1}{2}} C^{\lambda}_{\alpha p'} u_{p'}(a_{\alpha}). \tag{7.68}$$

We now see that the product $\Gamma^{\frac{1}{2}}_{\lambda(c)}\Gamma^{\frac{1}{2}}_{\lambda(\gamma\mu)}$ is proportional to $C^{\lambda}_{\alpha p'} u_{p'}(a_{\alpha}) C^{\mu}_{\alpha p''} \langle u_{p'}\varphi_{\alpha j'}||\mathscr{H}^{(\mathscr{L})}_{\mathrm{E}}||u_{p''}\varphi_{\alpha j''}\rangle$. We also find, by substituting eqn. (6.74) into eqn. (7.64), that $-\mathrm{i}e^{\mathrm{i}\phi_c}U^{\mathrm{D}}_{c\gamma\mu}$ is proportional to

$$\sum_{p'} \frac{(E_{p'}-E)}{(E_{p'}-E)^2+(W_{p'})^2} u_{p'}(a_{\alpha}) C^{\mu}_{\alpha p''} \langle u_{p'}\varphi_{\alpha j'}||\mathscr{H}^{(\mathscr{L})}_{\mathrm{E}}||u_{p''}\varphi_{\alpha j''}\rangle, \tag{7.69}$$

the sum including only those single-particle states p′ that can be coupled in the s-wave state. Clearly, the coefficient $\Gamma^{\frac{1}{2}}_{\lambda(c)}\Gamma^{\frac{1}{2}}_{\lambda(\gamma\mu)}(-\mathrm{i}e^{\mathrm{i}\phi_c}U^{\mathrm{D}}_{c\gamma\mu})$ of the interference term in eqn. (7.66) essentially has the sign of $(E_{p'}-E)$ in the neighbourhood of the single-particle s-wave resonance p′. For nuclei below the giant s-wave size resonance interference between resonant and direct capture will be constructive below the resonance (which is opposite to what is generally observed in elastic scattering). Nuclei above the size resonance show interference of the opposite kind.

Capture by odd and odd-mass nuclei is not so simple (except for $J = 0$ resonances in the cross-section of a spin $\frac{1}{2}$ target) even if the final state is a single-particle p-wave neutron state. The reason is that d-wave single-particle components coupled to the ground state core can now be present in the initial state and contribute to the photon reduced width amplitude. The sign of these contributions in the product $\Gamma^{\frac{1}{2}}_{\lambda(c)}\Gamma^{\frac{1}{2}}_{\lambda(\gamma\mu)}(-\mathrm{i}e^{\mathrm{i}\phi_c}U^{\mathrm{D}}_{c\gamma\mu})$ is unknown. However, we may reasonably expect that the nature of the interference will *usually* be that described above when the resonance has a very strong reduced neutron width for s-wave elastic scattering.

Impurity in the final state also introduces a degree of randomness into the sign of the interference term; more terms enter the sum over $\alpha p'p''$ in eqn. (7.67), and as the s-wave to p-wave single-particle component in the reduced width amplitude ceases to be predominant the sign of $\Gamma^{\frac{1}{2}}_{\lambda(\gamma\mu)}$ becomes random with respect to $\Gamma^{\frac{1}{2}}_{\lambda(c)}(-\mathrm{i}e^{\mathrm{i}\phi_c}U^{\mathrm{D}}_{c\gamma\mu})$.

The actual magnitude of the interference is very small. For the strong lowest-energy resonances of cobalt and gold, for example, it will only be of the order of 1 mbarn at three half-widths from the resonance energy.

This is difficult to measure and attempts to do so have not been very conclusive. Measurements on the transitions of energy 5·9 to 6·6 MeV from the 4·9-eV resonance in the gold cross-section (Wasson and Draper 1963) indicate that the non-resonant component of the cross-section is of the order of or less than 10 mbarns at 1 eV. The interference with resonance capture is constructive on the low-energy side of the resonance. The thermal neutron cross-sections of the high-energy transitions of some heavy and intermediate nuclei have been estimated and compared with data using the assumptions that the final state has single-neutron p-wave character, the potential capture has the value given by the strong-coupling model and only the incident channel contribution to the resonant capture is of importance (Lane and Lynn 1960*b*). The last assumption is only valid provided that local levels are not too near the incident neutron energy; close to a local level the assumption gives not only an incorrect value of the cross-section but also the wrong energy dependence for it. For heavy nuclei these estimates were usually too low but for nuclei in the mass-number-60 region they were mostly of the correct order of magnitude giving an indication, although not a proof, of the existence of direct capture.

A difficulty in the interpretation of these small interference effects is provided by the existence of resonance-resonance interference given by the last term of eqn. (7.66). For narrow resonances this vanishes, on average, for the usual compound-nucleus radiative transition. When the final state is a pure p-neutron state, however, the γ-ray transition amplitude is correlated in sign with the neutron amplitude and it can be shown that the average cross-section for the s-wave resonance-resonance interference is

$$\bar{\sigma}_{\gamma}(\text{r-r}) = \pi^3 \lambda\!\!\!^{-2} \frac{\Gamma_{(\text{n})}}{D} \cdot \frac{\Gamma_{(\gamma\mu)}}{D}. \qquad (7.70)$$

The energy dependence of the unaveraged cross-section is fairly mild, not showing strong resonance effects. It can also be shown (Lane and Lynn 1960*a*) that the average resonance-resonance interference cross-section is just the cross-section resulting from the real part (strictly it is $e^{-i\phi_c}\text{Re}\, e^{i\phi_c}\langle\rangle$) of the matrix element between the state describing s-wave neutron bombardment of a complex potential well and a final p-wave state in the real part of the potential. Results of such calculations have been published by Lane and Lynn (1960*b*) and they indicate the $\bar{\sigma}_{\gamma}(\text{r-r})$ is of the same order of magnitude as the potential capture cross-section.

Any successful attempt to identify potential capture must, therefore, take this into account. An attempt by Wasson and Draper (1965) to do this in studying neutron capture by ^{55}Mn showed how severe the problems can be. They observed the ratio of the yield of the 7·26-MeV primary γ-ray (the transition to the $I^{\pi} = 3^{+}$ ground state of ^{56}Mn) to the yield of γ-rays between 2·6 and 4·1 MeV as a function of neutron energy. This was found to peak above the 337 eV ($J^{\pi} = 2^{-}$) neutron resonance and reach a minimum below it. They found that the energy dependence of the ratio could be explained equally well in terms of certain arrangements of resonance-resonance interference alone, of resonance-potential capture interference alone, or by a mixture of both. The only result of certainty was an upper limit of 160 mbarns at 1 eV for the potential capture.

Conditions in cobalt seem to be much more favourable, however. The main problem in interpreting the manganese data was provided by the strong bound level, established by Cote *et al.* (1964*b*) as having parameters $J = 2$, $E_{\lambda} = -2830$ eV, $\gamma^{2}_{\lambda(\mathrm{n})} = 2300$ eV, but with unknown radiation properties. In ^{60}Co the *s*-wave resonances have spin and parity 3^{-} and 4^{-}, and the ground state spin and parity are 5^{+}, so that only the 4^{-} resonances can make electric dipole transitions to it (with energy of 7·49 MeV). A multi-level analysis of the neutron cross-section of ^{59}Co reveals that while there is a rather important bound 3^{-} level (with parameters $E_{\lambda} \approx -80$ eV, $\gamma^{2}_{\lambda(\mathrm{n})} \approx 127$ eV) influencing this cross-section the effect of bound 4^{-} levels is very weak at slow-neutron energies (see Table 1.2). This is confirmed by polarization measurements (Schermer 1963) showing that 22 per cent of the thermal absorption cross-section is due to a 3^{-} level while the remainder is accounted for by the parameters of the 130 eV resonance ($\gamma^{2}_{\lambda(\mathrm{n})} = 200$ eV, $\Gamma_{\lambda(\gamma\mathrm{T})} = 0{\cdot}44$ eV) with spin and parity 4^{-}. The most important 4^{-} resonance above this is the one at 4327 eV with $\gamma^{2}_{\lambda(\mathrm{n})} = 606$ eV and a total radiation width of about 0·5 eV (Moxon 1965). This can hardly contribute more than about 1 mbarn to the cross-section at 1 eV for capture to the ground state, but to confirm this it is still necessary to measure the partial radiation widths of the transition from this resonance. These favourable conditions have led Wasson *et al.* (1966) to make an experimental study of the interference in this transition through the 130-eV resonance. The ratio, normalized to unity, of the cross-section for the ground state transition to the total capture cross-section is shown in Fig. 7.14. There is clear evidence of interference asymmetry through the resonance, and it is constructive on the low-energy side. The calculated curve assuming no potential capture is to be compared with this; it is not constant because the bound 2^- level at -80 eV contributes a varying amount to the total cross-section and nothing to the ground-state transition. The experimental results have to be explained by introducing a non-resonant interfering component of $9{\cdot}2 \pm 2{\cdot}4$ mbarns (at 1 eV). That this is potential capture rather than a contribution from higher resonances is indicated by the fact that it is so much higher than our provisional estimate for the latter effect. Confirmatory evidence is provided by the absence of the interference effect

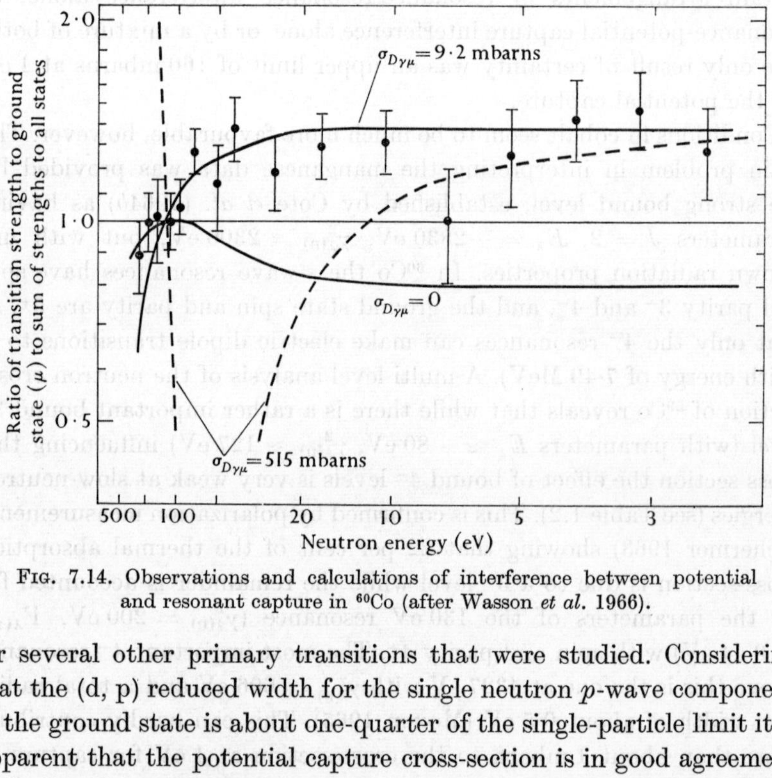

FIG. 7.14. Observations and calculations of interference between potential and resonant capture in ^{60}Co (after Wasson *et al.* 1966).

for several other primary transitions that were studied. Considering that the (d, p) reduced width for the single neutron *p*-wave component of the ground state is about one-quarter of the single-particle limit it is apparent that the potential capture cross-section is in good agreement with the theoretical estimates. In view of what was written above about the sign of the interference it is not certain that the observation of constructive interference below the resonance is significant. If it is, it is certainly in agreement with what we expect from the more sophisticated complex-potential analyses of neutron-scattering data. Here we must invoke first the vibrational coupling which introduces a splitting into the giant resonance in the strength function, and corresponding extra structure in the theoretical potential-capture mass number dependence, and second the target spin, projectile spin coupling, the evidence for which from ^{51}V and ^{59}Co suggests that the $J = 4$ states of ^{60}Co lie just below the second, subsidiary maximum in this giant-resonance structure.

H. MAGNETIC DIPOLE TRANSITIONS

So far in this discussion it has been tacitly assumed that all the significant transitions in neutron capture are electric dipole in nature. The importance of magnetic dipole radiation has now to be considered.

1. Valency-nucleon model

(a) Strong coupling

In this section we consider a valency-nucleon model of the same kind as that discussed in Section F. Using the same expansions for the wave functions X_λ and X_μ and the magnetic dipole operator of eqn. (7.18b), with the nuclear magneton factorized out, we can obtain for the partial width of a magnetic dipole transition to a state μ

$$\Gamma_{\lambda(\gamma\mathrm{M1})} = \frac{16\pi\kappa^3}{9}\sum_{\alpha\mathrm{p}'\mathrm{p}''} C^{\lambda 2}_{\alpha\mathrm{p}'} C^{\mu 2}_{\alpha\mathrm{p}''}\left(\frac{e\hbar}{2Mc}\right)^2 \left|\int_0^\infty \mathrm{d}r\, u_{\mathrm{p}'}(r) u_{\mathrm{p}''}(r)\right|^2 \times \frac{|\langle I_\alpha j', J_\lambda||\mathscr{H}^{(1)}_{\mathrm{M}}||I_\alpha j'', J_\mu\rangle|^2}{(2J_\lambda+1)} \tag{7.71}$$

where the spin component of the operator has the form (Lane and Lynn 1960*a*)

$$\mathscr{H}^{(1)}_{\mathrm{M0}} = \left(\frac{3}{4\pi}\right)^{\frac{1}{2}}\left(\frac{\mu_{\alpha_1}}{I_{\alpha_1}} I_{z\alpha_1} + \frac{\mu_{\alpha_2}}{I_{\alpha_2}} I_{z\alpha_2}\right). \tag{7.72}$$

Here α_1 and α_2 represent the two particles of the channels with particle label α, μ_{α_1} and μ_{α_2} their magnetic moments in nuclear magnetons and $I_{z\alpha_1}$ and $I_{z\alpha_2}$ the z-projection of the intrinsic angular momentum operators. The reduced matrix element may be calculated for the case where the initial and final states have specific channel spins s_λ and s_μ (in general, the physical case has spin-orbit coupling, eqn. 7.71). It is

$$\frac{\langle \alpha\mathrm{p}', J_\lambda||\mathscr{H}^{(1)}_{\mathrm{M}}||\alpha\mathrm{p}'', J_\mu\rangle}{(2J_\lambda+1)^{\frac{1}{2}}} = \left(\frac{3}{4\pi}\right)^{\frac{1}{2}}\delta_{l'l''}\{(2s_\lambda+1)(2J_\mu+1)\}^{\frac{1}{2}} \times W(1s_\mu J_\lambda l'; s_\lambda J_\mu)\{(2I_{\alpha_1}+1)^{\frac{1}{2}}(2s_\mu+1)^{\frac{1}{2}} W(1I_{\alpha_1}s_\lambda I_{\alpha_2}; I_{\alpha_1}s_\mu) \times \mu_{\alpha_1}\left(\frac{I_{\alpha_1}+1}{I_{\alpha_1}}\right)^{\frac{1}{2}} + (2I_{\alpha_2}+1)^{\frac{1}{2}}(2s_\mu+1)^{\frac{1}{2}} W(1I_{\alpha_2}s_\lambda I_{\alpha_1}, I_{\alpha_2}s_\mu) \times (-)^{s_\lambda - s_\mu}\mu_{\alpha_2}\left(\frac{I_{\alpha_2}+1}{I_{\alpha_2}}\right)^{\frac{1}{2}}\Bigg\} \tag{7.73}$$

This must be modified, by weighting with Racah coefficients and summing, for states that contain mixtures of channel spins. In the simplest case of $I_{\alpha_1} = 0$, $l' = l'' = 0$, $I_{\alpha_2} = \frac{1}{2}$ (e.g. even-target ground state and single nucleon)

$$\frac{|\langle J_\lambda || \mathscr{H}_{\mathrm{M}}^{(1)} || J_\mu \rangle|^2}{(2J_\lambda+1)} = \frac{3}{4\pi} \cdot 3\mu_{\alpha_2}^2. \tag{7.74}$$

If the particle α_2 is a neutron this has the numerical value 10·95 $(3/4\pi)$.

The expansion coefficients, $C_{\alpha\mathrm{p}'}^{\lambda 2}$, are now related to the reduced widths, $\gamma_{\lambda(\mathrm{c})}^2$, by the usual equation, eqn. (7.49). It is assumed that the initial state λ is at least as complicated as the final state and hence, for every component $\alpha\mathrm{p}''$ of the final state μ, there is a significant connecting component in the state λ. The average of the partial M1 width may now be written in terms of the average value of the reduced width $\overline{\gamma_{\lambda(\mathrm{c})}^2} = \bar{D}_\lambda s_{\lambda(\mathrm{c})}$, for which the strong-coupling value, from eqn. (6.58c), $\bar{D}_\lambda/(\pi K a)$, is substituted, the average value of a single-particle matrix element and the sum over the coefficients $C_{\alpha\mathrm{p}''}^{\mu 2}$. The last quantity has the value unity from the orthonormality relation, eqn. (6.5). The radial wave functions of the single-particle states p′ and p″ almost completely overlap, even when there is spin-orbit splitting between them, so the radial integral of eqn. (7.71) is approximately unity. For the spin part of the matrix element, eqn. (7.74) is taken to give a reasonable average. The average partial radiation width turns out to be

$$\Gamma_{\lambda(\gamma\mathrm{M1})}(\text{in meV}) \approx 4{\cdot}9 \times 10^{-7} a(\text{in fm}) \varepsilon_\gamma^3(\text{in MeV}) \bar{D}_\lambda(\text{in eV}). \tag{7.75}$$

This is smaller than the corresponding estimate for electric dipole transitions, eqn. (7.54), by a factor of $A^{\frac{1}{3}}/4$; this is not a large factor and suggests that magnetic dipole transitions are rather important in slow neutron capture.

It is supported by experimental evidence on neutron capture by ^{238}U (Jackson 1963, Bergquist, 1965). The ground state for ^{239}U has even parity and is reached by M1 transitions from levels excited in s-wave neutron capture and by E1 transitions from levels excited by p-wave capture. The transition to the ground state is four times more intense in the spectrum of 30-keV capture than it is in the s-wave resonances.

(*b*) *Intermediate coupling*

No explicit calculations have been made for this model, but, qualitatively, it suggests that the magnetic dipole strength, divided by the

ε_γ^3 factor, should be clustered partly at low gamma-ray energies, corresponding to single-particle matrix elements in which p′ and p″ are the same, and partly at energies of the order of 3 to 6 MeV, i.e. the spin-orbit splitting. The energy behaviour of the first part is suggested by a simple model in which the $s_{1/2}$ single-particle state is partially dissolved among initial states by an imaginary potential component and the final state is a pure $s_{1/2}$ state (Lynn 1963*b*), and it is shown in Fig. 7.15.

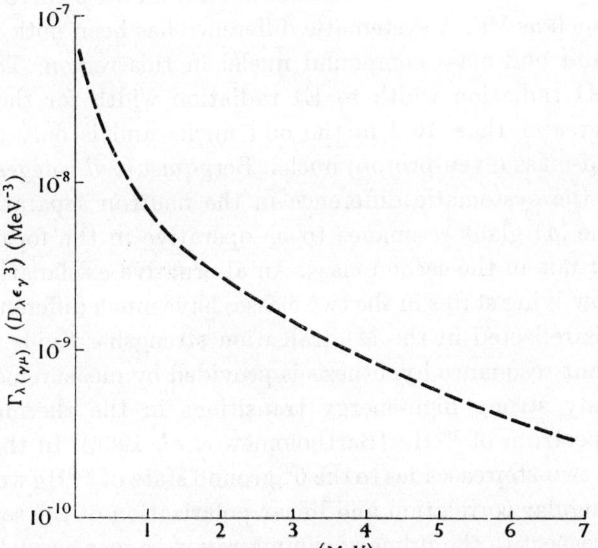

FIG. 7.15. Intermediate-coupling model calculation of partial radiation width for a magnetic dipole transition.

2. Giant-resonance model

The possibility exists that magnetic dipole transitions of nucleons from an empty state to a nearly full subshell of a potential well are a cooperative phenomenon (Mottelson 1960), just as they are for electric dipole transitions. If this is so, a large part of the magnetic dipole strength will be concentrated in a giant resonance. Starfelt (1964) has hypothesized that this is the cause of the anomalously strong high-energy γ-ray spectrum of nuclei like gold and cesium which are close to the filling of the $1i_{13/2}$ and $1h_{11/2}$ subshells respectively. Starfelt finds that a giant resonance in the γ-ray spectrum, of energy 5·5 MeV, width 1·5 MeV and strength 1 per cent of the electric dipole sum rule, is sufficient to allow him to fit both these spectra (see Fig. 7.11). The electric dipole strength was assumed to have the form given in Section E on the photonuclear model.

Support for this point of view is found in the observation of strong, high-energy M1 transitions in many light nuclei in the 2*s*–1*d* shell (Bergquist *et al.* 1965). An example is the *s*-wave 35-keV resonance in the cross-section of ^{27}Al. This resonance has spin and parity 3^+ and exhibits strong transitions to the 2^+ and 3^+ states near ground in ^{28}Al. Such strong M1 transitions are also observed from the *p*-wave resonances of nuclei such as ^{19}F. A systematic difference has been noticed between the odd and odd-mass compound nuclei in this region. The ratio of average M1 radiation width to E1 radiation width for the low-lying states is greater than 10^{-1} in the odd nuclei and is only about 10^{-2} for the odd-mass (even-proton) nuclei. Bergquist *et al.* suggest that this is due to the systematic difference in the neutron separation energy causing the M1 giant resonance to be operative in the former class of nuclei and not in the second class. An alternative explanation may be that the low-lying states in the two classes have much different structure and this is reflected in the M1 transition strengths. Evidence against the M1 giant-resonance hypothesis is provided by measurements on the anomalously strong high-energy transitions in the thermal neutron capture spectrum of ^{199}Hg (Bartholomew *et al.* 1965). In these experiments the two-step cascades to the 0^+ ground state of ^{200}Hg were selected and the angular correlation and linear polarization of the secondary γ-ray with respect to the primary gamma-ray were measured. The results showed that the intermediate states at the termination of the prominent primary γ-rays are of even parity, and since the *s*-wave resonant states in ^{200}Hg have odd parity, the primary transitions are electric dipole.

Finally, to emphasize the very elementary state of the theory of magnetic dipole transitions in slow neutron capture, we draw attention to the observation of Urbanec *et al.* (1965) of a very prominent transition to the 0^+ ground state and 2^+ first excited state of ^{136}Ba from the 24·3-eV resonance in the cross-section of ^{135}Ba. This resonance has been established as due to *s*-wave neutrons by observation of resonance-potential scattering interference (Kim Hi San *et al.* 1965) and to have spin and parity 1^+. Thus the transition is magnetic dipole and is at least forty times stronger than the mean M1 partial radiation width observed for other resonances in this cross-section. This is a much larger factor than one would expect even on the basis of the Porter–Thomas distribution, and at present there is no explanation for it.

I. AVERAGE NEUTRON CAPTURE CROSS-SECTIONS

At neutron energies above several keV in heavy-nuclei individual resonances cannot be resolved and only an average capture cross-section can be measured. Many measurements of such cross-sections are available; they have been made with the principal object of determining the neutron strength function for p-wave resonances. The theory of average capture cross-sections is reviewed here to ascertain the reliability of this method of determining strength functions and the possibility of extracting other interesting quantities from these data.

The average capture cross-section over resonances of spin J and parity π is obtained from eqn. (6.44)

$$\sigma_{\gamma T}(J^\pi) = 2\pi^2 \bar{\lambda}^2 g_J \frac{1}{\bar{D}(J^\pi)} \left\{ \overline{\sum_{s=|I-\frac{1}{2}|}^{I+\frac{1}{2}} \sideset{}{'}\sum_{l=|J-s|}^{J+s} \frac{\Gamma_{(nsl)}(J^\pi)\Gamma_{(\gamma T)}(J^\pi)}{\Gamma_{(T)}(J^\pi)}} \right\} \tag{7.76}$$

where the prime on the sum over l indicates that only those values consistent with parity conservation, $(-)^l \pi_T = \pi$, are included. For neutron energies below 50 keV, only one term will appear in practice in the sum over l, either s-wave or p-wave depending on the parity π. The total width $\Gamma_{(T)}(J^\pi)$ is

$$\Gamma_{(T)}(J^\pi) = \sideset{}{'}\sum_{s,l} \Gamma_{(nsl)}(J) + \sideset{}{''}\sum_{n's'l'} \Gamma_{(n's'l')}(J^\pi) + \Gamma_{(\gamma T)}(J^\pi) \tag{7.77}$$

where $\Gamma_{(n's'l')}$ is the width for an inelastic process which leaves the residual nucleus in a given excited state, the emitted neutron having orbital angular momentum l' consistent with parity conservation and the exit channel spin being s'. It is usual to write average cross-sections explicitly in terms of strength functions by introducing the mean widths, using eqns. (6.45) and (6.47), and dividing by $\bar{D}(J^\pi)$. The average capture cross-section over many resonances is

$$\bar{\sigma}_{\gamma T} = 2\pi^2 \bar{\lambda}^2 \sum_{J,\pi} g_J \times \frac{\sum_{s=|I-\frac{1}{2}|}^{I+\frac{1}{2}} \sideset{}{'}\sum_{l=|J-s|}^{J+s} (\bar{\Gamma}_{(nsl)}(J^\pi)/\bar{D}(J^\pi))(\Gamma_{(\gamma T)}(J^\pi)/\bar{D}(J^\pi))}{\sideset{}{'}\sum_{sl} (\Gamma_{(nsl)}(J^\pi)/\bar{D}(J^\pi)) + \sideset{}{''}\sum_{n's'l'} \Gamma_{(n's'l')}(J^\pi)/\bar{D}(J^\pi) + \Gamma_{(\gamma T)}(J^\pi)/\bar{D}(J^\pi)} \times \mathscr{S}_\gamma^{(1+\delta)}(J^\pi). \tag{7.78}$$

Below 50 keV, $\delta = 0$ when the parity is that of the target nucleus. It is either zero or one, for opposite parity, depending on whether unit orbital angular momentum can be coupled with one or both values of the channel spin to give the total angular momentum. It is to be noticed that in eqn. (7.78) the components of the p-wave neutron strength function are not weighted simply by g_J as they are in the total cross-section. Furthermore, the weighting depends on energy, other compound-nucleus parameters and the target-nucleus spin.

The assumptions that have to be made to extract the p-wave strength function from the average capture cross-section at a particular energy, e.g. 27 keV which is the energy of photoneutrons generated by a Sb-Be source, are, (a) that the s-wave strength function and level density are known from resonance spectroscopy, (b) the level densities for the same angular momentum but opposite parity are equal, (c) the level density is proportional to $(2J+1)$, (d) the total radiation width is independent of the spin and parity of the level. Assumption (b) is probably satisfied for most nuclei to within 10 per cent and perhaps assumption (c) also. Assumption (d) can be wrong by a factor of 2 or more; this is apparent on theoretical grounds, as shown in our discussion of the valency-nucleon model, and is supported by experimental evidence (Jackson 1963).

Some of these assumptions can be discarded if the average capture cross-section is available as a function of energy. The difficulty remains, however, that the spin-orbit splitting of the p-wave strength function gives rise to an energy dependence of the weighted average strength function (Margolis 1963). For these reasons, none of the p-wave strength functions that have been analysed from capture cross-section data are unambiguous, and these data have had to be discarded in the discussion of Chapter VI, Section D.7. It seems to be much better to obtain p-wave neutron strength functions from, say, average transmission data and to use these in the analysis of capture data for the extraction of information about p-wave resonance radiation widths.

VIII

NEUTRON-INDUCED FISSION

A. FISSION THEORIES

1. Liquid-drop model

NUCLEAR fission is a vast topic and we cannot hope to present anything like an adequate survey in the space available here. Some of the features of slow neutron-induced fission are, however, of particular interest and have shed much light on important aspects of the fission phenomenon, making it possible to write about these features as an almost self-contained topic. We begin with a very brief survey of the development of fission theory.

The initial discovery of the radiochemical evidence for fission (Hahn and Strassmann 1939) led Bohr and Wheeler (1939) to employ the liquid-drop model to study the energy systematics of the process. The analysis of the mass systematics of stable and near-stable nuclei shows that a stable nucleus has five main components of energy: these are terms proportional to the mass number A, a Coulomb repulsion energy term proportional to $Z^2/A^{1/3}$, a term depending on the neutron–proton symmetry factor $(A-2Z)$, a term proportional to $A^{2/3}$, and an empirically observed term depending on the odd or even character of the nucleon numbers. These terms are summarized in the Weizsâcker (1935) semi-empirical formula for the nuclear ground-state energies:

$$E = -u_V A + \frac{u_C Z(Z-1)}{A^{1/3}} + \frac{u_\tau (A-2Z)^2}{4A} + u_S A^{2/3} + \delta(Z, A). \qquad (8.1)$$

A recent analysis of available data (Green 1959) gives the following values for the coefficients of the formula: $u_V = 15{\cdot}826$ MeV, $u_C = 0{\cdot}7183$ MeV, $u_\tau = 94{\cdot}068$ MeV, $u_S = 17{\cdot}970$ MeV; δ is the function described in eqn. (4.40). From this formula it is possible to show that the energy of a heavy nucleus is considerably greater than the sum of the energies of two medium-weight nuclei of the same total mass. The energy difference is of the order of 200 MeV. The observed near-stability of the heavy nuclei indicates that their potential energy must go through a maximum as a heavy nucleus is deformed and eventually split into two smaller nuclei. The large energy difference between these initial and final states comes principally from the term in $A^{2/3}$ and the Coulomb energy terms of eqn. (8.1). Bohr and Wheeler (1939) took the step of assuming that these terms were the surface energy and Coulomb energy of an electrically-charged incompressible liquid drop. They initiated the study of the properties of such a liquid drop with respect to its division into two or more parts.

The ratio of the strength of the disrupting Coulomb forces to the strength of the restoring surface-tension force is proportional to the quantity Z^2/A. When this quantity has the value $(Z^2/A)_{\text{crit}} = 2u_s/u_c$ (numerically, this is 50, using the constants of Green 1959; see eqn. (4.71b)) the spherical liquid drop is in unstable equilibrium; any small deformation will cause it to undergo fission. The ratio of Z^2/A with respect to this critical quantity $(Z^2/A)_{\text{crit}}$ is denoted by the parameter x. A drop with a value of x less than unity is stable to small deformations from spherical; the lower the value of x the greater is its stability. When x is less than 0·34 the drop has absolute stability.

Much effort has been expended in studying the potential energy surface of the deformed liquid drop. When a drop with x smaller than unity (but greater than 0·384) is deformed the rate of increase of surface energy is at first greater than the rate of decrease of Coulomb energy. Eventually a critical deformation is reached at which this state of affairs begins to be reversed; the potential-energy curve has reached a maximum, beyond which scission of the drop into two parts is energetically favourable (see Fig. 8.1b). There is a multitude of possible paths of deformation, of course, and this is what makes the theoretical study so difficult. Most studies (e.g. Bohr and Wheeler 1939, Frankel and Metropolis 1947, Cohen and Swiatecki 1962) have employed the coefficients of a spherical harmonic analysis of the drop surface (eqn. (4.69)) as the set of parameters describing deformation. If the potential energy is plotted as contours on a surface using as coordinates the two principal parameters β_2 and β_4 of a symmetric deformation, a col or saddle point becomes apparent (see Fig. 8.1(a)). A similar saddle point would be apparent in a contour plot on a many-dimensional surface defined by coordinates which included also the higher order coefficients of the expansion. It is the principal object of liquid-drop calculations to find the energy at the saddle point with respect to the energy of the undeformed drop, for this is the threshold of the fission reaction.

It is beyond the scope of this book to give any details of the liquid-drop calculations and only the very briefest summary of results will be given here. For the values of x appropriate to the heavy fissionable nuclei ($x \sim 0{\cdot}7$) the fission thresholds calculated from the liquid-drop model are of the order of 10 to 15 MeV; the experimentally observed thresholds are at about 5 to 6 MeV above the ground state of the fissioning nuclei. The values of β_2, the principal deformation parameter, at the saddle point range from 0·74 for $x = 0{\cdot}74$ (Frankel and Metropolis 1947) to 1·72 for $x = 0{\cdot}68$ (Cohen and Swiatecki 1962). It is in just this region of x that Cohen and Swiatecki have discovered that there are at least two families of unstable equilibrium shapes for liquid drops. One of these families is characterized by a thin neck and the other by a thick neck. Between the two configurations there is a slight minimum of potential energy. The total barrier through which the system must pass on its way to fission is thus very broad. It appears also that the liquid drop is stable at the saddle point against small asymmetric deformations (Cohen and Swiatecki 1962) but it is necessary to bear in mind that the potential energy surface of a charged liquid drop remains inadequately studied.

The dynamics of the charged liquid drop have been studied even less. A solution of the hydrodynamic equations for the special case of $x = 0{\cdot}72$ with 50 MeV kinetic energy injected into the P_2 mode has been given by Hill (1958) and for this case a time development of the shape of the drop is available. The details of the shapes concern us rather less, however, than an account of the reaction rate. A semi-classical formula based on the methods of statistical mechanics (Wigner 1938) by treating the fissioning nucleus as a monomolecular reaction proceeding through a 'transition state' at the saddle point gives the ratio of the mean fission width $\Gamma_{(\mathrm{F})}$ of the states of the excited nucleus (with a defined set of good quantum numbers) to the spacing, $\bar{D}$, of these states (Bohr and Wheeler 1939):

$$\frac{\Gamma_{(\mathrm{F})}}{\bar{D}} = \frac{N}{2\pi}. \tag{8.2}$$

Here, the quantity N is the number of levels in the 'transition state' energetically available to the reaction:

$$N = \int_{E_{\mathrm{F}}}^{E} \mathrm{d}E'\rho^*(E'-E_{\mathrm{F}}) \tag{8.3}$$

where ρ^* is the density of the levels at the saddle point and E_{F} is the fission threshold energy. Each level corresponds to the nucleus, or quantal drop, being in a particular state of internal excitation, the remainder of the total energy E being partly potential energy and partly kinetic energy of deformation. In modern terminology the term 'transition state' is usually applied to these individual levels; this is in distinction to the usage of Wigner and of Bohr and Wheeler who used the term to describe the overall wave-function of the system as it passes over the saddle point. From here onward we use the modern definition of the term. To be more precise, the transition state in this sense is really the product of a particular state function of internal excitation

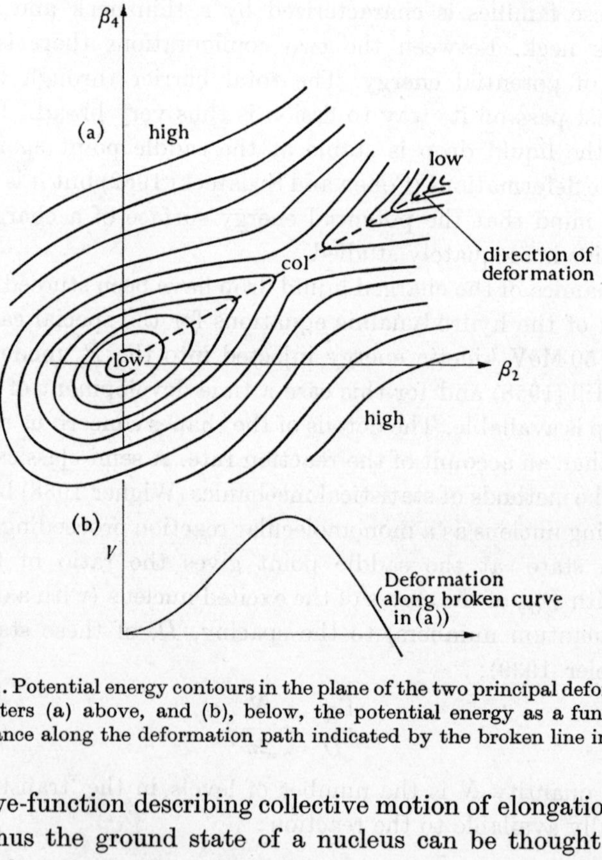

FIG. 8.1. Potential energy contours in the plane of the two principal deformation parameters (a) above, and (b), below, the potential energy as a function of distance along the deformation path indicated by the broken line in (a).

and a wave-function describing collective motion of elongation towards fission. Thus the ground state of a nucleus can be thought of as the product of an internal ground state function and the lowest wave-function in the potential well of deformation; the latter function governs the rate of spontaneous fission. In contrast to this, to say that a highly excited state fissions through the 'ground' transition state implies that although the nucleus is in its internal ground state during fission the deformation wave-function is a much more highly excited one.

In the study of a quantal liquid drop the effects of barrier penetration have to be considered. If the number of available transition states N is large then the effect of barrier penetration can be ignored. If N is zero on the other hand ($E < E_F$) tunnelling of the barrier can occur. A theoretical estimate (Frankel and Metropolis 1947) of the Gamow factor T_F for tunnelling is based on the liquid-drop calculation with irrotational motion through the saddle point and $x = 0{\cdot}74$:

$$T_F = e^{18{\cdot}1\,(E-E_F)}. \tag{8.4}$$

Penetration through the barrier at energies either greater or less than the threshold value has been considered by Hill and Wheeler (1953). If the potential barrier is assumed to have the form of an inverted one-dimensional harmonic oscillator, the tunnelling or transmission factor is

$$T_F = \frac{1}{1+\exp\{2\pi(E_F-E)/\hbar\omega\}} \tag{8.5}$$

where ω is the circular frequency of the harmonic oscillator. Estimates of $\hbar\omega$ based on the mass parameter for surface vibrations of the liquid drop of order $\lambda = 2$, together with an expression for the curvature of the barrier, vary strongly with x (Wilets 1964), showing a maximum of 0·85 MeV at $x = 0{\cdot}83$ and falling to zero in the region of $x \sim 0{\cdot}7$ where the barrier becomes very broad (Cohen and Swiatecki 1962). The result of Frankel and Metropolis (1947), eqn. (8.4), is in agreement with these values, and so is the factor, $\hbar\omega \approx 0{\cdot}38$ MeV, calculated from the spontaneous fission half-life of ^{238}U ($x \approx 0{\cdot}725$) (Halpern 1959).

2. The unified model

(a) *Intrinsic excitations in a deformed potential*

Despite the qualitative successes of the liquid-drop model in explaining the fission phenomenon it was apparent by the early 1950s that the success of the shell model of nuclear structure made it desirable to investigate the role of individual-particle motion in nuclear fission (Hill and Wheeler 1953). It was soon recognized that a few nucleons outside a closed nucleon shell structure exert a strong polarizing force on the shell core (Rainwater 1950). This force is sufficiently strong that for a few extra-shell nucleons the nucleus is 'soft' to deformations although it is still spherical at stable equilibrium. For rather more extra-shell nucleons the nucleus is permanently deformed in stable equilibrium. The shell-model study of the ground state properties of nuclei was completed by calculating the single-particle states of nucleons in a deformed potential well. The total energy of the nucleons in the well was then minimized as a function of deformation to obtain the preferred deformation of the nucleus and hence its ground-state spin

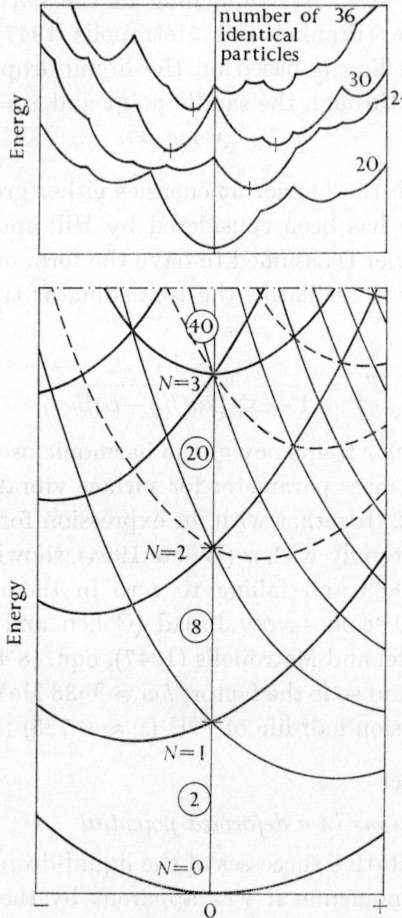

FIG. 8.2. Energies of single nucleon orbits in a harmonic oscillator potential without spin-orbit coupling as a function of spheroidal deformation (below) (after Moszkowski 1957). Numbers in circles indicate number of nucleons required to fill the orbits below. In the upper part of the diagram the total energy for given numbers of nucleons occupying the lowest possible orbits is shown and the positions of the minima are indicated by crosses.

and quadrupole moment (Nilsson 1955). These were found to agree largely with the data.

The energies of a typical set of nucleon orbitals as functions of the deformation parameter are shown in Fig. 8.2 for a harmonic oscillator potential without spin-orbit coupling. The lines in the upper part of this diagram are the minimum total energy (for 20, 24, 30, 36 nucleons) and are therefore essentially the potential energy curve of the nuclear model as a function of deformation. Two conditions are necessary so that the model may be valid in this sense and also satisfy the adiabatic condition that collective motions of the potential well have a period much greater than that of the individual nucleon motion. One is that there should be residual forces between the nucleons so that level crossings as shown in Fig. 8.2 do not occur (Hill and Wheeler, 1953). The result of perturbing forces is to smooth out the level surfaces and to cause transitions between the levels in the time development of the system. The transition probability between orbits a and b, integrated over all time, is given by

$$T_{ab} = 1 - \exp\left(-\frac{4\pi|H'_{ab}|^2}{\hbar|\dot{\beta}_2 d(E_a - E_b)/d\beta_2|}\right) \tag{8.6}$$

where H'_{ab} is the matrix element of the perturbing part of the Hamiltonian and $\dot{\beta}_2$ is the rate of deformation. The other condition is that the potential energy curve should not exhibit sharp curvature.

(*b*) *Collective excitations*

Within this deformed potential well one or more nucleons can be placed in higher single-particle orbits to form excited states of the nucleus. In addition to these intrinsic excited states there are excitations that correspond to collective motions of the nucleus as a whole (Bohr and Mottelson 1953, Hill and Wheeler 1953). Such collective motions appear to be due to long-range components of the residual nuclear forces (Elliott 1958). The short-range components of these forces lead to a highly correlated wave-function amongst the nucleons that are paired together in shell-model orbits (Bohr *et al.* 1958). This correlated state is lowered in energy below other states that correspond to occupation of the same single-particle orbits but without pairing. The energy gap is readily apparent in the spectra of heavy even nuclei, the 0^+ ground state being separated from the intrinsic states by about 1 MeV. The separation of the intrinsic states is of the order of 100 keV. In the spectra of odd-mass nuclei the gap contains single-particle intrinsic excitations and in odd nuclei it contains two-particle excitations.

The energy of each of these excitations, intrinsic or collective, will depend on the deformation of the nucleus. It is expected that each energy surface will resemble qualitatively the liquid-drop potential energy shown schematically in Fig. 8.1. For the heavy fissionable nuclei ($A > 233$) the minimum of the lowest energy surface, that of the ground state, occurs for $\beta_2 \approx 0{\cdot}3$, corresponding to a prolate spheroid. At the much greater deformation of the saddle point the energy surfaces form a set of transition states that govern the rate and manner of the decay of the nucleus through fission.

(c) *The transition-state spectrum of an even nucleus*

It was A. Bohr (1956) who first drew attention to the dependence of the fission process on the expected properties of the transition states. Wheeler (1963) has tabulated the properties of the collective transition states, and we summarize these here. In an even compound nucleus the lowest transition state at the fission threshold energy E_{F} has angular momentum and parity quantum numbers $I^{\pi} = 0^{+}$, and its quantum number K for the projection of angular momentum along the nuclear symmetry axis is 0. Associated with this state, which we shall refer to as the 'ground' state, is a rotational band of states all with $K = 0$ and angular momenta and parity, $I^{\pi} = 2^{+}, 4^{+}, 6^{+} \ldots$ This sequence of spins is limited to even values so that the overall wave-function of the system is invariant to an inversion of the nuclear surface through the centre of the nucleus. The symmetric top wave-function that describes the rotation of a cylindrically symmetric body is just the spherical harmonic $Y_M^{(I)}$ when $K = 0$, and the nuclear wave-function is the product of this and the intrinsic wave-function. The inversion invariance requirement, therefore, is that $Y_M^{(I)}$ has the same parity as the latter, which is even for the ground state. The energies of the rotational states relative to 'ground' are

$$E^{I} = \frac{\hbar^2}{2\mathscr{I}_{\perp}} I(I+1) \tag{8.7}$$

where $\mathscr{I}_{\perp}$ is the moment of inertia of the system about an axis perpendicular to the symmetry axis. In their shapes of stable equilibrium the heavy nuclei have moments of inertia equal to about half the value of an equivalent rigid body. At the saddle point the nucleus is much more deformed and should, in consequence, have a much larger moment of inertia; according to the liquid-drop model it should be twice as large, for uranium, as the spherical rigid body value. The separation of the transition states comprising the lowest rotational band should be correspondingly smaller than observed in the heavy nuclei spectra, the 2^+ state being at about 11 keV and the 4^+ state at about 37 keV above the 0^+ threshold.

Above this rotational band a sequence of collective vibrations is expected. In the spectra of the heavy nuclei three types of vibration have been identified. The first type is the β-vibration corresponding to collective motion about the equilibrium deformation along the axis of symmetry. Collective motion along the axis of symmetry is the principal feature of the act of fission, however, so this vibration does not have any counterpart among the transition states. The β-vibration is, in fact, a state that can spontaneously fission through the 'ground' transition state. It is explicitly a nearly pure transition state, being a product of the ground state internal function and a function of one phonon of collective vibration in the elongation parameter; the leakage of the latter through the potential barrier governs the rate of spontaneous fission. The second type is the γ-vibration corresponding to periodic collective deformation about axial symmetry—a wave crest on the surface running around the cylindrical symmetry axis. The quantum numbers of the one-phonon state are $I^\pi = 2^+$, $K = 2$. Like the ground state it is the parent of a rotational band but, unlike it, the spins of these rotational states are not limited to even values. At twice the energy of the one-phonon state there should be a two-phonon state with $I^\pi = 4^+$, $K = 4$ and, lying in a small energy range above this, there should be another rotational band with $K = 4$, $I^\pi = 5^+, 6^+ \ldots$ At the same energy there should be a two-phonon state and associated rotational band with $K = 0$, $I^\pi = 0^+, 2^+, 4^+, \ldots$ At still higher energies there will occur multi-phonon states and their rotational bands. The energy of the γ-phonon E_γ is observed to vary from $\sim$790 keV for ^{232}Th to $\sim$1200 keV for ^{244}Cm. Wheeler (1963) suggests that it should be greater at the saddle point, but observations on the angular distribution of fission fragments from the (d, pf) reaction have been interpreted to give $E_\gamma \sim 0{\cdot}7$ MeV (Britt *et al.* 1963).

The third type of vibration is associated with octupole deformation of a spherical body. It is observed in the spectra of heavy nuclei as a state with $K = 0$, $I^\pi = 1^-$ and is interpreted as one phonon of a mode in which material is transferred from one end of the prolate body to the other; this is known popularly as the sloshing mode or mass asymmetry vibration. It stems from the term in $Y_0^{(3)}$ in the spherical harmonic expansion of a surface about its undeformed value. In the spherical nucleus this is a degenerate member of the octupole vibration at about 3-MeV excitation. With cylindrical extension of the nucleus it falls in energy, and at stable equilibrium in the actinide nuclei it has energies E_S ranging from 230 keV (^{226}Th) to 788 keV (^{234}U). A rotational band is associated with it, the members having $I^{\pi} = 3^-, 5^-, \ldots$ The limitation of the rotational band to odd members is again a consequence of inversion invariance, the non-rotational part of the wave-function this time having odd parity. Yet another vibration with relatively low energy is expected at the saddle point; this is the 'bending' vibration with $K = 1$, $I^{\pi} = 1^-$ (Wheeler 1963). It stems from the $Y_1^{(3)}$ and $Y_{-1}^{(3)}$ terms in the expansion of a deformed surface about a spherical shape, and its classical analogy is a wave running about the surface at an angle $\text{acos}\{1/\sqrt{(12)}\}$ to the cylindrical deformation axis. The wave has reflection symmetry across a plane perpendicular to this axis, so there is no sense in which material is being transferred from one end of the body to the other, as in the mass asymmetry vibration. Its associated rotational band has members with $I^{\pi} = 2^-, 3^-, 4^-, \ldots$ All that is known about its energy is that it should be considerably less than the 3 MeV of the octupole vibration of spherical nuclei from which it is derived, and that a band with odd parity and $K = 1$ has been observed at 954 keV in ^{230}Th. One would expect this energy to further decrease with increasing extension of the nucleus towards the saddle point.

Little that is definite can be said about the multi-phonon states of these modes. There appear to be two possible interpretations of the sloshing mode. One is that the nucleus is soft to deformations in β_3, the octupole deformation parameter (see the expansion eqn. (6.111)), the potential well in this coordinate being of harmonic oscillator form. The 0^+ state is the zero-vibrational level of this oscillator, the 1^- state is the first vibrational level, and at an energy above this equal to the difference between the 0^+ and 1^- states there should be a second vibrational level, and so on. Each of these higher levels will carry a rotational band which consists of either even or odd spins depending on the parity of the parent state. The second interpretation is that the nucleus is stable for a non-zero value of β_3 (i.e. is pear-shaped); the potential energy curve as a function of β_3 shows a local maximum at $\beta_3 = 0$. Suppose that this maximum were extremely high as shown in Fig. 8.3(a). Then the wave-function would be zero at $\beta_3 = 0$ and would show two maxima at the positions of stable equilibrium. The relative signs of the two portions of the wave-function curve would be immaterial to the eigenvalue; in other words the wave-function is degenerate, there being a symmetric form and an anti-symmetric form. If the intermediate maximum at $\beta_3 = 0$ were now reduced to a finite value the degeneracies between these two forms would be removed, the symmetric state being lowered in energy. It can be shown that the energy difference between the two states is equal to the product of Planck's constant and the tunnelling frequency between the two wells (Strutinsky 1956). Higher

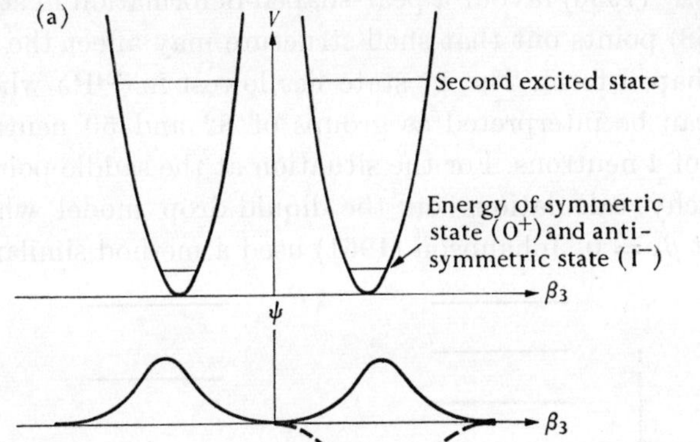

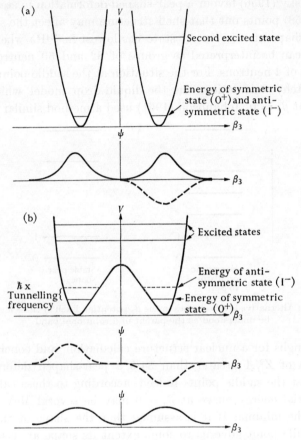

FIG. 8.3. Wave-functions in the β_3-potential.

excited states of the system would be similarly based on the excited states of the individual minima of Fig. 8.3(a). Each excited state of Fig. 8.3(a) is split into two components when the maximum between the wells is reduced to a finite value. In this picture the excited states above the 1^- level are expected to lie considerably higher than the energy separation of the 0^+ and 1^- levels. A comparison of the two interpretations is shown in Fig. 8.4.

It is not certain which interpretation is valid. For stable nuclei

Lee and Inglis (1957) have estimated from a perturbation calculation based on the spheroidal harmonic oscillator potential that the nucleus is merely soft to pear-shaped deformation. They point out, however, that they ignore spin-orbit coupling in the nucleon state and that this is a factor which would favour a stable deformation. The calculations of Strutinsky (1956) favour a pear-shaped deformation in stable nuclei. Inglis (1958) points out that shell structure may affect the stability of the pear-shaped form. The 1^- state lies lowest in ^{224}Ra where the 136 neutrons can be interpreted as groups of 82 and 50 neutrons joined by a neck of 4 neutrons. For the situation at the saddle point there are some sketchy calculations on the liquid-drop model which favour stability at $\beta_3 = 0$. Johannson (1961) used a method similar to that of

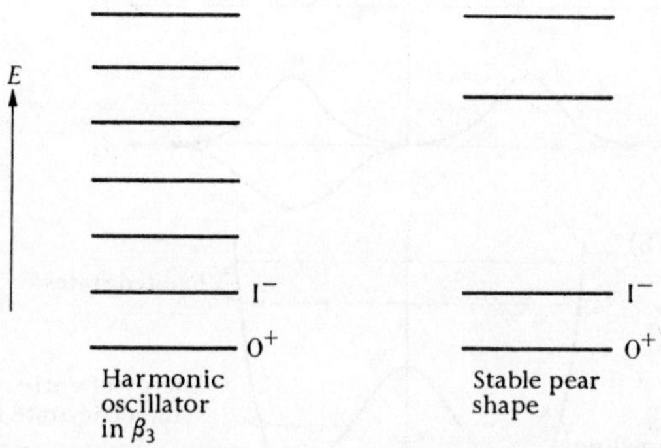

FIG. 8.4. Alternative level schemes in the β_3-potential. Each of these levels is to be understood as the parent of a rotational band.

Lee and Inglis for a nuclear structure calculation, and concluded that for values of Z^2/A greater than 34·3 a pear-shaped deformation is favoured at the saddle point; indeed, according to these calculations, the potential energy curve at $\beta_3 = 0$ may be several MeV above its value in the minima. If it is assumed that the shape of the nucleus at the saddle point governs to some extent its shape at scission, then the observed fission mass yields are in accord with Johansson's work. According to this assumption the mass yield curve is related to the β_3-dependence of the wave-function of the transition state, the maxima and minima of the mass ratios corresponding to the maxima and minima of the wave-function. The spontaneous fission of the heavy even nuclei must proceed mainly through the $K = 0$, $I^\pi = 0^+$ transition state. Symmetric mass yield is observed to be very infrequent in these reactions suggesting a minimum of the transition state wave-function at $\beta_3 = 0$. This corresponds to Fig. 8.3 with a high maximum in the potential energy curve at $\beta_3 = 0$. The second and higher excited states of the mass asymmetry mode therefore lie at a very much higher energy than the first excited state.

Other collective transition states can be formed from combinations of these types, but there are probably not many that can be distinguished by their energy from the levels of intrinsic excitation. In the spectrum of an even nucleus the intrinsic states lie above the ground state by an energy gap, 2Δ. Above this energy the intrinsic states are dense. Little can be said about their specific properties even at stable deformation and virtually nothing about them at the saddle point. The magnitude of the energy gap is of the order of 1 MeV at stable deformation but appears to be rather greater at the saddle point (the evidence for this is described in Section C.3). This is perhaps not surprising since theoretical calculations of the energy gap in infinite nuclear matter indicate that it is very small, suggesting that it is a surface phenomenon (Blatt and Thompson 1963).

(*d*) *The transition-state spectrum of an odd-mass nucleus*

In an odd mass nucleus the lowest transition states are states of intrinsic excitation of a single nucleon, and their associated rotational bands. In principle, the order of the single-particle states can be calculated by extension of Nilsson's spheroidal potential model with spin-orbit interaction to higher deformation. This has been done by Johansson (1959) who has calculated the neutron levels for neutron numbers from 139 to 160 (Fig. 8.5) and the proton levels for proton numbers from 91 to 106 up to deformations $\delta \approx 0{\cdot}6$. He calculates that saddle-point deformations should range from about $\delta = 0{\cdot}41$ for ^{249}Cf to $\delta = 0{\cdot}51$ for ^{235}U. The deformation parameter δ is related to β_2 by the expression $\delta \approx 0{\cdot}95\, \beta_2\, \{1-0{\cdot}48\, \beta_2+O\,(\beta^2)\}$.

(*e*) *Low-energy fission and the characteristics of the transition states*

Bohr (1956) used these considerations of the properties of the transition states to explain a number of fission phenomena. A compound-nucleus state at moderate or high excitation energy is expected to have only two constants of motion, total angular momentum I and parity π. The very many modes of motion of the nucleus in this state include the deformation of the nucleus towards the saddle point. With increasing deformation the nucleus makes transitions from one energy surface of the unified model to another at a rate which would be governed by eqn. (8.6) if the residual forces were small. Finally, at the saddle point, a

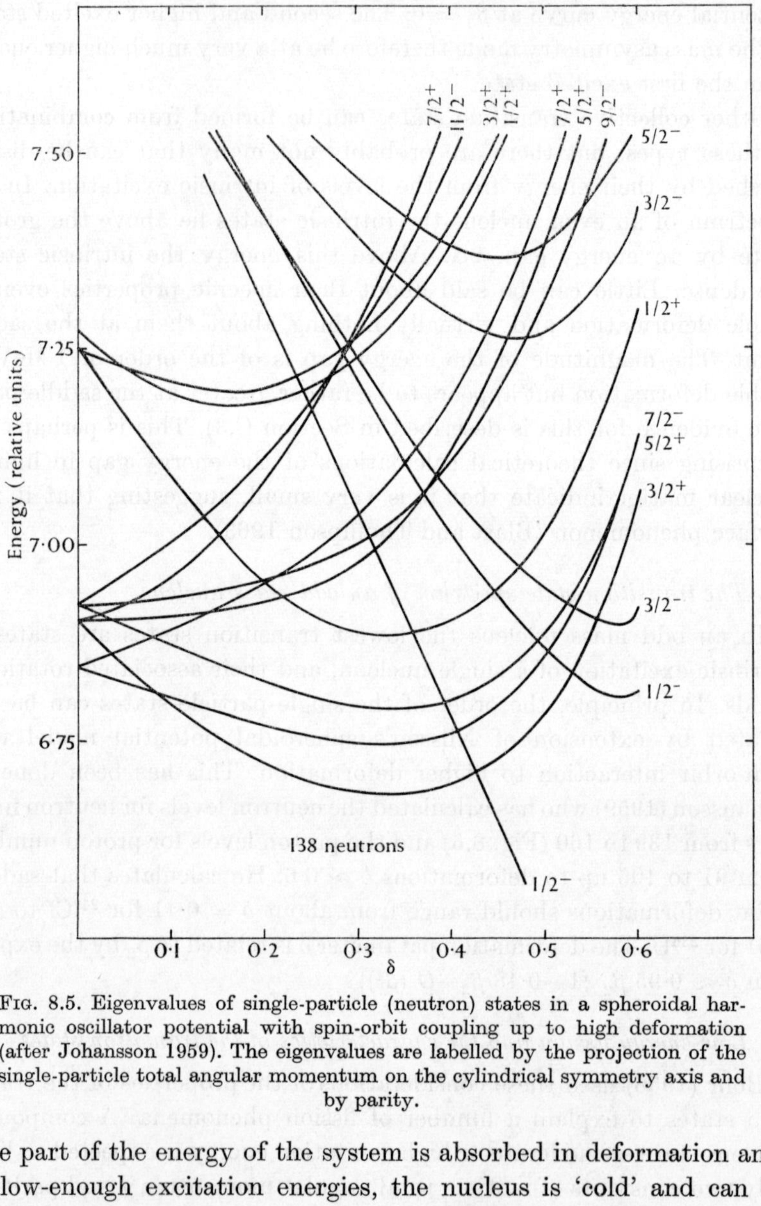

FIG. 8.5. Eigenvalues of single-particle (neutron) states in a spheroidal harmonic oscillator potential with spin-orbit coupling up to high deformation (after Johansson 1959). The eigenvalues are labelled by the projection of the single-particle total angular momentum on the cylindrical symmetry axis and by parity.

large part of the energy of the system is absorbed in deformation and, for low-enough excitation energies, the nucleus is 'cold' and can be regarded as being in one or a few energetically available transition states. In making its transitions from one unified-model energy surface to another the nucleus conserves total angular momentum and parity. Consequently, the saddle-point transition states that are available to a given compound-nucleus state must have the same total angular momentum and parity as the latter; the available transition states in low energy fission are limited by the available angular momentum and parity as well as by energy.

Perhaps the most striking phenomenon explained by Bohr was the angular distribution of the products resulting from the photo-fission (just above threshold) of even nuclei. The compound states which are strongly excited in photo-absorption by such nuclei have spin and parity quantum numbers 1^- (electric dipole absorption) and angular momentum projection on the direction of incident photons, $M = \pm 1$. The lowest transition state with $I^\pi = 1^-$ is believed to be the sloshing vibration with K, the projection of angular momentum along the nuclear symmetry axis, equal to zero. Thus, in the transition state, the fissioning nucleus will be aligned preferentially with its axis of symmetry perpendicular to the photon direction. Since K is expected to remain a good quantum number as the nucleus passes from the saddle point to scission the angular distribution of the fission products will also favour the direction perpendicular to the photon beam. The second transition state with $I^\pi = 1^-$ is the bending vibration with $K = 1$. The nuclear symmetry axis is aligned along the photon direction in this case and the fission product distribution follows suit. Thus, as the photon energy is raised so that the transmission factors through both transition states approach unity the character of the angular distribution of the fission products approaches isotropy. This behaviour has been experimentally observed, e.g. by Baerg *et al.* (1959), and interpreted to give the energy difference between the mass asymmetry vibration and the bending vibration at the saddle point. The fission product angular distribution resulting from fast neutron-induced fission and other particle-induced fission, such as the (d, pf) and (t, pf) reactions, have been explained in a similar manner (Bohr 1956, Wilets and Chase 1956). These and other successes give heartening confirmation of the usefulness of the unified model in understanding fission. The details of its application to slow neutron induced fission are given in Section D.

B. CROSS-SECTION FORMALISM

1. General remarks

In the slow neutron cross-sections of non-fissile nuclei the resonances are nearly always found to be very much narrower than the spacing between them. In consequence, the single-level Breit–Wigner formula is usually a very good approximation and is used as the basis for the analysis of nearly all the cross-section data on these nuclei. In contrast, the resonances in the cross-sections of the fissile nuclei are found to be little narrower than their spacing. Attempts to make detailed single-level fits to the cross-sections have usually failed (Sailor 1956, Lynn and Pattenden 1956). Analysis of these data must rely on many-level formulae and in this section we discuss some of the more useful results.

Most of the commonly employed many-level formulae start from the general R-matrix (1947) formalism. Of the limited forms of the R-matrix theory that still require the inversion of a matrix there are two useful classes available. One class is Thomas' (1955) channel reduction of the R-matrix expression using the elimination method of Teichmann and Wigner (1951) (see Chapter II, Section E.2). The expression for the elements of the reduced R-matrix for the retained channels, eqn. (2.60), was derived on the assumptions that the partial widths of all the channels to which explicit reference is eliminated are very much smaller than the level spacing and that their amplitudes are uncorrelated in sign.

As an alternative to inverting a channel matrix it is possible to rewrite the formalism so that a level matrix has to be inverted (Lane and Thomas 1958). The result is quoted in Chapter II, Section E.1, eqns. (2.48), (2.49). This form is of advantage when only a few levels need be considered in the analysis. Its particular application to slow neutron fission cross-sections is described below.

2. Application of the level matrix formalism to fission

The two more general classes of many-level formalism have their own advantages and disadvantages. According to Bohr's unified-model theory of fission, slow neutron-induced fission should behave as if it were a few-channel phenomenon and Thomas' reduced R-matrix treatment would seem to be ideally suited to its treatment; it was first applied by Reich and Moore (1958). The difficulty, however, is that the number of fission channels is not known *a priori*. This difficulty is avoided by the level-matrix formalism which was applied to the analysis of neutron-induced fission by Vogt (1958). The expression required for the fission cross-section σ_{F} is the sum over the cross-sections for the separate fission channels f:

$$\sigma_{\mathrm{F}} = \pi\lambda\!\!\!^{-2}\sum_{J} g_J \sum_{\mathrm{f}} |U_{\mathrm{nf}}|^2 \tag{8.8a}$$

$$= \pi\lambda\!\!\!^{-2}\sum_{J} g_J \sum_{\mathrm{f}} \left| \tfrac{1}{2}\sum_{\lambda\mu} \Gamma^{\frac{1}{2}}_{\lambda(\mathrm{n})}\Gamma^{\frac{1}{2}}_{\mu(\mathrm{f})} A_{\lambda\mu}(J) \right|^2. \tag{8.8b}$$

Vogt has shown that it is not necessary to know the values of the separate fission width amplitudes $\Gamma^{\frac{1}{2}}_{\mu(\mathrm{f})}$. The parameters required in addition to the single-level parameters, the neutron widths $\Gamma_{\lambda(\mathrm{n})}$, the total radiation widths $\Gamma_{\lambda(\gamma\mathrm{T})}$ and the total fission widths $\Gamma_{\lambda(\mathrm{f})}$, can be taken to be the $N(N-1)/2$ off-diagonal components of the N-order matrix $\mathbf{A}^{-1}$. These components may be written as $-\mathrm{i}/2$ times the scaler product of vectors whose components are the width amplitudes of the channels:

$$(A^{-1})_{\lambda\mu} = (-\mathrm{i}/2)\mathbf{g}_{\lambda} \cdot \mathbf{g}_{\mu}. \tag{8.9}$$

At very low neutron energies the neutron widths of the resonances of the fissionable nuclei are usually very much smaller than the total widths. The partial radiation widths are also very small and their amplitudes have random sign. As a result of these facts it is usually quite accurate to limit the space in which the vectors $\mathbf{g}_{\lambda}$ are defined; this limited space is defined simply by the fission channels. With this limitation, in which the vectors are now denoted by $\mathbf{g}_{\lambda\mathrm{F}}$, the fission cross-section, eqn. (8.8b), is

$$\sigma_{\mathrm{F}} = \pi\bar{\lambda}^2 \sum_J g_J \sum_{\lambda\lambda'\lambda''\lambda'''}^{J} \Gamma^{\frac{1}{2}}_{\lambda(\mathrm{n})}\Gamma^{\frac{1}{2}}_{\lambda'(\mathrm{n})}\mathbf{g}_{\lambda''\mathrm{F}} \cdot \mathbf{g}_{\lambda'''\mathrm{F}} A_{\lambda\lambda''}A^{*}_{\lambda'\lambda'''}. \tag{8.10}$$

The scattering cross-section is

$$\sigma_{\mathrm{n}} = \pi\bar{\lambda}^2 \sum_J g_J \left| 1-e^{-2\mathrm{i}ka}\left\{1+\mathrm{i}\sum_{\lambda\lambda'}^{J} \Gamma^{\frac{1}{2}}_{\lambda(\mathrm{n})}\Gamma^{\frac{1}{2}}_{\lambda'(\mathrm{n})}A_{\lambda\lambda'}\right\}\right|^2. \tag{8.11}$$

The capture cross-section is

$$\sigma_{\gamma} = \pi\bar{\lambda}^2 \sum_J g_J \sum_{\lambda\lambda'\lambda''}^{J} \Gamma_{\lambda(\gamma\mathrm{T})}\Gamma^{\frac{1}{2}}_{\lambda'(\mathrm{n})}\Gamma^{\frac{1}{2}}_{\lambda''(\mathrm{n})}A_{\lambda\lambda'}A^{*}_{\lambda\lambda''}. \tag{8.12}$$

The squares of the length of the vectors $\mathbf{g}_{\lambda\mathrm{F}}$ are just the fission widths:

$$|\mathbf{g}_{\lambda\mathrm{F}}|^2 = \mathbf{g}_{\lambda\mathrm{F}} \cdot \mathbf{g}_{\lambda\mathrm{F}} = \sum_{\mathrm{f}} \Gamma^{\frac{1}{2}}_{\lambda(\mathrm{f})}\Gamma^{\frac{1}{2}}_{\lambda(\mathrm{f})}. \tag{8.13}$$

Their scalar products may be characterized by the angles $\theta_{\lambda\lambda'}$ between them

$$\mathbf{g}_{\lambda\mathrm{F}} \cdot \mathbf{g}_{\lambda'\mathrm{F}} = |\mathbf{g}_{\lambda\mathrm{F}}||\mathbf{g}_{\lambda'\mathrm{F}}|\cos\theta_{\lambda\lambda'}. \tag{8.14}$$

The values of the scalar products determined by fitting an N-level formula to the cross-sections can always be described in terms of only N channels. A definite assessment of the number of fission channels cannot be made from these scalar products but a statistical analysis of the cos $\theta_{\lambda\lambda'}$ values can give information about this quantity. Thus if there is only one channel all $\mathbf{g}_{\lambda F}$ will be parallel or anti-parallel (cos $\theta_{\lambda\lambda'} = \pm 1$), which would be very unlikely for more than a few levels if there were more than one channel. For m channels with components which have a Gaussian distribution with zero mean and the same variance in each channel the expectation value of $|\cos\theta_{\lambda\lambda'}|$ is

$$\langle|\cos\theta_{\lambda\lambda'}|\rangle = \frac{(m-1)\,!}{2^{m-1}\{\frac{1}{2}(m-1)\,!\}^2}, \qquad m \text{ odd} \qquad (8.15a)$$

$$= \frac{2(m-1)\,!}{\pi}\frac{1}{\{(m-1)\,!\,!\}^2}, \qquad m \text{ even} \qquad (8.15b)$$

$$\to \{2/\pi(m-1)\}^{\frac{1}{2}}, \qquad m \text{ large.} \qquad (8.15c)$$

3. Interference between two levels

(a) *The two-level formula in R-matrix parameters*

An explicit formula is available for the cross-section of two levels of the same spin J (Lane and Thomas 1958). Omission of the level shifts, which can be set equal to zero over a limited energy range by suitable choice of the R-matrix boundary conditions, gives the formula

$$\sigma_{cc'} = \pi\lambda\!\!\!^{-2} g_J \sum_{sls'l'} \frac{\{(E_2-E)\Gamma^{\frac{1}{2}}_{1(c)}\Gamma^{\frac{1}{2}}_{2(c')}+(E_1-E)\Gamma^{\frac{1}{2}}_{2(c)}\Gamma^{\frac{1}{2}}_{2(c')}\}^2+\frac{1}{4}\Big(\sum_{c''}\prod_{c''c}\prod_{c''c'}\Big)^2}{\{(E_1-E)(E_2-E)+\frac{1}{4}(\Gamma^2_{12}-\Gamma_1\Gamma_2)\}^2+\frac{1}{4}\{\Gamma_1(E_2-E)+\Gamma_2(E_1-E)\}^2} \qquad (8.16a)$$

where

$$\prod_{c''c} = \Gamma^{\frac{1}{2}}_{1(c'')}\Gamma^{\frac{1}{2}}_{2(c)}-\Gamma^{\frac{1}{2}}_{2(c'')}\Gamma^{\frac{1}{2}}_{1(c)}, \qquad (8.16b)$$

$$\Gamma_{12} = \sum_{c''} 2P_{c''}\gamma_{1(c'')}\gamma_{2(c'')}, \qquad (8.16c)$$

$$\Gamma_1 \equiv \Gamma_{11},$$
$$\Gamma_2 \equiv \Gamma_{22}. \qquad (8.16d)$$

Explicit formulae for more than two levels do not seem to be available.

The two-level formula, eqn. (8.16), is not of great value for the analysis of experimental data but is useful for the study of the stronger interference effects to be expected between levels. Previous studies of such interference effects have been confined to situations in which the levels are more widely spaced than their widths (Teichmann 1950, Vogt 1958).

For a partial cross-section $\sigma_{cc'}$ the minima between two resonances are of two types depending on the sign of the ratio $\gamma_{1(c)}\gamma_{1(c')}/\gamma_{2(c)}\gamma_{2(c')}$; if this is positive there is destructive interference between the resonances leading to a minimum of order $(\Gamma/D)^4$ times the peak cross-sections; if the ratio is negative the constructive interference between the levels leads to a minimum of order $(\Gamma/D)^2$ times peak value. Teichmann (1952) also presents an interesting special case of three or more level interference. If the value of R_{ab} from all levels except $\lambda = 1$ and 2 is greater than its contribution from these two levels everywhere between them,

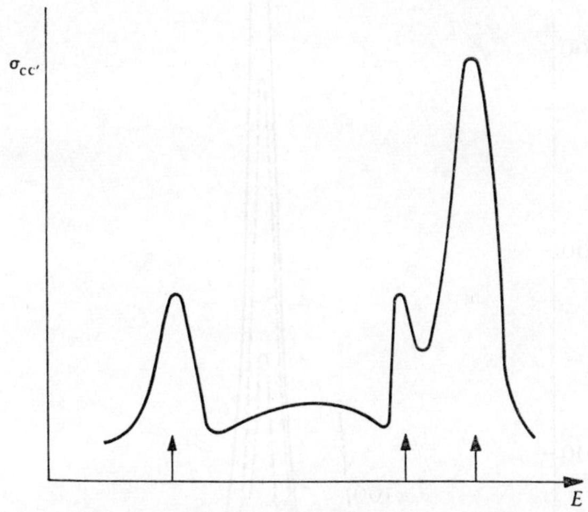

FIG. 8.6. The interference maximum that may occur in three-level interference. Positions of the levels are indicated by vertical arrows.

and if the ratio $\gamma_{1(c)}\gamma_{1(c')}/\gamma_{2(c)}\gamma_{2(c')}$ is negative, then an extra maximum occurs in the cross-section between them as illustrated in Fig. 8.6.

Equation (8.16) allows one to study the case where the spacing of two levels is less than their widths. Let us take, for example, the case in which the partial widths of one channel are much larger than those for any other. Then the square of the cross-width Γ_{12} is approximately equal to the product of Γ_1 and Γ_2. The cross-section has a single maximum lying between the levels, which is much sharper than the original widths suggest. In the special case of $\Gamma_1 = \Gamma_2$, and if we write $D = y\Gamma_1$, the 'resonance' term, given by the denominator of eqn. (8.16a), is higher by a factor of $4/y^2$ at its maximum than at the energies E_1 or E_2. The closer the levels (i.e. the smaller the value of y) the narrower and more intense is the single resultant resonance. The effective width

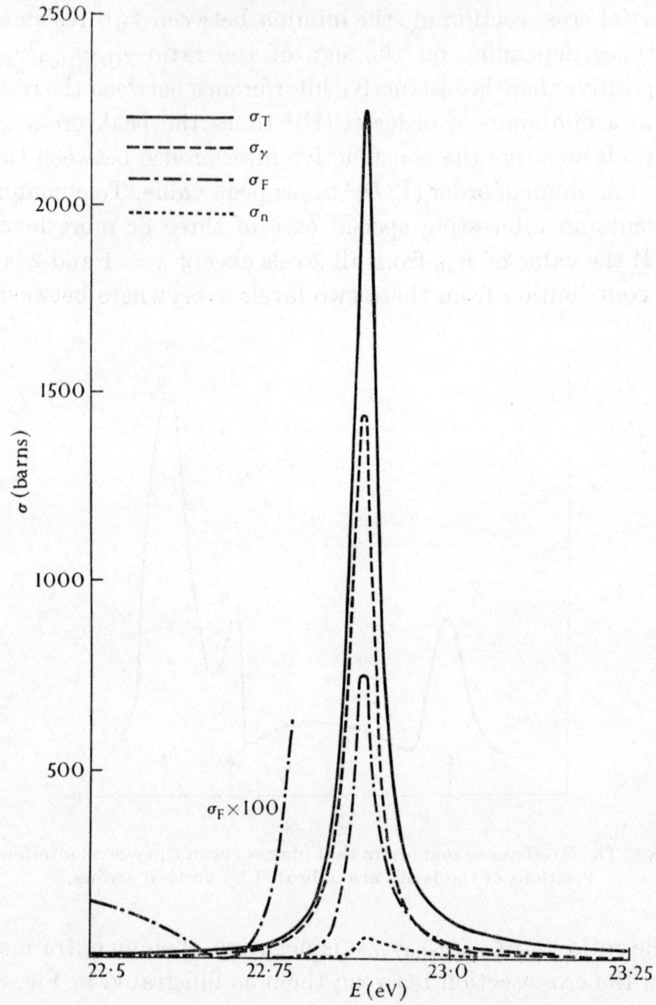

FIG. 8.7. Total and partial cross-sections for two close levels with R-matrix parameters

$$E_1 = 22{\cdot}81 \text{ eV}, \ \Gamma^{\frac{1}{2}}{}_{1(\mathrm{n})} = 0{\cdot}35 \ (\mathrm{meV})^{\frac{1}{2}}$$
$$\Gamma^{\frac{1}{2}}{}_{(1\mathrm{f})} = -0{\cdot}728 \ (\mathrm{eV})^{\frac{1}{2}}, \ E_2 = 22{\cdot}92 \text{ eV},$$
$$\Gamma^{\frac{1}{2}}{}_{2(\mathrm{n})} = 0{\cdot}84 \ (\mathrm{meV})^{\frac{1}{2}}, \ \Gamma^{\frac{1}{2}}{}_{2(\mathrm{f})} = 0{\cdot}574 \ (\mathrm{eV})^{\frac{1}{2}},$$
$$\Gamma_{1(\gamma\mathrm{T})} = \Gamma_{2(\gamma\mathrm{T})} = 0{\cdot}025 \text{ eV}.$$

of the 'resonance' is of the order $y^2\,\Gamma_1/2$. The numerator of eqn. (8.16a) contains interference terms as well as the more straightforward intensity terms. The interference can be either destructive or constructive depending upon the relative signs of the reduced width products $\gamma_{\lambda(c)}\gamma_{\lambda(c')}$; in the former case a strong minimum may be found not

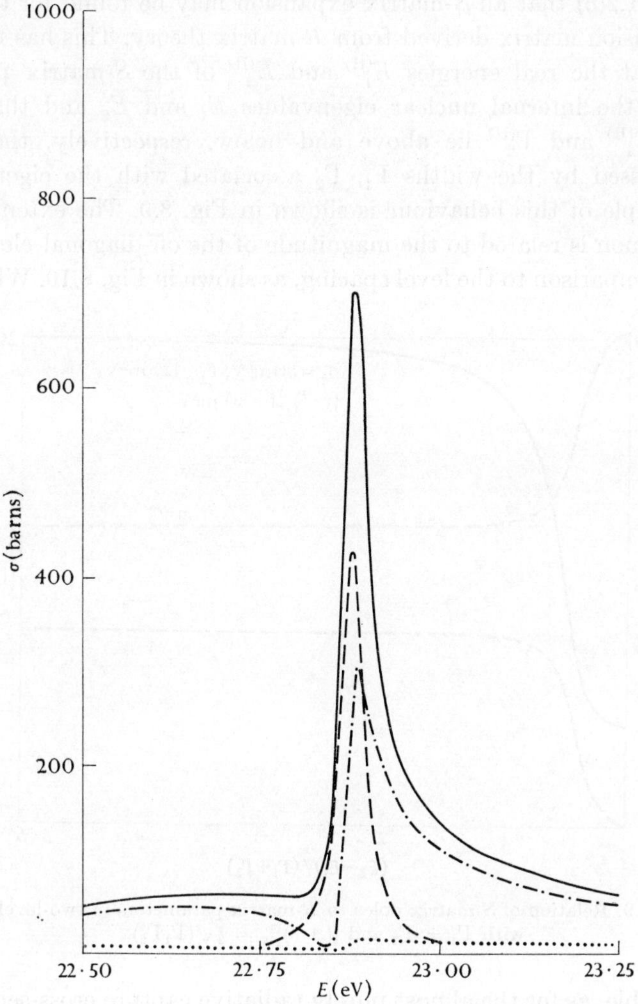

FIG. 8.8. Total and partial cross-sections for two close levels with R-matrix parameters as in Fig. 7.5 except for the reversal of sign of one reduced width amplitude.

far from the centre of the resonance. Typical examples of two-level behaviour are shown in Figs. 8.7 and 8.8.

(*b*) *S-matrix formalism*

The discussion of the two-level formula is more transparent if it is framed in the S-matrix formalism of Humblet and Rosenfeld (1961) as described in Chapter II, Section H. It was shown in Chapter II,

Section H.2(c) that an S-matrix expansion may be found for the two-level collision matrix derived from R-matrix theory. This has the property that the real energies $E_1^{(\mathrm{H})}$ and $E_2^{(\mathrm{H})}$ of the S-matrix poles lie between the internal nuclear eigenvalues E_1 and E_2 and that their widths $\Gamma_1^{(\mathrm{H})}$ and $\Gamma_2^{(\mathrm{H})}$ lie above and below, respectively, the range encompassed by the widths Γ_1, Γ_2 associated with the eigenvalues. An example of this behaviour is shown in Fig. 8.9. The extent of the phenomenon is related to the magnitude of the off-diagonal element of $\mathbf{A}^{-1}$ in comparison to the level spacing, as shown in Fig. 8.10. When this

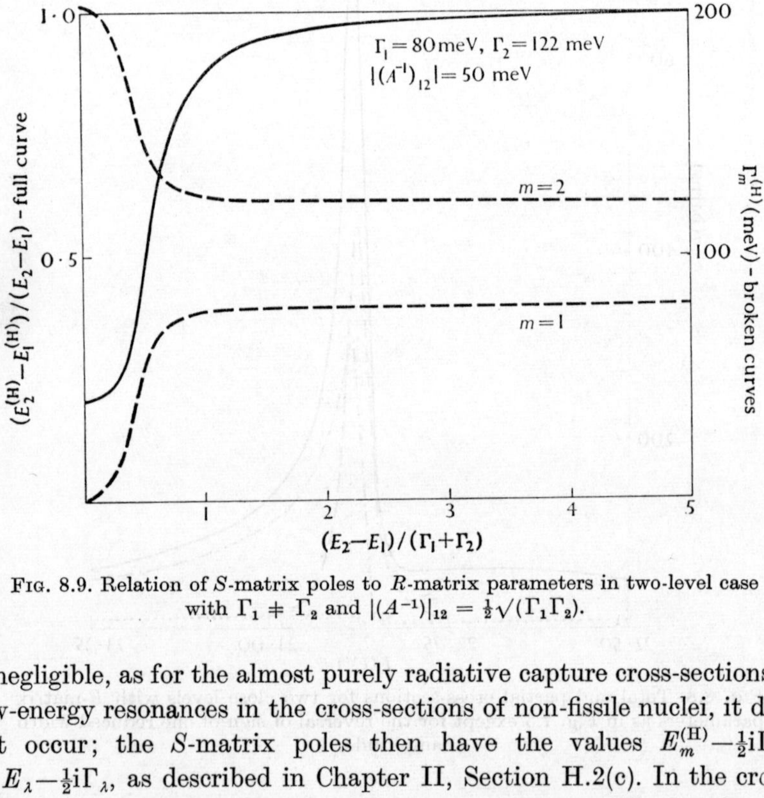

FIG. 8.9. Relation of S-matrix poles to R-matrix parameters in two-level case with $\Gamma_1 \neq \Gamma_2$ and $|(A^{-1})|_{12} = \frac{1}{2}\sqrt{(\Gamma_1\Gamma_2)}$.

is negligible, as for the almost purely radiative capture cross-sections of low-energy resonances in the cross-sections of non-fissile nuclei, it does not occur; the S-matrix poles then have the values $E_m^{(\mathrm{H})}-\frac{1}{2}\mathrm{i}\Gamma_m^{(\mathrm{H})} = E_\lambda-\frac{1}{2}\mathrm{i}\Gamma_\lambda$, as described in Chapter II, Section H.2(c). In the cross-sections of the fissionable nuclei, however, it is possible for the off-diagonal elements of the level matrix to be of the same order of magnitude as the level widths, giving a strong effect as in Fig. 8.9.

It is now apparent from the S-matrix formalism that the two-level cross-section is basically a superposition of two resonance forms, one narrow and one broad (see eqn. (2.114)). In general, this superposition will appear in the cross-section as a single narrow maximum and only careful analysis of the interference terms might reveal that it is a two-broad-level, rather than a single-narrow-level anomaly. Such a phenomenon is called a quasi-resonance (Lynn 1964 1966). Figs. 8.7 and 8.8, already referred to, show examples of quasi-resonances.

The parameters of the levels are: $E_1 = 22{\cdot}81$ eV, $(\Gamma_{1n})^{\frac{1}{2}} = 0{\cdot}3475$ (meV)$^{\frac{1}{2}}$, $(\Gamma_{1f})^{\frac{1}{2}} = -0{\cdot}728$ (eV)$^{\frac{1}{2}}$, $E_2 = 22{\cdot}92$ eV, $(\Gamma_{2n})^{\frac{1}{2}} = 0{\cdot}839$ (meV)$^{\frac{1}{2}}$,

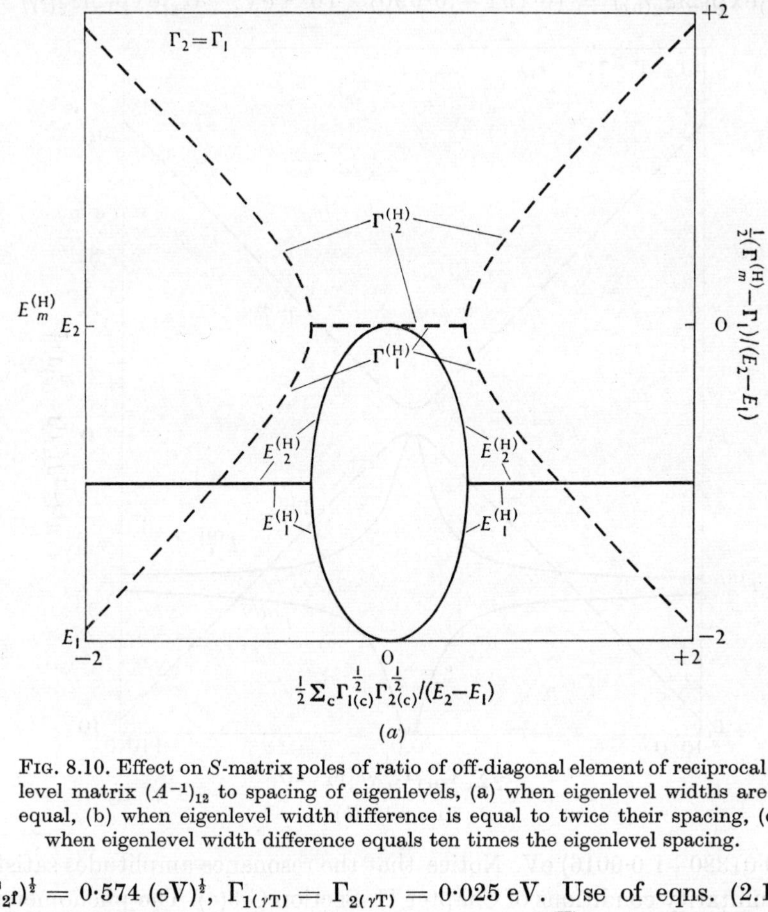

(a)

FIG. 8.10. Effect on S-matrix poles of ratio of off-diagonal element of reciprocal level matrix $(A^{-1})_{12}$ to spacing of eigenlevels, (a) when eigenlevel widths are equal, (b) when eigenlevel width difference is equal to twice their spacing, (c) when eigenlevel width difference equals ten times the eigenlevel spacing.

$(\Gamma_{2f})^{\frac{1}{2}} = 0{\cdot}574$ (eV)$^{\frac{1}{2}}$, $\Gamma_{1(\gamma T)} = \Gamma_{2(\gamma T)} = 0{\cdot}025$ eV. Use of eqns. (2.122) and (2.123) gives the S-matrix parameters: $E_1^{(H)} = 22{\cdot}852$ eV, $\Gamma_1^{(H)} = 0{\cdot}871$ eV, $G^2_{1(n)}\exp(2i\xi_{1(n)}) = (0{\cdot}0461 + i\ 0{\cdot}0535) \times 10^{-3}$ eV, $G^2_{1(f)}\exp(2i\xi_{1(f)}) = (0{\cdot}8733 + i\ 0{\cdot}0017)$ eV, $E_2^{(H)} = 22{\cdot}878$ eV, $\Gamma_2^{(H)} = 0{\cdot}0394$ eV, $G^2_{2(n)}\exp(2i\xi_{2(n)}) = (0{\cdot}7697 - i\ 0{\cdot}0535) \times 10^{-3}$ eV, $G^2_{2(f)}\exp(2i\xi_{2(f)}) = -(0{\cdot}01383 + i\ 0{\cdot}0017)$ eV, revealing that the strong, sharp resonance appearing in the cross-section is superimposed on a very broad, weak resonance. The complex nature of the resonance amplitudes ($G_{m(c)}$exp

$(i\xi_{m(c)})$) gives rise to complicated interference effects as in Fig. 8.8. Here, the same parameters as in Fig. 8.7 have been employed except for a change of sign in one of the partial width amplitudes. The Humblet–Rosenfeld parameters are: $E_1^{(H)} = 22\cdot852$ eV, $G^2_{1(n)}\exp(2i\xi_{1(n)}) = (0\cdot6217+i\ 0\cdot090)\times10^{-3}$ eV, $G^2_{1(f)}\exp(2i\xi_{1(f)}) = (0\cdot8733+i\ 0\cdot0016)$ eV, $\Gamma_1^{(H)} = 0\cdot871$ eV, $E_2^{(H)} = 22\cdot878$ eV, $\Gamma_2^{(H)} = 0\cdot0394$ eV, $G^2_{2(n)}\exp(2i\xi_{2(n)}) = (0\cdot194-i0\cdot090)\times10^{-3}$ eV, $G^2_{2f}\exp(2i\xi_{2(f)}) =$

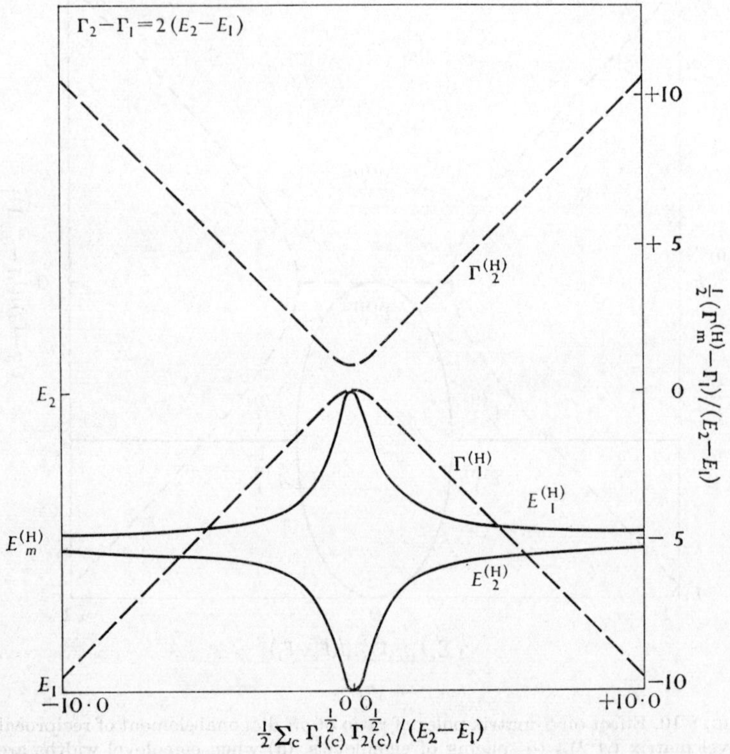

FIG. 8.10. (*b*)

$-(0\cdot01380+i\ 0\cdot0016)$ eV. Notice that the resonance amplitudes satisfy the unitarity conditions of Chapter II, Section G.3(c). The phenomenon of quasi-resonances is of considerable importance for the analysis of slow neutron fission cross-sections.

4. Average cross-sections

Perhaps the formally simplest many-level cross-section expression is the *S*-matrix formula of Humblet and Rosenfeld (1961). The cross-section for the process (a, b) is given in eqn. (2.113).

The averaging of this expression over energy is readily achieved using contour integration. On ignoring the background term Q_{ab} which is expected to be small in the typical compound-nucleus region the average

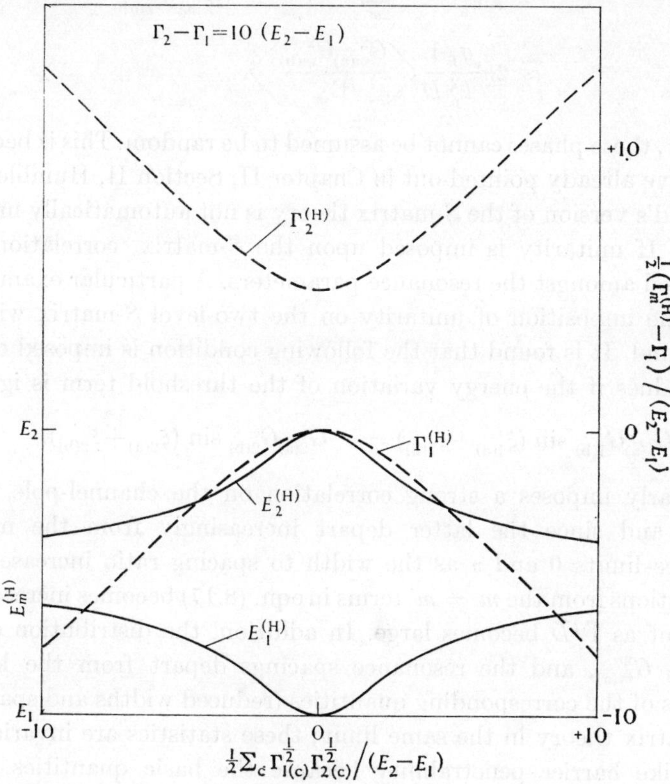

FIG. 8.10. (c)

cross-section over an energy interval ε containing many resonances is (for angular momentum component J)

$$\frac{1}{\varepsilon}\int_{\varepsilon} dE\sigma_{ab} \approx \frac{\pi^2}{\varepsilon}\frac{g_J}{k_a^2}\mathscr{P}_a^2\mathscr{P}_b^2 \sum_{m,m'}\left\{\frac{(\Gamma_m+\Gamma_{m'})G_{m(a)}G_{m(b)}G_{m'(a)}G_{m'(b)}\cos\Phi_{mm'}}{(E_{m'}-E_m)^2+\frac{1}{4}(\Gamma_m+\Gamma_{m'})^2} - \frac{(E_{m'}-E_m)\,2\,G_{m(a)}G_{m(b)}G_{m'(a)}G_{m'(b)}\sin\Phi_{mm'}}{(E_{m'}-E_m)^2+\frac{1}{4}(\Gamma_m+\Gamma_{m'})^2}\right\}\frac{1}{|\mathscr{P}_{ma}\mathscr{P}_{m'b}|^2}. \tag{8.17}$$

where $\Phi_{mm'} = \xi_{m(a)}-\xi_{m'(a)}+\xi_{m(b)}-\xi_{m'(b)}$. Now, if it is assumed that the phases $\Phi_{mm'}$ (which are zero for $m = m'$) are randomly distributed around the unit circle for all $m \neq m'$, or alternatively have similar distributions about zero and π, then the average cross-section reduces statistically to the single sum

$$\langle\sigma_{ab}\rangle = \frac{\pi^2}{\varepsilon}\frac{g_J}{k_a^2}\mathscr{P}_a^2\mathscr{P}_b^2\sum_m \frac{2G_{m(a)}^2 G_{m(b)}^2}{\Gamma_m}\frac{1}{|\mathscr{P}_{ma}\mathscr{P}_{mb}|^2}$$

$$\approx 2\pi^2\frac{g_J}{k_a^2}\frac{1}{D}\left\langle\frac{G_{m(a)}^2 G_{m(b)}^2}{\Gamma_m}\right\rangle. \tag{8.18}$$

However, these phases cannot be assumed to be random. This is because, as we have already pointed out in Chapter II, Section H, Humblet and Rosenfeld's version of the S-matrix theory is not automatically unitary in form. If unitarity is imposed upon the S-matrix, correlations are introduced amongst the resonance parameters. A particular example of this is the imposition of unitarity on the two-level S-matrix without background. It is found that the following condition is imposed on the pole residues if the energy variation of the threshold term is ignored

$$G_{1(a)}G_{1(b)}\sin(\xi_{1(a)}+\xi_{1(b)}) = -G_{2(a)}G_{2(b)}\sin(\xi_{2(a)}+\xi_{2(b)}). \tag{8.19}$$

This clearly imposes a strong correlation on the channel-pole phase factors, and since the latter depart increasingly from the narrow resonance limits 0 and π as the width to spacing ratio increases, the contributions from the $m \neq m'$ terms in eqn. (8.17) becomes increasingly important as $\bar{\Gamma}/\bar{D}$ becomes large. In addition, the distribution of the residues, $G_{m(a)}^2$, and the resonance spacings depart from the known statistics of the corresponding quantities (reduced widths and spacings) of R-matrix theory in the same limit; these statistics are invariant to things like barrier penetrability because the basic quantities of R-matrix theory are the eigensolutions of the Schrödinger equation within an internal region constricted only by real boundary conditions. The quasi-resonances provide an example of how the statistics are distorted; the S-matrix expansion of the two-level interference results in a pole spacing smaller than the level spacing, and widths respectively less than and greater than the two R-matrix level widths. Unfortunately these correlations and statistics of the S-matrix parameters are not nearly well enough established at the present time to allow calculations of the average cross-sections on the basis of eqn. (8.17). Average cross-sections are usually calculated on the basis of the approximate eqn. (8.18). In the narrow resonance approximation the R-matrix partial widths $\Gamma_{(a)}$ and $\Gamma_{(b)}$ can be substituted for $G_{m(a)}^2$ and $G_{m(b)}$ (see eqn. (2.120c)), and the averaging can be carried out on the basis of the known statistical behaviour of the R-matrix parameters. The necessary mathematical manipulation for this step was described in Chapter VI, Section B.3(b). The full expression for the partial cross-section averaged over all excited levels of different-total angular momentum is

$$\sigma_{\mathrm{ab}} = \frac{2\pi^2}{k_{\mathrm{a}}^2} \sum_{l} \sum_{s=|I_\alpha - \frac{1}{2}|}^{I_\alpha + \frac{1}{2}} \sum_{J=|l-s|}^{l+s} \frac{2J+1}{2(2I_\alpha+1)} \frac{1}{D(J)} \left\langle \frac{\Gamma_{\lambda J(\alpha s l)} \Gamma_{\lambda J(\mathrm{b})}}{\Gamma_{\lambda J(\mathrm{T})}} \right\rangle. \tag{8.20}$$

C. APPLICATION OF THE UNIFIED MODEL TO SLOW NEUTRON-INDUCED FISSION

1. Channel concept

In the formal definition of a channel in reaction theory the two particles which constitute the pair should be separated beyond the range of polarizing nuclear forces; the channel radius should be at least equal to this range. Each channel is defined not only by the nature of the particles but by their internal excitations and angular momentum couplings. With this definition there is obviously a large number of channels available for the fission process. By analogy with neutron capture radiation widths, one might thus expect the total fission widths to belong to a nearly uniform statistical distribution and interference effects between resonances to be negligible, the single-level Breit–Wigner formula being a nearly valid representation of the fission cross-section. Early measurements of the neutron-induced fission cross-sections over resonances showed that neither of these expectations were true (Sailor 1956, Lynn and Pattenden 1956).

These unexpected observations were explained by Bohr (1956) in his application of the collective model to the transition states through which the fission process passes at the saddle-point deformation. Only few transition states should be available, because of energy, angular momentum, and parity limitation, to compound nucleus states formed by the bombardment of odd-mass uranium and plutonium isotopes by slow neutrons. Suppose that only one transition state is available, fission through higher-energy transition states being negligible because of the tunnelling factor (eqn. (8.5)). The channel radii for the fission product pairs must necessarily include the saddle-point nucleus within the internal region, because nuclear forces between the incipient fission fragments are still acting until the system has at least passed the scission point. The values of the wave-function at the channel radii (i.e. the reduced width amplitudes for the formal fission channels) are related to the wave-function of the compound nucleus state at small deformation only through the wave-function of the transition state. Although their pattern of magnitudes and signs with respect to each other is unknown but probably random, for compound nucleus states with the same quantum numbers in the same energy region (defined by the availability of the single-transition state) this pattern will be identical. The only difference in these fission channel reduced width amplitudes from one compound state to another will lie in their mean square value, this being governed by the extent of the mixing of the transition state into the compound nucleus state. The coefficient of this mixing is in turn expected to be normally distributed with zero mean over the compound nucleus states and this gives rise to a Porter–Thomas distribution for both the partial and total fission widths:

$$p(\Gamma_{(\mathrm{f})})\mathrm{d}\Gamma_{(\mathrm{f})} = \frac{1}{\sqrt{(2\pi\bar{\Gamma}_{(\mathrm{f})}\Gamma_{(\mathrm{f})})}}\exp\left(-\frac{\Gamma_{(\mathrm{f})}}{2\bar{\Gamma}_{(\mathrm{f})}}\right)\mathrm{d}\Gamma_{(\mathrm{f})}. \tag{8.21}$$

Because of this statistical property of the fission widths and the associated resonance-resonance interferences that result from the complete correlation over the resonances of the partial fission width amplitudes, the term 'channel' in the fission process is usually taken to mean fission proceeding through a particular transition state. In this chapter we shall refer to such 'channels' as saddle-point channels to distinguish them from the true particle channels of reaction theory (we shall often refer to the latter as fission-product channels).

To extend this idea to the case of more than one level in the transition state it is necessary to write down the connexion between the reduced width amplitudes of the formally defined channels and the amplitudes of the transition state components in the compound nucleus levels in a more explicit way. Suppose the amplitude of a transition state f is denoted by $y_{\lambda\mathrm{f}}$ for eigenlevel λ. Then the reduced width amplitude of the level λ for channel c is

$$\gamma_{\lambda(\mathrm{c})} = \sum_{\mathrm{f}} b_{\mathrm{fc}} y_{\lambda\mathrm{f}}, \tag{8.22}$$

the coefficient b_{fc} giving the dependence of the wave-function at the channel entrance, $r_{\mathrm{c}} = a_{\mathrm{c}}$, on the transition state f. According to what we said in the paragraph above these coefficients do not depend on λ. If there is only one transition state f in eqn. (8.22),

$$\Gamma_{\lambda(\mathrm{c})} = 2P_{\mathrm{c}} b_{\mathrm{fc}}^2 y_{\lambda\mathrm{f}}^2, \tag{8.23}$$

and if this is summed over all formal fission channels c, we obtain the fission width

$$\Gamma_{\lambda(\mathrm{F})} = \Gamma_{\lambda(\mathrm{f})} = \sum_{\mathrm{c}} \Gamma_{\lambda(\mathrm{c})} = y_{\lambda\mathrm{f}}^{2} \sum_{\mathrm{c}} 2P_{\mathrm{c}} b_{\mathrm{fc}}^{2}, \tag{8.24}$$

Thus, $y_{\lambda\mathrm{c}}^{2}$ can be normalized to be equal to $\Gamma_{\lambda(\mathrm{f})}$, which we call the partial width for the saddle-point channel f, if $\sum_{\mathrm{c}} 2P_{\mathrm{c}} b_{\mathrm{fc}}^{2}$ is set equal to unity. If there is more than one transition state in the sum of eqn. (8.22) we obtain,

$$\Gamma_{\lambda(\mathrm{c})} = \sum_{\mathrm{f}} 2P_{\mathrm{c}} b_{\mathrm{fc}}^{2} y_{\lambda\mathrm{f}}^{2} + \sum_{\mathrm{f} \neq \mathrm{f}'} 2P_{\mathrm{c}} b_{\mathrm{fc}} b_{\mathrm{f}'\mathrm{c}} y_{\lambda\mathrm{f}} y_{\lambda\mathrm{f}'} \tag{8.25}$$

and the total fission width is clearly

$$\Gamma_{\lambda(\mathrm{F})} = \sum_{\mathrm{c}} \Gamma_{\lambda(\mathrm{c})} = \sum_{\mathrm{f}} y_{\lambda\mathrm{f}}^{2} \sum_{\mathrm{c}} 2P_{\mathrm{c}} b_{\mathrm{fc}}^{2} + \sum_{\mathrm{f} \neq \mathrm{f}'} y_{\lambda\mathrm{f}} y_{\lambda\mathrm{f}'} \sum_{\mathrm{c}} 2P_{\mathrm{c}} b_{\mathrm{fc}} b_{\mathrm{f}'\mathrm{c}}. \tag{8.26}$$

For the total fission width to be just the sum of the widths of the transition states (by eqn. (8.24) this is just the first term on the right-hand side of eqn. (8.26)) there must be a large number of formal channels c (so that the $2P_{\mathrm{c}} b_{\mathrm{fc}}^{2}$ are very small) and the sign pattern of the coefficients b_{fc} relating the channel-entrance wave-function values to the transition state must be random with respect to both f and c. With these conditions the second term on the right-hand side of eqn. (8.26) will be very small compared with the first. Similarly, the cross-product term of the level matrix formalism, $\sum_{\mathrm{c}} \Gamma_{\lambda(\mathrm{c})}^{\frac{1}{2}} \Gamma_{\mu(\mathrm{c})}^{\frac{1}{2}}$ (summed over fission-product channels), is

$$\sum_{\mathrm{c}} \Gamma_{\lambda(\mathrm{c})}^{\frac{1}{2}} \Gamma_{\mu(\mathrm{c})}^{\frac{1}{2}} = \sum_{\mathrm{f}} \Gamma_{\mu(\mathrm{f})}^{\frac{1}{2}} \Gamma_{\mu(\mathrm{f})}^{\frac{1}{2}} + \sum_{\mathrm{f} \neq \mathrm{f}'} \Gamma_{\lambda(\mathrm{f})}^{\frac{1}{2}} \Gamma_{\mu(\mathrm{f}')}^{\frac{1}{2}} \sum_{\mathrm{c}} 2P_{\mathrm{c}} b_{\mathrm{fc}} b_{\mathrm{f}'\mathrm{c}}. \tag{8.27}$$

With the same conditions as above the second term on the right-hand side is unimportant compared with the first.

With the approximation of neglecting these (assumed) minor terms it becomes apparent that the saddle-point channels can be treated just like true channels in the formal reaction theory, and, moreover, their use in this connexion has the advantage of taking care of the correlations (full or partial, depending on the number of transition states) amongst the reduced width amplitudes. The statistical properties of the total fission width are obtained from those of the partial widths of the saddle-point channels in the same way as for other total widths. In particular if N transition states are available with transmission factors all equal to unity then it is said that N saddle-point channels are fully open and the distribution over the resonances of the total fission widths is expected to have the chi-squared form with $\nu = N$ degrees of freedom (see eqn. (6.38)). In the general case, when the transmission factors are not equal, such a simple distribution function cannot be stated, only the mean and variance of the distribution being readily calculable.

It is clear from the above discussion that when there is more than one transition state the usefulness of this concept of the saddle-point channel depends on the summation of the fission-product channels in large groups. The partial width for a limited group of channels c′ has the same form as eqn. (8.26), and, by the same argument as before, this is proportional to the sum of the saddle-point widths weighted by the sums $\sum_{c'} 2P_{c'}b_{fc'}^2$ if the numbers of channels in the group is large. If this number if small however (i.e. when we are discussing the cross-sections for production of specific fission products in particular states of excitation) then the cross-product term cannot be neglected and this kind of proportionality breaks down. In practice, with the present state of experimental technique, this problem has not yet presented itself.

2. Statistics of fission parameters

(a) *Strong coupling*

An estimate of the mean value of the fission width at energy E is obtained from the formula (eqn. (8.2)) of Bohr and Wheeler (1939) with N taken as the sum of the transmission factors of the transition states, the energies of which are denoted by $E_{\mathfrak{f}}$:

$$N = \sum_{\mathfrak{f}} T_{\mathfrak{f}} \tag{8.28a}$$

$$= \sum_{\mathfrak{f}} 1/\{1+\exp 2\pi(E_{\mathfrak{f}}-E)/\hbar\omega_{\mathfrak{f}}\}, \tag{8.28b}$$

the sum being taken only over those transition states with the same angular momentum and parity as the compound-nucleus wave-function. Equation (8.2) may be derived using Wigner's (1938) theory of mono-molecular reactions or from the theory of Blatt and Weisskopf (1952), first applied to the derivation of mean neutron widths (see Chapter VI, Section C.1), giving the classical cycling time of a given configuration of a system of particles. These derivations clearly imply the assumption of strong coupling among the various modes of the system. This is particularly clear in the case of the second derivation; the wave-function of a nucleus summed over a sufficiently large number of levels to give a nearly classical description of the system is in fact being averaged over a very large energy interval that would wash out any residual structure of a particular mode. The validity of the strong-coupling assumption for the transition states of fission has been examined by Wilets (1959), starting from the perturbation theory expression (eqn.

(8.6)), who found that for high energies it certainly seems to be true, but expressed doubts that the lowest energy ($J = 0^+$, $K = 0$) transition state of even nuclei is strongly coupled to the compound nucleus motion. These doubts are based on plausibility arguments concerning the energy gap of even nuclei, rather than on quantitative assessments, and were intended to explain the low observed values of $\bar{\Gamma}_{(F)}/\bar{D}$ of the slow neutron-induced fission of the heavy odd-mass nuclei (see Section 3). However, it may also be argued that weak coupling of a transition state to the compound-nucleus wave-function could lead to 'giant resonance' effects in $\bar{\Gamma}_{(F)}/\bar{D}$, analogous to those observed in neutron strength-function data, and it follows that the observed values of $\bar{\Gamma}_{(F)}/\bar{D}$ need not necessarily be small.

As we have seen, eqn. (8.28) is based on the classical limit of quantal statistics combined with the quantal transmission of a potential barrier. Improvements in this estimate might result from calculations on models that contain more detail of the fission phenomenon. A complex potential in the variable of the deformation parameter, β, is introduced here as such a model. It is known that the potential energy of actinide nuclei is high for large negative values of the deformation parameter, reaches a minimum (the normal stable shape) at small positive values of β, rises to reach a local maximum (the saddle point) at a rather larger value of β and then descends through the scission point. Such a potential energy curve must be constructed for each state of intrinsic excitation of the nucleons or of collective excitation in other modes than those associated with deformation through the saddle point. In other words, the complex potential is a model for a particular saddle-point channel through the fission barrier. In this model the collective motion beyond the scission point would have to be pictured as a superposition of the wave-functions of all the fission product pairs in all their different states of excitation and relative angular momenta, and all such components of the complete wave-function would have coefficients and phases governed by the nature of the transition state.

For computational simplicity in some preliminary calculations the potential well has the form shown in Fig. 8.11. For values of the deformation parameter greater than zero the real part of the potential energy is given by the expression

$$V = \frac{V_c}{1+\exp\{(\beta-\beta_c)/d_c\}} + \frac{V_e}{1+\exp\{-(\beta-\beta_e)/d_e\}}, \tag{8.29}$$

and is infinite for β less than zero.

The values of β_c, d_c, β_e, and d_e are suggested by the liquid-drop model (see Fig. 8.1). The value of V_e is suggested by the observed release of kinetic energy in low-energy fission (i.e. about 180 MeV) and V_c is obtained from the known energy of the transition state E_f with respect to the nuclear ground state; typical values for this are of the order of 6 MeV. The mass parameter associated with the deformation is not a well-known quantity and probably varies with the degree of deformation. For small deformation the path towards fission is governed

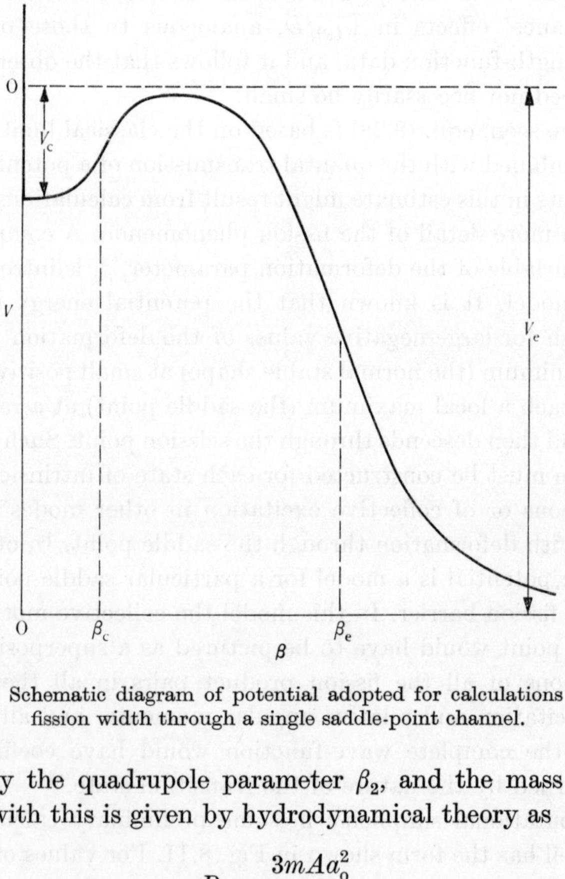

FIG. 8.11. Schematic diagram of potential adopted for calculations of mean fission width through a single saddle-point channel.

primarily by the quadrupole parameter β_2, and the mass parameter associated with this is given by hydrodynamical theory as

$$B_2 = \frac{3mAa_0^2}{8\pi}, \tag{8.30}$$

where m is the nucleon mass, A the nuclear mass number, and a_0 is the mean nuclear radius. Substitution of typical nuclear quantities in this expression gives a mass parameter B_2 of the order of $4{\cdot}5\times10^{-47}$ g.cm^2.

The fission-channel strength function is calculated from such a model in just the way described for the neutron strength-function in Chapter VI; the Schrödinger equation for the potential is integrated numerically and matched to an external wave-function to obtain the collision function. The difference between the modulus of this and unity is essentially the required quantity $2\pi\bar{\Gamma}_{(f)}/\bar{D}$. The results of a typical calculation with strong coupling of the transition-channel wave-function to the compound nucleus is shown in Fig. 8.12; the details of the

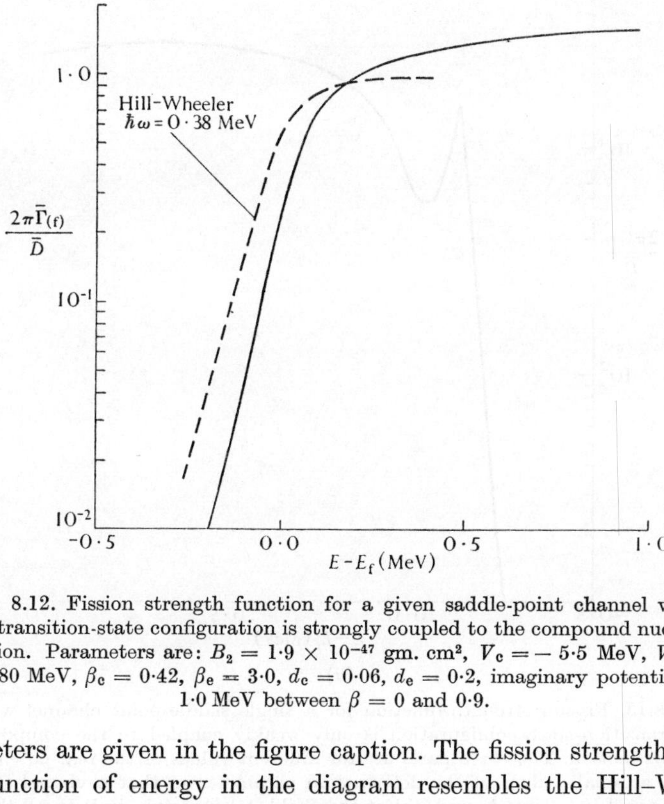

FIG. 8.12. Fission strength function for a given saddle-point channel when the transition-state configuration is strongly coupled to the compound nucleus motion. Parameters are: $B_2 = 1{\cdot}9 \times 10^{-47}$ gm. cm², $V_c = -5{\cdot}5$ MeV, $V_e = -180$ MeV, $\beta_c = 0{\cdot}42$, $\beta_e = 3{\cdot}0$, $d_c = 0{\cdot}06$, $d_e = 0{\cdot}2$, imaginary potential = 1·0 MeV between $\beta = 0$ and 0·9.

parameters are given in the figure caption. The fission strength shown as a function of energy in the diagram resembles the Hill–Wheeler form described by eqn. (8.28). The latter is shown as a broken curve in Fig. (8.12) for a tunnelling parameter, $\hbar\omega_f$, of 0·38 MeV. The new curve is, however, displaced upwards by 100 keV and shows the possibility of rising considerably above the asymptotic value of unity.

(*b*) *Weak coupling*

The same model allows one to calculate the fission strength-function when the collective motion in the fission mode is only weakly coupled to the compound-nucleus wave-function. Close to the threshold energy and below, almost discrete virtual states can exist in the real part of the potential well. In the weak-coupling complex-potential model these are broadened by the weak imaginary component giving Lorentz resonances in the absorption cross-section, or strength function, modified by the barrier-tunnelling factor. Above the threshold energy,

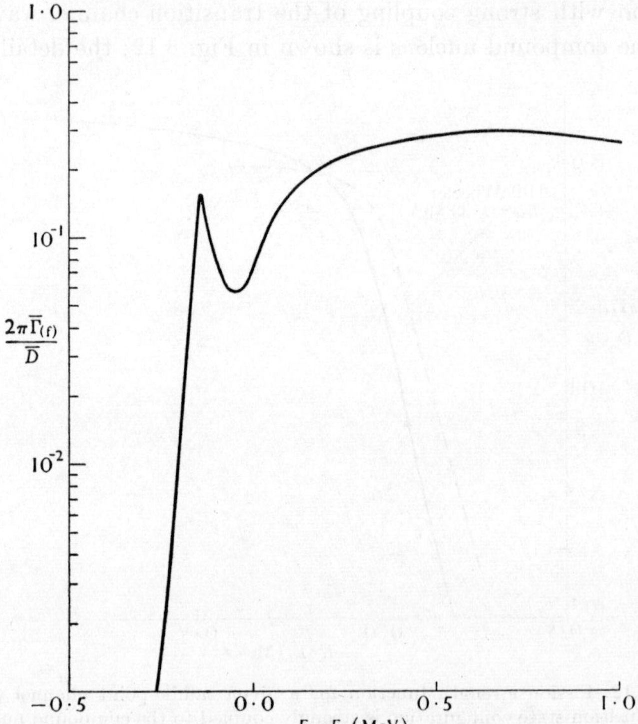

(*a*)

FIG. 8.13. Fission strength-function for a single saddle-point channel when the transition-state configuration is only weakly coupled to the compound nucleus motion. The three parts are for different values of the real potential depth at small values of the deformation parameter so that a virtual state in this well is (a) just bound, (b) at threshold, (c) just unbound. In all three cases the imaginary well depth is 30 keV.

virtual peaks of this kind are strongly damped by the large partial width associated with the motion in the fission deformation mode. Three typical situations are shown in Fig. 8.13; they only differ in the central well depth V_c. In the first case a virtual state exists 130 keV below the saddle point, and a quite well-developed sub-threshold peak in the strength function occurs. In the second case the well is shallower and the virtual state occurs almost exactly at the threshold energy. Here, the structure is most marked. In the third case the well is still shallower so as to move the virtual state up into the 'continuum', and very little structure is apparent.

(*c*) *Mean fission widths*

If we accept the strong-coupling assumption it is possible to make rough estimates of the ratios $\bar{\Gamma}_{(F)}/D$ to be expected for the slow

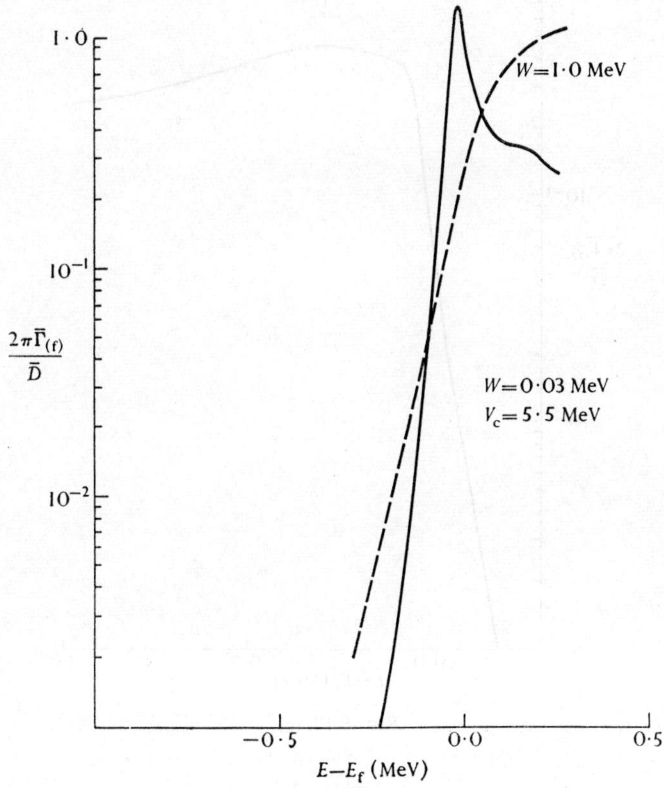

FIG. 8.13. (*b*)

neutron-induced fission of the heavy, odd-mass, even-charge nuclei, by counting the expected collective transition states at the saddle point. For such a target nucleus with ground-state spin and parity I^{π} there are two sets of levels formed in the even-compound nucleus by *s*-wave neutron bombardment, one set with total angular momentum and parity $J^{\pi}_{-} = (I-\frac{1}{2})^{\pi}$, and the other with $J^{\pi}_{+} = (I+\frac{1}{2})^{\pi}$. The states formed by slow neutron bombardment of the odd uranium and plutonium isotopes usually lie at least 1 MeV above the fission threshold (corresponding to the $K = 0$, $J = 0^+$ 'ground state' channel) and it appears from Table 8.1 that there will usually be one to three open saddle-point channels available for each set of states. In general it has not been possible to measure the spins of many of these resonances

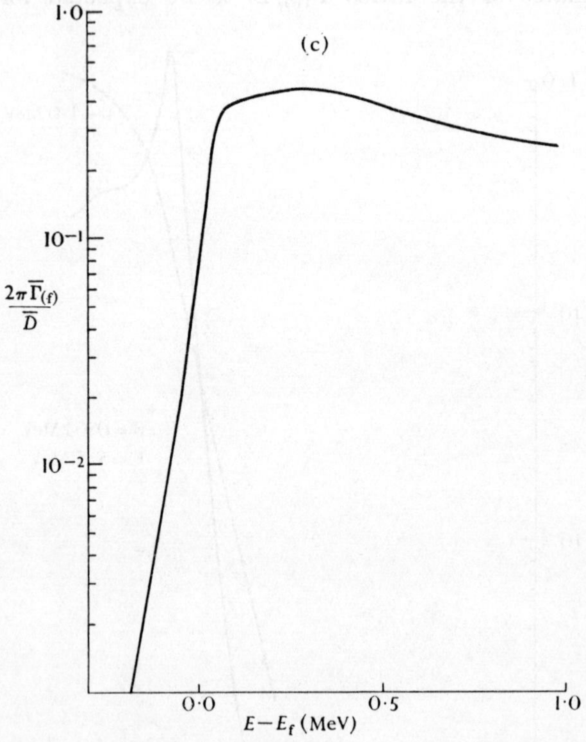

FIG. 8.13. (c)

so we define an average number of open saddle-point channels. The mean fission width over levels of both spins is

$$\bar{\Gamma}_{(F)} = \frac{\rho(J^{\pi}_{-})\Gamma_{(F)}(J^{\pi}_{-})+\rho(J^{\pi}_{+})\Gamma_{(F)}(J^{\pi}_{+})}{\rho(J^{\pi}_{-})+\rho(J^{\pi}_{+})} \tag{8.31}$$

and the mean level spacing is

$$\bar{D} = 1/\rho = 1/\{\rho(J^{\pi}_{-})+\rho(J^{\pi}_{+})\}. \tag{8.32}$$

The average number of open saddle-point channels per spin state is defined as

$$\frac{1}{2}\cdot\frac{2\pi\bar{\Gamma}_{(F)}}{\bar{D}} = \frac{1}{2}\left\{\frac{2\pi\bar{\Gamma}_{(F)}(J^{\pi}_{-})}{\bar{D}(J^{\pi}_{-})}+\frac{2\pi\bar{\Gamma}_{(F)}(J^{\pi}_{+})}{\bar{D}(J^{\pi}_{+})}\right\} \tag{8.33a}$$

$$= \tfrac{1}{2}(N(J^{\pi}_{-})+N(J^{\pi}_{+})) \tag{8.33b}$$

where N is given by eqn. (8.28a), the sums being confined to transition states with spin and parity J^{π}.

(d) The statistical-frequency function of fission widths

It has already been stated that, in general, the statistical frequency function of the fission widths will not belong exactly to the chi-squared family. The mean and variance of the distribution can be stated, however. The mean is (from eqns. (8.28))

$$\bar{\Gamma}_{(F)}(J^{\pi}) = \frac{\bar{D}(J^{\pi})}{2\pi}\sum_{f} T_{f} = \frac{\bar{D}(J^{\pi})}{2\pi}\,.\,N(J^{\pi}), \tag{8.34}$$

and the variance is

$$\text{var }\Gamma_{(F)}(J^{\pi}) = \sum_{f}\text{var }\Gamma_{(f)}(J^{\pi}) = 2\left(\frac{\bar{D}(J^{\pi})}{2\pi}\right)^{2}\sum_{f} T_{f}^{2}. \tag{8.35}$$

If the variance is equated to that of a chi-squared distribution (var $x = 2\bar{x}^2/\nu$) an effective number of degrees of freedom may be defined:

$$\nu_{\text{eff}}(J^{\pi}) = \left(\sum_{f} T_{f}\right)^{2}\Big/\left(\sum_{f} T_{f}^{2}\right) \tag{8.36}$$

which is greater than the value of $N(J^{\pi})$. The statistical distribution of the fission widths of both sets of levels considered together may be classified similarly; the effective value of ν which determines the overall variance is

$$\begin{aligned}\nu_{\text{eff}} = {} & 2\{N(J^{\pi}_{-})+N(J_{+})\}^{2}\rho(J^{\pi}_{-})\nu_{\text{eff}}(J^{\pi}_{-})\rho(J^{\pi}_{+})\nu_{\text{eff}}(J^{\pi}_{+}) \\ & /[N^{2}(J^{\pi}_{-})\rho\rho(J^{\pi}_{+})\nu_{\text{eff}}(J^{\pi}_{+})\{2+\nu_{\text{eff}}(J^{\pi}_{-})\}+N^{2}(J^{\pi}_{+})\rho\rho(J^{\pi}_{-}) \\ & \times\nu_{\text{eff}}(J^{\pi}_{-})\{2+\nu_{\text{eff}}(J^{\pi}_{+})\}-\{N(J^{\pi}_{-})+N(J^{\pi}_{+})\}^{2}\rho(J^{\pi}_{-})\nu_{\text{eff}}(J^{\pi}_{-})\rho(J^{\pi}_{+})\nu_{\text{eff}}(J^{\pi}_{+})].\end{aligned} \tag{8.37}$$

An alternative way of defining an effective ν value to classify the frequency function is to use the maximum likelihood principle described in Section B.2 of Chapter VI. If the frequency function for the total fission widths $\Gamma_{(\mathrm{F})}$ is denoted by $p(\Gamma_{(\mathrm{F})})$, then this alternative ν value, denoted by ν_{ML}, is given by the transcendental equation

$$\int_0^\infty \mathrm{d}x\,\ln x p(x) - \ln \bar{x} = \psi(\nu_{\mathrm{ML}}/2) - \ln(\nu_{\mathrm{ML}}/2) \tag{8.38}$$

(see eqn. (6.40)).

(*e*) *Statistics of quasi-resonances*

Before we turn to the comparison of these statistics with the experimental data it is necessary to clarify an important point. The statistics we have just discussed are those of real eigenfunctions at the edge of the nucleus, and the statistical spacing distributions discussed in Chapter V are those of real eigenvalues. Thus, we expect them to apply to the partial widths and eigenvalues of the R-matrix formalism but not generally to the complex quantities (or their square moduli) which occur in the S-matrix representation; the statistics of the latter must be derived from those of the former. In the study of the slow neutron cross-section of non-fissile nuclei the resonance spacings are nearly always very much larger than the resonance total widths, and the S-matrix parameters are virtually indistinguishable from the R-matrix parameters defined with the physical boundary conditions described in Section F of Chapter II. So, although it is the former that is really being derived (it is much more directly related to the cross-section) in the usual single-level type of cross-section analysis (see Chapter II, Section G.1 and 2(a)), the experimentally determined statistics (Porter–Thomas distribution of neutron widths, Wigner distribution of level spacings) are those of the latter.

This situation does not necessarily follow for the cross-sections of the fissionable nuclei. When the effective number of fission channels $N(J^\pi)$ for levels of one spin and parity class is of the order of, or greater than, unity there is an appreciable probability of two neighbouring levels being more closely spaced than the sum of their widths. In this case the parameters of the S-matrix resonant states can differ greatly from the parameters of the R-matrix internal nuclear eigenlevels, as shown in the examples of Section B.3(b). Obviously the statistical distributions of the S-matrix parameters can be altered by this effect, but what is even more important is the difficulty in resonance analysis that it introduces (Lynn 1964). If a cross-section quasi-resonance like that in Fig. 8.7 turned up in experiment it would almost certainly be assumed to be due to a single narrow level and would be analysed as such, the broad component of the quasi-resonance lying beneath the narrow component being almost unobservable. As a result the mean fission width of the levels will be greatly underestimated and their spacing over-estimated.

How likely is this effect? The striking situation illustrated in Fig. 8.7 occurred in the first run of a computer programme which randomly selected parameters and spacings for twenty levels from Porter–Thomas and Wigner distributions, respectively, assuming $N(J^{\pi}) = 1$ An explicit calculation of its probability can be made using the assumptions that (a) the levels for which the effect is likely to occur are fairly wide and therefore their fission widths predominate over the sum of their other partial widths, (b) their fission widths comprise n fully open saddle-point channels and no others. The frequency function of the sum of the widths x of two neighbouring levels is then given by

$$p(x)\mathrm{d}x = \Gamma(n)^{-1}(n/2\bar{x})^{n}x^{n-1}e^{-nx/2\bar{x}}\mathrm{d}x \tag{8.38}$$

where x is the mean total width of a single level. The probability that the sum is greater than a number k times their spacing D is

$$P_n(x \geqslant kD) = \Gamma(n)^{-1}\left(\frac{n}{2\bar{x}}\right)^{n}\cdot\frac{\pi}{2\bar{D}^2}\int\limits_0^{\infty}\mathrm{d}De^{-\pi D^2/4\bar{D}^2}\int\limits_{kD}^{\infty}\mathrm{d}xx^{n-1}e^{-nx/2\bar{x}}, \tag{8.39a}$$

which can be shown to be

$$P_n(x \geqslant kD) = \exp\left(\frac{n^2k^2\bar{D}^2}{8\pi\bar{x}^2}\right)\sum_{\mu=1}^{n}\mu\left(\frac{nk\bar{D}}{\bar{x}\sqrt{(2\pi)}}\right)^{\mu-1}\mathscr{D}_{-\mu-1}\left(\frac{nk\,D}{\bar{x}\sqrt{(2\pi)}}\right), \tag{8.39b}$$

where the $\mathscr{D}_{-\mu-1}(z)$ are the parabolic cylinder functions of order $(-\mu-1)$. These are related to the error function and may be calculated accurately from tables or asymptotic expansions of the latter by use of the expression

$$\mathscr{D}_{-\mu-1}(z) = \frac{(-)^{\mu}2^{\frac{1}{2}}}{\mu\,!}\exp\,(-z^2/4)\frac{\mathrm{d}^{\mu}}{\mathrm{d}z^{\mu}}\{\exp(z^2/2)\,\mathrm{Erfc}(z/2^{\frac{1}{2}})\} \tag{8.40a}$$

where

$$\mathrm{Erfc}(y) = \int\limits_y^{\infty}\mathrm{d}te^{-t^2}, \tag{8.40b}$$

$$\frac{\mathrm{d}}{\mathrm{d}z}\{\mathrm{Erfc}(z/2^{\frac{1}{2}})\} = -\frac{\exp(-z^2/2)}{2^{\frac{1}{2}}}. \tag{8.40c}$$

The results for the most important cases are

$$P_1(x \geqslant k\,D) \equiv P_1(m=1) = 1-\frac{mk\bar{D}}{\bar{x}\sqrt{\pi}}\exp\!\left(\frac{m^2k^2\bar{D}^2}{4\pi\bar{x}^2}\right)\mathrm{Erfc}\!\left(\frac{mk\bar{D}}{2\bar{x}\sqrt{\pi}}\right), \tag{8.41a}$$

$$P_2(x \geqslant kD) = 1-\frac{4k^2\bar{D}^2}{2\pi\bar{x}^2}P_1(m=2), \tag{8.41b}$$

$$P_3(x \geqslant kD) = 1+\frac{1}{2}\left(\frac{9k^2\bar{D}^2}{2\pi\bar{x}^2}+\frac{81k^4\bar{D}^4}{4\pi^2\bar{x}^4}\right)P_1(m=3)-\frac{9k^2\bar{D}^2}{4\pi\bar{x}^2}, \tag{8.41c}$$

$$P_4(x \geqslant kD) = 1-\frac{1}{6}\left(\frac{192k^4\bar{D}^4}{\pi^2\bar{x}^4}+\frac{512k^6\bar{D}^6}{\pi^3\bar{x}^6}\right)P_1(m=4)+\frac{32k^4\bar{D}^4}{3\pi^2\bar{x}^4}\cdot \tag{8.41d}$$

From Fig. 8.9 it is clear that the widths of the S-matrix poles begin to diverge considerably from those of the R-matrix levels when the sum of the half widths is greater than the level spacing. If we take this as the criterion for k ($k = 2$) in eqns. (8.41) above, and assume that $\bar{x} = n\bar{D}/2\pi$ (strong coupling), we find $P_1 = 0{\cdot}036$, $P_2 = 0{\cdot}10$, $P_3 = 0{\cdot}19$, $P_4 = 0{\cdot}25$ for the probabilities that a pair of R-matrix levels give rise to a quasi-resonance. Dramatic quasi-resonance effects can be expected for $k = 4$ for which the probabilities become $P_1 = 0{\cdot}0097$, $P_2 = 0{\cdot}029$, $P_3 = 0{\cdot}056$, $P_4 = 0{\cdot}099$. Values of n varying between 1 and 4 are actually expected for slow neutron-induced fission of the even-charge, odd-mass transuranic nuclei. These probabilities show that the statistics to be expected for the properties of the observed quasi-resonances can be different from those of the basic R-matrix level parameters.

(*f*) *Mixed resonances*

It is to be remembered also that the cross-sections of these nuclei are due to two sequences of levels of different spin. The probability that two levels of different spin are close neighbours is even greater. If we assume that the first level is a random point so far as the other sequence is concerned, the probability of the spacing to the next level lying between D and $D+\mathrm{d}D$ is (see Chapter V, Section C)

$$p(D)\mathrm{d}D = \frac{1}{\bar{D}}\exp\!\left(-\frac{\pi D^2}{4\bar{D}^2}\right)\mathrm{d}D, \tag{8.42}$$

where $\bar{D}$ is the mean spacing of levels in the second sequence. By the same arguments as above we find, in the case when the sequences have the same mean spacing and widths, that the probability that a level of the first sequence is masked by one of the second sequence is

$$P_n^M(x \geqslant k\bar{D}) = \frac{2^{\frac{1}{2}}}{\pi^{\frac{1}{2}}}\exp\left(\frac{\bar{D}^2}{2\pi}\frac{n^2k^2}{4\bar{x}^2}\right)\sum_{\mu=1}^{n}\left(\frac{knD}{\bar{x}\sqrt{(2\pi)}}\right)^{\mu-1}\mathscr{D}_{-\mu}\left(\frac{nk}{\bar{x}}\frac{D}{\sqrt{(2\pi)}}\right). \tag{8.43}$$

The explicit results for the lowest values of n are

$$P_1^M(x \geqslant kD) \equiv P_1^M(m=1) = \frac{2}{\sqrt{\pi}}\exp\left(\frac{m^2k^2D^2}{4\pi\bar{x}^2}\right)\mathrm{Erfc}\left(\frac{mkD}{2\bar{x}\sqrt{\pi}}\right), \tag{8.44a}$$

$$P_2^M(x \geqslant kD) \equiv P_2^M(m=2) = P_1^M(m=2)+\frac{mkD}{\bar{x}\pi}P_1(m=2), \tag{8.44b}$$

$$P_3^M(x \geqslant kD) = P_2^M(m=3)+\frac{9k^2D^2}{4\bar{x}^2\pi}\left\{\left(1+\frac{9k^2D^2}{2\bar{x}^2\pi}\right)P_1^M(m=3)-\frac{3kD}{\bar{x}\pi}\right\}. \tag{8.44c}$$

For strong coupling and complete masking (defined by $k = 2$, say) $P_1^M = 0{\cdot}15$, $P_2^M = 0{\cdot}30$, $P_3^M = 0{\cdot}41$.

A single maximum in the cross-section may thus be due to two (or more) levels of different spin (a mixed resonance) with the result that there is even more confusion in their properties.

3. Experimental data on neutron-induced fission; even-compound nuclei

(a) *Evidence from the (d, pf) and other reactions*

The compound nucleus formed in the (d, p) reaction is the same as that formed by neutron absorption in the same target. In the (d, p) reaction, however, states below the neutron emission threshold can be excited. The resolution is such, of course, that individual states cannot be resolved, and also states with a high range of angular momentum and both parities are formed. Nevertheless, the observation of fission following the (d, p) reaction can give important information about the fission properties of the compound nucleus states below zero neutron energy.

The striking yield curve of the ^{239}Pu (d, pf) reaction (Northrop *et al.*) is shown in Fig. 8.14. Since gamma radiation is the only reaction competing with fission in the decay of compound nucleus states below the neutron threshold, the (d, pf) yield will saturate for a set of states of a particular spin and parity at a considerable energy (of the order of

100 keV) below the lowest fission threshold energy E_f for that set of states. This is because the total radiation width of compound nucleus states probably changes little for the first few MeV of energy below the neutron threshold, and therefore has a value of a few tens of meV in this energy region, while the fission width is a fairly large, almost constant, fraction of the level spacing, which increases quite rapidly with decreasing energy below neutron threshold. The tunnelling factor T_f therefore has to be quite small before the fission and radiation widths are of comparable magnitude. The structure in a yield curve like that

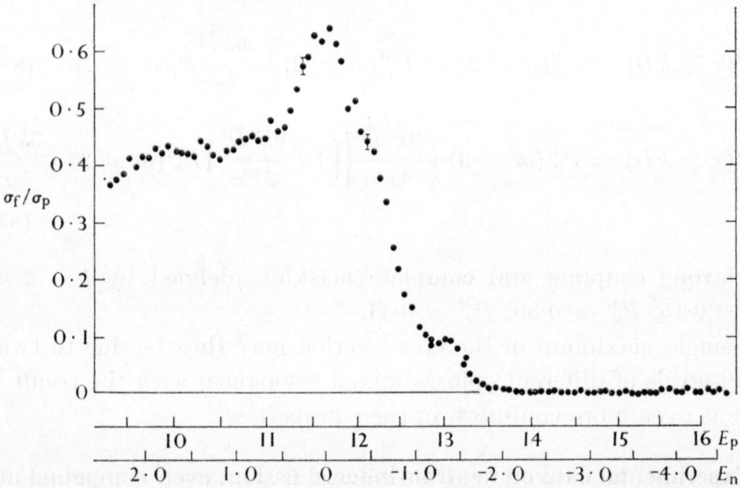

FIG. 8.14. Yield curve in (d, pf) reaction on ^{239}Pu. The lowest abscissa scale gives the excitation energy relative to the neutron emission threshold in ^{240}Pu. The proton energy is denoted by E_p and the total (d, p) cross-section by σ_p (after Northrop *et al.* 1959).

in Fig. 8.14 is thus due to the energy separation of the lowest fission thresholds of different classes of states. The first rise and plateau is probably due to fission of the 0^+, 2^+ 4^+, . . . sequence of states (the difference in threshold of the rotational sequence being too small to be observable against the exponential rise in the tunnelling factors). There will be negligible increase in the yield due to these states with the opening of their higher saddle-point channels. This first rise is therefore a measure of the position of the threshold of the $K^\pi = 0^+$ (ground) and associated rotational band of saddle-point channels; they are of the order of 100–200 keV above the mid-point of the rising curve. The second rise is probably due to the appearance of one or more of the set of thresholds $K^\pi = 0^-$, $I^\pi = \underline{1}^-, \underline{3}^-, \underline{5}^-, \ldots$, $K^\pi = 1^-$, $I^\pi = \underline{1}^-, \underline{2}^-, \underline{3}^-, \ldots$, $K^\pi = 2^+$, $I^\pi = 2^+, \underline{3}^+, 4^+, \underline{5}^+$, $K^\pi = 1^+$, $I^\pi = \underline{1}^+, 2^+, \underline{3}^+, \ldots$ (the underlined spins being those that will contribute to the increase in yield).

The lowest of these must be at least 500 keV (assuming $\hbar\omega \approx 0{\cdot}4$ MeV) above the $K^\pi = 0^+$ channel to allow a plateau to separate this rise from the first rise. Some useful information about the channel thresholds is thus obtained from the (d, pf) reaction. The reaction indicates that the fission threshold of ^{240}Pu is about 1·5 MeV below the neutron emission threshold.

The ^{233}U(d, pf) reaction shows a similar structure to ^{239}Pu(d, pf) with a similar fission-threshold relative to the neutron threshold of ^{234}U, but the ^{235}U(d, pf) does not show such structure; this indicates that the thresholds for the second and perhaps third or fourth groups of states are separated from each other by less than about 300 keV. The fission threshold of ^{236}U appears to lie between 0·6 and 0·9 MeV below the neutron threshold according to this reaction, but the ^{234}U(t, pf) reaction (also exciting compound nucleus levels in ^{236}U) shows that the fission threshold is at least 0·5 MeV below this estimate (Eccleshall and Yates 1965). The reason for the difference appears to be the assumption made in interpreting the (d, pf) results that compound nucleus levels of all spins and parities are excited to roughly the same degree. Specht *et al.* (1966) have calculated the differential cross-sections for forming single-particle neutron states in ^{236}U by the (d, p) reaction. The single-neutron states were assumed to be the Nilsson states of a deformed potential, and the cross-sections were calculated for all such Nilsson states expected within an energy region of 3 MeV around the fission threshold energy.

The results showed that only some of the even parity Nilsson orbitals are strongly excited by the reaction. These are coupled to the odd-parity neutron of the ground state of ^{235}U. If (as is very likely) these two quasi-particle states are dissolved into the compound nucleus over only a limited energy range then the compound nucleus states that are predominantly excited near the fission threshold are clearly those of odd parity, and the fission 'threshold' observed in the (d, pf) reaction really corresponds to the odd-parity levels in the transition-state spectrum. Thus the $K^\pi = 0^-$ transition state band (the mass asymmetry vibration) probably lies about 0·5 MeV above the $K^\pi = 0^+$ band. It has also been shown by use of the (t, pf) reaction that the fission threshold of ^{242}Pu is 0·7–1·0 MeV below its neutron threshold (Britt *et al.* 1966).

More information on the K-values of transition states can be obtained from measurements of the angular distributions of fission products from the (d, pf) reaction. These can be interpreted (Britt *et al.* 1963) to give the mean value of K^2 over all the transition state spectrum below the energy at which the measurement is made. Thus, the average value of K^2 as a function of energy for the compound nucleus ^{240}Pu is close to zero from the fission-threshold energy to about 700 keV above this, and there it rises to a value of about 3. It stays at this value until about 1600 keV where it increases again to about 8. The next increase, a continuing one, does not occur until about 2·3 MeV above the fission threshold. It is believed that the first step (at 700 keV) is the position of the γ-vibration ($K = 2$) band, and the second step would be the position of the two-phonon γ-vibrations (with $K = 0$ and $K = 4$). Strutinsky (1965) has argued, however, that the second step is due to excitations of two quasi-particles, in other words that the energy gap of even nuclei at the saddle point is about 1·6 MeV. The interpretation of Britt *et al.* is that the energy gap is higher, being associated with the big rise in K^2 in the region of 2·3–2·6 MeV. This is supported by the evidence of the angular distribution of fission products produced in fast neutron-induced fission (Griffin 1963), and by the appearance of a small step-like rise in the total fission cross-sections of a number of nuclei at about 2·2 MeV above the fission threshold (Stein *et al.* 1966). This implies that in the slow neutron-induced fission of even-charge, odd-mass nuclei, in which the available excitation energy is less than 2 MeV above the fission threshold, the properties of intrinsic transition states need not be considered. A summary (following Wheeler 1963) of much of our present information about the transition-state spectrum of an even nucleus is given in Table 8.1.

Although the energy E_f is the principal quantity we wish to know about each transition state, the tunnelling parameter, $\hbar\omega_f$, is also important. Usachev *et al.* (1964) have analysed the (d, pf) data and various photofission data in an attempt to extract this quantity. Their results, for even compound nuclei, range from 0·31 MeV in ^{240}Pu to 0·7 MeV in ^{238}U. It is difficult to assess the accuracy of these estimates. Their considerable variation is not necessarily an argument against them, because such changes in the thickness and curvature of the potential-energy barrier can be expected not only from nucleus to nucleus (see Section A on the liquid-drop model), but also from one transition level to another.

(*b*) ^{233}U

The target nucleus ^{233}U has ground state spin and parity $I^{\pi} = 5/2^{+}$. There are two sets of levels formed in the even compound nucleus ^{234}U by *s*-wave neutron bombardment; one set has total angular momentum and parity $J^{\pi} = 2^{+}$ and the other has $J^{\pi} = 3^{+}$. The fission threshold of ^{234}U has been observed in the ^{233}U (d, pf) reaction to lie between 1·3 and 1·5 MeV below the neutron-separation energy

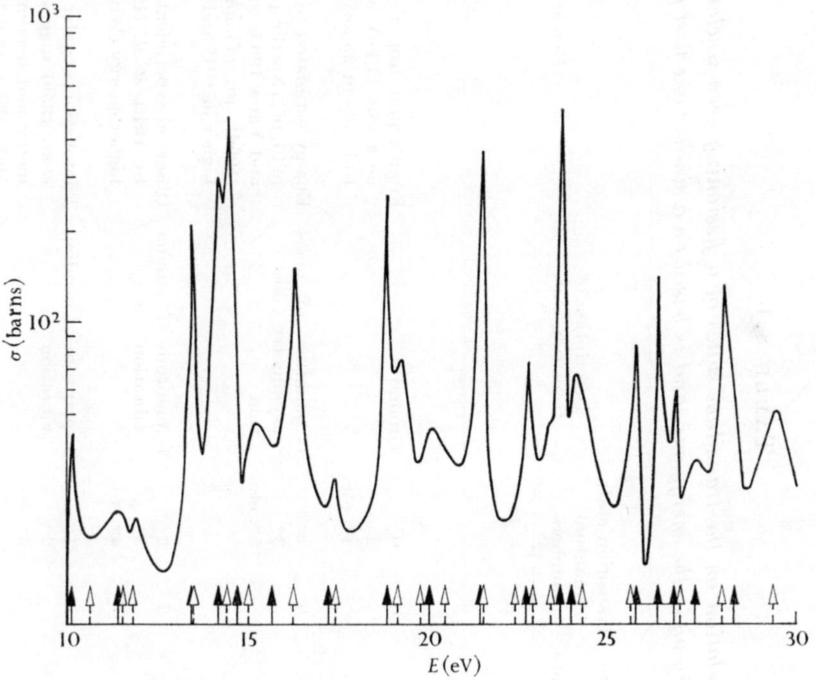

FIG. 8.15. Simulated cross-section with random generation of level parameters. Three open saddle-point channels for one spin and two open channels for the other were assumed. Level positions are indicated by vertical arrows (of different type for different spin). These conditions are expected to approximate those holding for slow neutron bombardment of ^{233}U.

(Northrop *et al.* 1959, Usachev *et al.* 1964). According to the conclusion of Griffin (1963) and Britt *et al.* (1963) that the energy gap of even nuclei at the saddle point is about 2·3 MeV, the neutron-separation energy of this and other fissioning even nuclei is well below the transition states of intrinsic excitation. From Table 8.1 it is apparent that there are between two and four open fission channels for the resonances in the slow neutron cross-section of ^{233}U with $J^{\pi} = 2^{+}$, and between one

TABLE 8.1

A summary of evidence and speculation on the transition states of a fissioning even nucleus. The table is confined to states of a simple collective nature lying in the energy gap, and is based on a similar one first presented by Wheeler (1963)

Approximate features on the energy scale (origin is the fission threshold)	Approximate energy of transition state (in MeV)	Transition state quantum numbers K^{π}	I^{π}	Description of transition state	Remarks and references
0·0 MeV (fission threshold) →	0·0	0^+	0^+, 2^+, 4^+, etc.	'Ground'	From liquid drop model, the 2^+ state is estimated to lie about 11 keV above 0^+ state, and the 4^+ state to lie about 35 keV above 0^+ state.
	~0·5	0^-	1^-, 3^-, 5^-, etc.	1 quantum of mass asymmetry vibration	Energy estimated from different observed thresholds of (d, pf) (Northrop *et al.* 1959) and (t, pf) (Eccleshall and Yates 1965) with interpretation of Specht *et al.* (1966). (d, pf) indicates that energy is perhaps higher in ^{234}U and ^{240}Pu than in ^{236}U.
$\approx E_{th,n}$ for ^{242}Pu ⟶	~0·7	2^+	2^+, 3^+, 4^+ etc.,	1 quantum of gamma vibration	Observed experimentally in (d, pf) angular distribution by Britt *et al.* (1963) for ^{240}Pu. Theory suggests higher energy (Wheeler 1963).
1·0 MeV ⟶	~0·9	1^-	1^-, 2^-, 3^-, etc.	1 quantum of bending vibration	Photofission angular distribution experiments (Baerg *et al.* 1959) suggest difference between mass asymmetry and bending vibrations to range from 0·23 MeV (^{240}Pu) to 0·5 MeV (^{234}U).

$\approx E_{\mathrm{th,n}}$ for ^{236}U ⟶	~1·2	2^-	2^-, 3^-, 4^-, etc.	1 quantum of mass asymmetry vibration combined with 1 quantum of gamma vibration	
$\approx E_{\mathrm{th,n}}$ for ^{234}U ⟶ $\approx E_{\mathrm{th,n}}$ for ^{240}Pu ⟶	~1·4	1^+	1^+, 2^+, 3^+, etc.	1 quantum of mass asymmetry vibration combined with 1 quantum of bending vibration	Important combination state suggested by Griffin (1965) and estimated by him from liquid-drop model to lie in range 1 to 1·5 MeV.
⟶ (Top of energy gap according to Strutinsky 1965)	~1·6	0^+ 4^+	0^+, 2^+, etc. 4^+, 5^+, etc.	2 quanta of gamma vibration	Observed in angular distribution of (d, pf) for ^{240}Pu (Britt *et al.* 1963); but interpreted by Strutinsky (1965) as 2 quasi-particle excitation marking top of energy gap.
	~1·7	1^- 3^-	1^-, 2^-, etc. 3^-, 4^-, etc.	1 quantum of gamma vibration combined with 1 quantum of bending vibration	
2·0 MeV ⟶ (Top of energy gap at saddle point according to Griffin 1963) ⟶					

and two open channels for those with $J^\pi = 3^+$. Thus, on the strong-coupling assumption

$$\overline{\Gamma}_{(\mathrm{F})}(J^\pi = 2^+) \approx 3(J^\pi\ \bar{D} = 2^+)/2\pi, \tag{8.45a}$$

$$\overline{\Gamma}_{(\mathrm{F})}(J^\pi = 3^+) \approx 1{\cdot}5\bar{D}(J^\pi = 3^+)/2\pi, \tag{8.45b}$$

and the average of $\pi\overline{\Gamma}_{(\mathrm{F})}/D$ per spin state (eqn. (8.33)) is about 2·25. The statistical distribution of fission widths will be of the Porter–Thomas form (chi-squared family with one degree of freedom) for the 3^+ states if there is only one channel open and will have an effective

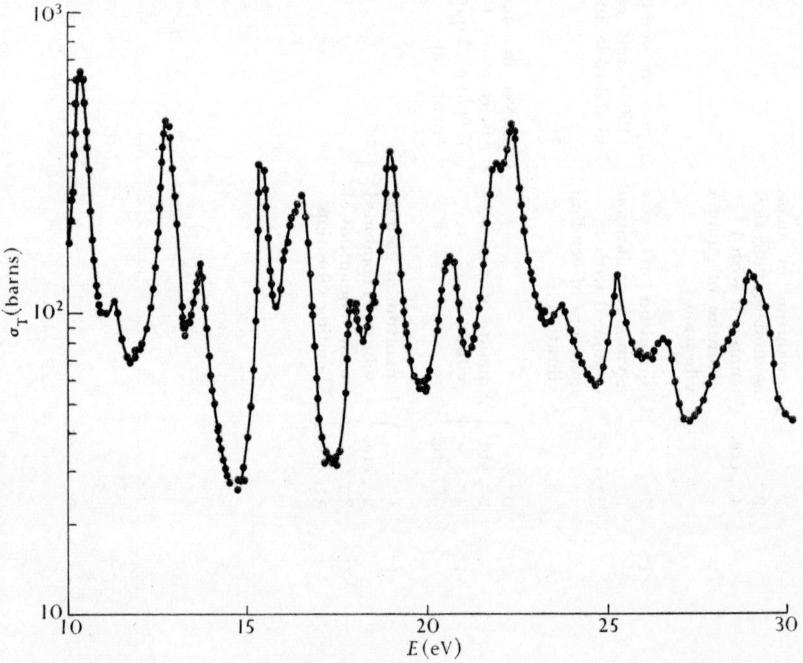

FIG. 8.16. Total cross-section of ^{233}U.

number of degrees of freedom between 1 and 2, otherwise. The distribution of the fission widths of the 2^+ state will have an effective number of degrees of freedom (eqn. (8.36)), ν^{2+}_{eff} between 2 and 3. The effective number of degrees of freedom of the overall distribution (eqn. (8.37)) is expected to lie between 1·4 and 2·7 with the weighting of probability towards the lower value. A typical total cross-section for such mean values and distributions of the fission widths is shown in Fig. 8.15. This is a calculated cross-section in which the R-matrix level parameters were randomly selected for each spin from a Wigner level-spacing distribution with a mean value of $\bar{D}(2^+) = \bar{D}(3^+) = 1$ eV, a Porter–Thomas distribution of neutron widths, and fission width distributions appropriate to three open channels for the 2^+ levels and two open channels for the 3^+ levels. The curve may be compared visually with the actual cross-section (Fig. 8.16) of ^{233}U in the same energy interval; the two have similar features, if anything the experimental data appearing more 'damped', which indicates even larger mean fission widths than those employed for the simulated curve. The important feature of the latter is the number of 'missed' or 'hidden' levels that it contains.

The detailed results of single-level analyses of the slow neutron cross-sections of ^{233}U are shown in Table 8.2. It will be remarked that most of these analyses employed many-level formalism but suffer from the defect, mentioned above, that a single peak in the cross-section is generally taken to correspond to a single level in the R-matrix scheme; in the analyses of the very detailed data below 2 eV, however, it has been found necessary to include two levels where no definite maximum appears (at 0·1 eV and 1·6 eV) as well as strong bound levels. It is significant that the properties ascribed to these levels by different workers are very different. In particular the fission width of the 0·1 eV level is quoted as 994 meV by Vogt (1960) and as 60 meV by Moore and Reich (1960). Such a large difference is partially explained by the inclusion of a strong non-interfering $E^{-\frac{1}{2}}$ absorption term in the cross-section by Moore and Reich. It is apparent that these many-level analyses are by no means unambiguous (indeed, the authors have never claimed that they are unique) but the widths that are assigned to the *observed* cross-section maxima are not very different from those that would be determined by a single-level treatment of the data. The main conclusion that has been drawn from this type of many-level analysis is that there are a few saddle-point channels available for fission of levels of both spins (Vogt 1960). The conclusion is based, not on width to spacing ratios, but on the values of the interference parameters $\cos(\theta_\lambda - \theta_{\lambda'})$, (see eqns. (8.15) in Section B.2); the mean value of the modulus of this quantity appears to be less than unity but not negligible.

To indicate that the partial widths and spacings resulting from 'single-level' analyses of the cross-section data of fissionable nuclei are not necessarily those of the R-matrix formal basis we call them pseudo-widths and pseudo-spacings and place their symbols in inverted commas. The statistics of the pseudo-widths and pseudo-spacings of the ^{233}U cross-section are shown in Table 8.3 (final column). From the analyses of observed maxima up to 25 eV (see Stehn *et al.* 1965 for a

TABLE 8.2

Analyses of neutron cross-section of ^{233}U

λ	E_λ (eV)	J^π	$\Gamma^\circ_{\lambda(n)}$ (meV)	$\Gamma_{\lambda(\gamma T)}$ (meV)	Total fission width $\Gamma_{\lambda(F)}$ (meV)	Partial fission widths $\Gamma_{\lambda(f_1)}$ (meV)	$\Gamma_{\lambda(f_2)}$ (meV)	Relative sign of $\Gamma^{\frac{1}{2}}_{\lambda(n)}\Gamma^{\frac{1}{2}}_{\lambda(f_1)}$	$\Gamma^{\frac{1}{2}}_{\lambda(n)}\Gamma^{\frac{1}{2}}_{\lambda(f_2)}$	θ_λ	Remarks	Reference
1	−1·0	as $\lambda = 5$	0·10/2g	45 (assd.)	170					0°	1	Pattenden and Harvey (1960)
2	−0·3	not $\lambda = 5$	0·044/2g	45 (assd.)	960					0°	1	Pattenden and Harvey (1960)
3	0·10	not $\lambda = 5$	0·0586/2g	56	994					0°	2	Vogt (1960)
	0·150	3^+	0·00002	30	60	35	25	−	+		3	Moore and Reich (1960)
	0·188	as $\lambda = 5$	0·00046/2g	40	63					0°	1	Pattenden and Harvey (1960)
	0·195	3^+	0·00059	44	60	60		+			3	Moore and Reich (1960)
4	1·45	not $\lambda = 5$	0·152/2g	54	716					99·6°	2	Vogt (1960)
	1·55	2^+	0·165	60	562						3	Moore and Reich (1960)
	1·56	3^+	0·104	30	420	0	420	−	+		3	Moore and Reich (1960)
	1·61	not $\lambda = 5$	0·142/2g	45 (assd.)	600					150°	1	Pattenden and Harvey (1960)
5	1·755	3^+	0·162	36	186	186	0	−			3	Moore and Reich (1960)
	1·76	3^+	0·155	36	182	182		−			3	Moore and Reich (1960)
	1·76		0·235/2g	49	231					0°	2	Vogt (1960)
	1·785		0·225/2g	45 (assd.)	210					150°	1	Pattenden and Harvey (1960)

6	2·30	as $\lambda = 5$	0·116/2g	47	49					119·7°	2	Vogt (1960)
	2·305	3^+	0·086	34·6	48	45·6	2·4	+	−		3	Moore and Reich (1960)
	2·307	as $\lambda = 5$	0·115/2g	45 (assd.)	50					295°	1	Pattenden and Harvey (1960)
	2·31	3^+	0·086	34·6	48	48		+			3	Moore and Reich (1960)
7	3·61	3^+	0·060	62	174	174		+			3	Moore and Reich (1960)
	3·65	3^+	0·057	53	149	129	20	+	+		3	Moore and Reich (1960)
	3·64	as $\lambda = 5$	0·084/2g	48	212					210·7°	2	Vogt (1960)
	3·64	as $\lambda = 5$	0·074/2g	45 (assd.)	155					20°	1	Pattenden and Harvey (1960)
8	4·75	2^+	1·130	80	718	718					3	Moore and Reich (1960)
	4·825	3^+	0·105	80	850	750	100	+	−		3	Moore and Reich (1960)
	4·80	not $\lambda = 5$	0·164/2g	60	740					225°	2	Vogt (1960)
	4·79	not $\lambda = 5$	0·187/2g	45 (assd.)	950					240°	1	Pattenden and Harvey (1960)
9	5·82	3^+	0·047	80	316	316		−			3	Moore and Reich (1960)
	5·85	as $\lambda = 5$	0·041/2g	45 (assd.)	195					230°	1	Pattenden and Harvey (1960)
10	6·82	3^+	0·300	55	146	146		+			3	Moore and Reich (1960)
	6·77	as $\lambda = 5$	0·203/2g	50	160					210°	2	Vogt (1960)
	6·85	as $\lambda = 5$	0·41/2g	45 (assd.)	165					80°	1	Pattenden and Harvey (1960)
11	7·6	3^+	0·007	48	125	125		−			3	Moore and Reich (1960)
	7·57	as $\lambda = 5$	0·015/2g	45 (assd.)	90					200°	1	Pattenden and Harvey (1960)
12	8·7	3^+	0·010	40	300	300		−			3	Moore and Reich (1960)
	8·78	not $\lambda = 5$	0·067/2g	45 (assd.)	700					15°	1	Pattenden and Harvey (1960)

Remarks

1. Assumes two-channel fission.
2. Analysis includes a contribution of $\sigma_T = 3{\cdot}25/E^{\frac{1}{2}}$barns and $\sigma_F = 1{\cdot}30/E^{\frac{1}{2}}$barns from distant levels.
3. Analysis includes non-interfering component of $\sigma_T = 73/E^{\frac{1}{2}}$barns, $\sigma_F = 68/E^{\frac{1}{2}}$barns.

compilation of data above the energy range of Table 8.2) quantities such as the mean pseudo-spacing, pseudo-strength function, mean pseudo-fission width, and the characteristic parameters of the statistical distributions are calculated. The characteristic statistical parameter that has been universally employed is the number of degrees of freedom, ν_{ML}, of an assumed chi-squared distribution. This has been used, even for the resonance spacing distribution, which is known to be of different form, because it is easy to determine using the maximum likelihood method (see Chapter VI, Section B.2). Use of the second moment of the distribution, which is also easy to calculate from the observed data, has been discarded because of the much larger relative standard deviation associated with its determination for chi-squared distributions with a small number of degrees of freedom. Having found these statistical parameters of the data we can compare them with similar ones found for simulated cross-section curves like that in Fig. 8.15.

While this 'single-resonance' approach seems to be a good way of cataloguing the properties of the cross-section maxima we also need a way of treating the minima because it is in the minima that the low, broad components of the quasi-resonances and the mixed resonances will have their greatest relative influence. Two methods have been used for dealing with them. One recognizes that in the narrow level limit the cross-section in the minimum is usually just the potential scattering cross-section. Resonance scattering is usually negligible at low energies in the fissionable nuclei cross-section so the absorption cross-section, $\sigma_{(\mathrm{a})}$, is used as a measure of the filling-in of the minima due to resonance overlap. The mean value of the quantity $\sigma_{(\mathrm{a})}(\mathrm{min})E^{\frac{1}{2}}$ (denoted hereafter by S_1) has been calculated for the cross-section data and for the simulated cross-sections, together with an effective ν-value, labelled ν_{s1}, for its distribution. Two auxiliary quantities, $\sigma_{(\mathrm{a})}(\mathrm{min})E^{\frac{1}{2}}`D'/\langle `g\Gamma^0_{(\mathrm{n})}'\rangle$ (denoted by S_2) and $\sigma_{(\mathrm{a})}(\mathrm{min})E^{\frac{1}{2}}`D'^2/\{\langle `g\Gamma^0_{(\mathrm{n})}'\rangle(\langle `\Gamma_{(\mathrm{F})}'\rangle + \langle `\Gamma_{(\gamma)}'\rangle)\}$ (denoted by S_3), have also been examined in an attempt to reduce the influence of the high minima between pairs of close, strong maxima.

The second method recognizes that fission will greatly predominate over capture in the broad components of the quasi-resonances, so the statistics of α, the ratio of capture to fission, in the minima, have been examined in the cases in which there are data on this quantity (Brooks and Jolly, 1963, 1965). The statistics of α have also been computed for the maxima as a matter of interest. In the calculations of the statistics of α, the distorting effect of the (n, γF) reaction has been taken into

Table 8.3

Comparison of the statistics of simulated cross-sections with those of the experimental data on ^{233}U and ^{241}Pu

$T_f(J^\pi = 2^+)$	1·0, 1·0, 0·08	1·0, 1·0, 0·33	1·0, 1·0, 0·67	1·0, 1·0, 1·0	0·2, 0·2, 0·2, 0·2	Data on ^{233}U	Data on ^{241}Pu
$T_f(J^\pi = 3^+)$	1·0, 0·0	1·0, 0·33	1·0, 0·67	1·0, 1·0	0·2, 0·2, 0·2, 0·2		
$\langle 'D' \rangle$	0·82 ± 0·07	0·76 ± 0·07	0·80 ± 0·07	0·87 ± 0·07		1·03 ± 0·1	1·1 ± 0·2
ν_D	5·5 ± 1·0	5·7 ± 1·1	8·0 ± 1·6	5·7 ± 1·1		7·7 ± 2·1	6·2 ± 1·4
$\langle 'g\Gamma^{\circ}_{(n)}' \rangle / \langle 'D' \rangle$	0·56 ± 0·09	0·80 ± 0·12	0·81 ± 0·13	0·53 ± 0·06		0·97 ± 0·16	1·3 ± 0·2
ν_n	1·5 ± 0·3	1·6 ± 0·3	1·5 ± 0·3	1·7 ± 0·3		2·9 ± 0·8	1·8 ± 0·4
$\pi \langle '\Gamma_{(F)}' \rangle / \langle 'D' \rangle$	0·45 ± 0·07	0·66 ± 0·08	0·74 ± 0·07	0·72 ± 0·08		0·95 ± 0·12	0·64 ± 0·1
ν_F	1·7 ± 0·3	3·0 ± 0·6	4·7 ± 0·9	3·0 ± 0·6		4·8 ± 1·3	2·4 ± 0·5
S_1	122 ± 16	168 ± 11	158 ± 20	152 ± 20	97 ± 20	202 + 25	270 ± 50
ν_{S_1}	2·2 ± 0·4	3·7 ± 0·8	3·1 ± 0·6	2·8 ± 0·6	1·9 ± 0·5	7·4 ± 2·4	2·7 ± 0·7
S_2	1530 ± 200	1700 ± 170	1500 ± 150	2100 ± 200	700 ± 100	2210 ± 400	
S_3	8·2 ± 1·3	7·2 ± 1·0	5·0 ± 0·7	8·6 ± 1·1	3·0 ± 0·5	7·6 ± 1·5	
$\langle \alpha_{(max)} \rangle$	1·3 ± 0·2	0·73 ± 0·1	0·29 ± 0·03	0·38 ± 0·04		0·21 ± 0·05	
$\nu_{\alpha(max)}$	1·3 ± 0·2	1·8 ± 0·3	6·2 ± 1·2	2·9 ± 0·6		4 ± 2	
$\langle \alpha_{(min)} \rangle$	0·60 ± 0·07	0·42 ± 0·05	0·42 ± 0·05	0·36 ± 0·04		0·13 ± 0·04	
$\nu_{\alpha(min)}$	3·5 ± 0·6	3·4 ± 0·7	3·1 ± 0·6	2·6 ± 0·5		6·5 ± 3	

account. In the case of ^{235}U the (n, γF) reaction will set an upper limit of between 10 and 20 on α (see Section C.4).

The first striking feature of Table 8.3 is the characteristic parameter of the pseudo-resonance spacing distribution $\nu_{\text{`D'}} = 7{\cdot}7 \pm 2{\cdot}1$. For a sequence of levels with the same set of good quantum numbers (Wigner distribution, eqn. (5.11)) it is expected to be $\nu_{\text{D}} = 6{\cdot}3$, and for two superposed sequences with the same mean value $\nu_{\text{D}} = 3{\cdot}3$. The observed result at first suggests that the observed resonances are of one spin only (presumably 3^+) and this agrees with the suggestion of Moore and Reich (1960) that the strong $E^{-\frac{1}{2}}$ absorption cross-section necessary to their fit is due to the levels of the other spin (2^+). This suggestion is untenable on the grounds that numerical experiments show very strong fluctuations in the total cross-section even when there are as many as twelve fully open fission channels available: the 2^+ component of the cross-section cannot be a smooth $E^{-\frac{1}{2}}$ curve. Other important features of Table 8·3 are the value of $\pi\langle\text{`}\Gamma_{\text{F}}\text{'}\rangle/\langle\text{`}D\text{'}\rangle$ ($= 0{\cdot}95 \pm 0{\cdot}12$, considerably lower than the expected value of about 2·25) and the value of $\nu_{\text{`F'}}$ ($= 4{\cdot}8 \pm 1{\cdot}3$, rather higher than the expected value). An unexpected feature of the ^{233}U data that is not included in Table 8·3 is the fluctuation in pseudo-total radiation widths (from 30 to 80 meV according to Table 8.2). The high value of the cross-section between resonances (to which attention has been drawn by the inclusion of the $E^{-\frac{1}{2}}$ term in the detailed fits) is shown in Table 8.3 by including the results of the analysis of the absorption cross-section minima.

All these results can be explained by applying the channel theory of fission to obtain the expected R-matrix theory parameters of the cross-section. Numerical experiments in which level parameters have been selected at random from Wigner distributions for the spacings and Porter–Thomas distributions for the channel widths have been carried out using a digital computer (Lynn 1966); the total and partial cross-sections generated from these (a typical total cross-section curve has already been shown in Fig. 8.15) have been analysed using the single-level procedure usually employed for experimental data (see Chapter I). In this, a background term is removed from under each identifiable resonance peak and, from the resulting resonance width and total and partial peak cross-sections, the pseudo-partial widths are calculated. The statistical analysis of the results for various assumptions concerning the fission channels are given in Table 8·3 and some of them are plotted in Fig. 8.17. The other mean parameters assumed in these calculations were $\bar{D}^{(2+)} = \bar{D}^{(3+)} = 1$ eV, $\bar{\Gamma}^{\circ}{}_{(\text{n})}/\bar{D} = 1\times10^{-4}$, $\Gamma_{(\gamma\text{T})} = 0{\cdot}040$ eV. The

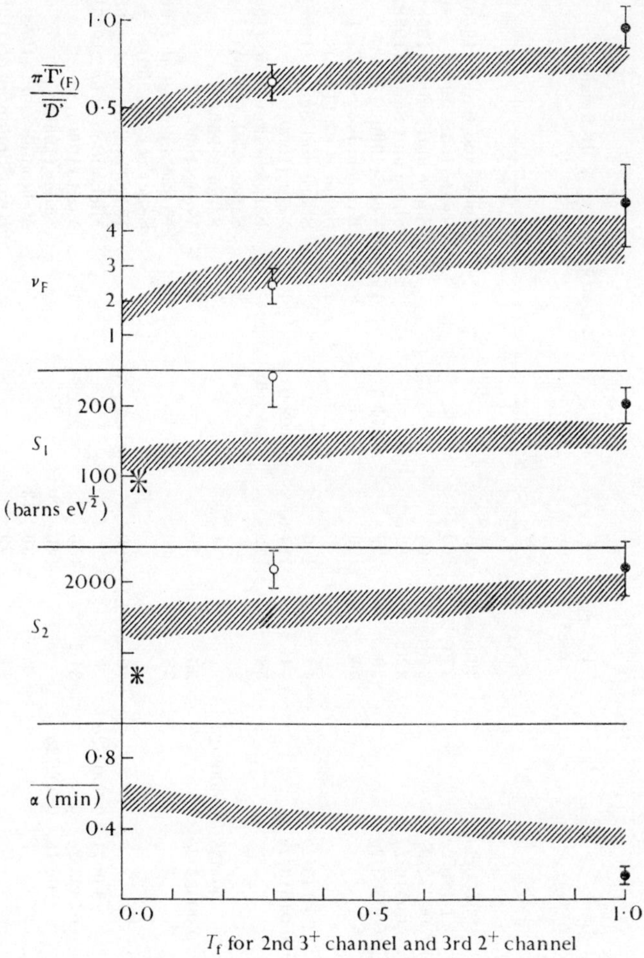

FIG. 8.17. Statistics of the cross-sections of ^{233}U and ^{241}Pu. For the theoretical simulated cross-sections (statistics shown by hatching) it was assumed the first and second 2^+ and first 3^+ channels had transmission factors of unity. Statistics from ^{233}U data are shown by full circles and those from ^{241}Pu data by open circles, while those from the simulation of a simple interpretation are shown by asterisks.

results for the case $N(J_+) \approx 2$, $N(J_-) \approx 3$ are in reasonable agreement with the experimental data of Table 8·3; indeed the results indicate that an even higher (probably 2-γ phonon, $K = 0$) transition state is open to some degree. Furthermore, this case results in fluctuations of pseudo-radiation width values by a factor of more than 2. There appears to be no disagreement with the unified theory of the transition states.

TABLE 8.4

Analyses of neutron cross section of ^{235}U

λ	E_λ (eV)	J^π	$\Gamma^\circ_{\lambda(n)}$ (meV)	$\Gamma_{\lambda(\gamma T)}$ (meV)	$\Gamma_{\lambda(F)}$ (meV)	θ_λ	Remarks	Reference
1	−1·45	not $\lambda = 3$	3·056/2g	33 (assd.)	223			Shore and Sailor (1958)
	−0·95	as $\lambda = 3$	1·488/2g	27·6	169·4	0°	1	Vogt (1958, 1960)
2	−0·02	not $\lambda = 3$	0·00072/2g	34 (assd.)	63			Shore and Sailor (1958)
3	0·282		0·00516/2g	32·2	82·5			Shore and Sailor (1958)
	0·273		0·00563/2g	29	99	277·5°	1	Vogt (1960)
	0·300			36	99			Kirpichnikov *et al.* (1964)
		3⁻(?)					2	Sailor *et al.* (1966)
4	1·138	as $\lambda = 3$	0·0143/2g	42	106			Shore and Sailor (1958)
	1·140	as $\lambda = 3$	0·01613/2g	44	124·6	103·9°	1	Vogt (1960)
	1·14			38	112	155±5°		Kirpichnikov *et al.* (1964)
		not $\lambda = 3$					2	Sailor *et al.* (1966)
5	2·035±·005		0·0055±0·0003/2g		14±5			Sailor (1956)
	2·035	not $\lambda = 3$	0·00537/2g	35	12		1	Vogt (1960)
	2·04			38	10			Kirpichnikov *et al.* (1964)
		as $\lambda = 3$					2	Sailor *et al.* (1966)
6	2·80			40 (assd.)	160	−65±5°		Kirpichnikov *et al.* (1964)
	2·83		0·0071±0·0008/2g					Michaudon *et al.* (1965)
7	3·16	as $\lambda = 3$	0·01823/2g	31·1	155	225°	1	Vogt (1960)
	3·14±·05		0·018±0·002/2g		140±70			Sailor (1956)
					36±13			Melkonian *et al.* (1958)
	3·13			44	79			Kirpichnikov *et al.* (1964)
	3·14		0·0158±0·0008/2g	51±9	116±15			Michaudon *et al.* (1965)
8	3·599	as $\lambda = 3$	0·0243/2g	37	45			Shore and Sailor (1958)
					97±50			Melkonian *et al.* (1958)
	3·60			40	43	±~150°		Kirpichnikov *et al.* (1964)

	3·61		$0·025 \pm 0·001/2g$	46 ± 5	47 ± 5		Michaudon *et al.* (1965)
9	$4·84 \pm ·03$		$0·0282 \pm 0·0015/2g$		19 ± 7		Sailor (1956)
					2·9		Bowman *et al.* (1963)
	4·84			44	4		Kirpichnikov *et al.* (1964)
	4·84		$0·027 \pm 0·0013/2g$	37 ± 4	38 ± 5		Michaudon *et al.* (1965)
10	5·45			40 (assd.)	23		Kirpichnikov *et al.* (1964)
	5·45		$\approx 0·0038/2g$				Michaudon *et al.* (1965)
11	6·20				12		Bowman *et al.* (1963)
	6·20				260		Kirpichnikov *et al.* (1964)
	6·19		$0·014 \pm 0·0015/2g$				Michaudon *et al.* (1965)
12	6·40	as $\lambda = 3$	$0·100/2g$	33 (assd.)	9		Shore and Sailor (1958)
	6·38				6·4		Havens *et al.* (1959)
	6·40				7·2		Bowman *et al.* (1963)
	6·40				11		Kirpichnikov *et al.* (1964)
	6·38		$0·103 \pm 0·006/2g$	33 ± 3	12 ± 2		Michaudon *et al.* (1965)
13	7·09			33 (assd.)	16		Havens *et al.* (1959)
	7·10				31		Bowman *et al.* (1963)
	7·09			40 (assd.)	25		Kirpichinkov *et al.* (1964)
	7·07		$0·047 \pm 0·002/2g$	36 ± 5	28 ± 4		Michaudon *et al.* (1965)
14	8·795	as $\lambda = 3$	$0·257/2g$	33 (assd.)	60		Shore and Sailor (1958)
		as $\lambda = 3$				2	Sailor *et al.* (1966)
	8·79			33 (assd.)	30		Havens *et al.* (1959)
	8·78		$0·04 \pm 0·02/2g$	50 ± 10	82 ± 10		Michaudon *et al.* (1965)
	8·85				54		Bowman *et al.* (1963)
		3				3	Poortmans *et al.* (1966)
15	9·28			33 (assd.)	4·4		Havens *et al.* (1959)
	9·3				19		Bowman *et al.* (1963)
	9·28		$0·066 \pm 0·012/2g$	65 ± 35	95 ± 40		Michaudon *et al.* (1965)
16	9·75				4·1		Bowman *et al.* (1963)
	9·74		$0·0083 \pm 0·0015/2g$				Michaudon *et al.* (1965)
17	10·10				35		Bowman *et al.* (1963)
18	10·20				13		Bowman *et al.* (1963)
	10·18		$0·020 \pm 0·002/2g$	37 ± 19	58 ± 14		Michaudon *et al.* (1965)
19	11·6		$0·171 \pm 0·015/2g$		9^{+11}_{-9}		Simpson *et al.* (1956)
	11·64			33 (assd.)	2·6		Havens *et al.* (1959)
	11·70				2·3		Bowman *et al.* (1963)

TABLE 8.4 (cont.)

Analyses of neutron cross section of ^{235}U

λ	E_λ (eV)	J^π	$\Gamma^\circ_{\lambda(n)}$ (meV)	$\Gamma_{\lambda(\gamma T)}$ (meV)	$\Gamma_{\lambda(F)}$ (meV)	θ_λ	Remarks	Reference
	11·66		0·173 ± 0·012/2*g*	36 ± 6	3·5 ± 0·6			Michaudon *et al.* (1965)
20	12·4		0·396 ± 0·025/2*g*		16 ± 12			Simpson *et al.* (1956)
	12·39		0·368 ± 0·025/2*g*	44 ± 6	24 ± 5			Michaudon *et al.* (1965)
	12·38			33 (assd.)	12			Havens *et al.* (1959)
	12·45				10·1			Bowman *et al.* (1963)
		4					3	Poortmans *et al.* (1966)
21	12·8		0·014 ± 0·005/2*g*					Simpson *et al.* (1956)
	12·90				17			Bowman *et al.* (1963)
	12·85		0·0111 ± 0·0012/2*g*	23 ± 12	60 ± 15			Michaudon *et al.* (1965)
22	13·3		0·030 ± 0·005/2*g*					Simpson *et al.* (1956)
	13·30				3·7			Bowman *et al.* (1963)
	13·28		0·015 ± 0·004/2*g*					Michaudon *et al.* (1965)
23	14·1		0·092 ± 0·010/2*g*					Simpson *et al.* (1956)
	14·1 ± 0·1			40 (assd.)	74			Ignat'ev *et al.* (1964)
	13·98		0·090 ± 0·02/2*g*					Michaudon *et al.* (1965)
24	14·7		0·032 ± 0·005					Simpson *et al.* (1956)
	14·53			33 (assd.)	40			Havens *et al.* (1959)
	14·5 ± 0·1			40 (assd.)	40			Ignat'ev *et al.* (1964)
	14·54		0·033 ± 0·0025/2*g*	29 ± 9	23 ± 7			Michaudon *et al.* (1965)
25	15·5		0·054 ± 0·005					Simpson *et al.* (1956)
	15·4		0·064 ± 0·005/2*g*	49 ± 15	49 ± 10			Michaudon *et al.* (1965)
	15·45				17			Bowman *et al.* (1963)
	15·5 ± 0·1				33			Ignat'ev *et al.* (1964)
26	16·2		0·087 ± 0·005					Simpson *et al.* (1956)
	16·0		0·092 ± 0·005/2*g*	37 ± 6	19 ± 4			Michaudon *et al.* (1965)

	16·07		33 (assd.)	9·2	Havens *et al.* (1959)
	16·15			9·5	Bowman *et al.* (1963)
	16·2 ± 0·1		40 (assd.)	17	Ignat'ev *et al.* (1964)
27	16·8	0·055 ± 0·005			Simpson *et al.* (1956)
	16·6	0·0685 ± 0·005/2g	52 ± 15	86 ± 15	Michaudon *et al.* (1965)
	16·64		33 (assd.)	23	Havens *et al.* (1959)
	16·70			27	Bowman *et al.* (1963)
	16·7 ± 0·1		40 (assd.)	37	Ignat'ev *et al.* (1964)
28	18·2	0·079 ± 0·003			Simpson *et al.* (1956)
	18·07		33 (assd.)	46	Havens *et al.* (1959)
	18·10			25	Bowman *et al.* (1963)
	18·2			37	Ignat'ev *et al.* (1964)
	18·05	0·085 ± 0·007/2g	70 ± 20	90 ± 20	Michaudon *et al.* (1965)
29	19·5 ± 0·2	0·63 ± 0·04		79 ± 22	Simpson *et al.* (1956)
	19·29	0·705 ± 0·035/2g	50 ± 8	52 ± 7	Michaudon *et al.* (1965)
	19·27		33 (assd.)	40	Havens *et al.* (1959)
	19·40			25	Bowman *et al.* (1963)
	19·4			24	Ignat'ev *et al.* (1964)
30	20·1			~250	Michaudon and Ribon (1961)
	20·15	0·029 ± 0·005/2g			Michaudon *et al.* (1965)

Remarks

1. Analysis includes distant level contribution of $\sigma_T = 2{\cdot}0/\sqrt{E}$ barns and $\sigma_F = 1{\cdot}3/\sqrt{E}$ barns.
2. From polarized nucleus and neutron measurements.
3. From scattering yield measurements combined with other partial cross-section yields.

(*c*) ^{235}U

The ground state of the ^{235}U nucleus has spin and parity $I^{\pi} = 7/2^-$; the *s*-wave neutron resonances correspond to levels of ^{236}U with total angular momentum and parity $J^{\pi} = 3^-$ and 4^-. The fission threshold of ^{236}U is more than 1 MeV below the neutron separation energy (Eccleshall and Yates 1965) and we conclude from Table 8.1 that $N(3^-)$ should lie between 1 and 2 and $N(4^-)$ between 0 and 1. The average value of $\pi\bar{\Gamma}_{(\mathrm{F})}/D$ per spin state should lie between 0·5 and 1·5. The fission widths of the 4^- states will belong to a Porter–Thomas distribution. The effective number of degrees of freedom $\nu_{\mathrm{eff}(3-)}$ of the fission widths of the 3^- levels will be in the range 1 to 2 and the overall value of ν_{eff} will probably be less than unity.

The results of analysis of the experimental data on the neutron cross-sections of ^{235}U up to 20 eV are given in Table 8.4. We note here that a number of resonances quoted by Pilcher *et al.* (1956) after a detailed single-level analysis have not been included because they do not correspond to observed maxima. The statistics of the quasi-resonances and mixed resonances are shown in Table 8.5. The number of degrees of freedom of the pseudo-resonance spacing distribution is high; that this is due to a dearth of small spacings has been shown by Michaudon *et al.* (1963, 1965) in a histogram of the distribution. In addition to the statistics shown in the table, it is known, even more definitely than in the case of ^{233}U, that there are fluctuations of the pseudo-radiation widths of the maxima (Michaudon and Ribon 1961, Michaudon *et al.* 1965).

Again, the superficial equating of the properties of the cross-section maxima with those of the basic *R*-matrix parameters gives apparent disagreement with the unified-model transition state theory. However, the results of analyses of simulated cross-sections shown in Table 8.5 and Fig. 8.18 reveal that the pseudo-statistics can be reproduced if $N(J_+)$ is assumed to be $\approx 0{\cdot}3$ and $N(J_-)$ is of the order of 1·3; this agrees reasonably well with the theory, and suggests that while the mass asymmetry ($K = 0$, odd parity) band of transition states lies well below the neutron separation energy, the first 4^- transition state for fission (probably based on the bending mode, $K = 1$ with odd parity) lies between 50 and 150 keV above the neutron threshold, or, in other words, some 1100 to 1500 keV above 'ground' at the saddle point. The analysis also results in the strength function value $\bar{\Gamma}_{\mathrm{n}}/D \approx (1{\cdot}0 \pm 0{\cdot}2)\times 10^{-4}$ and level spacing (per spin state) $D \approx 1{\cdot}0 \pm 0{\cdot}1$ eV.

TABLE 8.5

Comparison of the statistics of simulated cross-sections with those of the experimental data on ^{235}U

$T_f(J^\pi = 3^-)$ $T_f(J^\pi = 4^-)$	1·0, 0·1, 0·02 0·1, 0·02	1·0, 0·3, 0·06 0·3, 0.06	1·0, 0·5, 0·1 0·5, 0·1	1, 0·9, 0·18 0·9, 0·18	0·16, 0·16 0·06, 0·06	Data
$\langle 'D' \rangle$	0·67 ± 0·05	0·68 ± 0·05	0·73 ± 0·07	0·79 ± 0·07		0·67 ± 0·07
ν_D	6·5 ± 1·2	7·4 ± 1·3	5·3 ± 1·1	7·6 ± 1·5		5·8 ± 1·3
$\langle 'g\Gamma^{\circ}_{(n)}' \rangle / \langle 'D' \rangle$	0·72 ± 0·1	0·71 ± 0·1	0·96 ± 0·14	0·47 ± 0·07		0·70 ± 0·15
ν_n	1·6 ± 0·25	1·4 ± 0·2	1·6 ± 0·3	2·1 ± 0·4		1·5 ± 0·35
$\pi \langle '\Gamma_{(F)}' \rangle / \langle 'D' \rangle$	0·24 ± 0·04	0·36 ± 0·05	0·50 ± 0·06	0·53 ± 0·06	0·14 ± 0·02	0·22 ± 0·04
ν_F	1·3 ± 0·2	1·7 ± 0·26	2·5 ± 0·5	2·7 ± 0·5	2·8 ± 0·5	1·6 ± 0·4
S_1	108 ± 16	113 ± 13	166 ± 17	117 ± 15	52 ± 7	114 ± 16
ν_{S_1}	1·5 ± 0·3	2·4 ± 0·4	2·3 ± 0·4	2·7 ± 0·5	2·0 ± 0·3	2·4 ± 0·5
S_2	820 ± 80	1200 ± 130	1130 ± 130	1950 ± 230	370 ± 40	1290 ± 160
ν_{S_2}	3·3 ± 0·6	3·2 ± 0·5	4·1 ± 0·8	4·2 ± 0·8	5·1 ± 0·6	3·5 ± 0·8
S_3	5·7 ± 0·7	6·7 ± 0·9	5·5 ± 0·7	8·8 ± 1·0	3·1 ± 0·3	11·8 ± 0·8
ν_{S_3}	2·4 ± 0·4	2·4 ± 0·4	2·6 ± 0·5	2·7 ± 0·5	4·2 ± 0·8	2·6 ± 0·6
$\langle \alpha_{(max)} \rangle$	3·0 ± 0·5	1·6 ± 0·3	0·84 ± 0·12	0·74 ± 0·10	2·3 ± 0·3	1·3 ± 0·16
$\nu_{\alpha(max)}$	1·7 ± 0·3	1·4 ± 0·3	2·9 ± 0·6	2·2 ± 0·4	3·5 ± 0·5	2·7 ± 0·5
$\langle \alpha_{(min)} \rangle$	1·8 ± 0·2	0·90 ± 0·09	0·73 ± 0·09	0·55 ± 0·06	2·0 ± 0·25	0·87 ± 0·08
$\nu_{\alpha(min)}$	2·6 ± 0·4	3·2 ± 0·5	3·3 ± 0·6	3·4 ± 0·7	3·6 ± 0·7	4·7 ± 1·0

(d) ^{239}Pu

This nucleus has ground-state spin and parity $I^\pi = \frac{1}{2}^+$, and hence an *s*-wave neutron cross-section with components of total angular momentum and parity $J^\pi = 0^+$ and 1^+. The fission threshold of ^{240}Pu lies

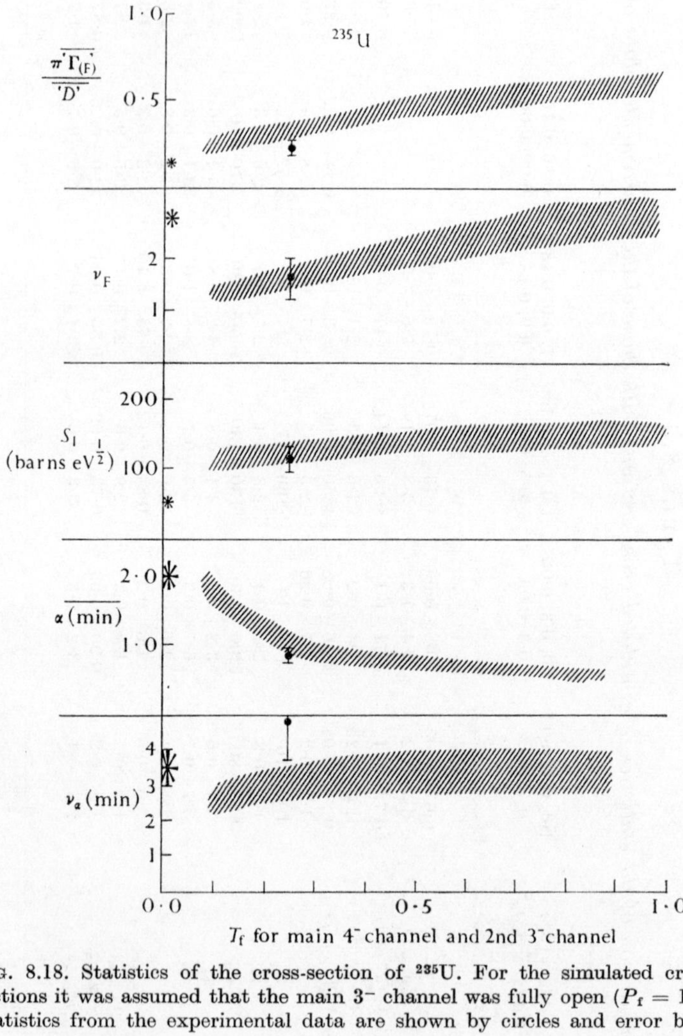

FIG. 8.18. Statistics of the cross-section of ^{235}U. For the simulated cross-sections it was assumed that the main 3^- channel was fully open ($P_f = 1{\cdot}0$). Statistics from the experimental data are shown by circles and error bars.

1·4 to 1·6 MeV below the neutron separation energy (Northrop *et al.* 1959, Usachev *et al.* 1964). From Table 8.1, we see that $N(0^+)$ should be at least 1 and may be as high as 2, whereas $N(1^+)$ may have any value between 0 and 1. Fission widths of the 1^+ levels should have a Porter–

Thomas distribution and the effective value of ν for the overall distribution of fission widths from both sets of levels may be very much less than unity owing to the large mean spacing and fission width of the 0^+ levels (see eqn. (8.37)).

Table 8.6 shows the detailed results of analysis of the cross-section of ^{239}Pu up to 260 eV. Vogt (1960) concludes from the interference parameters that only a single channel, with some small contributions from other channels, is open. The difficulties and ambiguities of the many-level analyses, particularly for making spin assignments, are well exemplified by these low-energy results. Using the definite assignment of the 7·8-eV resonance as having spin 1, Vogt, tentatively, and Kirpichnikov *et al.*, more positively, assign spin 1 to the 15·5-eV resonance. Kirpichnikov *et al.* also assign spin 1 to the 14·3-eV resonance and spin 0 to the 14·7-eV resonance. Scattering cross-section measurements on the latter resonance combined with fission cross-section and total cross-section data show that it has in fact spin 1 (Asghar 1966, Sauter and Bowman 1965). From the lack of interference between this and the 15·5-eV resonance, Sauter and Bowman then deduce the spin of the latter to be 0, in contrast to the other results. Most of the spins given in Table 8.6 have in fact been deduced by the usually sound techniques of single-level analysis of the partial cross-section areas under the resonances.

The statistics of cross-section maxima are displayed in Table 8.7. Simulated cross-sections of a spin $\frac{1}{2}$ target nucleus have been calculated assuming mean level spacings, $\bar{D}(J = 1) = 3$ eV, $\bar{D}(J = 0) = 9$ eV, a total radiation width of 40 meV and a neutron strength function $\Gamma^0_{(n)}/\bar{D} = 1\times 10^{-4}$. The statistics of the single-level analyses of the cross-sections are also shown in Table 8.7. Comparisons of simulations and data on the pseudo-parameters suggest that the 0^+ (ground state) fission channel is fully open and that a second 0^+ channel (perhaps the 2γ-phonon state) is open to an appreciable degree (perhaps with $T_f \approx 0{\cdot}5$). It is more difficult to assess the transmission factor of the one expected 1^+ channel (corresponding to the combination of mass asymmetry vibration and bending vibration). If it were very small, one would expect the appearance of very small fission widths leading to a value of ν_f much smaller than unity; on the other hand such small widths could be masked by the (n, γf) reaction (see Section C.4). The general assessment of the cross-section statistics in comparison with the simulated statistics indicates that the order of magnitude of $T_f(1^+)$ is about 0·1. The results also indicate that the strength function $\Gamma^0_n/\bar{D}$

TABLE 8.6

Analyses of neutron cross-section of ^{239}Pu

Part A. Below 65 eV

λ	E_λ (eV)	J^π	$\Gamma^\circ_{\lambda(n)}$ (meV)	$\Gamma_{\lambda(\gamma T)}$ (meV)	$\Gamma_{\lambda(F)}$ (meV)	θ_λ	Reference	Remarks
1	−1·200	Not $\lambda = 2$	1·156/2g	39	201	0°	Vogt (1960)	1
	−0·26		0·085 ± 0·03	40 (assd.)	160 ± 20		Bollinger *et al.* (1958)	
2	0·296		0·209/2g	38·6	55·4		Vogt (1960)	
	0·296	Assd. 1+	0·149 ± 0·006	39 ± 2	62 ± 2		Bollinger *et al.* (1958)	
	0·296 ± 0·002		0·224 ± 0·005/2g	31 ± 8	58 ± 6		Egelstaff *et al.* (1958)	
3	7·90	Not $\lambda = 2$	0·47/2g	38	42	126·9°	Vogt (1960)	1
	7·83	Assd. 1+	0·464 ± 0·01/2g	40·6 ± 3	41·5 ± 3		Bollinger *et al.* (1958)	
	7·8	1+					Fraser and Schwartz (1961)	
	7·84	1+	0·486 ± 0·012/2g		35		Kirpichnikov *et al.* (1964)	2
	7·9	1+					Sauter and Bowman (1965)	
4	11·0	Not $\lambda = 2$	0·83/2g	32	147	180°	Vogt (1960)	1
	10·93	Assd. 1+	0·83 ± 0·013/2g	31·5 ± 9	147 ± 7		Bollinger *et al.* (1958)	
	10·95		1·02 ± 0·1/2g				Egelstaff *et al.* (1958)	
	10·9	1+					Fraser and Schwartz (1961)	
	10·9	1+	0·675 ± 0·07/2g		81	0°	Kirpichnikov *et al.* (1964)	2
	10·9	1+					Sauter and Bowman (1965)	
5	11·90	Assd. 1+	0·464 ± 0·02/2g	40·9 ± 5	22 ± 2		Bollinger *et al.* (1958)	
	11·95 ± 0·05		0·56 ± 0·06/2g				Egelstaff *et al.* (1958)	
	11·9	1+					Fraser and Schwartz (1961)	

	11·9	1^+	$0{\cdot}39 \pm 0{\cdot}1/2g$		23	180°	Kirpichnikov *et al.* (1964)	2
	11·9	1^+					Sauter and Bowman (1965)	
6	14·28		$0{\cdot}22 \pm 0{\cdot}05/2g$	40 (assd.)	60 ± 7		Bollinger *et al.* (1958)	
	14·3	1^+			34	0°	Kirpichnikov *et al.* (1964)	2
	14·3	1^+					Sauter and Bowman (1965)	
7	14·68	Assd. 0^+	$0{\cdot}66 \pm 0{\cdot}04/2g$	40 (assd.)	33 ± 4		Bollinger *et al.* (1958)	
	14·7	0^+					Fraser and Schwartz (1961)	
	14·69	1^+					Asghar (1966)	
	14·7	0^+			23		Kirpichnikov *et al.* (1964)	2
	14·7	1^+					Sauter and Bowman (1965)	
8	15·5	Not $\lambda = 2$	$0{\cdot}32/2g$	40	760	180°	Vogt (1960)	1
	15·5	Assd. 0^+	$0{\cdot}305 \pm 0{\cdot}05/2g$	40 (assd.)	760 ± 100		Bollinger *et al.* (1958)	
	15·5	1^+	$0{\cdot}341 \pm 0{\cdot}05/2g$		1000	180°	Kirpichnikov *et al.* (1964)	2
	15·5	0^+					Sauter and Bowman (1965)	3
9	17·6	Assd. 1^+	$0{\cdot}571 \pm 0{\cdot}04/2g$	39 ± 5	46 ± 5		Bollinger *et al.* (1958)	
	17·6	1^+					Fraser and Schwartz (1961)	
	17·65	1^+					Asghar (1966)	
	17·6	1^+	$0{\cdot}521 \pm 0{\cdot}07/2g$		29		Kirpichnikov *et al.* (1964)	2
	17·6	1^+					Sauter and Bowman (1965)	
10	22·2		$0{\cdot}715 \pm 0{\cdot}04/2g$	35 ± 4	75 ± 4		Bollinger *et al.* (1958)	
	22·2	0^+					Fraser and Schwartz (1961)	
	22·28	1^+					Asghar (1966)	
	22·6	0^+	$0{\cdot}70 \pm 0{\cdot}08/2g$		49		Kirpichnikov *et al.* (1964)	2
	22·2	1^+					Sauter and Bowman (1965)	
11	23·9		$0{\cdot}026 \pm 0{\cdot}003/2g$	40 (assd.)	42 ± 5		Bollinger *et al.* (1958)	
12	26·2		$0{\cdot}521 \pm 0{\cdot}04/2g$	40 (assd.)	37 ± 3		Bollinger *et al.* (1958)	

TABLE 8.6 (cont.)

Analyses of neutron cross-section of ^{239}Pu

Part A. Below 65 eV

λ	E_λ (eV)	J^π	$\Gamma^\circ_{\lambda(n)}$ (meV)	$\Gamma_{\lambda(\gamma T)}$ (meV)	$\Gamma_{\lambda(F)}$ (meV)	θ_λ	Reference	Remarks
	26·5		$0{\cdot}429 \pm 0{\cdot}08/2g$		25		Ignat'ev *et al.* (1964)	
	26·26	1^+					Asghar (1966)	
13	27·3		$0{\cdot}38 \pm 0{\cdot}08/2g$	40 (assd.)	3 ± 1		Bollinger *et al.* (1958)	
14	32·3		$0{\cdot}076 \pm 0{\cdot}008/2g$	40 (assd.)	190 ± 5		Bollinger *et al.* (1958)	
	32·3	0^+					Sauter and Bowman (1965)	
15	35·3		$0{\cdot}079 \pm 0{\cdot}008/2g$	40 (assd.)	4 ± 1		Bollinger *et al.* (1958)	
	35·3	1^+					Sauter and Bowman (1965)	
16	41·4	Assd. 0^+	$1{\cdot}43 \pm 0{\cdot}04/2g$	47 ± 9	11 ± 2		Bollinger *et al.* (1958)	
	41·4	1^+					Fraser and Schwartz (1961)	
	41·5	1^+					Asghar (1966)	
	41·5		$0{\cdot}87 \pm 0{\cdot}3/2g$	40 (assd.)	6·5		Ignat'ev *et al.* (1964)	
	41·4	1^+					Sauter and Bowman (1965)	
17	44·5	Assd. 1^+	$1{\cdot}44 \pm 0{\cdot}02/2g$	40 ± 10	4 ± 1		Bollinger *et al.* (1958)	
	44·5	1^+					Ashar (1966)	
	44·5		$1{\cdot}125 \pm 0{\cdot}23/2g$	40 (assd.)	4·5		Ignat'ev *et al.* (1964)	
	44·5	1^+					Sauter and Bowman (1965)	
18	47·6		$0{\cdot}39 \pm 0{\cdot}04/2g$	40 (assd.)	310 ± 50		Bollinger *et al.* (1958)	

	47·7	0^+				Asghar (1966)
	47·7		$0{\cdot}44 \pm 0{\cdot}15/2g$	40 (assd.)	74	Ignat'ev *et al.* (1964)
	47·6	0^+				Sauter and Bowman (1966)
19	50·0		$0{\cdot}96 \pm 0{\cdot}06/2g$	40 (assd.)	33 ± 4	Bollinger *et al.* (1958)
	50·0		$0{\cdot}72 \pm 0{\cdot}24/2g$	40 (assd.)	27	Ignat'ev *et al.* (1964)
	50·2	1^{+1}				Asghar (1966)
20	52·6	Assd. 1^+	$3{\cdot}1 \pm 0{\cdot}2/2g$	34 ± 5	8 ± 2	Bollinger *et al.* (1958)
	52·6	1^+				Asghar (1966)
	52·3		$1{\cdot}4 \pm 0{\cdot}7/2g$	40 (assd.)	8	Ignat'ev *et al.* (1964)
	52·6	1^+				Sauter and Bowman (1965)
21	55·63		$0{\cdot}29 \pm 0{\cdot}01/2g$	35	22	Derrien *et al.* (1966)
22	57·5			40 (assd.)	160	Ignat'ev *et al.* (1964)
	57·44		$0{\cdot}86/2g$	40 (assd.)	~ 460	Derrien *et al.* (1966)
23	59·5			40 (assd.)	160	Ignat'ev *et al.* (1964)
	59·3	0^+				Asghar (1966)
24	62·5			40 (assd.)	360	Ignat'ev *et al.* (1964)
	63·08		$0{\cdot}16 \pm 0{\cdot}04/2g$	43	111 ± 37	Derrien *et al.* (1966)

Remarks

1. All these parameters were determined by many level fits to cross-sections between 0·01 eV and 10 eV.
2. Spin assignments from many-level analysis.
3. Spin assignment from apparent absence of resonance-resonance interference with 14·7-eV level.

TABLE 8.6

Part B. Parameters above 65 eV

λ	E_λ(eV)	J	$2g\Gamma^{\circ}_{\lambda(n)}$(meV)	$\Gamma_{\lambda(\gamma T)}$(meV)	$\Gamma_{\lambda(F)}$(meV)	Ref.
25	65·71	1	2·24±0·06	50±8	74±8	1
		1				3
26	66·57		0·15±0·03	40 (assd.)	~140	1
27	74·05		0·45±0·03	37±6	32±4	1
		1				3
28	74·95	1	3·8±0·2	41±6	84±9	1
		1				3
29	78·95		0·018	40 (assd.)	~140	1
30	82·68		0·08±0·02	40 (assd.)	~30	1
31	85·48		1·28±0·02		17±9	1
		0				3
32	90·75	1	1·94±0·05	39±6	9±2	1
		1				3
33	92·97		0·11±0·005	47±6	9	1
34	95·36		0·32±0·02	58	37±5	1
		0				3
35	96·49		0·68±0·03		1670±400	1
36	102·9		0·25±0·02	40 (assd.)	85±40	2
	103·0		0·24±0·01	33±5	13±4	1
		0				3
37	105·3		0·86±0·09			2
	105·3		0·68±0·05	38±7	6±1	1
		1				3
38	106·7		1·16±0·05			2
	106·7	1	1·35±0·04	40±4	26±2	1
		1				3
39	110·3		0·13±0·02			2
	110·4		0·063±0·006	30	13	1
40	115·1		0·03±0·01	40 (assd.)	~160	1
41	116·0		0·46±0·04	40 (assd.)	175±20	2
	116·0		0·50±0·01	36	215±20	1
		0				3
42	118·8		2·02±0·2	40 (assd.)	78±26	2
	118·8	1	2·38±0·06	42±5	43±3	1
		1				3
43	120·9		0·38±0·04			2
	121·0		0·34±0·02	35±7	39±7	1
44	123·3		0·070±0·007			2
	123·4		0·063±0·006	40 (assd.)	18±13	1
45	126·2		0·25±0·04			2
	126·2		0·26±0·01	40 (assd.)	56±10	1
46	127·5		0·071±0·007			2
	127·5		0·097±0·01	40 (assd.)	120±30	1
47	131·7		1·52±0·15		~3800	2
	131·7		1·59±0·12		3300±50	1
		0				3
48	133·7		0·69±0·05			2
	133·8		0·72±0·03		7	1
		1				3
49	136·7		0·41±0·04			2
	136·7		0·44±0·02	33±8	88±10	1

TABLE 8.6 (cont.)

Part B. Parameters above 65 eV

λ	E_λ(eV)	J	$2g\Gamma^{\circ}_{\lambda(n)}$(meV)	$\Gamma_{\lambda(\gamma T)}$(meV)	$\Gamma_{\lambda(F)}$(meV)	Ref.
		0				3
50	139·3		0·015			1
51	142·9		0·41±0·02	56	76±15	1
52	143·5		0·51±0·02	36	41±7	1
53	146·2		0·96±0·05			2
	146·2	0	0·88±0·03	36	13±2	1
		1				3
54	147·9		0·16±0·02			2
	148·2		0·06±0·01	40 (assd.)	~110	1
55	149·3		0·18±0·04			2
	149·4		0·21±0·01	62	55±14	1
56	151·8		0·05±0·01			2
57	156·9		1·39±0·14	40 (assd.)	700±60	2
	157·1		1·37±0·03	40 (assd.)	600±50	1
		0				3
58	160·8		0·016			1
59	164·4		2·96±0·3			2
	164·5	1	3·28±0·2	43±8	8±1	1
		1				3
60	166·8		0·66±0·04			2
	167·1	1	0·67±0·03	32±6	74±7	1
		1				3
61	170·5		0·34±0·02		1250±200	2
62	175·7		0·24±0·02			2
	176·0		0·24±0·01	41±8	29	1
63	177·0		0·43±0·03			2
	177·2		0·40±0·01	41±6	5	1
		1				3
64	178·7		0·15±0·02			2
	178·9		0·14±0·01	42±7	14	1
65	183·4		0·26±0·03			2
	183·6		0·17±0·01			1
66	185·1		0·52±0·06	40 (assd.)	~1700	2
	184·9		0·73±0·16		1570±500	1
67	188·1		0·05±0·005			2
	188·3		0·07±0·007	41	11	1
68	190·4		0·17±0·02			2
	190·6		0·18±0·01	56	9	1
69	195·1		1·76±0·18	40 (assd.)	≈330	2
	195·4		2·14±0·07	36±12	350±42	1
		0				3
70	196·4		0·54±0·05			2
	196·7		0·50±0·03	46±11	59±12	1
		1				3
71	199·2		0·95±0·1	40 (assd.)	105±40	2
	199·4	1	1·03±0·05	33±8	90±10	1
		1				3
72	203·5		0·42	40 (assd.)	~150	1
73	203·9		1·85±0·08	40 (assd.)	~360	1
		0				3
74	207·1		0·69±0·03			2

TABLE 8.6 (cont.)

Part B. Parameters above 65 eV

λ	E_{λ}(eV)	J	$2g\Gamma^{\circ}_{\lambda(n)}$(meV)	$\Gamma_{\lambda(\gamma T)}$(meV)	$\Gamma_{\lambda(F)}$(meV)	Ref.
	207·4	1	0·73±0·03	44±5	7±2	1
		1				3
75	210·9		0·12			2
	211·1		0·096	40 (assd.)	~760	1
76	212·0		0·082	40 (assd.)	~1460	1
77	213·3		0·048	40 (assd.)	160±60	1
78	216·3		0·65±0·02			2
	216·5	1	0·64±0·04	39±6	10	1
79	219·5		0·36±0·02	40 (assd.)	25±15	1
80	220·2	1	0·75±0·04	33	4	1
81	222·8		0·31±0·02			2
	223·2		0·34±0·01		~2	1
82	224·6		0·15±0·02			2
	224·9		0·17±0·01	40 (assd.)	42±17	1
83	227·5		0·21±0·03			2
	227·9		0·17±0·01	28	37	1
84	231·1		1·0±0·05			2
	231·4	1	1·17±0·05	27	4	1
		1				3
85	234·0		0·89±0·05			2
	234·3		1·00±0·05	45	14	1
		0				3
86	238·7		0·51±0·05		~65	2
	239·0	0	0·53±0·03	47	17	1
		0				3
87	240·6		0·003			1
88	242·6		0·55±0·04		~50	2
	242·9	1	0·64±0·03	32±7	58±6	1
		1				3
89	247·1		0·08			2
	247·5		0·09±0·02	40 (assd.)	270±60	1
90	248·5		1·39±0·08			2
	248·9	1	1·40±0·06	41	6	1
		1				3
91	250·9		2·27±0·1			2
	251·2	1	2·60±0·1	41±7	14±2	1
		1				3
92	254·2		0·24±0·02			2
	254·6		0·26±0·02	40 (assd.)	10±10	1
93	255·8		0·52±0·04			2
	256·1		0·59±0·03	40 (assd.)	41±16	1
		1				3
94	261·8		2·6±0·2		~6300	2
	262·4		3·1		~6000	1
		0				3

References
1—Derrien *et al.* (1966)
2—Uttley (1965)
3—Asghar (1967)

TABLE 8.7

Comparison of the statistics of simulated cross-sections with those of the experimental data on ^{239}Pu

$T_f(J^\pi = 0^+)$ $T_f(J^\pi = 1^+)$	1·0 0·1	1·0 0·3	1·0 0·5	1·0, 0·5 0·5	1·0, 1·0 0·1	0·4 0·4	Data
'D'	2·9 ± 0·2	2·7 ± 0·25	3·2 ± 0·3	2·7 ± 0·25	2·6 ± 0·15		3·1 ± 0·17
ν_D	5·7 ± 1·0	7·0 ± 1·4	4·6 ± 0·9	7·1 ± 1·4	7·3 ± 2·3	4·1 ± 0·7	6·1 ± 1·0
$\langle$'$g\Gamma_n^\circ$'$\rangle/\langle$'D'$\rangle$	0·5 ± 0·1	0·6 ± 0·1	0·7 ± 0·1	0·9 ± 0·13	0·6 ± 0·15		1·2 ± 0·12
ν_n	1·1 ± 0·16	1·4 ± 0·2	1·6 ± 0·3	1·3 ± 0·2	1·9 ± 0·6		1·9 ± 0·3
$\pi\langle$'$\Gamma_{(F)}$'$\rangle/\langle$'D'$\rangle$	0·11 ± 0·02	0·25 ± 0·05	0·26 ± 0·05	0·48 ± 0·08	0·24 ± 0·05	0·23 ± 0·04	0·35 ± 0·06
ν_F	0·9 ± 0·1	0·8 ± 0·1	0·92 ± 0·15	0·88 ± 0·14	0·81 ± 0·06	1·04 ± 0·14	0·58 ± 0·05
S_1	58 ± 10	70 ± 12	77 ± 11	81 ± 12	120 ± 20		154 ± 20
ν_{S_1}	1·1 ± 0·15	1·8 ± 0·4	1·8 ± 0·3	2·3 ± 0·4	2·0 ± 0·13		1·9 ± 0·3
S_2	365 ± 45	750 ± 120	570 ± 160	700 ± 80	500 ± 50		1000 ± 100
ν_{S_2}	2·2 ± 0·35	2·5 ± 0·5	3·7 ± 0·7	3·2 ± 0·6	2·7 ± 0·4		3·2 ± 0·5

is about $(1{\cdot}3 \pm 0{\cdot}15) \times 10^{-4}$, and this value is confirmed by measurements of the average total cross-section (Uttley 1965).

These results on the mean fission widths imply that level overlap is in some ways not as serious a problem in the cross-section of ^{239}Pu as it is in the other nuclei. This is especially so because the narrow 1^+ levels constitute about three-quarters of the s-wave excited levels (by level density theory); thus there is very little chance of quasi-resonance formation in the majority group of levels. The mean fission width of the 0^+ levels is such that about 5–10 per cent of these levels (i.e. only 1–3 per cent of all 0^+ and 1^+ levels) will combine as quasi-resonances. The mixed resonance problem is not too serious either; again this is because of the much larger level spacing of the 0^+ levels. Usually, the width of a 1^+ level is so much smaller than that of a 0^+ level (by a factor of perhaps 25 on average) that a 1^+ resonance will be clearly superimposed on its 0^+ neighbour. The most difficult problem that remains is the masking of 0^+ resonances by the more closely spaced 1^+ resonances overlying them. This will be particularly serious for those resonances with below average neutron widths and above average fission widths. These considerations imply that it may be a practical possibility to describe the ^{239}Pu cross-section in detail in terms of a full set of individual level parameters.

The resonance parameters listed in Table 8.6 do not form such a complete set for the energy range they cover. A particularly strong discrepancy occurs in the region of 80 eV. The total and fission cross-sections between 70 eV and 120 eV as measured by Derrien *et al.* (1966) are shown in Fig. 8.19. The sharp resonance at 85·5 eV (listed in Table 8.6) is clearly superposed directly on a strong but lower and much wider resonance. This in turn seems to be part of a generally high and wide region on which is sitting the other sharp maximum that is listed in Table 8.6. Derrien *et al.* have attempted to fit this region with a superposition of Breit–Wigner terms. They found that two wide terms are insufficient to fit the data and therefore have to postulate Breit–Wigner resonances at 81·76 eV ($\Gamma = 2050$ meV), 83·5 eV ($\Gamma = 1750$ meV), and 85·3 eV ($\Gamma = 2300$ meV). It is very unlikely that these provide a unique fit, and, as Derrien *et al.* point out, with such broad levels interference would be very strong. This region is probably worth detailed investigation, which may even lead to the discovery of an actual experimental example of a quasi-resonance. Other regions that appear anomalously high after the subtraction of Breit–Wigner terms describing the observed peaks are around 60 eV (where Derrien *et al.* postulate two extra resonances of widths 1100 meV and 6000 meV), at 100 eV (Derrien *et al.* suggest a resonance of width 6000 meV), at 212 eV (explained by a hidden resonance of 1500 meV width) and at 227 eV (where it is believed that a resonance of width greater than 6 eV underlies a great deal of fine structure).

The general conclusion that the 0^+ resonances are broad on average and the 1^+ resonances are very much narrower is borne out by a detailed study of the parameters shown in Table 8.6 in conjunction with

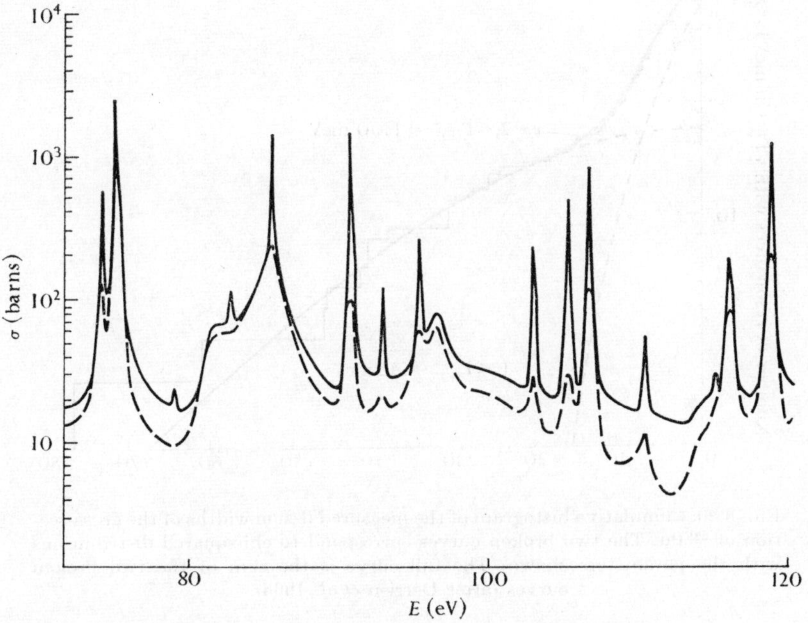

FIG. 8.19. Total (full curve) and fission (broken curve) cross sections of ^{239}Pu between 70 eV and 120 eV (after Derrien *et al.* 1966).

the spin assignments. Some of the spin assignments, particularly by Vogt (1960) and Kirpichnikov *et al.* (1964) for the lowest energy resonances have already been remarked on; they are based on multi-level analysis, and therefore cannot be trusted too strongly in view of what has been said about hidden levels, but most of the others are probably sound. Of these there are very many assignments to the 1^+ class, and the broadest is the resonance at 10·9 eV with a fission width of 147 meV. Many of the assigned 0^+ resonances have fission widths greater than this, and two in particular are extremely wide (3800 and 6000 meV). The division of the resonances into two classes with very different mean values of the fission width is also illustrated by a diagram due to Derrien *et al.* (1966) which is a cumulative histogram of the measured fission widths (Fig. 8.20). This includes the estimates of 'hidden' broad levels mentioned above. The structure of the histogram is indicative of the superposition of two distributions, one a Porter–Thomas distribution, containing three-quarters of the resonances and with a mean width of 42 meV, the other an exponential distribution

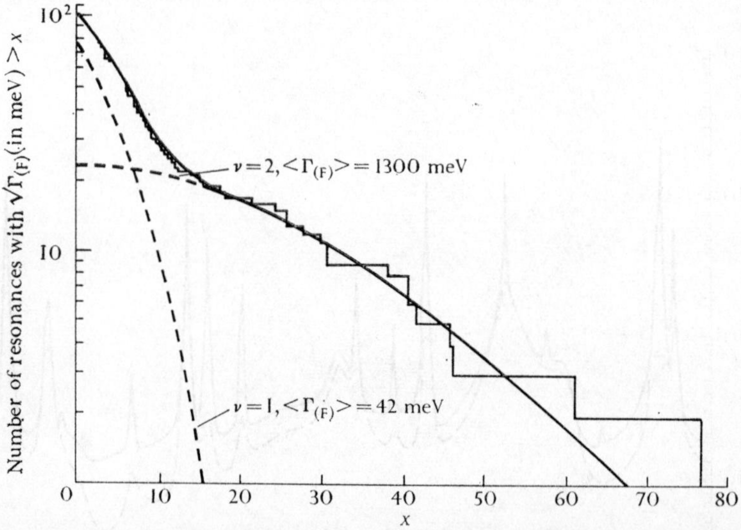

FIG. 8.20. Cumulative histogram of the measured fission widths of the cross-section of ^{239}Pu. The two broken curves correspond to chi-squared distributions with the parameters shown. The full curve is the sum of the two broken curves (after Derrien *et al.* 1966).

with a mean width of 1300 meV. These correspond to effective saddle-point channel numbers, $N(1^+) \approx 0{\cdot}12$, $N(0^+) \approx 1{\cdot}0$.

(*e*) ^{241}Pu

This nucleus has the same spin and parity properties as ^{233}U. The position of its fission threshold with respect to the neutron separation energy has been observed in the (t, pf) reaction (Britt *et al.* 1966); it is about 0·8 to 0·9 MeV.

From Table 8·1 we see that probably two saddle-point channels should be open for 2^+ states and one saddle-point channel for the 3^+ states. The pseudo-parameters of the ^{241}Pu cross-section are given in Table 8.8 and their statistics in Table 8.3. Comparison of these with the simulated statistics of Table 8.3 again show reasonable agreement of the data with the unified model; 1·3 open saddle-point channels for one spin state and 2·3 for the other spin are indicated by the comparison (see also Fig. 8.17).

It appears that the neutron strength function is of the order of $1{\cdot}5 \times 10^{-4}$ and the resonance spacing (per spin state) is about 1·3 eV. Simulations of the cross-section have also been made by Moore and Simpson (1966) who assumed $\sum_f T_f$ to be equal to 1·3 for 2^+ levels and to 0·3 for 3^+ levels. They found that about 30 per cent of the levels were not observed as resonances. This led them to include about 30 per cent 'unobserved' levels in making a many level R-matrix fit to recent data on the ^{241}Pu fission cross-section. The results of the fitting agreed quite well with the distribution of parameters of the simulated levels.

(*f*) *Average cross-sections*

At higher neutron energies many measurements of average cross-sections have been made. As far as the study of fission is concerned the most interesting function of these is the ratio of the average capture cross-section to the average fission cross-section, usually denoted by $\bar{\alpha}$. From this ratio it is possible to learn something about the saddle-point channels that are open for p-wave excited resonances (Bell 1966).

For neutron energies of less than 1 keV interacting with ^{233}U, $\bar{\alpha}$ (for cross-sections averaged over intervals of the order of 50–100 eV) varies from about 0·2 to 0·5 (Yeater *et al.* 1961), Calculations of $\bar{\alpha}$ using eqn. (8.20) for the average cross-section and the results of Section C.3(b) for the average saddle-point channel widths give a value for comparison of 0·23. These calculations are approximate to the extent that they ignore level-level interference; the Porter–Thomas distribution is assumed in all partial-width channels, rather than the modified statistics that the S-matrix parameters must have in broad resonance conditions. If these effects were to be properly taken into account $\bar{\alpha}$ would be higher, but on the other hand the (n, γf) reaction (see Section C.4) has also been ignored in making the calculations and its proper inclusion would tend to have the opposite effect. It must be concluded that the calculation is not too inaccurate. The calculated value of $\bar{\alpha}$ is thus in not too bad agreement with the observations.

At higher neutron energies odd-parity levels are excited in the ^{234}U compound nucleus, and so far we have not discussed in detail the structure of the odd-parity saddle-point channels. In fact, the analysis of the s-wave data on this nucleus does not throw much more light on these channels than is already contained in Table 8.1. According to the

TABLE 8.8

Analyses of neutron cross-section of ^{241}Pu

λ	E_{λ} (eV)	J^{π}	$\Gamma^{\circ}_{\lambda(n)}$ (meV)	$\Gamma_{\lambda(\gamma T)}$ (meV)	$\Gamma_{\lambda(F)}$ (meV)	Remarks	Reference
1	−0·160	as $\lambda = 2$	0·075/2g	40 (assd.)	60(+)	1	Simpson and Moore (1961)
2	0·264		0·101/2g	40 (assd.)	72(−)	1	Simpson and Moore (1961)
3	4·28	as $\lambda = 2$	0·255/2g	40 (assd.)	45(−)	1	Simpson and Moore (1961)
	4·275		0·404/2g	40 (assd.)	21(B, +)	2	Moore *et al.* (1964)
4	4·56	not $\lambda = 2$	0·194/2g	40 (assd.)	190(+)	1	Simpson and Moore (1961)
	4·58		0·204/2g	40 (assd.)	140(A, −)	2	Moore *et al.* (1964)
5	5·91	not $\lambda = 2$	1·020/2g	40 (assd.)	1350(+)	1	Simpson and Moore (1961)
	5·91		1·020/2g	40 (assd.)	1350(A, −)	2	Moore *et al.* (1964)
6	6·94	as $\lambda = 2$	0·218/2g	40 (assd.)	95(+)	1	Simpson and Moore (1961)
	6·915		0·275/2g	40 (assd.)	93(B, −)	2	Moore *et al.* (1964)
7	8·60	as $\lambda = 2$	0·268/2g	40 (assd.)	70(+)	1	Simpson and Moore (1961)
	8·585		0·324/2g	40 (assd.)	70(B, +)	2	Moore *et al.* (1964)
8	9·56	as $\lambda = 2$	0·035/2g	40 (assd.)	100(−)	1	Simpson and Moore (1961)
	9·48		0·068/2g	40 (assd.)	125(B, −)	2	Moore *et al.* (1964)
9	10·20	not $\lambda = 2$	0·400/2g	40 (assd.)	1000(−)	1	Simpson and Moore (1961)
	10·11		0·47/2g	40 (assd.)	900(A, +)	2	Moore *et al.* (1964)
10	12·84		0·220/2g	40 (assd.)	266(1, +)	3	James (1965)
	12·77		0·220/2g	40 (assd.)	250(A, −)	2	Moore *et al.* (1964)
	12·75 ± ·07		0·20 ± 0·06/2g	40 (assd.)	195 ± 70		Pattenden (1964)
11	13·45		0·596/2g	40 (assd.)	42(2, −)	3	James (1965)
	13·38		0·5/2g	40 (assd.)	50(B, −)	2	Moore *et al.* (1964)
	13·39 ± ·08		0·70 ± 0·04/2g	40 (assd.)	15 ± 10		Pattenden (1964)
12	14·04		0·048/2g	40 (assd.)	214(1, −)	3	James (1965)

13	14·78	1·513/2*g*	40 (assd.)	105(1, +)	3	James (1965)
	14·73	1·61/2*g*	40 (assd.)	135(A, +)	2	Moore *et al.* (1964)
	14·75 ± ·08	1·67 ± 0·06/2*g*	40 (assd.)	110 ± 20		Pattenden (1964)
	14·74 ± ·05	1·6 ± 0·3/2*g*	40 (assd.)	110 ± 50		Craig and Westcott (1964)
14	16·06	0·344/2*g*	40 (assd.)	360(1, −)	3	James (1965)
	16·01	0·36/2*g*	40 (assd.)	500(A, −)	2	Moore *et al.* (1964)
	15·94 ± ·07	0·390 ± 0·015/2*g*	40 (assd.)	460 ± 100		Pattenden (1964)
	15·96 ± ·08	0·45/2*g*	40 (assd.)	560 ± 150		Craig and Westcott (1964)
15	16·70	0·323/2*g*	40 (assd.)	180(2, +)	3	James (1965)
	16·65	0·36/2*g*	40 (assd.)	300(B, +)	2	Moore *et al.* (1964)
	16·6 ± ·1	0·27 ± 0·02/2*g*	40 (assd.)	170 ± 20		Pattenden (1964)
	16·7 ± ·08	0·28/2*g*	40 (assd.)	210 ± 100		Craig and Westcott (1964)
16	17·78	0·41/2*g*	40 (assd.)	80(B, +)	2	Moore *et al.* (1964)
	17·8 ± ·1	0·77 ± 0·04/2*g*	40 (assd.)	13^{+20}_{-13}		Pattenden (1964)
	17·85 ± ·05	0·76 ± 0·2/2*g*	40 (assd.)	10^{+90}_{-10}		Craig and Westcott (1964)
17	18·2 ± ·1	0·037 ± 0·004/2*g*	40 (assd.)	27 ± 10		Pattenden (1964)
18	20·5 ± ·1	0·04 ± 0·02/2*g*				Pattenden (1964)
19	20·63	0·08/2*g*	40 (assd.)	40(B, −)		James (1965)
	20·7 ± ·1	0·077 ± 0·009/2*g*	40 (assd.)	50 ± 40		Pattenden (1964)
	20·75 ± ·17	0·07/2*g*	40 (assd.)	50^{+100}_{-50}		Craig and Westcott (1964)
20	21·9 ± ·1	0·033 ± 0·007/2*g*	40 (assd.)	60 ± 30		Pattenden (1964)
	21·99 ± ·24	0·028/2*g*	40 (assd.)	160 ± 100		Craig and Westcott (1964)
21	22·86	0·24/2*g*	40 (assd.)	400(B, +)	2	Moore *et al.* (1964)
	23·0 ± ·1	0·23 ± 0·02/2*g*	40 (assd.)	270 ± 40		Pattenden (1964)
	23·04 ± ·3	0·32/2*g*	40 (assd.)	560 ± 250		Craig and Westcott (1964)
22	23·7 ± ·1	0·059 ± 0·009/2*g*	40 (assd.)	140 ± 40		Pattenden (1964)
23	23·96	0·31/2*g*	40 (assd.)	230(B, −)	2	Moore *et al.* (1964)
	24·0 ± ·1	0·33 ± 0·03/2*g*	40 (assd.)	150 ± 30		Pattenden (1964)
	24·12 ± ·16	0·29 ± 0·2/2*g*	40 (assd.)	180 ± 140		Craig and Westcott (1964)
24	24·7 ± ·1	0·009 ± 0·007/2*g*	40 (assd.)	$20 +^{+30}_{-20}$		Pattenden (1964)
25	26·34	0·82/2*g*	40 (assd.)	280(B, +)	2	Moore *et al.* (1964)
	26·4 ± ·2	0·88 ± 0·05	40 (assd.)	250 ± 30		Pattenden (1964)
	26·45 ± ·17	0·84 ± 0·2/2*g*	40 (assd.)	300 ± 100		Craig and Westcott (1964)
26	28·0 ± ·2	0·02 ± 0·4/2*g*	40 (assd.)	110 ± 50		Pattenden (1964)
27	28·75	1·12/2*g* 01/2*g*	40 (assd.)	750(A, +)	2	Moore *et al.* (1964)
	28·8 ± ·2	0·81/2*g*	40 (assd.)	530 ± 60		Pattenden (1964)

TABLE 8.8 (cont.)

Analyses of neutron cross-section of ^{241}Pu

λ	E_λ (eV)	J^π	$\Gamma^\circ_{\lambda(n)}$ (meV)	$\Gamma_{\lambda(\gamma T)}$ (meV)	$\Gamma_{\lambda(F)}$ (meV)	Remarks	Reference
	28·97 ± ·22		0·93/2*g*	40 (assd.)	680 ± 100		Craig and Westcott (1964)
28	29·35		0·10/2*g*	40 (assd.)	40(B, −)	2	Moore *et al.* (1964)
	29·4 ± ·2		0·15 ± 0·03/2*g*	40 (assd.)	90 ± 30		Pattenden (1964)
	29·57 ± ·25		0·066/2*g*				Craig and Westcott (1964)
29	30·88		0·45/2*g*	40 (assd.)	300(B, +)	2	Moore *et al.* (1964)
	30·9 ± ·2		0·55 ± 0·05/2*g*	40 (assd.)	310 ± 50		Pattenden (1964)
	31·03 ± ·21		0·43 ± 0·1/2*g*	40 (assd.)	320 ± 100		Craig and Westcott (1964)
30	33·0		0·07 ± 0·02/2*g*	40 (assd.)	360 ± 100		Pattenden (1964)
31	33·7		0·20 ± 0·02/2*g*	40 (assd.)	460 ± 60		Pattenden (1964)
32	34·90		0·45/2*g*	40 (assd.)	1200(A, −)	2	Moore *et al.* (1964)
	35·0 ± ·1		0·34 ± 0·02/2*g*	40 (assd.)	500 ± 60		Pattenden (1964)

Remarks

(1) Parameters from multi-level fit assuming 6 levels of one spin and 3 levels of the other spin. A single-fission channel is assumed. The relative sign of $\Gamma^{\frac{1}{2}}_{\lambda(n)}\Gamma^{\frac{1}{2}}_{\lambda(f)}$ is placed in brackets following the fission width entry.

(2) Parameters from multi-level fit assuming 3 levels of one spin and 4 of opposite spin in range 4·275 to 10·11 eV, 3 of each spin in range 12·77 to 17·78 eV, 3 of one spin in range 20·63 to 23·96 eV, and 2 of one and 3 of the other in the range 26·34 to 34·90 eV. The fission widths of the two groups are denoted by A and B, and this and the relative sign of $\Gamma^{\frac{1}{2}}_{\lambda(n)}\Gamma^{\frac{1}{2}}_{\lambda(f)}$ (within the indicated energy ranges) are given in brackets following the fission width entries.

(3) Parameters from 6-level fit. Two fission channels assumed but there is the further assumption that only one is open at each level. The open channel is indicated after each fission width entry with the sign of $\Gamma^{\frac{1}{2}}_{\lambda(n)}\Gamma^{\frac{1}{2}}_{\lambda(f)}$.

table there should be two fully open channels for 2^- and 4^- levels and three open channels for 1^- and 3^- levels. With this information the value of $\bar{\alpha}$ at 30 keV—well in the *p*-wave region—is calculated to be 0·23. The measured value (Hopkins and Diven 1962) of $0{\cdot}11 \pm 0{\cdot}02$ is considerably lower, suggesting that the next odd-parity bands of transition states (combinations of gamma vibration and bending vibration) are already close to the neutron emission threshold in ^{234}U.

The measurements of $\bar{\alpha}$ for ^{235}U are more difficult to reconcile with the analysis of the resonance data. With the saddle-point channel widths given at the end of Section C.3(c) the value of $\bar{\alpha}$ in the *s*-wave region is calculated to be 0·91. Now, while $\bar{\alpha}$ in the region 1–100 eV is about this magnitude, at higher energies it is generally much lower; if the cross-sections are averaged over 100-eV intervals to define $\bar{\alpha}$, the mean value for the nine intervals between 100 and 1000 eV is only 0·57. The root mean square value of the fluctuations of $\bar{\alpha}$ about this mean is 0·19. If this is corrected for the experimental error the inherent fluctuation is $\pm 0{\cdot}12$. The observed mean can be explained by the assumption that there are two fully open 3^- channels and one fully open 4^- channel (Bell 1966); these give $\bar{\alpha} = 0{\cdot}52$. The fluctuations can also be explained; a calculation of $\bar{\alpha}$ for 80-eV intervals with random selection of resonance parameters from the mean fission widths of these channels gave a root-mean-square value of 0·11 (from twelve individual values of $\bar{\alpha}$). The resonance data can only be reconciled with these channel widths by assuming that the observed resonance region is an extreme local fluctuation. In the *p*-wave region the observed value of $\bar{\alpha}$ ($0{\cdot}33 \pm 0{\cdot}02$ at 60 keV; Hopkins and Diven 1962) can be explained by assuming that the saddle-point channel corresponding to either the combination state of mass asymmetry and bending vibration or to the gamma vibration state is almost fully open (in addition to the 'ground' channel).

In the neutron-induced fission of ^{239}Pu the value of $\bar{\alpha}$ in the *s*-wave region is not too well established but appears to have the value of about 0·6 in the 100 to 200 eV region and to lie between 1 and 1·5 in the 1–2 keV region (Patrick and Sowerby 1967). Above 10 keV it falls rather rapidly, reaching a value of $0{\cdot}30 \pm 0{\cdot}02$ at 30 keV and $0{\cdot}16 \pm 0{\cdot}02$ by 70 keV (de Saussure *et al.* 1966). This behaviour is explained rather well by a transition-state spectrum based on Table 8.1. It is shown specifically in Table 8.9. We have already seen that this explains the resonance data rather well. It also gives a value of $\bar{\alpha}$ of 0·7 in the *s*-wave region, and at 30 keV it gives $\bar{\alpha} = 0{\cdot}26$, a satisfactory result. Although the *s*-wave value agrees with that observed in the 100–200 eV range,

Table 8.9

Transition states used in calculation of $\bar{\alpha}$ and mass yield ratio to about 70 keV in neutron-induced fission of ^{239}Pu (ground state spin and parity $I^\pi = \frac{1}{2}^+$)

Component of neutron beam		Transition state properties					
Orbital ang. mom. l	Channel spin s	J^π	K	Collective vibration	β_3-sym.	E_f(MeV) (relative to $E_{(\mathrm{th,n})}$)	Remarks
0	0	0^+	0	'ground'	+	−1·5	From (d, pf) reaction
			0	2 gamma quanta	+	∼0·0	Inferred from (d, pf) angular distribution data

	1	1^+	1	mass asymmetry + bending	−	$\sim+0{\cdot}15$	From (n, f) data in neutron resonance region
1	0	1^-	0	mass asymmetry	−	$\sim-0{\cdot}9$	Assumption
			1	bending	+	$\sim-0{\cdot}45$	From above plus data for $K^\pi = 1^+$
			0	2 gamma quanta + mass asymmetry	−	$\sim+0{\cdot}6$	From combination of above
			1	1 qu. gamma + bending	+	$\sim+0{\cdot}3$	From combination of above
	1	0^-		Unknown			
		1^-	See	$J^\pi = 1^-$ above			
		2^-	1	Bending	+	$\sim-0{\cdot}45$	
			2	1 qu. gamma + mass asymmetry	−	$\sim-0{\cdot}15$	From combination of above
			0	2 qu. gamma + mass asymmetry	+	$\sim+0{\cdot}6$	From combination of above
			1	1 qu. gamma + bending	+	$\sim+0{\cdot}3$	From combination of above

the discrepancy over the larger 1–2 keV region suggests that $N(1+)$ may be rather lower than 0·1 at the neutron threshold, the resonances observed in this region providing a rather high sample mean.

4. The (neutron, gamma fission) reaction

In the calculation of the statistics of simulated cross-sections for Tables 8.5 and 8.7 it was observed that when fission for one spin state was through a single, only partially open channel some extremely small individual fission widths appeared. Such small fission widths (0·5 meV and less) have never been observed for the resonances of the odd-neutron, even-charge actinide target nuclei, even though (as for ^{235}U and ^{239}Pu) both the theory of transition states and comparison of other features of the data with the simulated statistics indicate that, for one spin, there is just one or perhaps two partially open channels. A possible explanation of this particular discrepancy is that, in addition to the one partially open channel, there is fission through many more nearly closed channels; the statistical frequency function of the total width through these channels will show a pronounced maximum at a value of a few meV and will give very small probability of having a value much smaller than this.

An alternative, and more likely, explanation is that there is only the one partially-open fission channel for compound nucleus states of a particular spin and parity and extra fission is observed following radiative transitions to a lower compound-nucleus state of different spin and/or parity (Lynn 1965). This is the (n, γF) reaction illustrated schematically in Fig. 8.21.

Estimates of the width for this process may be made from the unified model of the transition states and the theory of capture γ-ray spectra given in Chapter VII. It is first assumed that an intermediate state for which a fission channel is fully open will decay predominantly by fission rather than by radiating. This is very plausible for, at an energy about 1 MeV below the neutron threshold, the spacing of compound nucleus states (of one spin and parity) will be of the order of 10 eV, the fission width will be about one-sixth of this and the radiation width will be about the same as for states at the neutron separation energy, i.e. about 40 meV. The fission width is therefore about two orders of magnitude greater than the radiation width and, indeed, will not equal it until the energy is of the order of $\frac{1}{2}\hbar\omega_{\mathrm{f}}$ below the transition state energy E_{f}. Thus, in the part of the primary radiation spectrum with γ-ray energy below $E_{\mathrm{th,n}}-E_{\mathrm{f}}+\frac{1}{2}\hbar\omega_{\mathrm{f}}$ the cascade is broken by fission;

the total width for this part of the spectrum is observed as fission and the remainder leads to the observation of radiative capture. The fraction $P(\varepsilon_\gamma)$ of the electric dipole primary spectrum with energy less than ε_γ is shown in Fig. 8.22. This calculation was made for ^{236}U using Newton's shell model of level density (see Chapter IV, Section B.5), but with single-particle level density given by $\rho_S = 0{\cdot}045\ (\bar{j}_N + \bar{j}_Z + 1)$

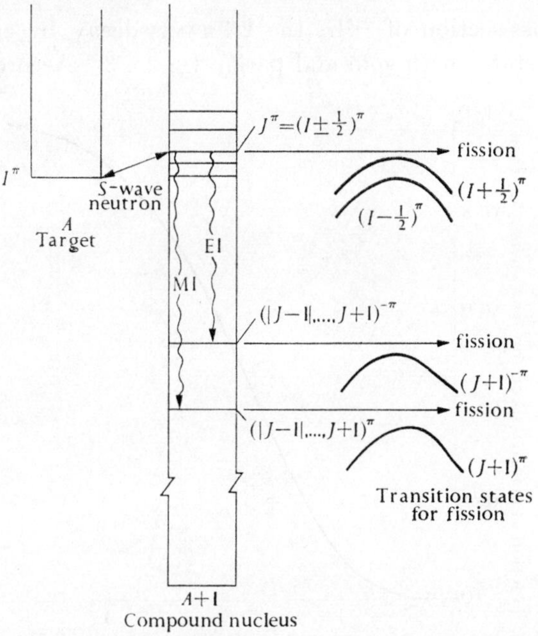

FIG. 8.21. Schematic diagram of the (n, γF) reaction. The inverted parabolic curves on the right indicate the transition states at the saddle point in the deformation energy, through which the compound nucleus must pass in the process of fission. Only the lowest transition states for different spin and parity are schematically indicated. In a typical case the ground state of the compound nucleus will lie about 6 MeV below the neutron separation energy while the very lowest transition state for fission will be up to 1·5 MeV below the neutron separation energy.

$A^{2/3}$, and the photonuclear giant-resonance model (see Chapter VII, Section E) for the radiative capture matrix elements.

The formula quoted in Chapter VII, Section D for the relative variance, V^2, of total radiation widths may be used to obtain a crude estimate of the fluctuation in this process; in eqn. (7.41) the neutron separation energy is replaced by the maximum energy of γ-rays that can be followed by fission, i.e. $E_{\text{th,n}} - E_f + \frac{1}{2}\hbar\omega_f$. It is found that for the heavy even-compound nuclei V^2 is of the order of 2×10^{-5} when this energy is in the region of 1 MeV, and at much lower energies it has the asymptotic form $V^2 = 32/\{7(E_{\text{th,n}} - E_{\text{f}} + \frac{1}{2}\hbar\omega_{\text{f}})\rho(E_{\text{th,n}})\}$ where $\rho(E_{\text{th,n}})$ is the density of final states at the neutron emission threshold. If the energy variation of the partial radiation widths is assumed to be different from the usual cubic form, and has the form ε_γ^n say, then the coefficient of 32/7 in the asymptotic formula for V^2 is replaced by $2(n+1)^2/(2n+1)$.

In the cross-section of ^{233}U, the 2^+ levels decay by electric dipole radiation to states with spin and parity 1^-, 2^-, 3^-. According to Table

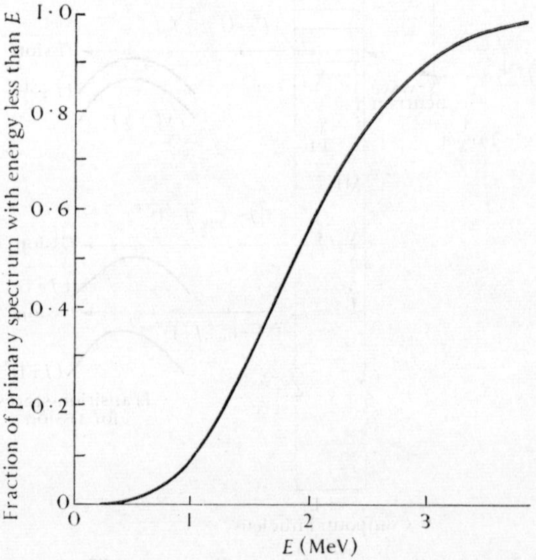

FIG. 8.22. Fraction of primary gamma-ray spectrum with gamma-ray energy less than E.

8.1 the 1^- and 3^- transition states may lie 0·5 MeV above the lowest fission threshold, i.e. about 0·8 MeV below the neutron threshold. Thus, about 10 per cent of primary transitions to the 1^- and 3^- states, and about 1 per cent of those to 2^- states are followed by fission; this implies that the width of the (n, γF) process is about 7 per cent of the total radiation width, i.e. about 3 meV. Similarly, for the 3^+ levels it is about 4 per cent of $\Gamma_{(\gamma\text{T})}$ or 1·5 meV. These values are much smaller than any observed fission width in the cross-section of ^{233}U (see Table 8.2) and consequently we conclude that the reaction is unimportant for this nucleus.

In the cross-section of ^{235}U, on the other hand, it may be a significant contributor to the statistical behaviour of the 4^- levels. Electric dipole transitions occur from these to states of spin and parity 3^+, 4^+, and 5^+. The 3^+ and 5^+ fission transition states are members of the γ-vibration-rotation band (see Table 8.1) some 700 keV or more above the fission threshold which lies about 1200 keV below the neutron threshold. These states will not contribute greatly to the width of the (n, γF) reaction. The 2^+ states, however, may fission through the ground transition-state rotational band and the width is about 10 per cent or more of the total radiation width of these states, giving $\Gamma_{(\gamma F)} \approx 2$ meV. This width will be virtually constant from level to level, because it is summed from perhaps many thousands of primary transitions, so its role in the resonance statistics is to add a small, constant component to each member of the population of widths for 'direct' fission; this adequately explains the discrepancy between observations and simulations described at the beginning of this section. The minimum values of fission widths recorded in Table 8.4 are of the order of 3 to 4 meV in reasonable agreement with the necessary crude estimate given above.

A similar calculation on ^{239}Pu indicates that the width $\Gamma_{(\gamma F)} \approx 3$ meV for the 1^+ states, again in rough agreement with the minimum observed values of 3 to 4 meV. In this a significant contribution to the gamma-fission width could also come from magnetic dipole transitions to 0^+ and 2^+ states for which there is an available fission-transition state 1·4 MeV below neutron threshold. Use of the model of Chapter VII, Section H, for magnetic dipole capture, indicates that this contribution will also be of the order of 1 meV. In the calculations of statistics of the ratio α of capture cross-section to fission cross-section, described in the last section, the (n, γF) reaction was taken into account.

5. Angular distribution of fission products in slow neutron-induced fission

It has already been pointed out (in Section A.2(e)) that, because the projection of total angular momentum on the nuclear symmetry axis, K, is a good quantum number for the low levels of the transition state, the angular distribution of fission products has forms characteristic of the transition-state spectrum. The orientation of the nuclear cylindrical symmetry axis is governed, in these low-lying states, by the wave function of a symmetric top, $D^I_{MK}(\theta, \phi, \chi)$, in which θ and ϕ are the polar angles giving the direction of the symmetry axis of the top with respect to a space fixed axis, χ is the angle of rotation of the top about its symmetry axis, I is the total angular momentum of the top, and M is the projection of the last on the space axis. The

Schrödinger equation for the rotator can be separated for each variable, so the wave-function is

$$D^I_{MK}(\theta,\phi,\chi) = d^I_{MK}(\theta)e^{iM\phi}e^{iK\chi}, \tag{8.46}$$

the first factor being the solution of

$$\sin\theta\frac{d}{d\theta}\left\{\sin\theta\frac{dd^I_{MK}(\theta)}{d\theta}\right\} + \{I(I+1)\sin^2\theta - M^2 - K^2 + 2MK\cos\theta\}d^I_{MK}(\theta) = 0. \tag{8.47}$$

The general solution of this is (Wigner 1959)

$$d^I_{MK}(\theta) = \sum_n \frac{(-)^n\{(I+K)!(I-K)!(I+M)!(I-M)!\}^{\frac{1}{2}}}{(I-M-n)!(I+K-n)!n!(n+M-K)!} \times \cos^{2I+K-M-2n}(\theta/2)\sin^{2n+M-K}(\theta/2) \tag{8.48}$$

(where the integer n is such that the factorial arguments are not less than zero), and tables for specific values of I, K, and M have been published by Wheeler (1963). It is assumed that the fission products are emitted in the direction of the symmetry axis, in which case their distribution for unit solid angle in the direction θ is

$$W^I_{MK}(\theta) = |d^I_{MK}(\theta)|^2 + |d^I_{M-K}(\theta)|^2. \tag{8.49}$$

The angular distribution is obviously incoherent for states of different I and M, but it is necessary to enquire more closely into the angular distribution from a compound nucleus level which may decay through saddle-point channels of different K values. If the angular distribution in a single fission-product channel were being considered, the discussion of Section C.1 shows that in fact an amplitude type of summing of d^I_{MK} terms, followed by squaring, would be required to find the angular distribution. But the arguments of the same section can be used to show that if the angular distribution of all fission-product channels is under discussion it is obtained simply by summing eqn. (8.49) over K. This is also true if the distribution is over a selected, but large, group (say for a specific mass ratio), with the provision that the different terms in K are weighted according to the fraction of fission products in the group that might be associated with each K value.

Fission following s-wave neutron absorption in unpolarized targets is isotropic. The reason for this is very general; the s-wave is spherically symmetric in space so there is no physical axis about which an angular distribution can appear. In a more detailed way this result can be seen as a consequence of the different magnetic substates of a level in the compound nucleus being excited with such (equal) weights that their individual contributions to the angular distribution balance out to leave only isotropy. To produce angular distributions in s-wave neutron-induced fission it is necessary to alter the relative weights of the excited magnetic substates, and this can be done by polarizing or aligning the nuclei. In polarization the nuclear spins all tend to point in a particular direction. Ideally, only a specific magnetic substate of the excited level is occupied. In alignment, the nuclear spins tend to lie along a particular axis irrespective of direction, and ideally, only the two magnetic substates, $M = \pm J$, of a level with angular momentum J are occupied. In practice, only the latter method has been used in studying fission, so we limit ourselves here to discussion of the angular distribution of fission products from aligned nuclei.

Let the spin function of the compound system of target and neutron in a state of total angular momentum J and projection M along a space axis (which from now is assigned as the direction of alignment) be denoted by $\mathscr{Y}^M_{JI\sigma}$. Here I and σ are the spins of the target and neutron respectively. Now it can be shown from the properties of the Clebsch–Gordan coefficients that the product of the spin functions of the target and neutron (respectively denoted by ζ and ξ) can be expressed as a superposition of the spin functions of the compound system.

$$\zeta_{Im}\xi_{\sigma m'} = \sum_{J=|I-\sigma|}^{I+\sigma} C_{I\sigma}(JM;\, mm')\mathscr{Y}^M_{JI\sigma}. \tag{8.50}$$

The neutron intrinsic spin is $\frac{1}{2}$ so we can substitute the specific values of the Clebsch–Gordan coefficients in eqn. (8.50) to obtain the result

$$\zeta_{Im}\xi_{\sigma m'} = \left(\frac{I\pm m}{2I+1}\right)^{\frac{1}{2}}\mathscr{Y}^{m+m'}_{I-\frac{1}{2},\,I\frac{1}{2}} + \left(\frac{I+1\mp m}{2I+1}\right)^{\frac{1}{2}}\mathscr{Y}^{m+m'}_{I+\frac{1}{2},I\frac{1}{2}}, \tag{8.51}$$

the upper sign referring to $m' = -\frac{1}{2}$ and the lower to $m' = +\frac{1}{2}$. In the ideal case of complete alignment of the *target* nucleus it can now be seen that the compound system with angular momentum $I+\frac{1}{2}$ appears in magnetic substates $\pm(I+\frac{1}{2})$ (with weighting 1/2) and in magnetic substates $\pm(I-\frac{1}{2})$ (with weighting $1/\{2(2I+1)\}$. The compound state with total angular momentum $I-\frac{1}{2}$ is completely aligned, appearing only in magnetic substates $\pm(I-\frac{1}{2})$. When the target nucleus has a high spin there is thus a very strong (though not always perfect) alignment of the compound nucleus spin in the same direction. This high value of $|M|$ governs the orientation of the transition-state nucleus. In particular if the resonance state has a high partial width for a saddle-point channel with a low value of K then the fissioning nucleus will tend to lie with its axis of cylindrical symmetry perpendicular to the direction of alignment of the target, and the fission product escape will be preferentially in this perpendicular plane.

The detailed angular distributions can now be calculated for any specified degree of alignment and set of transition-state levels (with given partial widths in the resonances) from eqn. (8.51), to give the weighting in different magnetic substates, and from eqns. (8.49) and (8.48) giving the angular distribution for each magnetic substate. In practice perfect alignment of the target nuclei cannot be achieved. For the rather small degrees of alignment that can in fact be obtained Dabbs *et al.* (1965) have derived a simpler expression for the angular distribution. For a resonant state of total angular momentum J it is

$$W_K^J(\theta) = 1+\frac{3K^2-J(J+1)}{J(J+1)}\left\{\frac{5(2I-1)(2I+1)(2I+3)}{8I(2I+2)}\right\}^{\frac{1}{2}} S_2 P_2(\cos\theta), \tag{8.52}$$

where P_2 is the Legendre polynomial of order 2 and S_2 is a parameter giving the degree of alignment of the target nuclei.

Dabbs *et al.* have made measurements of the angular anisotropy of fission products from neutron interaction with ^{235}U. The alignment of the target nuclei was achieved by the method of electric quadrupole coupling with the electric field in a crystal $UO_2Rb\,(NO_3)_3$. The crystal was cooled to temperatures as low as 0·4°K to obtain a suitable degree of alignment. The experiment is difficult to interpret because the precise value of the quadrupole coupling constant is not known (except that it is negative), but measurements at 0·28, 1·1, and 8 eV showed a degree of forward peaking (in the direction of alignment) in the angular distributions that indicated the fission to be predominantly through channels with K values between 0 and 2 in these resonances rather than through those with much higher values of K. The anisotropy is almost equal in the 1·14-eV and 8·8-eV resonances, and has a value nearly twice that of the 0·282-eV resonance. Tentative spin assignments for the resonances are shown in Table 8.4. The assignment of spin 3^- for the 0·282-eV and 8·8-eV resonances together with the anisotropy results shows that the latter has a greater proportion of its fission through a $K = 0$ channel than does the former. The assignment of spin 4^- to the 1·14-eV resonance shows very clearly that the $K = 0$ channel is not predominant in the two 3^- levels; the $K = 1$ and perhaps even the $K = 2$ channels are playing as important a role.

6. The mass distribution of fission products

Certain features of the fission phenomenon can be explained by the unified model if it is assumed that some of the properties of the transition states remain good quantum numbers, or are otherwise 'frozen-in', as the nucleus passes from the saddle point to the scission point. This is the adiabatic model (see Section A.2) the basic assumptions of which are that the collective deformation is slow compared with the typical period of nucleon motion, and that the residual interactions among the nucleons are negligible. This latter assumption is difficult to justify, as has been shown by Fong (1964) and Wilets (1964), but the success of fission product angular distribution theory strongly suggests that at least the quantum number K, the projection of the total angular momentum on the axis of cylindrical symmetry is a reasonably good quantum number between saddle and scission. It is thus arguable that the symmetry character of the wave-function with respect to the octupole deformation parameter, β_3, in the spherical harmonic expansion of the nuclear surface eqn. (4·69), is also a constant of the motion, in which case the mass division ought to be governed by the transition states at the saddle point.

The behaviour of the wave-function with respect to the octupole coordinate was rather fully described in Section A.2(c). If a stable pear-shaped configuration for the nucleus between the saddle and scission points is expected, the lowest transition states will have wave-functions with a minimum value at $\beta_3 = 0$; this will hinder symmetric mass distribution in low-energy fission, in agreement with observation.

Applied in greater detail, the theory raises the expectation that the ratio of symmetric to asymmetric fission may differ for levels of different spin (Wheeler 1956). To show this we refer back to Fig. 8.3. The ground state (and its rotational band) in the octupole potential is symmetric with respect to the octupole coordinate and the wave-function at the origin, although small, need not be zero. Thus a small amount of symmetric mass division may occur when this state is a component of the saddle-point channel. The first excited state (one phonon of mass asymmetry vibration) in the octupole potential is anti-symmetric, so perfectly symmetric mass division is forbidden when this state governs the saddle-point channel. The best target nucleus for searching for this effect experimentally is probably ^{239}Pu which forms ^{240}Pu in states of spin and parity 0^+ and 1^+ upon absorption of s-wave neutrons. The 0^+ resonant states cannot decay through saddle-point channels that contain one phonon of mass asymmetry vibration (see Table 8.1), so we expect some symmetric mass division in these resonances. The 1^+ resonant states can decay only through the saddle-point channel that is believed to be a combination of one phonon of mass asymmetry vibration and one phonon of bending vibration; so symmetric division is expected to be suppressed. Cowan *et al.* (1966) have made observations on the ratio R of ^{115}Cd (a nearly symmetric fission product) to ^{99}Mo (a product in one of the asymmetric peaks of the mass division) produced at a large number of resonances in the cross-section of ^{239}Pu. The results are shown in Table 8.10. In addition to these the ratio of the same products has been measured at thermal neutron energies and at the 0·296-eV resonance; the former is higher than the latter by a factor of about 2·5 (Regier *et al.* 1960). The results as a whole tend to confirm the theoretical expectations. All the resonances that are certainly spin 1 have a low value of the ^{115}Cd to ^{99}Mo ratio (the largest is $1{\cdot}8\times10^{-2}$, and many are less than 1×10^{-2}). A number of resonances that have been found to have zero spin have values of this ratio ranging from about 2×10^{-2} to 5×10^{-2}. In addition some resonances that probably have zero spin (because they are so broad) have values of R between $2{\cdot}5\times10^{-2}$ and 3×10^{-2}. These data seem sufficient to establish the expected correlation, but there are some exceptions to the general rule. In particular the resonances at 15·4 eV and 47·7 eV (both spin zero) have low values of R, suggesting perhaps that they are not due to single levels. The results for the 0·296-eV resonance and the thermal region are not consistent with the many-level analysis of Vogt (1960); they suggest a reversal of the spin assignments between the positive and 'negative' energy resonances.

Similar arguments may be applied to the s-wave neutron induced fission of ^{235}U. According to Table 8.1, fission of a 3^- level should proceed through a fully open saddle-point channel with one quantum of mass asymmetry vibration (and rotation), implying no symmetric fission. It may also proceed through a partially- or fully-open channel corresponding to bending vibration and, likewise, the 4^- compound-nucleus states may fission through such a channel, for which symmetric fission is allowed. The average ratio of symmetric to asymmetric fission is consequently expected to be smaller, on average, for the 3^- compound-nucleus levels than for the 4^- levels. The fluctuating ratio of yields of fission products ^{111}Ag and ^{99}Mo up to a neutron energy of 60 eV (Cowan

Table 8.10

Ratio of symmetric to asymmetric mass division in resonance fission of the compound nucleus ^{240}Pu. Ratios preceded by $\sim$ are poorly known, either because of poor statistics or poor resolution. Spins in brackets are rather uncertain. Some attempt has been made to correct the results above the broken line for the wings of neighbouring resonances

Resonance energy (eV)	Spin (consensus of results in Table 8.6)	Ratio $\frac{^{115}\text{Cd}}{^{99}\text{Mo}}$ ($\times 10^2$)
15·4	(0)†	0·78‖
17·6	1	0·89
22·2	1	1·0
26·2	1	0·74
32·3	0	$\sim$4·7
41·5	1	0·69
44·5	1	1·14
47·7	0	0·80
50·2	1	0·7
52·6	1	1·16
55·8		$\sim$0·4
57·6	†	2·8
59·5	0	$\sim$1·4
61·1	‡	3·0
65·8	1	$\sim$1·9
66·8		2·79
75·0	1	0·7
81·7	§	2·85
– – –	– – –	– – –
82·4	§	2·36
84·3	§	2·12
86·0	0§	2·27
90·9	1	1·40
92·6		2·13
96·7	1	2·36
106·7	1	1·83
116	0	1·52
119	1	1·17
132	0	2·09
143		0·69
157	0	1·91
161		0·81
164	1	0·34
185	†	2·59
195	0	1·80

† This is a broad resonance so probably has spin zero.

‡ One of the broad hidden resonances postulated by Derrien *et al.* (1966); probably spin-zero.

§ These energies belong to the complex around 80 eV that is probably dominated by very strong spin-zero levels.

‖ This ratio was actually measured off resonance so there is the possibility that it is dominated by a hidden level of different spin.

et al. 1961, 1963) may be evidence of this effect. It has been observed, for example, that the ratio of ^{111}Ag to ^{99}Mo is lower for the 8·8-eV than for the 0·282-eV resonance, both of which are believed to have total angular momentum of 3. According to the results of angular anisotropy of fission fragments from aligned nuclei (see Section C.5) this is not surprising, the ratio of the $K^{\pi} = 0^{-}$ partial fission width to the total fission being greater for the former resonance.

The behaviour of the symmetric-to-asymmetric mass yield ratios has been measured at higher energies by Cuninghame *et al.* (1961, 1966) for ^{235}U and ^{239}Pu. In the former case they found the (at first sight) surprising result that fission induced by 60-keV neutrons shows less symmetric yield than that induced by *s*-wave neutrons. This can be explained, however, if it is assumed that the even-parity resonant states excited in ^{236}U by *p*-wave neutrons can decay by fission through the transition states of combined mass asymmetry and bending vibration. We have already seen in our discussion of $\bar{\alpha}$ of ^{235}U at 60-keV neutron energy that it seems necessary for either this saddle-point channel or the gamma vibration channel to be almost fully open; it now appears that it has to be the former that is open, while the latter would seem to be nearly closed. The behaviour of the mass yield ratios in neutron-induced fission of ^{239}Pu up to a few hundred keV can also be explained by the channel theory. Using the *s*-wave resonance data on mass yields and assuming the transition states given in Table 8.9, a direct calculation of the ratio certainly gives the observed magnitude and also shows the monotonically increasing dependence on energy that the data has.

Despite these apparent successes of the adiabatic theory it ought to be pointed out that there are other classes of theory which seek to explain the ratio of mass division observed in fission. One such is the statistical model (Fong 1956, 1963; Newton 1956) on which the only detailed quantitative calculations have been done: these have met with some success. The statistical model is based on the hypothesis that the reduced widths for the individual fission-product channels are equal; the mass distribution is therefore governed by the number of energetically available excited states of the fission products (i.e. by their level density behaviour) and the centrifugal and Coulomb barrier penetration factors for the fission product channels. The general assumption behind the model is that the time of collective deformation from saddle point to scission is long compared with the time of inter-nucleon collisions. Fong (1964) has attempted to justify this by showing that the lower limit for the former time, based on the Coulomb force between the incipient fission products, is greater than an estimate for the latter time, calculated from the optical potential as deduced from studies of nuclear reactions. This justification is weak in that it assumes that the imaginary part of the optical potential is the same between saddle and scission as it is in the more central part of configuration space involved in the nucleon scattering reactions; in so far as the intrinsic excitation energy of the nucleus between saddle and scission is low compared with the excitation energy of a compound nucleus in a scattering reaction, the imaginary potential may also be much lower and, therefore, the inter-nucleon collision period may be much higher. However, even if

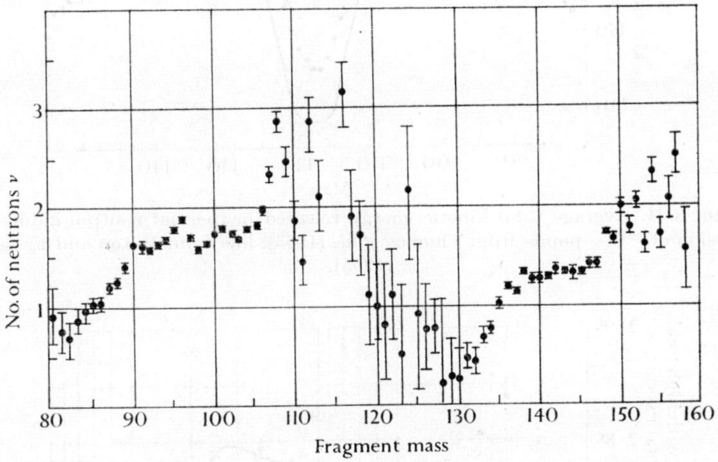

FIG. 8.23. Number of neutrons produced per fission in thermal neutron induced fission of ^{235}U as a function of fragment mass number (from Milton and Fraser 1965).

the statistical theory is correct to the extent that the basic energy surfaces provided by the unified model are mixed between the saddle and scission points there may still be some reason to suspect the influence of the transition-state levels in low-energy fission. This is because the mixing of the unified-model states will be confined to those with the same values not only of total angular momentum and parity but of angular momentum projection on the symmetry axis. Actually the conservation of J and π alone, together with the assumption that the mixing is limited to a resonable energy range (say less than $\frac{1}{2}$ MeV), is sufficient to explain the plutonium results. In the case of ^{236}U, K conservation may be necessary in addition to confine the mass symmetry vibration to states of one spin rather than the other.

7. Kinetic energy of fission products

Certain other features of fission are related to the mass distribution. One of these is the neutron emission that follows fission. The number of neutrons emitted per fission, ν, as function of the masses of the fission

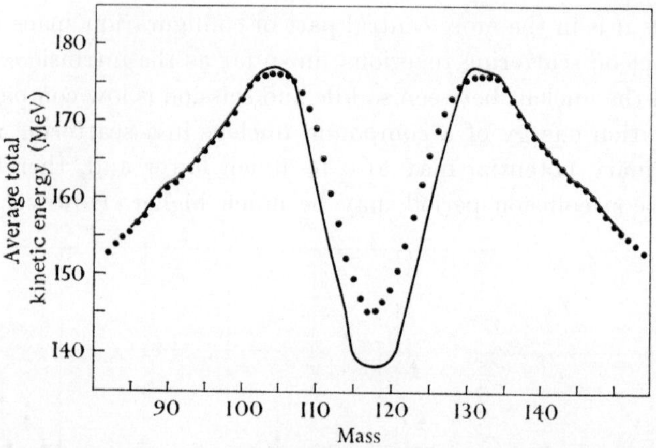

Fig. 8.24. Average total kinetic energy released in thermal neutron-induced fission of ^{235}U—points from Thomas *et al.* (1965), line from Milton and Fraser (1965).

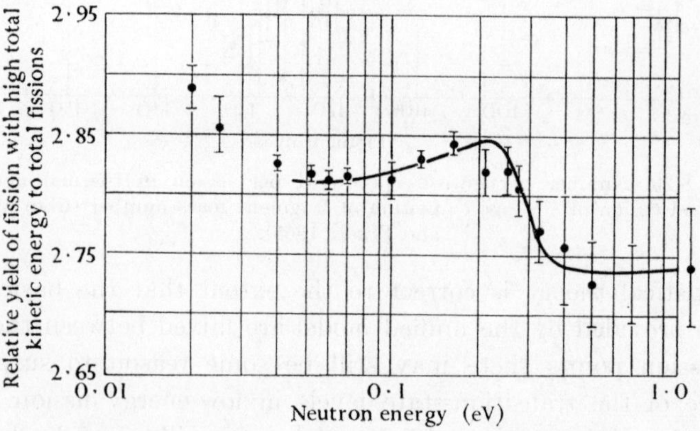

Fig. 8.25. Dependence of total kinetic energy released in neutron-induced fission of ^{235}U on neutron energy (from Moore and Miller 1965).

products is shown in Fig. 8.23 for fission induced by thermal neutrons. It follows from the large number of neutrons emitted following symmetric division that the internal excitation of the fragments is large and their kinetic energy low for this particular mass yield ratio. This particular behaviour has also been observed and is shown in Fig. 8.24.

It implies that as the ratio of symmetric to asymmetric division varies through neutron resonances the average kinetic energy of the fragments varies also, tending to be high when the fraction of symmetric fission is low, and vice versa. Some measurements of this quantity have been made at very low energies with ^{235}U as the target (Moore and Miller 1965). The results, shown in Fig. 8.25, do show these qualitative features.

8. Neutron-induced fission of even-target nuclei

The measured fission widths of the cross-sections of even-target nuclei are, in general, much less than those of the odd-mass, even-charge

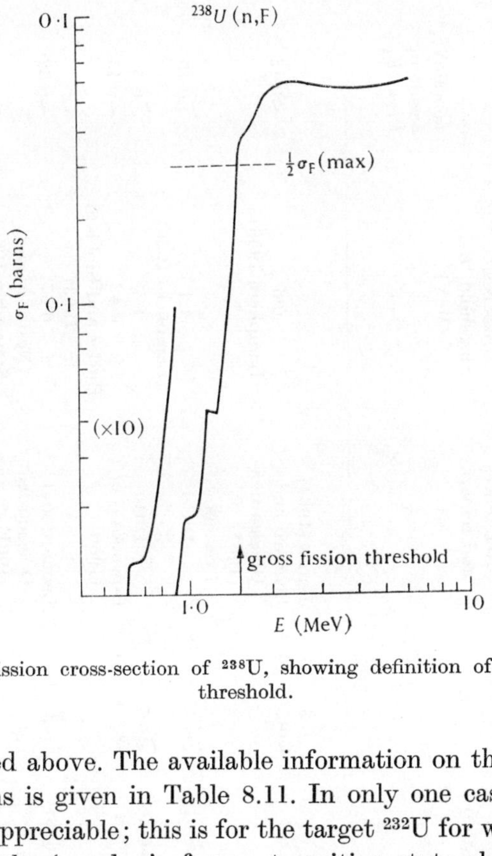

FIG. 8.26. Fission cross-section of ^{238}U, showing definition of gross fission threshold.

nuclei discussed above. The available information on the mean values of these widths is given in Table 8.11. In only one case is the mean fission width appreciable; this is for the target ^{232}U for which the effective N-value, the 'number' of open transition state channels, is $0{\cdot}30 \pm 0{\cdot}15$. This indicates that in the compound nucleus ^{233}U the $\frac{1}{2}^+$ fission threshold is close to the neutron separation energy. A maximum likelihood analysis of the eight measured fission widths in this cross-section to find the parameter of the best fitting chi-squared distribution gives a

TABLE 8.11

Mean fission widths for even target nuclei

Target nucleus	$\bar{\Gamma}_{(F)}$(meV)	$\dfrac{2\pi\bar{\Gamma}_{(F)}}{\bar{D}}$	References and remarks	Gross fission threshold 'E_F' (MeV)	Deductions about properties of $\frac{1}{2}^+$ saddle-point channel: $\hbar\omega_f$(MeV), assuming E_f = 'E_F'	E_f(MeV) assuming $\hbar\omega_f = 0{\cdot}4$MeV	E_f(MeV), assuming $\hbar\omega_f = 0{\cdot}6$MeV
^{232}U	360 ± 130	$0{\cdot}3 \pm {\cdot}15$	James (1964)			0·05	0·08
^{234}U	$\sim 0{\cdot}7$	$\sim 0{\cdot}24 \times 10^{-3}$	Leonard and Odegaarden (1961) 1 resonance	0·6 (Lamphere 1956)	$\sim 0{\cdot}45$	$\sim 0{\cdot}53$	$\sim 0{\cdot}8$
^{236}U	$\lesssim 0{\cdot}001$	$\lesssim 0{\cdot}35 \times 10^{-6}$	Ditto	1·1 (Lamphere 1956)	$\lesssim 0{\cdot}45$	$\gtrsim 0{\cdot}95$	$\gtrsim 1{\cdot}5$
^{238}U	$\lesssim 0{\cdot}0002$	$\lesssim 0{\cdot}7 \times 10^{-7}$	Ditto	1·5	$\lesssim 0{\cdot}5$	$\gtrsim 1{\cdot}05$	$\gtrsim 1{\cdot}7$
^{238}Pu	$4{\cdot}7 \pm 2$	$(2{\cdot}3 \pm 1) \times 10^{-3}$	Bowman *et al.* (1966)	0·42 (Butler and Sjoblom 1963)	$\sim 0{\cdot}45$	$\sim 0{\cdot}39$	$\sim 0{\cdot}58$
^{240}Pu	$\sim 0{\cdot}006$	$\sim 2 \times 10^{-6}$	Leonard and Odegaarden (1961) 1 resonance	0·67 (Nesterov and Smirenkin 1960)	$\sim 0{\cdot}32$	$\sim 0{\cdot}84$	$\sim 1{\cdot}4$
^{242}Pu	$\lesssim 0{\cdot}02$	$\lesssim 0{\cdot}7 \times 10^{-5}$	Ditto	0·76 (Butler 1960)	$\lesssim 0{\cdot}4$	$\gtrsim 0{\cdot}76$	$\gtrsim 1{\cdot}2$

value of ν of $1{\cdot}9 \pm 0{\cdot}8$, indicating that the Porter–Thomas distribution ($\nu = 1$) may be valid (James 1964). A many-level fit to the cross-section (using the reduced R-matrix method) has also been made by James, and he finds that the fit is quite satisfactory using only one saddle-point channel. There is no very strong reason for expecting appreciable

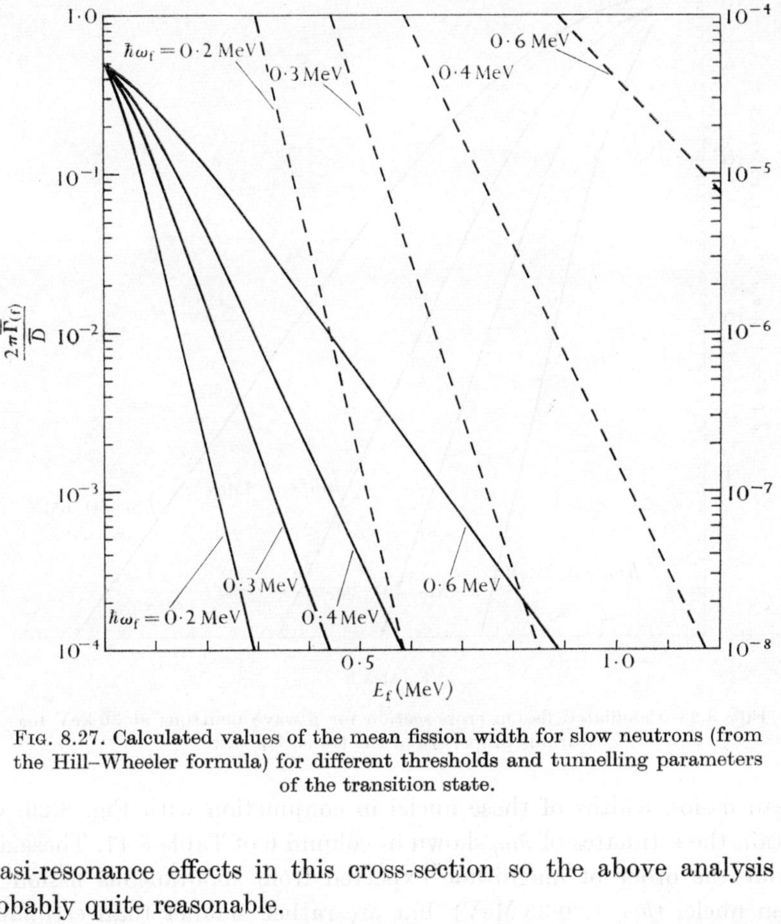

FIG. 8.27. Calculated values of the mean fission width for slow neutrons (from the Hill–Wheeler formula) for different thresholds and tunnelling parameters of the transition state.

quasi-resonance effects in this cross-section so the above analysis is probably quite reasonable.

In the other compound nuclei listed in Table 8.11 the $\frac{1}{2}^{+}$ fission threshold is clearly at a much higher energy. First of all, we discuss the s-wave resonance fission widths in terms of the 'gross' fission thresholds of these nuclei. The latter term is defined as the energy at which the average fission cross-section of an even nucleus attains half its plateau value in the MeV region. This is illustrated for the case of ^{238}U in Fig. 8.26. These gross thresholds are listed in Table 8.11. (But see p. 459 *ff.*)

Estimates of the mean fission widths of low-energy resonances (in the eV region) can be made from the Hill–Wheeler formula, eqns. (8.28), (8.33), for different values of $\hbar\omega_f$ and E_f for only one transition state. Such estimates are shown in Fig. 8.27. If the gross fission thresholds are used for E for the nuclei in Table 8.11, and $\hbar\omega_f$ is deduced from the

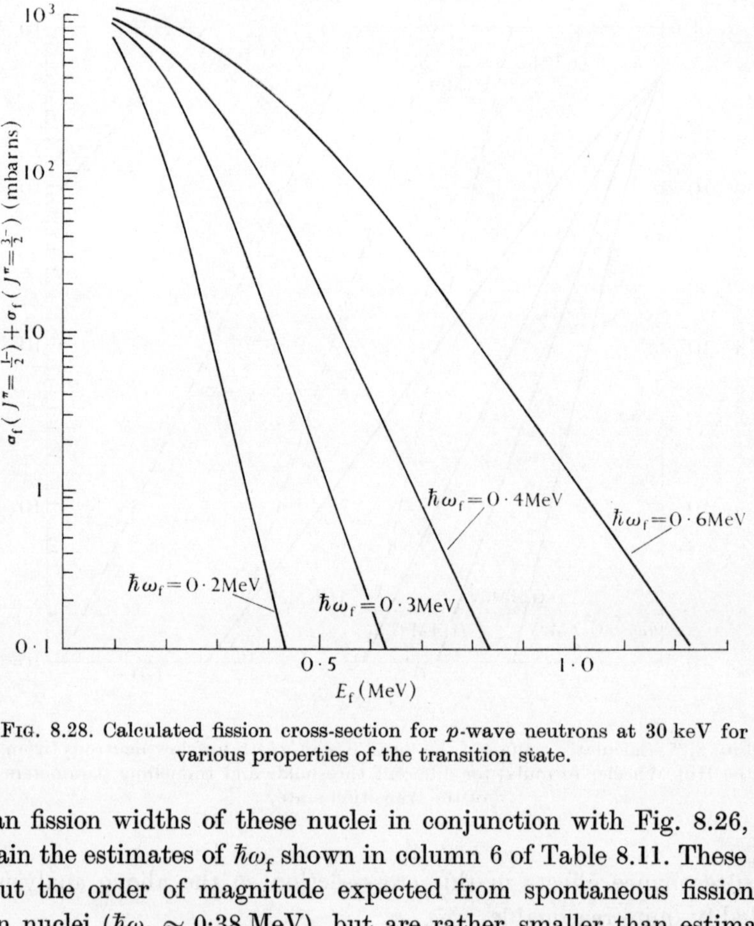

FIG. 8.28. Calculated fission cross-section for p-wave neutrons at 30 keV for various properties of the transition state.

mean fission widths of these nuclei in conjunction with Fig. 8.26, we obtain the estimates of $\hbar\omega_f$ shown in column 6 of Table 8.11. These are about the order of magnitude expected from spontaneous fission of even nuclei ($\hbar\omega_f \approx 0{\cdot}38$ MeV), but are rather smaller than estimates obtained from other sources of information. The latter range from about 0·3 to 0·6 MeV in the (d, pf) reaction, and from about 0·4 to 0·7 MeV in the photofission reaction (Usachev *et al.* 1964). The spontaneous fission estimate may itself be an indication of higher values of $\hbar\omega_f$ in particle induced fission, because at very low energies the fission barrier departs from the parabolic shape assumed for the Hill–Wheeler transmission formula.

The deduction to be made from this possible discrepancy (Rae 1965) may be that the $\frac{1}{2}^+$ fission threshold lies at a considerably higher energy than the gross fission threshold (estimates of this threshold for $\hbar\omega_f = 0{\cdot}6$ MeV are shown in column 8 of Table 8.11); the transition states responsible for the latter are of higher spin projection (K) and spin value than the $\frac{1}{2}^+$ level, or have opposite parity. This hypothesis is supported by studying the average p-wave neutron fission cross-section, which may be calculated from the Hill–Wheeler formula and

TABLE 8.12

Fission cross-sections of even-target nuclei at neutron energies of about 30 keV

Target nucleus	σ_F(mbarns) at about 30 keV	Reference	Deductions about properties of $\frac{1}{2}^-$ or $\frac{3}{2}^-$ saddle-point channels		
			$\hbar\omega_f$(MeV) assuming E_f = 'E_F'	E_f(MeV) assuming $\hbar\omega_f = 0{\cdot}4$ MeV	E_f(MeV) assuming $\hbar\omega_f = 0{\cdot}6$ MeV
^{234}U	15 ± 4	Perkin *et al.* (1965)	$\sim 0{\cdot}5$	0·54	0·77
^{236}U	<4	Perkin *et al.* (1965)	$<0{\cdot}7$	$>0{\cdot}6$	$>0{\cdot}9$
	probably ~ 1	From data at 127 keV by White *et al.* (1965)	$\sim 0{\cdot}65$	$\sim 0{\cdot}7$	$\sim 1{\cdot}05$
^{238}Pu	~ 1000	Vorontnikov *et al.* (1966)		$\lesssim 0$	$\lesssim 0$
^{240}Pu	106 ± 18	Ruddick and White (1964)	$\sim 0{\cdot}75$	$\sim 0{\cdot}38$	$\sim 0{\cdot}56$

the average cross-section formula in Section B (eqn. (8.20)). A typical set of cross-sections for fission induced by p-wave neutrons at the energy of 30 keV is shown in Fig. 8.28. In these a $K^\pi = \frac{1}{2}^-$ transition state is assumed. Observed fission cross-sections at 30-keV energy are shown in Table 8.12. Their magnitudes can be explained (using Fig. 8.28) by assuming either that E_f for the saddle-point channel is equal to the gross fission threshold, in which case the deduced value of $\hbar\omega_f$ is given in column 4, or by assuming a specific value of $\hbar\omega_f$ to deduce E_f. With the former assumption it appears that $\hbar\omega_f$ lies in the range 0·5–0·75 MeV. De Vroey *et al.* (1965) have measured the fission cross-section of ^{240}Pu from 30 keV to above the gross threshold energy at 0·67 MeV and have fitted the data up to a few hundred keV, allowing for competition from the experimentally observed inelastic scattering. To obtain an adequate fit it appears necessary to have the $K^\pi = \frac{1}{2}^-$ fission threshold close to the gross fission threshold, in which case the tunnelling parameter $\hbar\omega_f$ must be of the order of or greater than 0·6 or 0·7 MeV.

Whatever the value of $\hbar\omega_f$ may be, it appears from the s-wave and p-wave neutron-induced fission data of even targets that, generally speaking, the $K^\pi = \frac{1}{2}^+$ saddle-point channel lies a few hundred keV above the lowest $K = \frac{1}{2}^-$ or $K = \frac{3}{2}^-$ channel (^{234}U appears to be an exception). This result is in qualitative agreement with Johannson's scheme of the Nilsson orbitals at high deformation ($\delta \approx 0{\cdot}5$)—see Fig. 8.5. It also leads to the speculation that in one or two cases, like ^{238}Pu, when the odd-parity or higher-spin fission thresholds (e.g. $K^\pi = \frac{1}{2}^-$ or $\frac{3}{2}^+$) are below the neutron emission threshold, while the s-wave induced-fission threshold is above, the observed fission in the s-wave resonances may be due mainly to the (n, γf) reaction. Bowman *et al.* (1966) have analysed their measurements of ten fission widths varying from 1·2 to 8·7 meV in the low energy cross-section of ^{238}Pu to test this. Using the maximum likelihood method, they find $\nu = 8 \pm 2$ for an assumed chi-squared distribution. While this is high, the expected value for the normal fission process being $\nu = 1$ (the Porter–Thomas distribution), it is not nearly high enough to signify that a large part of the width is due to the indirect γf process; it was pointed out in Section 4 that V^2, the relative variance of the γf widths, related to the effective ν value by $V^2 = 2/\nu_{\text{eff}}$, will be of the order of 10^{-4} to 10^{-3}. The magnitude of these fission widths is also too large for it to appear plausible that the (n, γf) reaction is playing an important role. A width for the γf process greater than 1 meV is calculated only when the fission barrier of the final states following gamma-ray emission is more than $\frac{1}{2}$ MeV below the neutron threshold. For the more likely value of 100–200 keV in the difference of the two thresholds the γf width would be of the order of $\frac{1}{10}$ meV.

9. Fission of odd-proton targets

(a) *Even-neutron targets*

Neutron absorption by these targets leads to odd-compound nuclei. The most elementary transition states in such nuclei will be two quasi-particle states and will be very numerous. No attempt has been made to classify or calculate them at the saddle point so the rather sparse cross-section data cannot be correlated in any way. The mean fission widths with deductions about the s-wave saddle-point channels are given in Table 8.13. The most complete data are those on ^{241}Am. An analysis of the fission-width fluctuations in this cross-section indicates a chi-squared distribution with an effective ν value of $2{\cdot}9 \pm 0{\cdot}6$ (Bowman *et al.* 1965). (See p. 459 *ff.*)

(*b*) *Odd-neutron targets*

Although the fission widths of the cross-sections of the odd-neutron, even-proton targets are very small, the odd actinide nuclei are, by

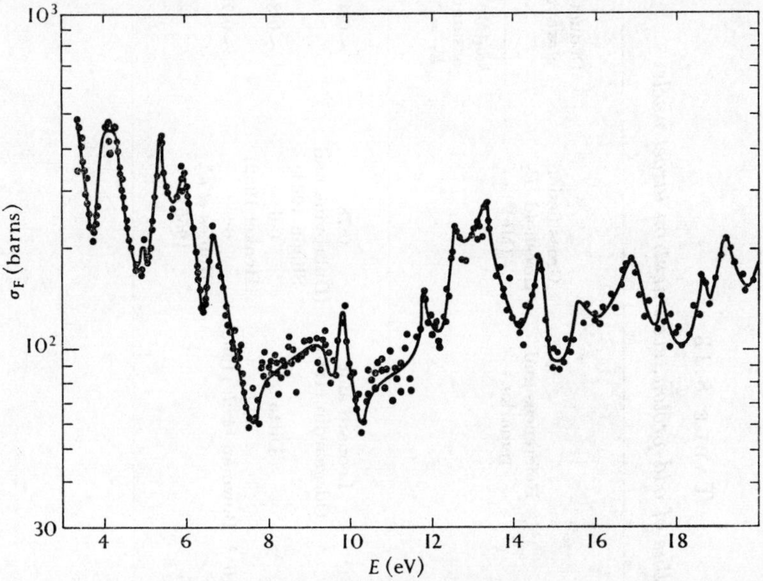

FIG. 8.29. Slow neutron fission cross-section of ^{242m}Am (from Bowman and Auchampaugh 1966).

contrast, highly fissile. This is known from their very high fission cross-sections at thermal neutron energies: ^{230}Pa, 1500 ± 250 barns, ^{232}Pa, 700 ± 100 barns, ^{234}Np, 900 ± 300 barns, ^{236}Np, 2800 ± 800 barns, ^{238}Np, 1600 ± 100 barns, ^{242}Am, 2900 ± 100 barns, ^{242m}Am (152a), 6000 ± 500 barns, ^{244}Am, 2300 ± 300 barns, nearly all of which are several times greater than those of the odd-mass, even-charge nuclei. The reason is the high neutron-separation energy of the odd-Z compound nuclei. There only seems to be one of these nuclei for which the resonance structure of the cross-section has been measured. This is the metastable isomer ^{242m}Am, the half-life of which is 152a, the spin is 5^-, and its energy above the ground state is $48{\cdot}8$ keV. The cross-section, measured by Bowman and Auchampaugh (1966), is shown in Fig. 8.29. The qualitative features here of very broad maxima and very high minima indicate that the number of open saddle-point channels must be large indeed.

TABLE 8.13

Mean fission widths of odd-proton, even-neutron target nuclei

Target nucleus and spin and parity, I^{π}	$\bar{\Gamma}_{(F)}$(meV)	$\frac{2\pi\Gamma_{(F)}}{\bar{D}}$	References and remarks	Gross fission threshold 'E_F' (MeV)	Deductions about properties of S-wave saddle-point channels	
					$\hbar\omega_f$(MeV), assuming E_f = 'E_F'	E_f(MeV), assuming $\hbar\omega_f = 0{\cdot}4$MeV
$^{231}Pa(\frac{3}{2}-)$	$0{\cdot}006 \pm {\cdot}004$	$(1{\cdot}9 \pm 1) \times 10^{-5}$	Leonard and Odegaardin (1961)	0·78 (Dubrovina and Shigin 1964)	~0·45	~0·69
$^{237}Np(\frac{5}{2}+)$	$0{\cdot}0028 \pm {\cdot}002$	$(1{\cdot}5 \pm 1) \times 10^{-5}$	Ditto	0·6 (Henkel 1952)	~0·34	~0·71
$^{241}Am(\frac{5}{2}-)$	$0{\cdot}18 \pm {\cdot}06$	$(0{\cdot}65 \pm {\cdot}25) \times 10^{-3}$	Bowman *et al.* (1965)	0·9 (Nobles *et al.* 1955)	~0·75	~0·46

10. Angular distribution of fission products from fast neutron-induced fission

In the analysis of a plane wave into its spherical components only the spherical harmonics $Y_0^{(l)}$, corresponding to zero projection of the orbital angular momentum in the direction of the beam, appear. In the bombardment of a target nucleus with a low spin (e.g. an even nucleus) with fast neutrons it is therefore possible to excite resonant states with high angular momentum J (corresponding to excitations by neutrons with high orbital angular momentum l) and low values of the magnetic quantum number M. As we have seen in earlier sections this kind of limitation on the value of M can lead to strong angular distributions of the fission products from the excited states if only one or a few transition states are energetically available at the saddle point. For example, a nucleus in a transition state with a high value of K will be constrained to lie perpendicular to the beam direction with the result that the fission products show a 'sideways' peaking in their angular distribution. On the other hand, if the predominant transition state has a low value of K (i.e. is one of the high-spin members of a rotational band with low K) the fission products tend to appear in cones about the neutron beam directions; the lower the value of K the smaller is the angle of the cone.

The detailed distributions for particular cases can be obtained from the symmetric top wave-functions given in eqn. (8.48). For even-target nuclei the magnetic quantum numbers of the compound nucleus are limited to the two values $\pm\frac{1}{2}$, and the angular distribution of the fission products from a resonant state of total angular momentum J through a saddle-point channel belonging to a rotational band K is

$$W_K^J(\theta) \propto |D^J_{\pm\frac{1}{2}K}|^2 + |D^J_{\pm\frac{1}{2}-K}|^2 \tag{8.53}$$

(Wilets and Chase 1956). The expressions for J values corresponding to the first three rotational levels of the band are explicitly

$$W_K^K(\theta) = \frac{(2K)!}{\{(K-\frac{1}{2})!\}^2 2^{2K}} \sin^{2K-1}\theta, \tag{8.54a}$$

$$W_K^{K+1}(\theta) = \frac{(2K+1)!}{\{(K+\frac{1}{2})!\}^2 2^{2K+2}} \sin^{2K-1}\theta\{1+4K(K+1)\cos^2\theta\}, \tag{8.54b}$$

$$W_{K+2}^K(\theta) = \frac{(2K+3)!}{(K+\frac{1}{2})!(K+\frac{3}{2})!2^{2K+4}} \sin^{2K-1}\theta\{1-4K\cos^2\theta+4K(K+2)\cos^4\theta\} \tag{8.54c}$$

By maximizing these expressions it is found that the angular distribution can only have forward peaking (a maximum W at $\theta = 0$) for $K = \frac{1}{2}$ and $J > K$. The greater the value of J the more pronounced is the forward angular distribution. Other things being equal, high neutron energy is most favourable for observing this phenomenon.

It has been observed, as a general rule, that in fast neutron-induced fission of even nuclei forward-peaking occurs in the sub-threshold region. Among the target nuclei showing this effect most strongly are ^{230}Th (Vorotnikov *et al.* 1965, Lamphere 1965), ^{232}Th and ^{238}U (Lamphere 1965). It is also exhibited to a lesser extent by ^{240}Pu and ^{234}U (Lamphere 1965). An exception to the rule is ^{236}U. The result shows that the lowest transition state for fission of these nuclei except ^{236}U belong to a $K = \frac{1}{2}$ band. Lamphere has attempted to fit the angular anisotropy as a function of energy in more detail in order to obtain the K values and parities of a sequence of bands, but the results are probably rather ambiguous because it is necessary to use the complex-potential model to calculate the neutron cross-sections for compound nucleus formation in each state of total angular momentum and parity, and the model is hardly capable yet of providing the necessary accuracy for this. In particular Lamphere usually gives the parity of the lowest $K = \frac{1}{2}$ band as even, yet, as we have seen, the fission cross-sections in the s-wave and p-wave regions strongly suggest that it should be odd, at least for the nuclei ^{236}U, ^{238}Pu, ^{240}Pu. (See also Vandenbosch, 1967.)

11. Fast neutron-induced fission of even-target nuclei

So far it seems that the channel theory explains many features of neutron-induced fission rather well. But now let us look at the other side of the coin. In contrast to the very heavy odd-mass nuclei, even targets are not normally fissile to slow neutrons but show a threshold effect at several hundred keV. Our reason for considering fast neutron fission cross-sections in this book is that only a limited fraction of the angular momentum and parity states of the compound nucleus may actually decay by fission in the threshold region, and thus it may be possible to interpret them profitably from the viewpoint of resonant states. Above the threshold, dips are often found in the fission cross-sections; these are usually explained as the effect of inelastic neutron competition after a single channel (or group of channels in a rotational band) has become fully open for fission (Wheeler 1956, 1963). At this point the fission cross-section flattens off to an almost constant value, but when an inelastic scattering channel opens at a higher energy the fission cross-section falls again. This rising and falling is expected to continue successively as new saddle-point channels and then new inelastic channels open in turn.

One wonders, however, if the theory of inelastic scattering competition is fully capable of explaining these dips. In the cross-section of ^{232}Th (shown in Fig. 8.30), for example, the first peak falls by nearly a factor of 2 with an energy increase of only 80 keV. Assuming only about fifteen levels below about 1·6 MeV in ^{232}Th available for inelastic

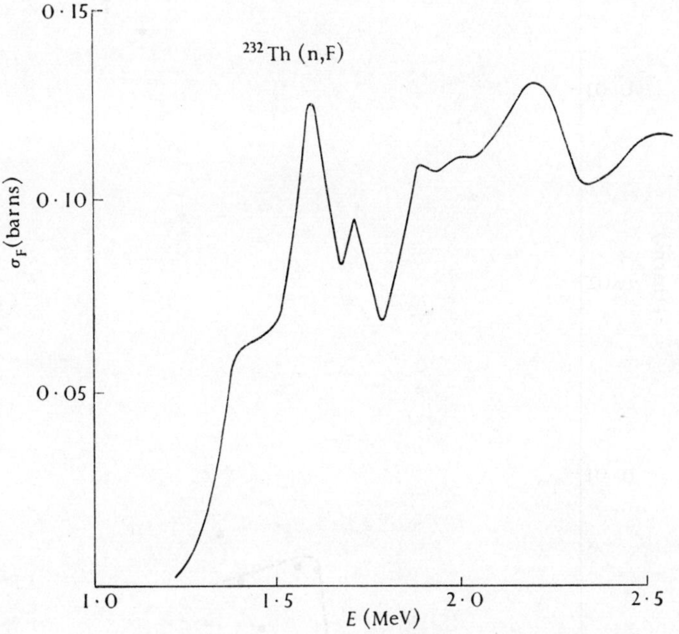

FIG. 8.30. Fission cross-section of ^{232}Th.

scattering, we calculate that the level density in this nucleus would suddenly have to increase to at least a few thousand per MeV at 1·6 MeV to provide sufficient inelastic scattering to explain this fall. Now a sudden increase in the level density at about this energy is certainly possible; it is associated with the top of the energy gap in the pairing-correlation theory of nuclear structure. A calculated level density curve (by Kluge 1964) from this theory is shown in Fig. 4.14. However this calculation indicates that the density above the energy gap is only a few hundred per MeV. Furthermore, the required degree of inelastic scattering should also have its effect on the radiative capture cross-section, but the rather sparse data on this (Miskal *et al.* 1962) indicate that it falls by less than a factor of 2 between 1·5 and 2·0 MeV. Yet again, the available fission channels are not expected to appear with a density comparable to that of the inelastic scattering channels until a neutron energy of nearly 4 MeV is reached. So it may be asked why the fission cross-section does not show an overall decline from 1·5 to 4 MeV.

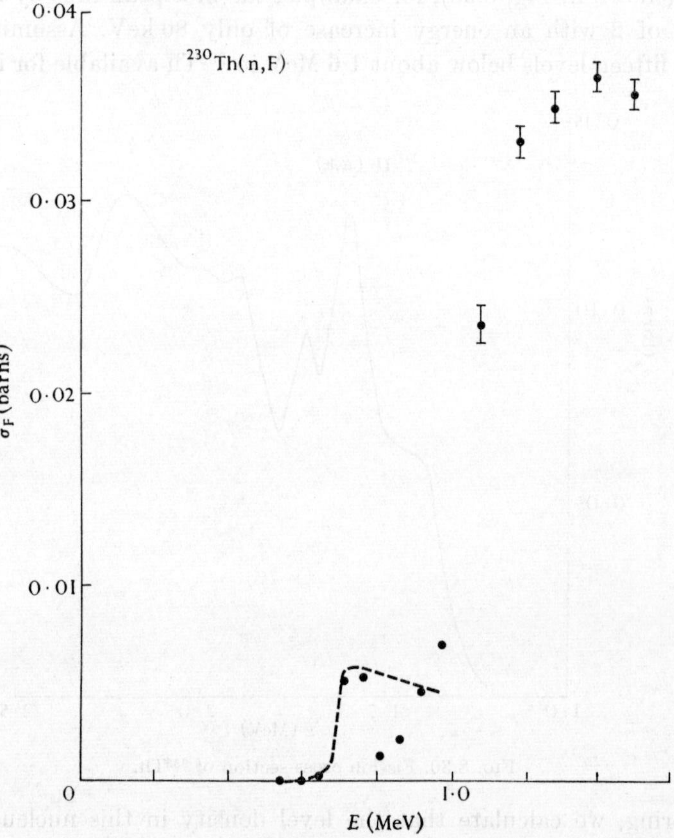

FIG. 8.31. Fission cross-section of ^{230}Th. The broken curve is an attempt to calculate the cross-section from strong-coupling theory of the transition state, assuming the transition state to be $K^\pi = 7/2^-$, including inelastic scattering competition to all known residual states of ^{230}Th. Assumed parameters for this saddle-point channel are $E_f = 0{\cdot}68$ MeV, $\hbar\omega_f = 0{\cdot}1$ MeV.

Our doubts about the inelastic scattering competition theory are further intensified when we turn to the fission cross-section of ^{238}U (Fig. 8.26). This is a rather similar nucleus to ^{232}Th and the fission threshold is very close. Yet apart from some breaks in the sub-threshold region, its cross-section is very smooth.

But the greatest difficulty that the competition theory has to face is provided by the fission cross-section of ^{230}Th (Fig. 8.31). This exhibits a narrow peak (Evans and Jones 1965), in what is commonly called the sub-threshold region, rising to about 50 mbarns and then falling to about one-quarter of this value. The energy at which this occurs is only 700 keV so there is no chance at all of invoking the large onset of inelastic scattering channels at the top of the energy gap to explain it. In fact the most favourable assumptions about the states known to exist in ^{230}Th will only allow a small drop in the fission cross-section, as shown in Fig. 8.31. In this calculation the fission channel is assumed to have spin projection (on the symmetry axis) and parity of $K^{\pi} = 7/2^{-}$; this, and the higher spin members of its rotational band, would allow the fission of compound nucleus levels excited only by neutron f-waves and waves of higher odd orbital angular momentum. A smaller choice of K would allow states excited by lower orbital angular momenta to fission and a much higher fission cross-section at the plateau would be expected. This in itself is a difficulty: measurements of the angular distribution of fission products (due to Gokhberg *et al.* 1959) indicate that a $K = \frac{1}{2}$ channel is open, so the observed peak in the cross-section really is a sub-threshold effect and is not just the contribution from a partial wave below the neutron centrifugal potential barrier.

A possible weak point at the root of a quantitative channel theory of fission may be the estimate of channel-fission width, both in magnitude and in barrier penetration. The estimate that $\Gamma_{(f)}/D = 1/2\pi$ for a single open fission channel really comes from the classical limit of quantal statistical mechanics. Furthermore, perhaps the penetrability formula of Hill and Wheeler leaves room for improvement. This latter visualizes the motion of the fissioning nucleus over the barrier as a wave progressing from an infinitely low value of the deformation parameter, β, of the nucleus through an inverted harmonic oscillator potential towards an indefinitely high value.

In Section C.2 we discussed a more sophisticated model for estimating the strength function of a saddle-point channel; this embraced both strong-coupling and weak-coupling aspect of the mixing of the transition state into the compound-nucleus wave-function. The intriguing features of the model are found in the 'weak coupling' calculations. In the result of Fig. 8.13b, W is only 30 keV. A rather sharp peak is found in the fission strength function very close to the threshold energy. One is tempted to hypothesize that this may be the explanation of the peaks in the fission cross-section of ^{232}Th. The peak corresponds to a virtual state in the (real) potential well of the model. With the kinds of parameters used the spacing of such states is of the order of 2 or 3 MeV. Fairly small changes in the parameters will move the virtual states to different energies with respect to threshold. If V is changed from $-5{\cdot}4$ MeV to $-6{\cdot}0$ MeV the virtual state moves from just above threshold to a binding energy of 130 keV. The fission strength function then has the form shown in Fig. 8.13(a) and could provide the explanation of the sub-threshold fission strength-function of ^{230}Th. The occurrence of the virtual state at an energy considerably above threshold would give a much damped peak owing to the large partial width associated with the motion in the deformation parameter (seeFig.8.13 (c)). Thus the model seems to have the property of being able to explain the variety of structure observed in fission cross-sections ranging from the fully-developed peaks in the ^{232}Th(n, f) cross-section, through the sub-threshold peaks in ^{230}Th(n, f) to the rather featureless cross-section of ^{238}U(n, f). This hypothesis is, of course, only a phenomenological model for what appears to be happening in these reactions. The explanation at a deeper level would lie in answering why the imaginary component is so low. This question has not yet been completely satisfactorily answered in the related problem of nucleon scattering by nuclei, but at least existing theory suggests that there is no reason for expecting W in this case to be the same as in the nucleon scattering case. There are other examples of elementary types of excitation being only weakly coupled to the compound nucleus. The outstanding example is the isobaric anologue state, revealed by (p, n) and, (p, p) reactions, which has been found to be spread over energy intervals as small as 10 keV even at excitation energies greater than 10 MeV.

This is a suitable note of uncertainty on which to close both this chapter and this book. 'Intermediate structure' is a topic that dominates discussions in low- and medium-energy nuclear reaction physics at the present time. In only one instance has its existence been decisively proved; this is the isobaric analogue structure already referred to. Strictly speaking, the model that we have just invoked to explain the strength function in a fission saddle-point channel is not one that gives intermediate structure (which would be analogous to the 'doorway state' structure tentatively believed to be revealed in neutron strength function data) but, rather, gives gross structure (analogous to the size resonances due to single-particle states in the neutron-scattering case). However, the occurrence of such structure in the fission strength function must be due basically to the same cause as intermediate structure in the strength functions of nucleon channels; namely, weak coupling of the actual compound nucleus to excitation modes of an elementary nature gives a low value of the imaginary component of the complex-potential model of the interaction as well as fluctuations in this value. The field of neutron spectroscopy is already becoming well-poised for investigations into this whole question of intermediate structure. For example, there is no sign yet that the intensity of pulsed neutron sources has reached its limit, so we may still expect considerable increases in neutron energy resolution, and hence increases in the effective energy range over which neutron resonance reactions can be measured, as well as increases in the number of sophisticated experiments that can be undertaken. Thus it may become possible to resolve the problem in the most satisfactory way; that is, from the 'microscopic' point of view.

12. Intermediate structure in neutron-induced fission

(a) *Shell-corrected liquid-drop calculations*

Since the above concluding paragraphs were written and delivered to the publisher a number of important theoretical and experimental developments have converged to give evidence of a situation of great interest both to nuclear structure studies and to the understanding of fission. First, we deal with the theoretical developments.

In the last few years advanced studies of the liquid-drop model have continued (see e.g. Nix and Swiatecki 1965), and at the same time far-reaching attempts have been made to calculate the potential energy surface of the nucleus as a function of deformation, using only the summed single-particle and pairing energies in a deformed shell-model potential (Nilsson 1967). So far these have encountered difficulties at high deformations and have failed, in the actinide region, to reproduce the saddle point, for example. Theories that combine the extreme view-points of both liquid drop and shell model are now turning out to be more promising than either. Thus, Myers and Swiatecki (1966) have analysed 1200 nuclear masses and 240 quadrupole moments, using the liquid-drop model with a shell-model correction term (depending on neutron and proton number) that declines in a Gaussian manner with increasing deformation from the spherical form. They found constants for the semi-empirical mass formula that are very close to those of Green, but, with the shell-correction term, were able to get much closer agreement with observation in calculating the observed saddle-point energies. An even more sophisticated model of this type has recently been produced by Strutinsky (1967). In this, the shell-correction term, as a function of deformation, has been calculated directly from the summed Nilsson single-particle energies of the deformed shell-model potential. Strutinsky finds that the minima in the shell-correction term occur at deformations where a gap is left in the structure of unfilled single particle levels immediately above the Fermi energy. The most striking of these minima occur for magic nuclei (e.g. ^{208}Pb) in their spherical configurations. But, although the major gaps in the single-particle level structure occur for spherical shapes, other gaps occur at non-zero deformations (see e.g. Fig. 4.6). Thus, for the mid-shell nuclei like the rare earths the most important gap occurs at a deformation of $\beta \approx 0{\cdot}2$, and this is sufficient to cause such nuclei to have a permanent stable deformation. A feature of special interest is the recurrence of gaps with increasing deformation. Because of this the nuclei below lead, for instance, in spite of having a deep minimum in the potential energy surface at the spherical configuration, are expected to have another less deep minimum at a fairly high prolate deformation. The important point for fission is this: Strutinsky calculates that many of the actinide nuclei should have a second minimum roughly in the region of the liquid-drop saddle point (see Fig. 8.32); its depth is expected to be of the order of 2 or 3 MeV.

This theory provides a possible explanation (Bjørnholm *et al.* 1967) of the phenomenon of spontaneous-fissioning isomeric states found in the odd americium isotopes (Flerov and Polikanov 1964). These have lifetimes of the order of 1 ms, and recently it has been discovered that they lie about 3 MeV above the ground state (e.g. for ^{240m}Am, $T_{\frac{1}{2}} \approx 0{\cdot}6$ ms, $E = 3{\cdot}15 \pm 0{\cdot}25$ MeV, $T_{\frac{1}{2}}(\gamma) > 0{\cdot}9$ ms; Bjørnholm *et al.* 1967). The great puzzle has been why, at this excitation energy, decay by gamma-radiation is so inhibited. The normal explanation for an isomeric state is that it should have such a high spin that it can only decay by emitting radiation of high multipole order. Analysis of the data on nuclear reactions leading to the spontaneous-fission isomers reveals that their spins are not excessively high (Jägare 1967). With the Strutinsky theory the isomer would be explained by postulating that it is the 'ground' state associated with zero-point vibration in the second minimum, whereupon its decay by gamma-radiation is inhibited by tunnelling through the first maximum, and is thus dominated by spontaneous fission through the second maximum.

(b) *Narrow intermediate structure in resonance fission*

The hypothesis of a second minimum in the potential energy surface also explains the very recent observations of structure in the pattern of resonance fission widths in the sub-threshold region. Narrow structure in the *average* fission cross-section of ^{241}Am has been observed by Seeger *et al.* (1967), and also in that of ^{237}Np (Paya *et al.* 1967), where the first intermediate resonance has also been found to be split into a number of true (fine structure) resonances with fission widths much larger than any observed at lower energies. But the most dramatic evidence of intermediate structure has been observed by Weigman and Schmid (1967) and Migneco and Theobald (1967) in their work on the resonances in the cross-section of ^{240}Pu.

The mean resonance spacing in this cross-section is 13 ± 2 eV, and they are of one spin (and parity), $J^{\pi} = \frac{1}{2}^{+}$. Fission in the lowest resonances has been observed to be very weak, and in fact has only been measured for the 1·0-eV resonance, which has a fission width of 0·006 meV. Migneco and Theobald confirm that fission is weak (certainly less than 1 meV), in all the resonances up to nearly 750 eV, where there is a group of five resonances with easily observable fission widths ranging up to the order of 100 meV; their parameters are shown in Table 8.14. Thereafter, fission is not measurable up to 1400 eV, where

TABLE 8.14

Resonance parameters of resonances with a measurable rate of fission in the cross-section of ^{240}Pu *below* 2 *keV* (after Migneco and Theobald 1967)

E_{λ} (eV)	$\Gamma_{\lambda(n)}$ (meV)	$\Gamma_{\lambda(f)}$ (meV)
750	$68{\cdot}2 \pm 3{\cdot}4$	$7{\cdot}8 \pm 1{\cdot}0$
782	$3{\cdot}0 \pm 0{\cdot}9$	$132 \pm ^{400}_{85}$
791	$23{\cdot}9 \pm 1{\cdot}4$	$12{\cdot}9 \pm 1{\cdot}7$
810	$213{\cdot}0 \pm 10{\cdot}7$	$9{\cdot}6 \pm 1{\cdot}2$
820	$110{\cdot}0 \pm 5{\cdot}5$	$1{\cdot}0 \pm 0{\cdot}2$
1402	$5{\cdot}2 \pm 1{\cdot}0$	60 ± 13
1408	$10{\cdot}9 \pm 6{\cdot}5$	60 ± 31
1426	$36{\cdot}7 \pm 3{\cdot}7$	$4{\cdot}0 \pm 0{\cdot}5$
1842	126 ± 10	$10{\cdot}1 \pm 1{\cdot}2$
1916	36 ± 6	$42{\cdot}3 \pm 7{\cdot}3$
1956	261 ± 18	$24{\cdot}5 \pm 6{\cdot}7$
2033	102 ± 10	$7{\cdot}2 \pm 0{\cdot}9$
2053	68 ± 7	$1{\cdot}9 \pm 0{\cdot}2$

there is a group of three fissioning resonances. Beyond this, fission is observed in groups of resonances at 1950 eV, 2700 eV, 3000 eV, 3400 eV, 5000 eV, 5300 eV, 6400 eV, 7500 eV, and 8000 eV. Resonances are only resolved in the first two of these, the higher groups being observed as single peaks in the average fission cross-section.

The theoretical explanation of this phenomenon is based on the properties of the vibrational states belonging to the potential energy curve shown in Fig. 8.32. For our development these are assumed to

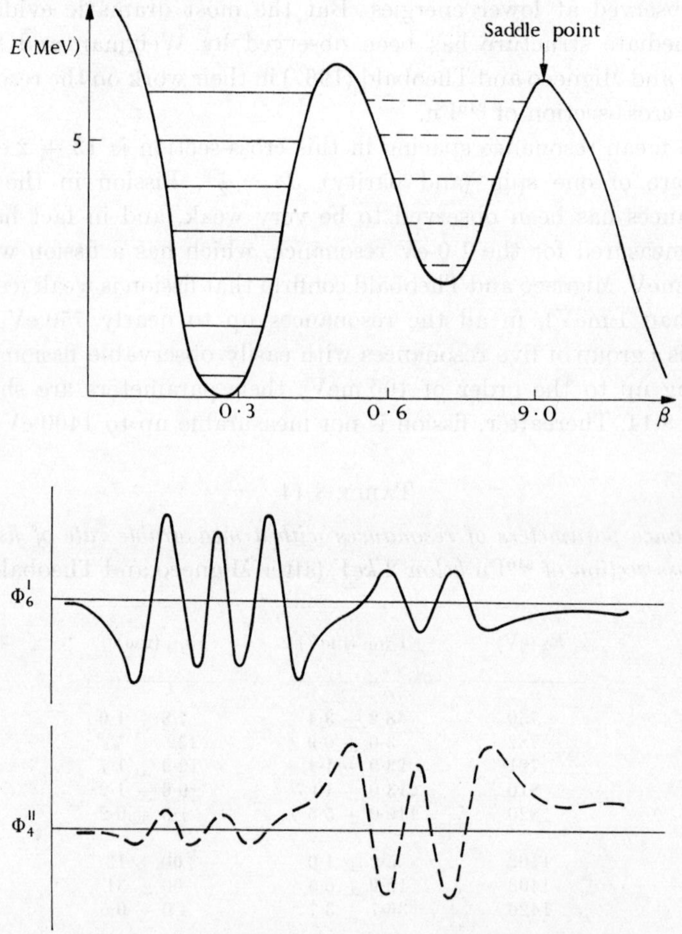

FIG. 8.32. Schematic diagram through the nuclear potential energy surface in the direction of prolate deformation towards fission, according to Strutinsky's theory. The full horizontal lines indicate the positions of class I vibrational levels, and the broken lines indicate class II vibrational levels. Schematic wave-functions for high vibrational states of each class are shown below. Note the relative amplitudes after tunnelling through the saddle point.

be discrete and, in the spirit of the R-matrix technique, can be made so by imposing a suitable real boundary condition near the deformation at the second maximum (the saddle point). Because we are interested in total fission, and not in the cross-sections for individual fission-product channels, the fact that nuclear forces are operative beyond the saddle point does not concern us (see Section C.1). Two typical vibrational wave-functions are indicated schematically in Fig. 8.32, and it is seen that, in general, below the energy of the first maximum in the potential energy curve the states will fall into one of two classes depending on whether the bulk of the wave-function falls within the region of deformation where the normal potential energy minimum resides, or within the region of the second potential energy minimum. We denote the two sets as 'class I' and 'class II' vibrational states, respectively, with notation $E_\nu^{(\mathrm{I})}$, $\Phi_\nu^{(\mathrm{I})}(\beta)$, $E_{\nu'}^{(\mathrm{II})}$, $\Phi_{\nu'}^{(\mathrm{II})}(\beta)$ for the eigenvalues and wave-functions. We also need to refer to the eigenvalues and eigenfunctions for the dynamical motion of the nucleus in all the other degrees of freedom, i.e. intrinsic nucleonic motion, rotational motion, and collective vibration in modes other than that of spheroidal elongation leading eventually to fission; these overall eigenvalues and eigenfunctions are denoted by E_μ, χ_μ. The simple product functions $\Phi_\nu \chi_\mu$, with energy $E_\nu + E_\mu$, may now be used as a basis for diagonalizing the nuclear Hamiltonian of the internal region, there being a residual term, H', describing interplay between vibrational and other degrees of freedom, which has not been used in defining either the vibrational states Φ_ν or the 'intrinsic' states χ_μ. It is now perfectly possible to diagonalize the sub-matrix referring only to basic states with vibrational eigenfunctions of class I, and the sub-matrix referring only to basic states with vibrations of class II, separately. In this way we obtain two sets of (R-matrix) eigenfunctions, the one, $X_\lambda^{(\mathrm{I})}$ with eigenvalues $E_\lambda \mathrm{I}$, being related to what we might call compound states of class I with vibrational motion in the first minimum, and the other, $X_\lambda^{(\mathrm{II})}$, being related to compound states of class II. There is still a residual interaction between these two sets, the matrix elements for which are given by

$$\langle \lambda^{(\mathrm{I})} | H' | \lambda^{(\mathrm{II})} \rangle = \sum_{\nu^{\mathrm{I}},\mu;\nu^{\mathrm{II}},\mu'} \langle \lambda^{(\mathrm{I})} | \nu^{(\mathrm{I})}\mu \rangle \langle \nu^{(\mathrm{I})}\mu | H' | \nu^{(\mathrm{II})}\mu' \rangle \langle \nu^{(\mathrm{II})}\mu' | \lambda^{(\mathrm{II})} \rangle. \tag{8.53}$$

We see from this that if the energy of the compound nucleus is sufficiently far below the top of the first maximum, vibrational states that 'tunnel' only weakly through this potential energy peak are involved in the sum in eqn. (8.53). Consequently the overlap of class I and class II vibrational states is very small and so, in consequence, is the residual interaction matrix element. Clearly, this is a situation that can apply only to sub-threshold fission. Once the energy is above the fission barrier (which means certainly above the first maximum, whether or not this is lower than that of the second maximum) there is no clear distinction between the highest class I and class II vibrational states admixed into the X_λ; their overlap is large, not only with each other but also with the lower vibrational states of opposite class, and the residual interaction matrix element is no longer small.

The density of the class II compound states at a given energy will normally be considerably lower than the density of class I states, owing to the greater amount of energy tied up in deformation in the former case. In many ways the properties of the two classes will be very different. Thus, the fission width amplitudes associated with the class II levels are governed by the amplitude of the highest admixed class II vibrational state after it has tunnelled through the saddle point barrier. The fission width amplitudes of the class I levels will be much smaller because they depend on the amplitude of a class I vibrational wave-function after it has tunnelled through both the saddle-point barrier and the intermediate maximum (see Fig. 8.32). The difference in relative fission widths is further increased by the level density difference between the two classes. The amplitudes for (elastic) neutron emission will have opposite behaviour; because the residual nucleus has to be left in its ground state, the vibrational wave-function of which is the zero-point state of the first minimum, the class II levels are associated with zero neutron width. Thus, in the absence of coupling to the class I compound states, they cannot be excited by slow neutron bombardment. Radiation properties are also quite different. The cascade of gamma rays from a state of particular class will mostly be through lower levels of the same class; cross-transitions to the other class will again be inhibited by the tunnelling of the vibrational wave-functions through the intermediate maximum. Qualitatively, the gamma-ray spectra of class II levels will be characterized by widely-spaced transitions (enhanced relative to the class I transitions by the difference in initial level density) at rather low gamma-ray energies.

The interpretation of the ^{240}Pu neutron cross-section data is now straightforward. Each group of strongly fissioning resonances is centred on the position of a class II compound state. The very weak interaction between the class I and class II states causes mixing of their wave-functions and thus a spreading of the large class II fission width into a few of the resonances nearby. From the data we see that the mean spacing of the class II states, $\bar{D}^{\mathrm{II}}$, is about 650 eV, a factor of 50 greater than the normal resonance spacing of 13 eV, which is essentially the class I spacing, $\bar{D}^{\mathrm{I}}$. From this difference we obtain an estimate of the effective excitation energy available for the class II states, i.e. a measure of the difference of potential energy of the two minima. Using Newton's level density formula, eqn. (4.43), with Lang's constant, $\alpha = 0{\cdot}0227$, we find $E^{*}_{\mathrm{II}} \approx 3{\cdot}8$ MeV; since $E_{\mathrm{th,n}} = 5{\cdot}5$ MeV for ^{241}Pu, this implies that the potential energy difference is 1·7 MeV. Using Lang and Le Couteur's formula, eqn. (4.77), we find that the difference is about 1·9 MeV.

If we examine the data in Table 8.14 we find that there is normally one resonance in each group with a predominant fission width. This suggests that this resonance corresponds to a largely pure class II state with only small admixtures of class I states. Correspondingly, the neighbouring resonances result from mainly class I states with a small admixture of a single class II state. In this situation we can use perturbation theory to interpret the results. To second-order we find,

$$X_{\lambda'} \approx X^{(\mathrm{I})}_{\lambda'} + \frac{H'_{\lambda'\lambda''}\,X^{(\mathrm{II})}_{\lambda''}}{E^{\mathrm{I}}_{\lambda'} - E^{\mathrm{II}}} + \sum_{(\neq\lambda',} \frac{H_{\lambda'''\lambda''}\,H_{\lambda''\lambda'}\,X^{(\mathrm{I})}_{\lambda'''}}{(E^{\mathrm{I}}_{\lambda'} - E^{\mathrm{I}}_{\lambda'''})(E^{\mathrm{I}}_{\lambda'} - E^{\mathrm{II}}_{\lambda''})} \tag{8.54a}$$

$$E_{\lambda'} \approx E^{(\mathrm{I})}_{\lambda'} + H'^{\,2}_{\lambda'\lambda''}/(E^{\mathrm{I}}_{\lambda'} - E^{\mathrm{II}}_{\lambda''}), \tag{8.54b}$$

$$X_{\lambda''} \approx X^{(\mathrm{II})}_{\lambda''} + \sum_{\lambda'(\neq\lambda'')} \frac{H'_{\lambda'\lambda''}\,X^{(\mathrm{I})}_{\lambda'}}{E^{\mathrm{II}}_{\lambda''} - E^{\mathrm{I}}_{\lambda'}}, \tag{8.54c}$$

$$E_{\lambda''} \approx E^{\mathrm{II}}_{\lambda''} + \sum_{\lambda'(\neq\lambda'')} H'^{2}_{\lambda''\lambda'}/(E^{\mathrm{II}}_{\lambda''} - E^{\mathrm{I}}_{\lambda'}), \tag{8.54d}$$

the new eigenvalues and eigenfunctions being denoted by dropping the superscripts I or II. From the eigenfunctions X_{λ} the fission and neutron widths are obtained, e.g. the fission width of the new state λ' is, from eqn. (8.54a), just

$$\Gamma_{\lambda'(\mathrm{f})} = H'^{2}_{\lambda'\lambda''}\;\Gamma^{\mathrm{II}}_{(\mathrm{f})}/(E^{\mathrm{I}}_{\lambda'} - E^{\mathrm{II}})^{2}.$$

From this we see that the fractional admixture of the class II state into the resonant state λ' is $\Gamma_{\lambda'(\mathrm{f})}/\Gamma^{\mathrm{II}}_{\mathrm{f}}$, and $\Gamma^{\mathrm{II}}_{\mathrm{f}}$, the sum of all the fission widths in the group, is the fission width of the pure class II state at $E^{\mathrm{II}}_{\lambda''}$.

The neutron width of the resonance that carries the bulk of the class II state comes from the admixtures of the class I state into this resonance. The amplitudes of these admixtures are given by the square roots of $\Gamma_{\lambda'(f)}/\Sigma_{\lambda'''}\Gamma_{\lambda'''(f)}$ but with unknown sign. Hence, the neutron width of resonance λ'' is (assuming n resonances λ' in the group)

$$\Gamma_{\lambda''(n)} = \{\textstyle\sum_{\lambda'=1}^{n} \pm \sqrt{(\Gamma_{\lambda'(n)}\Gamma_{\lambda'(f)}/\Gamma^{\rm II}_{(f)})}\}^2 \tag{8.55}$$

giving us 2^{n-1} possibilities. The average of these is $\Sigma_{\lambda'}\Gamma_{\lambda'(n)}\Gamma_{\lambda'(f)}/\Gamma^{\rm II}_{(f)}$, and there is an upper limit to its value. The neutron width data of Table 8.14 all satisfy these relations in the weak sense of lying well below the upper limit, and even below the average established by eqn. (8.55). A more precise test would have to await more accurate determinations of the resonance parameters, in which case we could see whether the neutron width of the strongest fission width coincided with one of the possible discrete values calculated from the other parameters.

This kind of correlation of the resonance parameters is important to establish. For one thing it tests the theory by seeing whether the class II state has its predicted neutron width amplitude value of zero. For another, we still have not dealt with the possibility that the saddle-point maximum lies far below the intermediate maximum, to the extent that tunnelling of the class II vibrational wave-functions towards fission is not seriously inhibited. Up to this point in our discussion we have assumed that we are dealing entirely with narrow resonances, in which case we obtain their parameters directly from the R-matrix eigenfunctions (see Chapter II, Section H). But now we have the possibility that a very large fission width (up to the order of 100 eV) is associated with the class II state. If mixing with the neighbouring class I states is appreciable, the new R-matrix states thus formed acquire large fission widths (perhaps of the same order of magnitude as their spacing), and to investigate the resonance structure of the cross-section we must find the S-matrix poles and residues, which can be very different from the R-matrix parameters. At the present time this kind of problem has usually to be carried through numerically. Qualitatively, however, we can expect very strong quasi-resonance formation—the appearance of narrow fission resonances on a very low and extremely broad resonance term carrying most of the fission width. Experimentally this background term would probably be extremely difficult to detect. Its interference with the narrow resonance terms would be easier to find, although still difficult. However, there would no longer be any correlation among the parameters of the narrow resonances. This is because the class II state, to which this type of correlation applies, is mostly in the underlying background.

For the ^{240}Pu cross-section resonances the neutron width correlation does seem to hold, so we assume that in this case the class II states are well confined by the saddle-point maximum. Thus we can deduce from the data that the mean class II fission width $\Gamma^{\mathrm{II}}_{(\mathrm{f})}$ is of the order of 100 meV, and the mean interaction matrix element $\overline{H'^2_{\lambda'\lambda''}} \approx 250\ (\mathrm{eV})^2$ Both quantities fluctuate considerably from one class II state to another, and the second fluctuates with respect to the class I levels also, as we would expect from the complicated nature of the interacting states. From the ratio $\Gamma^{\mathrm{II}}_{(\mathrm{f})}/\bar{D}^{\mathrm{II}} \approx T_{\mathrm{f}}/2\pi$, the tunnelling factor through the saddle point appears to be of the order of 10^{-3}, but if weak-coupling effects are operating in this fission mode, the estimate could be out by a factor of 10 or more either way. The average fission cross-section behaviour at higher energies suggests that there is some weak coupling; the sub-threshold fission cross-section in the neutron energy range 30 to 100 keV may not be due to p-wave neutrons (as suggested on p. 449) after all.

We now turn to the ^{237}Np cross-section data of Paya *et al.* (1967). The mean resonance spacing (two spin groups) is found to be 0·67 eV. The fission widths of the lowest resonances has been observed to be of the order of 0·002 meV, but around 39 eV there are a few resonances with fission widths of the order of 0·5 meV, and one (at 39·9 eV) with a fission width of 6 meV. From the average cross-section it is found that other groups of strong resonances occur at 105 eV, 195 eV, 225 eV, 250 eV, and 280 eV. From this it is apparent that the mean spacing of class II states (assumed to be of both spins) is $\approx$ 50 eV. The ratio of class I and class II spacings gives the potential energy of the second minimum relative to that of the first to be of the order of 2·3 MeV. The neutron width of the 39·9 eV resonance is well within the limits allowed by the correlation formula, eqn. (8.55), which indicates again that the saddle point is considerably higher than the neutron separation energy.

Finally, we have the ^{241}Am fission cross-section data (Seeger *et al.* 1967). The average fission width of the low-lying resonances is 0·18 meV and their spacing is about 0·7 eV (Bowman *et al.* 1965). There is no evidence for structure in the first thirty or so resonances and a smooth average fission cross-section follows on from them for the next keV or so of neutron energy. It appears, therefore, that these low energy resonances are of the class I type, the double tunnelling not being sufficient to suppress their intrinsic fission widths completely. Indications of class II levels are found in the average fission cross-section up to 10 keV neutron energy as quite well-marked spikes at intervals of roughly 1 keV. The ratio of class II to class I spacings is thus about 10^3 and indicates that the difference in the potential energies of the minima is about 2·8 MeV (using the Lang and Le Couteur formula); this is very close to the energy of the spontaneous fissioning isomeric state in ^{242}Am, $2{\cdot}9 \pm 0{\cdot}4$ MeV (Flerov *et al.* 1967), and provides excellent corroboration of the whole theory.

The appearance of sharp class II structure in the cross-section indicates a high barrier between the two minima, and this, in combination with the rather high observed fission widths of the supposed class I states at low energy (see Table 8.13), suggests that the saddle-point beyond the second minimum may be close to or below the neutron separation energy of ^{242}Am. The first maximum, by contrast, would perhaps be at the position of the 'gross' fission threshold revealed in the fast neutron cross-section of ^{241}Am, i.e. about 950 keV above the neutron separation energy. In this way, we see that we can begin to learn about the features of the new complicated deformation curve in a quantitative manner.

This structure of the deformation curve makes the phenomenon of weak-damping of fission modes in the sub-threshold region much more understandable. In the first place we see that for above-threshold fission the wave-function for the relevant vibration covers a much larger region of deformation than do the sub-threshold vibrations. This is important if particle-vibration coupling is the main component of the residual Hamiltonian H'. It is perfectly possible therefore to have strong damping of the fission modes in the fissile nuclei (and as we have seen this seems to be necessary to explain the resonance properties of these nuclei) while weaker damping operates in sub-threshold modes. The lower excitation energy in the second minimum will also lead to weaker damping, and it is possible that in the Th nuclei, for which the most definite evidence of weakly-coupled fission modes is available, the second minimum is much shallower than in the higher-Z nuclei discussed above.

To conclude, it is only necessary to point out that this mechanism for intermediate structure is not necessarily confined to fissionable nuclei. As we mentioned above, a class II compound state will have a characteristic, somewhat low-energy, gamma-ray spectrum, and this will be superposed in varying degrees, but with identical pattern, on the resonances into which it is mixed (the pattern of the spectrum will, of course, differ from one class II state to another). This will exist irrespective of whether the class II state can fission or not; the important considerations are the existence of an intermediate maximum (determining the coupling strength) within a favourable range of height and thickness, and the depth of the second minimum (which determines the density of the class II states). Outside the actinide range, Strutinsky's calculations indicate that favourable nuclei for observing this effect may lie among the platinum, gold, mercury series of nuclei, which ought to have a strong, prolate secondary minimum, and perhaps in the rare earth region, centred on erbium, where there may exist an oblate, secondary minimum. So far, of course, these considerations are speculative and uncertain; what is certain is that a whole new dimension has been added to the field of research covered by neutron spectroscopy.

BIBLIOGRAPHY

ADAIR, R. K., BOCKELMAN, C. K., and PETERSON, R. E. (1949). *Phys. Rev* **76,** 308.

ADAMCHUK, YU. V., DANELYAN, L. S., MURADYAN, G. V., and SCHEPKIN, YU. G. (1966*a*). I.A.E.A. conf. on microscopic neutron cross-section data, Paris. Paper CN-23/108.

— MOSKALEV, S. S, and MURADYAN, G. V. (1966*b*). *Soviet J. nucl. Phys.* **3,** 801.

ADLER, F. T. and ADLER, D. B. (1966). *Proc. conf. on neutron cross-section technology, Washington*, p. 873. *U.S.A.E.C. Report No. CONF*-660303.

ALFIMENKOV, V. P., LUSHCHIKOV, V. I., NIKOLENKO, V. G., TARAN, YU. V., and SHAPIRO, F. L. (1966). *Soviet J. nucl. Phys.* **3,** 55.

AMALDI, E., D'AGOSTINO, O., FERMI, E., PONTECORVO, B., RASETTI, F., and SEGRÈ, E. (1935). *Proc. R. Soc.* **A149,** 522.

ASGHAR, M. (1964). D. Phil. Thesis, Oxford University (unpublished).

— (1967). *Nucl. Phys.* **A98,** 33.

— and BROOKS, F. D. (1966). *Nucl. Instrum. Meth.* **39,** 68.

— CHAFFEY, C. M., MOXON, M. C., PATTENDEN, N. J., RAE, E. R., and UTTLEY, C. A. (1966*a*). *Nucl. Phys.* **76,** 196.

— MOXON, M. C., and CHAFFEY, C. M. (1965). *Proc. int. conf. on study of nuclear structure with neutrons, Antwerp*, 1965. Contributed Paper 65.

— — and PATTENDEN, N. J. (1966*b*). I.A.E.A. conf. on microscopic neutron cross-section data, Paris. Paper No. CN-23/31.

AUCHAMPAUGH, G. F., BOWMAN, C. D., COOPS, M. S., and FULTZ, S. C. (1966). *Phys. Rev.* **146,** 840.

AXEL, P., MIN, K., STEIN, N., and SUTTON, D. C. (1963). *Phys. Rev. Lett.* **10,** 299.

BAERG, A. P., BARTHOLOMEW, R. M., BROWN, F., KATZ, L., and KOWALSKI, S. B. (1959). *Can. J. Phys.* **37,** 1418.

BARDEEN, J. and FEENBERG, E. (1938). *Phys. Rev.* **54,** 809.

— COOPER, L. N., and SCHRIEFFER, J. R. (1957). *Phys. Rev.* **108,** 1175.

BARSCHALL, H. H. (1952). *Phys. Rev.* **85,** 704.

BARTHOLOMEW, G. A. (1962). *Proc. conf. on electromagnetic lifetimes and properties of nuclear states, Gatlinberg*, 1961, p. 209. *Publication* 974, National Academy of Sciences–National Research Council.

BARTHOLOMEW, G. A. and HIGGS, L. A. (1958). *Chalk River Report A.E.C.L.* 669.

— EARLE, E. D., and GUNYE, M. R. (1965). *Proc. int. Conf. on study of nuclear structure with neutrons, Antwerp.* Paper 43.

BELL, G. I. (1966). *Proc. conf. on neutron cross-section technology, Washington. U.S.A.E.C. Report CONF* 660303, p. 454.

BELYAEV, S. T. (1959). *Comptes rendus du congrés international de physique nucléaire, Paris*, 1958 (Ed. GUGENHEIMER), p. 713. Dunod, Paris.

BERNABEI, A., BORST, L. B., and SAILOR, V. L. (1962). *Nucl. Sci. Engng.* **12,** 63.

BERNSTEIN, S., SHAPIRO, M. M., STANFORD, C. P., STEPHENSON, T. E., DIAL, J. B., FREED, S., PARKER, G. W., BROSE, A. R., HERBERT, G., and DEWITT, T. W. (1956). *Phys. Rev* **102,** 823.

BERGQUIST, I. (1966). *Nucl. Phys.* **74,** 15.

— BIGGERSTAFF, J. A., GIBBONS, J. H., and GOOD, W. M. (1965). *Proc. int. conf. on study of nuclear structure with neutrons, Antwerp*, 1965. Contributed Paper 129. Also *Phys. Lett.* **18,** 323.

— and STARFELT, N. (1962). *Nucl. Phys.* **39,** 353.

BETHE, H. A. (1935). *Phys. Rev.* **47**, 747.

— (1937). *Rev. mod. Phys.* **9**, 69.

BIANCHI, G., COLMIN, J., CORGE, C., HUYNH, V., JULIEN, J., MORGENSTERN, J., NETTER, F., and VASTEL, M. (1963). Société Francaise de Physique, Colloque de physique nucléaire, Orsay, May, 1963.

BIGGERSTAFF, J. A. and FARRELL, J. A. (1966). *Ann. Phys.* (in press).

BILPUCH, E. G., SETH, K. K., BOWMAN, C. D., TABONY, R. H., SMITH, R. C., and NEWSON, H. W. (1961). *Ann. Phys.* **14**, 387.

— — — WESTON, L. W., and NEWSON, H. W. (1959). Private communication reported by Stehn *et al.* (1964).

BIRD, J. R. (1959). *Proc. int. conf. peaceful uses atom. energy, Geneva*, 1958, Vol. 14, p. 294. United Nations, Geneva.

— MOXON, M. C., and FIRK, F. W. K. (1959). *Nucl. Phys.* **13**, 525.

BIRKS, J. B. (1964). *The theory and practice of scintillation counting.* Pergamon, Oxford.

BJØRNHOLM, S., BORGGREN, J., WESTGAARD, L., and KARNAUKHOV, V. A. (1967). *Nucl. Phys.* A**95**, 513.

BLATT, J. M. and WEISSKOPF, V. F. (1952). *Theoretical nuclear physics.* Wiley, New York.

— and THOMPSON, D. (1963). *Phys. Rev. Lett.* **10**, 332.

BLOCH, C. (1954). *Phys. Rev.* **93**, 1094.

— (1957). *Nucl Phys.* **4**, 503.

BLOCH, I., HULL, M. H., BROYLES, A. A., BOURICIUS, W. G., FREEMAN, B. E., and BREIT, G. (1950). *Phys. Rev.* **80**, 553.

— — — — — — (1951) *Rev. mod. Phys.* **23**, 147.

BLOCK, R. C. (1958). *Phys. Rev.* **109**, 1217.

— HAEBERLI, W., and NEWSON, H. W. (1958*a*). *Phys. Rev.* **109**, 1620.

— HARVEY, J. A., and SLAUGHTER, J. C. (1958*b*). *Bull. Am. phys. Soc.* Ser. II, **3**, 177.

BLOKHIN, G. E. *et al.* (1961). *Atomn. Energ.* **10**, 437.

BLUMBERG, S. and PORTER, C. E. (1958). *Phys. Rev.* **110**, 786.

BÖCKHOFF, K. H., DE KEYSER, A., HORSTMANN, H., KOLAR, W., and MARTIN, H. (1966). I.A.E.A. conf. on microscopic neutron cross-section data, Paris. Paper No. CN-23/89.

BOHR, A. (1956). *Proc. int. conf. peaceful uses atom. energy, Geneva*, 1955, Vol. 2, p. 220. United Nations, New York.

— and MOTTELSON, B. R. (1953). *Dan. Mat.-Fys. Medd.* **27**, No. 16.

— — and PINES, R. A. (1958). *Phys. Rev.* **110**, 936.

BOHR, N. (1936). *Nature, Lond.* **137**, 344.

— and WHEELER, J. A. (1939). *Phys. Rev.* **56**, 246.

BOLLINGER, L. M. (1958). *Proc. int. conf. peaceful uses atom. energy, Geneva*, 1958, Vol. 14, p. 239. United Nations, Geneva.

— COTÉ, R. E., CARPENTER, R. T., and MARION, J. P. (1963). *Phys. Rev.* **132**, 1640.

— — and JACKSON, H. E. (1964). *Comptes rendus du congrès international de physique nucleaire, Paris*, 1964 (Ed. P. GUGENBURGER), Vol. II, p. 673. Editions du Centre National de la Recherche Scientifique, Paris.

— — and THOMAS, G. E. (1959*a*). *Proc. int. conf. peaceful uses atom. energy, Geneva*, 1958, Vol. 15, p. 127. United Nations, Geneva.

— THOMAS, G. E., and GINTHER, R. G. (1959*b*). *Rev. scient. Instrum.* **30**, 1135.

BOLOTIN, H. H. and CHRIEN, R. E. (1959). *Bull. Am. phys. Soc.* Ser. II, **4**, 271.

— — (1960). *Bull. Am. phys. Soc.* Ser. II, **5**, 18.

— — (1963). *Nucl. Phys.* **42**, 676.

BOWMAN, C. D. and AUCHAMPAUGH, G. F. (1966). I.A.E.A. conf. on microscopic neutron cross-section data, Paris. Paper No. CN-23/38.
— — and FULTZ, S. C. (1963). *Phys. Rev.* **130**, 1482.
— — STUBBINS, W. F., YOUNG, T. E., SIMPSON, F. B., and MOORE, M. S. (1967). *Phys. Rev. Lett.* **18**, 15.
— BILPUCH, E. G., and NEWSON, H. W. (1962). *Ann. Phys.* **17**, 319.
— COOPS, M. S., AUCHAMPAUGH, G. F., and FULTZ, S. C. (1965). *Phys. Rev.* **137**, B326.
BREIT, G. (1959). *Encyclopedia of Physics*, Vol. 41 (Ed. S. FLÜGGE). Springer-Verlag, Berlin.
BRINK, D. M. (1955). D.Phil. Thesis, Oxford (unpublished).
— (1957). *Nucl. Phys.* **4**, 215.
BRITT, H. C., NEWSOME, R. W., and STOKES, R. H. (1966). *Bull. Am. phys. Soc.* **11**, 30.
— STOKES, R. H., GIBBS, W. R., and GRIFFIN, J. J. (1963). *Phys. Rev. Lett.* **11**, 343.
BROOKS, F. D. (1956). *Prog. nucl. Phys.* **5**, 252.
— (1959). *Nucl. Instrum. Meth.* **4**, 151.
— and JOLLY, J. E. (1963). *United Kingdom Atomic Energy Authority Report No. A.E.R.E. PR/NP6* (Ed. D. L. ALLAN), p. 13.
— — (1965). Private communication.
BROVETTO, P. and CANUTO, V. (1963). *Nucl. Phys.* **44**, 151.
BROWN, G. E. (1959). *Rev. mod. Phys.* **31**, 893.
— and BOLSTERLI, M. (1959). *Phys. Rev. Lett.* **3**, 472.
BRUGGER, R. M., EVANS, J. E., JOKI, E. G., and SHANKLAND, R. S. (1956). *Phys. Rev.* **104**, 1054.
BRUNHART, G., MARSHAK, H., REYNOLDS, C. A., SAILOR, V. L., SCHERMER, R. I. and SHORE, F. J. (1962). *Bull. Am. phys. Soc.* Ser. II, **7**, 305.
BRUNNER, J. and WIDDER, F. (1966). I.A.E.A. conf. on microscopic neutron cross-section data, Paris. Paper No. CN-23/20.
BUCK, B., STAMP, A. P., and HODGSON, P. E. (1963). *Phil. Mag.* **8**, 1805.
BUTLER, D. K. (1960). *Phys. Rev.* **117**, 1305.
— and SJOBLOM, R. K. (1963). *Bull. Am. phys. Soc.* **8**, 369.
BYERS, D. H., DIVEN, B. C., and SILBERT, M. G. (1966). *Proc. conf. on neutron cross-section technology, Washington*, p. 903. *U.S.A.E.C. Report No. CONF-660303*.
CAMERON, A. G. W. (1958). *Can. J. Phys.* **36**, 1040.
— (1959). *Can. J. Phys.* **37**, 322.
— (1960). Private communication.
CARPENTER, R. T. and BOLLINGER, L. M. (1960). *Nucl. Phys.* **21**, 66.
CARTER, R. S., HARVEY, J. A., HUGHES, D. J., and PILCHER, V. E. (1954). *Phys. Rev.* **96**, 113.
CEULEMANS, H. and POORTMANS, F. (1961). *J. Phys. Radium, Paris* **22**, 707.
CHASE, D. M., WILETS, L., and EDMONDS, A. R. (1958). *Phys. Rev.* **110**, 1080.
CHRIEN, R. E. (1966). *Phys. Rev.* **141**, B1129.
— BOLOTIN, H. H., and PALEVSKY, H. (1962). *Phys. Rev.* **127**, 1680.
— and MUGHABGHAB, S. F. (1965). *Proc. int. conf. on study of nuclear structure with neutrons, Antwerp*, 1965. Contributed Paper 69.
CINI, M. and FUBINI, S. (1955). *Nuovo Cim.* **10**, 75.
CLINE, J. E., MAGLEBY, E. H., and BURGESS, W. H. (1959). *Bull. Am. phys. Soc.* **4**, 270.
COHEN, S. and SWIATECKI, W. J. (1962). *Ann. Phys.* **19**, 67.

CORGE, C., HUYNH, V. D., JULIEN, J., MORGENSTERN, J., and NETTER, F. (1961). *J. Phys. Radium, Paris* **22**, 719.

COTÉ, R. E., BARNES, R. F., and DIAMOND, H. (1964*a*). *Phys. Rev.* **134**, B1281.

— BOLLINGER, L. M., BARNES, R. F., and DIAMOND, H. (1959). *Phys. Rev.* **114**, 505.

— — and LEBLANC, J. M. (1958). *Phys. Rev.* **111**, 288.

— — and THOMAS, G. E. (1964*b*). *Phys. Rev.* **134**, B1047.

— — — (1964*c*). *Phys. Rev.* **136**, B703.

COURANT, R. (1931). *Methoden der Mathematischen Physik*. Springer, Berlin.

COWAN, G. A., BAYHURST, B. P., and PRESTWOOD, R. J. (1963). *Phys. Rev.* **130**, 2380.

— — — GILMORE, J. S., and KNOBELOCH, G. W. (1966). *Phys. Rev.* **144**, 979.

— TURKEVITCH, A., BROWNE, C. I., and Los Alamos Radiochemistry Group (1961). *Phys. Rev.* **122**, 1286.

CRAIG, D. S. and WESTCOTT, C. H. (1964). *Can. J. Phys.* **42**, 2384.

CRITCHFIELD, C. L. and OLEKSA, S. (1951). *Phys. Rev.* **82**, 243.

CUNINGHAME, J. G., FRITZE, K., LYNN, J. E., and WEBSTER, C. B. (1966). *Nucl. Phys.* **84**, 49.

— KITT, G. P., and RAE, E. R. (1961). *Nucl. Phys.* **27**, 154.

DABBS, J. W. T., ROBERT, L. D., and BERNSTEIN, S. (1955). *Phys. Rev.* **98**, 1512.

— *et al.* (1965). Physics and chemistry of fission, *Proc. Symposium at Salzburg*, 1965, p. 39. I.A.E.A., Vienna.

DAHLBERG, D. A. and BOLLINGER, L. M. (1956). *Phys. Rev.* **104**, 1006.

DEARNALEY, G. and NORTHROP, D. C. (1966). *Semiconductor counters for nuclear radiation*, 2nd edn. Spon, London.

DERRIEN, H., BLONS, J., EGGERMANN, C., MICHAUDON, A., PAYA, D., and RIBON, P. (1966). I.A.E.A. conf. on microscopic neutron cross-section data, Paris. Paper CN-23/70.

DE SAUSSURE, G., WESTON, L. W., GWIN, R., INGLE, R. W., and TODD, J. H. (1966). I.A.E.A. conf. on microscopic neutron cross-section data, Paris. Paper CN-23/48.

DESJARDINS, J. S., ROSEN, J. L., HAVENS, W. W., and RAINWATER, J. (1960). *Phys. Rev.* **120**, 2214.

DE VROEY, M., FERGUSON, A. T. G., and STARFELT, N. (1965). *Proc. Symp. on physics and chemistry of fission, Salzburg*, 1965, p. 281. I.A.E.A., Vienna.

DIVEN, B. C. (1966). *Nuclear structure study with neutrons* (Eds. M. NÈVE DE MÉVERGNIES, P. VAN ASSCHE, and J. VERVIER), p. 441. North Holland, Amsterdam.

— TERRELL, J., and HEMMENDINGER, A. (1960). *Phys. Rev.* **120**, 556.

DOMANI, F. and PATRONIS, E. T. (1959). *Phys. Rev.* **114**, 1667; **118**, 1577.

— and SAILOR, V. L. (1960). *Phys. Rev.* **119**, 208.

DRAPER, J. E. and BAKER, C. P. (1954). *Phys. Rev.* **95**, 644.

DRESNER, L. (1957). *Proc. int. conf. on neutron interactions with the nucleus, New York. U.S.A.E.C. Report No. TID*-7547, p. 71.

DUBROVINA, S. M. and SHIGIN, V. A. (1964). *Dokl. Akad. Nauk SSSR* **157**, 561.

DUNNING, J. R., PEGRAM, G. B., FINK, G. A., and MITCHELL, D. P. (1935). *Phys. Rev.* **48**, 265.

DYSON, F. J. (1962*a*). *J. Math. Phys.* **3**, 140.

— (1962*b*). *J. Math. Phys.* **3**, 157.

— (1962*c*). *J. Math. Phys.* **3**, 166.

— (1962*d*). *J. Math. Phys.* **3**, 1199.

— and MEHTA, M. L. (1963). *J. Math. Phys.* **4**, 701.

Eccleshall and Yates (1965). *Proc. symp. on physics and chemistry of fission, Salzburg*, p. 77. I.A.E.A., Vienna.
Eckart, C. (1930). *Phys. Rev.* **35**, 1303.
Edmonds, A. R. (1957). *Angular momentum in quantum mechanics.* Princeton University Press, Princeton, N.J.
— and Flowers, B. H. (1952). *Proy. R. Soc.* **A214**, 515.
Egelstaff, P. A. (1958). *Proc. phys. Soc.* **71**, 910.
— Gayther, D. B., and Nicholson, K. P. (1958). *J. nucl. Energy* **6**, 303.
Elliott, J. P. (1958). *Proc. R. Soc.* **A245**, 128, 562.
— and Lane, A. M. (1957). *Encyclopedia of Physics* (Ed. S. Flügge), Vol. 39, p. 241.
Ericson, T. (1958). *Nucl. Phys.* **6**, 62.
— (1959). *Nucl. Phys.* **11**, 481.
— (1960). *Adv. Phys.* **9**, 425.
Evans, J. E., Joki, E. G., and Smith, R. R. (1955). *Phys. Rev.* **97**, 565.
— and Jones, G. A. (1965). Private communication.
— Kinsey, B. B., Waters, J. R., and Williams, G. H. (1959). *Nucl. Phys.* **9**, 205.
Everling, F., König. L. A., Mattauch, J. H. E., and Wapstra, A. H. (1960). *Nucl. Phys.* **18**, 521.
Farrell, J. A., Bilpuch, E. G., and Newson, H. W. (1966). *Ann. Phys.* **37**, 367.
— Kyker, G. C., Bilpuch, E. G., and Newson, H. W. (1965). *Phys. Lett.* **17**, 286.
Ferrell, R. A. (1957). *Phys. Rev.* **107**, 1631.
Feshbach, H. (1962). *Ann. Phys.* **19**, 287.
— Kerman, A. K., and Lemmer, R. H. (1965). *Comptes rendus du congrés international de physiques nucléaire, Paris*, 1964 (Ed. P. Geigenberger), Vol. 2, p. 693.
— — — (1967). *Ann. Phys.* **41**, 177.
— Peaslee, D. C., and Weisskopf, V. F. (1947). *Phys. Rev.* **71**, 145.
— Porter, C. E., and Weisskopf, V. F. (1954). *Phys. Rev.* **96**, 448.
Fiebiger, N. F. (1962). *Bull. Am. phys. Soc.* Ser. II, **7**, 11.
Fiedeldey, H. and Frahn, W. E. (1962). *Ann. Phys.* **19**, 428.
Firk, F. W. K., Lynn, J. E., and Moxon, M. C. (1963*a*). *Proc. phys. Soc.* **82**, 477.
— — — (1963*b*). *Nucl. Phys.* **44**, 431.
— — — (1963*c*). *Nucl. Phys.* **41**, 614.
— and Moxon, M. C. (1959). *Nucl. Phys.* **12**, 552.
Flerov, G. N. and Polikanov, S. M. (1964). *Comptes Rendus du Congrès international de physique nucléaire, Paris,* 1964. Vol. 1, p. 407. Editions du Centre National de la Researche Scientifique, Paris.
— Pleve, A. A., Polikanov, S. M., Tretyakova, S. P., Martalogu, N., Poenaru, D., Sezon, M., Vîlcov, I., and Vîlcov, N. (1967). *Nucl. Phys.* **A97**, 444.
Fluharty, R. G., Simpson, F. B., and Simpson, O. D. (1956). *Phys. Rev.* **103**, 1778.
Fong, P. (1956). *Phys. Rev.* **102**, 434.
— (1963). *Phys. Rev. Lett.* **11**, 375.
— (1964). *Phys. Rev.* **136**, 1338.
Foote, H. L. (1954). *Phys. Rev.* **94**, 790.
— Landon, H. H., and Sailor, V. L. (1953). *Phys. Rev.* **92**, 656.
Ford, K. W. and Bohm, D. (1950). *Phys. Rev.* **79**, 745.
Fowler, J. L. (1966). *Phys. Rev.* **147**, 870.
Fox, D. and Kahn, P. B. (1964). Unpublished.

FRANKEL, S. and METROPOLIS, N. (1947). *Phys. Rev.* **72,** 914.
FRASER, J. S. and SCHWARTZ, R. B. (1962). *Nucl. Phys.* **30,** 269.
FUKETA, T., KHAN, F. A., and HARVEY, J. A. (1963). *Bull. Am. phys. Soc.* **8,** 71.
FURUOYA, I. and SUGIE, A. (1963). *Nucl. Phys.* **44,** 44.
GARG, J. B., HAVENS, W. W., and RAINWATER, J. (1964*b*). *Phys. Rev.* **136,** B177.
— — — (1965). *Phys. Rev.* **137,** B547.
— RAINWATER, J., and HAVENS, W. W. (1966). Unpublished data reported by Stehn *et al.* (1966) (Vol. II).
— — PETERSON, J. S., and HAVENS, W. W. (1964*a*). *Phys. Rev.* **134,** B985.
GARRISON, J. D. (1964). *Ann. Phys.* **30,** 269.
GAUDIN, M. (1961). *Nucl. Phys.* **25,** 447.
GERASIMOV, V. F. (1966). I.A.E.A. conf. on microscopic neutron cross-section data, Paris. Paper CN-23/112.
GIBBONS, J. H., MACKLIN, R. L., MILLER, P. D., and NEILER, J. H. (1961). *Phys. Rev.* **122,** 182.
GOKHBERG, B. M., OSTROSCHENKO, G. A., and SHIGIN, V. A. (1959). *Dokl. Akad. Nauk SSSR* **128,** 1157.
GOLDHABER, M. and TELLER, E. (1948). *Phys. Rev.* **74,** 1046.
GOLDSMITH, E. (1947). *Revs. mod. Phys.* **19,** 259.
GOMES, L. C. (1959). *Phys. Rev.* **116,** 1226.
GOOD, W. M. and BLOCK, R. C. (1966). *Bull. Am. phys. Soc.* **11,** 28.
— PAYA, D., WAGNER, R., and TAMURA, T. (1966). *Phys. Rev.* **151,** 912.
— and MILLER, P. D. (1958). Unpublished.
— NEILER, J., and GIBBONS, J. H. (1958). *Phys. Rev.* **109,** 926.
GOVE, H. E., LITHERLAND, A. E., and BATCHELOR, R. (1961). *Nucl. Phys.* **26,** 480.
GREEN, A. E. S. (1958). *Proc. int. conf. peaceful uses atom. energy,* Vol. 14, p. 406. United Nations, Geneva.
GRIFFIN, J. J. (1963). *Phys. Rev.* **132,** 2204.
— (1965). Physics and chemistry of fission, *Proc. Symp. at Salzburg,* 1965, p. 23. I.A.E.A., Vienna.
GRIMM, G. W. (1956). *Columbia University Report CU*-155.
GRIN', YU. T. and STRUTINSKI, V. M. (1965). *Soviet J. nucl. Phys.* **1,** 420.
GROENWALD, H. J. and GROENDIJK, H. (1947). *Physica* **13,** 141.
GROSHEV, L. V., DEMIDOV, A. M., LUTSENKO, V. N., and PELEKHOV, V. I. (1959). *Atlas of γ-ray spectra from radiative capture of thermal neutrons.* Pergamon Press, London.
— — and PELEKHOV, V. I. (1960). *Nucl. Phys.* **16,** 645.
GUNSON, J. (1962). *J. Math. Phys.* **3,** 752.
GUREVICH, I. I. and PEVZNER, M. I. (1956). *Physica* **22,** 1132.
HADDAD, E., FRIESENHAHN, J. S., FRÖHNER, F. H., and LOPEZ, W. M. (1965). *Phys. Rev.* **140,** 850.
HAHN, O. and STRASSMANN, F. (1939). *Naturwissenschaften* **27,** 11.
HARVEY, J. A., BLOCK, R. C., SLAUGHTER, J. C., MARTIN, C., and PARKER, D. (1958*a*). *Proc. conf. peaceful uses atom. energy, Geneva,* 1958, Vol. 16, p. 150. United Nations, Geneva.
— — — (1958*b*). *Bull. Am. phys. Soc.* Ser. II, **3,** 364.
— — — (1959). *Bull. Am. phys. Soc.* Ser. II, **4,** 34.
— and HUGHES, D. J. (1958). *Phys. Rev.* **109,** 471.
— — CARTER, R. S., and PILCHER, V. E. (1955). *Phys. Rev.* **99,** 10.
— and SLAUGHTER, G. G. (1965). *Proc. int. conf. on study of nuclear structure with neutrons, Antwerp.* Contributed Paper 77.
— — (1966). *Oak Ridge National Laboratory Report No.* 3924, p. 28.

Harvey, R. R., Caldwell, J. T., Bramblett, R. L., and Fultz, S. C. (1964). *Phys. Rev.* **136**, B126.
Havens, W. W., Melkonian, E., Rainwater, J., and Rosen, J. L. (1959). *Phys. Rev.* **116**, 1538.
— and Rainwater, L. J. (1951). *Phys. Rev.* **83**, 1123.
Haxel, O., Jensen, J. H., and Suess, H. E. (1949). *Phys. Rev.* **75**, 1766.
Heitler, W. (1954). *Quantum theory of radiation.* Oxford University Press.
Henkel, R. L. (1952). *Los Alamos National Laboratory Report LA*-1495.
Hill, D. L. (1956). *Encyclopedia of physics* (Ed. S. Flügge), Vol. 39, p. 178. Springer-Verlag, Berlin.
— (1958). *Proc. int. conf. peaceful uses atom. energy, Geneva*, 1958, Vol. 15, p. 244. United Nations, Geneva.
— and Wheeler, J. A. (1953). *Phys. Rev.* **89**, 1102.
Hopkins, J. C. and Diven, B. C. (1962). *Nucl. Sci. Engng.* **12**, 169.
Hughes, D. J. and Harvey, J. A. (1955). *Phys. Rev.* **99**, 1032.
— Magurno, B. A., and Brussels, M. K. (1959). *Brookhaven National Laboratory Report, BNL* 325, 2nd edn., Supp. 1.
— and Schwartz, R. B. (1958). *Brookhaven National Laboratory Report, BNL* 325, 2nd edn.
— Zimmerman, R. L., and Chrien, R. E. (1958). *Phys. Rev. Lett.* **1**, 461.
Hughes, L. B., Kennett, T. J., and Prestwick, W. V. (1966). *Nucl. Phys.* **80**, 131.
Humblet, J. (1952). *Mém. Soc. r. Sci. Liége* **12**, No. 4.
— (1964*a*). *Nucl. Phys.* **50**, 1.
— (1964*b*). *Nucl. Phys.* **57**, 386.
— and Rosenfeld, L. (1961). *Nucl. Phys.* **26**, 529.
Hurwitz, H. and Bethe, H. A. (1951). *Phys. Rev.* **81**, 898.
Huynh, V. D., de Barros, S., Chevillon, P. L., Julien, J., Le Poittevin, G., Morgenstern, J., and Samour, C. (1965). *Proc. int. conf. on study of nuclear structure with neutrons, Antwerp*, 1965. Contributed Paper 73.
Ignatèv, K. G., Kirpichnikov, I. V., and Sukhoruchkin, S. I. (1964). *Atomn. Energ.* **16**, 110.
Igo, G. (1955). *Phys. Rev.* **100**, 1338.
— and Landon, H. H. (1956). *Phys. Rev.* **101**, 726.
Iliescu, N., Kim Hi San, Pikelner, L. B., Sharapov, E. I., and Sirazhet, H. (1965). *Nucl. Phys.* **72**, 298.
Inglis, D. R. (1962). *Nucl. Phys.* **30**, 1.
Jackson, H. E. (1963). *Phys. Rev.* **131**, 2153.
— Julien, J., Samour, C., Bloch, A., Lopata, C., Morgenstern, J., Mann, H., and Thomas, G. E. (1966). *Phys. Rev. Lett.* **17**, 656.
— and Lynn, J. E. (1962). *Phys. Rev.* **127**, 461.
Jägare, S. (1967). *Nucl. Phys.* **A103**, 241.
Jain, A. P. (1964). *Nucl. Phys.* **50**, 157.
James, G. D. (1964). *Nucl. Phys.* **55**, 517.
— (1965*a*). *Nucl. Phys.* **65**, 353.
— (1961). *Neutron time-of-flight methods* (Ed. J. Spaepen), p. 115. Euratom, Brussels.
— (1965*b*). Physics and chemistry of fission, *Proc. I.A.E.A. Symposium, Salzburg*, 1965, p. 235. I.A.E.A., Vienna.
Jeffries, C. D. (1963). *Dynamical nuclear orientation.* Interscience, New York.
Jensen, J. H. D. and Luttinger, J. M. (1952). *Phys. Rev.* **86**, 907.
Jeukenne, J. P. (1964). *Nucl. Phys.* **58**, 1.

JOHANSSON, S. A. E. (1959). *Nucl. Phys.* **12**, 449.

— (1961). *Nucl. Phys.* **22**, 529.

JOHNSON, M. H. and TELLER, E. (1955). *Phys. Rev.* **98**, 783.

JULIEN, J., DE BARROS, S., BIANCHI, G., CORGE, C., HUYNH, V. D., LE POITTEVIN, G., MORGENSTERN, J., NETTER, F., SAMOUR, C., and VASTEL, R. (1966). *Nucl. Phys.* **76**, 391.

— — CHEVILLON, P. L., HUYNH, V. D., LE POITTEVIN, G., MORGENSTERN, J., NETTER, F., and SAMOUR, C. (1965). *Proc. int. conf. on study of nuclear structure with neutrons, Antwerp.* Paper 80.

— BIANCHI, G., CORGE, C., HUYNH, V., LE POITTEVIN, G., MORGENSTERN, J., NETTER, F., and SAMOUR, C. (1964). *Physics. Lett.* **10**, 86.

— CORGE, C., HUYNH, V., MORGENSTERN, J., and NETTER, F. (1962*a*). *C.r.hebd. Séanc. Acad. Sci., Paris*, **254**, 4004.

— — — — — (1962*b*). *Physics Lett.* **3**, 69.

KAHN, P. B. (1963). *Nucl. Phys.* **41**, 159.

— and PORTER, C. E. (1963). *Nucl. Phys.* **48**, 159.

KALEBIN, S. M., IVANOV, R. N., PALEY, P. N., KORALLOVA, Z. K., KUKAVADZE, G. M., PYZHOVA, V. I., SHIBAEVA, N. P., and RUKOLAINE, G. V. (1966). I.A.E.A. conf. on microscopic neutron cross-section data, Paris. Paper CN-23/104.

KAMMURI, T. (1964). *Prog. theor. Phys., Osaka*, **31**, 595.

KAPUR, P. L. and PEIERLS, R. (1938). *Proc. R. Soc.* **A166**, 277.

KENDALL, M. G. (1946). *The advanced theory of statistics*, Vol. II, Chap. 17. Griffin, London.

KENNETT, T. J., BOLLINGER, L. M., and CARPENTER, R. T. (1958). *Phys. Rev. Lett.* **1**, 76.

KIM HI SAN, PIKELNER, L. B., SHARAPOV, E. I., and SIRAZHET, KH. (1965). *Proc. int. conf. on study of nuclear structure with neutrons, Antwerp.* Papers 185 and 188.

KIRPICHNIKOV, I. V., IGNATÈV, K. G., and SUKHORUCHKIN, S. I. (1964). *Atomn. Energ.* **16**, 211.

KLUGE, G. (1964). *Nucl. Phys.* **51**, 41.

KOFOED-HANSEN, O. (1955). *Phys. Rev.* **99**, 154.

KRUEGER, T. K. and MARGOLIS, B. (1961). *Nucl. Phys.* **28**, 578.

KURATH, D. (1956). *Phys. Rev.* **101**, 216.

LADENBURG, R. and REICHE, F. (1913). *Annln. Phys.* **42**, 181.

LAMB, W. E. (1939). *Phys. Rev.* **55**, 190.

LAMPHERE, R. W. (1956). *Phys. Rev.* **102**, 797.

LANDOLT-BÖRNSTEIN TABLES (1961). Vol. I. Springer-Verlag, Berlin.

LANDON, H. H. (1955). *Phys. Rev.* **100**, 1414.

— and RAE, E. R. (1957). *Phys. Rev.* **107**, 1333.

— and SAILOR, V. L. (1955). *Phys. Rev.* **98**, 1267.

LANE, A. M. (1959). *Nucl. Phys.* **11**, 625.

— (1960). *Rev. mod. Phys.* **32**, 519.

— (1962). *Phys. Rev. Lett.* **8**, 171.

— (1964). *Nuclear theory.* Benjamin, New York.

— and LYNN, J. E. (1957*a*). *United Kingdom Atomic Energy Authority Research Group Report No. AERE T/R* 2210.

— — (1957*b*). *Proc. phys. Soc.* **A70**, 557.

— — (1960*a*). *Nucl. Phys.* **17**, 563.

— — (1960*b*). *Nucl. Phys.* **17**, 586.

— — MELKONIAN, E., and RAE, E. R. (1959). *Phys. Rev. Lett.* **2**, 424.

— — and Story, J. S. (1956). *Atomic Energy Research Establishment Report No. AERE T/M* 137.
— and Pendlebury, E. (1960). *Nucl. Phys.* **15,** 39.
— and Soper, J. (1962). *Nucl. Phys.* **37,** 663.
— and Thomas, R. G. (1958). *Rev. mod. Phys.* **30,** 257.
— — and Wigner, E. P. (1955). *Phys. Rev.* **98,** 693.
— and Wandel, C. (1955). *Phys. Rev.* **98,** 1524.
— and Wilkinson, D. H. (1955). *Phys. Rev.* **97,** 1199.
Lang, D. W. (1961). *Nucl. Phys.* **26,** 434.
— and Le Couteur, K. J. (1960). *Nucl. Phys.* **14,** 21.
Lang, J. M. B. and Le Couteur, K. J. (1953). *Proc. phys. Soc.* **A67,** 586.
Leblanc, J. M., Coté, R. E., and Bollinger, L. M. (1959). *Nucl. Phys.* **14,** 120.
Lee, K. and Inglis, D. R. (1957). *Phys. Rev.* **108,** 774.
Leonard, B. R. and Odegaarden, R. H. (1961). *Bull. Am. phys. Soc.* **6,** 8.
— Seppi, E. J., Friesen, W. J., and Kinderman, E. M. (1956). *Bull. Am. phys. Soc.* Ser. II, **1,** 248.
Le Poittevin, G., de Barros, S., Huynh, V. D., Julien, J., Morgenstern, J., Netter, F., and Samour, C. (1965). *Nucl. Phys.* **70,** 497.
Levin, J. S. and Hughes, D. J. (1956). *Phys. Rev.* **101,** 1328.
Levinger, J. S. and Bethe, H. A. (1950). *Phys. Rev.* **78,** 115.
Lynn, J. E. (1958). *Nucl. Phys.* **7,** 599.
— (1960). *Nucl. Instrum. Meth.* **9,** 315.
— (1963*a*). *Proc. phys. Soc.* **82,** 903.
— (1963*b*). *Proc. conf. on direct interactions and nuclear reaction mechanisms, Padua,* 1962, p. 183. Gordon and Breach, New York.
— (1964). *Phys. Rev. Lett.* **13,** 412.
— (1965). *Phys. Lett.* **18,** 31.
— (1966). *Proc. int. conf. on study of nuclear structure with neutrons, Antwerp,* 1965 (Eds. M. Nève de Mévergnies, P. Van Assche, and J. Vervier), p. 125. North-Holland, Amsterdam.
— Firk, F. W. K., and Moxon, M. C. (1958*a*). *Nucl. Phys.* **5,** 603.
—, Moxon, M. C., and Firk, F. W. K. (1958*b*). *Nucl. Phys.* **7,** 613.
— — (1967). To be published.
— and Pattenden, N. J. (1956). *Proc. int. conf. peaceful uses atom. energy, Geneva,* 1955, Vol. 4, p. 210. United Nations, New York.
— and Rae, E. R. (1956). *J. nuc. Energy* **4,** 418.
McCallum, G. J. (1957). *Atomic Energy Research Establishment Report No. AERE NP/M*81.
Macfarlane, M. H. and French, J. B. (1960). *Rev. mod. Phys.* **32,** 567.
Macklin, R. L., Pasma, P. J., and Gibbons, J. H. (1964). *Phys. Rev.* **136,** B695.
MacRobert, T. M. (1947). *Functions of a complex variable,* 3rd edn. Macmillan, London.
Mahaux, C. (1966). *Nucl. Phys.* **79,** 481.
— (1965). *Nucl. Phys.* **71,** 241.
Malyshev, A. V. (1963). *Soviet Phys. JETP* **45,** 316.
Mann, D. P., Watson, W. W., Chrien, R. E., Zimmermann, R. L., and Schwartz, R. B. (1959). *Phys. Rev.* **116,** 1516.
Margenau, H. and Murphy, G. H. (1946). *Mathematics of physics and chemistry.* Van Nostrand, New York.
Margolis, B. (1963). *Proc. conf. on direct interactions and nuclear reaction mechanisms, Padua,* 1962, Gordon and Breach, New York.
— and Troubetzkoy, E. S. (1957). *Phys. Rev.* **106,** 105.

MARSHAK, H. and NEWSON, H. W. (1957). *Phys. Rev.* **106**, 110.

— POSTMA, H., SAILOR, V. L., SHORE, F. J., and REYNOLDS, C. A. (1962). *Phys. Rev.* **128**, 1287.

— and SAILOR, V. L. (1958). *Phys. Rev.* **109**, 1219.

MAYER, M. G. (1949). *Phys. Rev.* **75**, 1969.

MEHTA, M. L. (1960). *Nucl. Phys.* **18**, 395.

— and DYSON, F. J. (1963). *J. Math. Phys.* **4**, 713.

MEITNER, L. and FRISCH, O. R. (1939). *Nature, Lond.* **143**, 239.

MELKONIAN, E., HAVENS, W. W., and RAINWATER, L. J. (1953). *Phys. Rev.* **92**, 702.

— PEREZ-MENDEZ, V., MELKONIAN, M. L., and HAVENS, W. W. (1958). *J. nucl. Sci. Engng.* **3**, 435.

MICHAUDON, A., DERRIEN, H., RIBON, P., and SANCHE, M. (1963). *Phys. Lett.* **7**, 211.

— — — — (1965). *Nucl. Phys.* **69**, 545.

— and RIBON, P. (1961). *J. Phys. Radium, Paris* **220**, 712.

MIGNECO, E. and THEOBALD, J. P. (1967). Private communication and paper to be submitted to *Nucl. Phys.*

MILLER, D. W., FIELDS, R. E., and BOCKELMAN, C. K. (1952). *Phys. Rev.* **85**, 704.

MILLER, P., GOOD, W., GIBBONS, J. H., and NEILER, J. (1959). *Bull. Am. phys. Soc.* II **4**, 42.

MILTON, J. C. D. and FRASER, J. S. (1965). *Proc. symp. on physics and chemistry of fission, Salzburg*, Vol. 2, p. 46. I.A.E.A., Vienna.

MISKEL, J. A., MARSH, K. V., LINDNER, M., and NAGLE, R. J. (1962). *Phys. Rev.* **128**, 2717.

MOLDAUER, P. A. (1959). Unpublished.

— (1963). *Nucl. Phys.* **47**, 65.

MOON, P. B. and TILLMAN, R. (1936). *Proc. R. Soc.* **153**, 421.

MOORE, J. A., PALEVSKY, H., and CHRIEN, R. E. (1963). *Phys. Rev.* **132**, 801.

MOORE, M. S. and MILLER, L. G. (1965). *Proc. symp. on physics and chemistry of fission, Salzburg*, p. 87. I.A.E.A., Vienna.

— and REICH, C. W. (1960). *Phys. Rev.* **118**, 718.

— and SIMPSON, O. D. (1966). *Proc. conf. on neutron cross-section technology, Washington. U.S.A.E.C. Report CONF*-660303, p. 840.

— — and WATANABE, T. (1964). *Phys. Rev.* **135**, B945.

MORGENSTERN, J., BIANCHI, G., CORGE, C., HUYNH, V., JULIEN, J., NETTER, F., LE POITTEVIN, G., and VASTEL, M. (1965*a*). *Nucl. Phys.* **62**, 529

— DE BARROS, S., BIANCHI, G., CORGE, C., HUYNH, V., JULIEN, J., LE POITTEVIN, G., NETTER, F., and SAMOUR, C. (1965*b*). *Proc. int. conf. on study of nuclear structure with neutrons, Antwerp*, 1965. Contributed Paper No. 86.

MOSKALEV, S. S., MURADIAN, H. V., and ADAMCHUK, YU. V. (1964). *Nucl. Phys.* **53**, 667.

MÖSSBAUER, R. L. (1958). *Z. Phys.* **151**, 124.

MOSZKOWSKI, S. (1957). *Handbuch der Physik* (Ed. S. FLÜGGE), Vol. 39, p. 411.

MOTT, N. F. and SNEDDON, I. N. (1948). *Wave mechanics and its applications.* Oxford University Press.

MOTTELSON, B. R. (1960). *Proc. int. conf. on nuclear structure, Kingston*, 1960, p. 525. University of Toronto Press, Toronto.

MOXON, M. C. (1964). Private communication.

— (1965). *Proc. int. conf. on study of nuclear structure with neutrons, Antwerp*, 1965. Contributed Paper No. 88.

— and RAE, E. R. (1961). *Neutron time-of-flight methods* (Ed. J. SPAEPEN), p. 439. Euratom, Brussels.

MURADYAN, H. V. (1965). *Phys. Lett.* **14,** 123.

— and ADAMCHUK, YU. V. (1965). *Nucl. Phys.* **68,** 549.

— — (1966). I.A.E.A. conf. on microscopic neutron cross-section data, Paris. Paper CN-23/107.

MYERS, L. and SWIATECKI, W. (1966). *Nucl. Phys.* **81,** 1.

NESTEROV, V. G. and SMIRENKIN, G. N. (1960). *Atomn. Energ.* **9,** 16.

— — (1962). *J. nucl. Energy* **16,** 51.

NEWSON, H. W. (1965). *Nuclear structure study with neutrons* (Eds. M. NÉVE DE MÈVERGNIES, P. VAN ASSCHE, and J. VERVIER), p. 195. North Holland, Amsterdam.

— BLOCK, R. C., NICHOLS, P. F., TAYLOR, A., and FURR, A. K. (1959). *Ann. Phys.* **8,** 211.

— and DUNCAN, M. M. (1959). *Phys. Rev. Lett.* **3,** 45.

— GIBBONS, J. H., MARSHAK, H., BILPUCH, E. G., ROHRER, R. H., and CAPP, P. (1961). *Ann. Phys.* **14,** 346.

NEWTON, T. D. (1956*a*). *Can. J. Phys.* **34,** 804.

— (1956*b*). *Proc. symp. on physics of fission. Chalk River Laboratory* (*A.E.C.L.*) *Report No. CRP* 642*A*.

NICHOLS, P. F., BILPUCH, E. G., and NEWSON, H. W. (1959). *Ann. Phys.* **8,** 250.

NILSSON, S. G. (1955). *Dan. Mat. Fys. Medd.* **29,** No. 16.

NILSSON, S. G. (1967). Lectures on Nucleonic Structure of Equilibrium and Fission Deformations at International School of Physics, Varenna, Italy.

NIX, J. R. and SWIATECKI, W. (1965). *Nucl. Phys.* **71,** 1.

NOBLES, R. A., HENKEL, R. L., and SMITH, R. K. (1955). *Phys. Rev.* **99,** 616.

NORTHROP, J. A., STOKES, R. H., and BOYER, K. (1959). *Phys. Rev.* **115,** 1277.

PALMER, R. R. and BOLLINGER, L. M. (1956). *Phys. Rev.* **102,** 228.

PATRICK, B. H. and SOWERBY, M. J. (1967). Private communication.

PATTENDEN, N. J. (1964). Private communication.

— (1965*a*). *Proc. int. conf. on study of nuclear structure with neutrons, Antwerp*, 1965. Contributed Paper No. 92.

— (1965*b*). *Proc. int. conf. on study of nuclear structure with neutrons, Antwerp*, 1965. Contributed Paper No. 93.

— and HARVEY, J. A. (1960). *Proc. int. conf. on nuclear structure, Kingston*, 1960, p. 882. University of Toronto Press, Toronto.

PATTERSON, J. R. and HARVEY, J. A. (1962). *Bull. Am. phys. Soc.* Ser. II, **7,** 22.

PAYA, D., DERRIEN, H., FUBINI, A., MICHAUDON, A., and RIBON, P. (1966). *I.A.E.A. conf. on microscopic neutron cross-section data, Paris.* Paper CN23/69.

PERKIN, J. L., WHITE, P. H., FIELDHOUSE, P., AXTON, E. J., CROSS, P., and ROBERTSON, J. C. (1965). *J. nucl. Energy* A/B, **19,** 423.

PETERSON, R. E., BARSCHALL, H. H., and BOCKELMAN, C. K. (1950). *Phys. Rev.* **79,** 593.

PEVZNER, M. I., ADAMCHUK, YU. V., DANELYAN, L. S., EFIMOV, B. V., MOSKALEV, S. S., and MURADYAN, G. V. (1963). *Soviet Phys. JETP* **44,** 1187.

PILCHER, V. E., HARVEY, J. A., and HUGHES, D. J. (1956). *Phys. Rev.* **103,** 1342.

POOLE, M. J. and WIBLIN, E. R. (1958). *Proc. int. conf. peaceful uses atom. energy*, Vol. 14, p. 266. United Nations, Geneva.

POORTMANS, F., CEULEMANS, H., and NEVE DE MÉVERGNIES, M. (1966). I.A.E.A. conf. on microscopic neutron cross-section data, Paris. Paper No. CN-23/79.

POPOV, YU. P. and FENIN, YU. I. (1962). *Dubna preprint* P-1010.

—— and SHAPIRO, F. L. (1961). *Soviet Phys. JETP* **13,** 1132.

PORTER, C. E. (1955). *Phys. Rev.* **100**, 935.

— (1963). *Brookhaven National Laboratory Report No. BNL* 6763.

— and ROSENZWEIG, N. (1960). *Suomalaisen Tiedeakatemian Tomituksia A VI*, No. 44.

— and THOMAS, R. G. (1956). *Phys. Rev.* **104**, 483.

POSTMA, H., MARSHAK, H., SAILOR, V. L., SHORE, F. J., and REYNOLDS, C. A. (1962). *Phys. Rev.* **126**, 979.

PRESTWICH, W. V. and COTÉ, R. E. (1967). *Argonne Nat. Lab. Preprint.*

RADKEVICH, I. A., VLADIMIRSKY, V. V., and SOKOLOWSKY, V. V. (1956). *Atomn. Energ.* **1**, 55.

RAE, E. R. (1954). *Proc.* 1954 *Glasgow conf. on nuclear and meson physics* (Eds. E. H. BELLAMY and R. G. MOORHOUSE), p. 71. Pergamon, London.

— (1965). Physics and chemistry of fission, *Proc. of I.A.E.A. Symp., Salzburg*, 1965, p. 187. I.A.E.A., Vienna.

— and BOWEY, E. M. (1953). *Proc. phys. Soc.* **A66**, 1073.

— COLLINS, E. R., KINSEY, B. B., LYNN, J. E., and WIBLIN, E. R. (1958). *Nucl. Phys.* **5**, 89.

— MOYER, W., FULLWOOD, R. R., and ANDREWS, J. L. (1967). *Phys. Rev.* **155**, 1301.

RAINWATER, J. (1950). *Phys. Rev.* **79**, 432.

— HAVENS, W. W., and GARG, J. B. (1964). *Rev. scient. Instrum.* **35**, 263.

— WYNCHANK, S., HAVENS, W. W., and GARG, J. B. (1965). *Proc. int. conf. on study of nuclear structure with neutrons, Antwerp*, 1964. Contributed Paper No. 95.

RASETTI, F., SEGRÉ, E., FINK, G., DUNNING, J. R., and PEGRAM, G. B. (1936). *Phys. Rev.* **49**, 104.

RAYLEIGH, LORD (1879). *Proc. R. Soc.* **A29**, 91.

REGIER, P. B., BURGUS, W. H., TROMP, R. L., and SORENSEN, B. H. (1960). *Phys. Rev.* **119**, 2017.

REICH, C. W. and MOORE, M. S. (1958). *Phys. Rev.* **111**, 929.

RIBON, P., DIMITRIJEVICK, Z., MICHAUDON, A., and WAGNER, P. (1961). *J. Phys. Radium, Paris*, **22**, 708.

— MICHAUDON, A., and DIMITRIJEVICK, Z. (1962). *C.r.hebd. Séanc. Acad. Sci., Paris* **254**, 2546.

ROHR, G., FRIEDLAND, E., and NEBE, J. (1966). I.A.E.A. conf. on microscopic neutron cross-section data, Paris. Paper No. CN-23/9.

ROMANOV, S. A. and SHAPIRO, F. L. (1965). *Soviet J. nucl. Phys.* **1**, 229.

ROSE, M. E. (1957). *Elementary theory of angular momentum.* Wiley, New York.

— MIRANKER, W., LEAK, P., and RABINOWITZ, G. (1954). *Brookhaven National Laboratory Report BNL* 257.

ROSEN, J. L., DESJARDINS, J. S., RAINWATER, J., and HAVENS, W. W. (1960). *Phys. Rev.* **118**, 687.

ROSENZWEIG, N. (1958). *Phys. Rev. Lett.* **1**, 101.

— (1963). *Phys. Lett.* **6**, 123.

— (1965). *Proc. int. conf. on study of nuclear structure with neutrons, Antwerp*, 1965. Contributed Paper No. 174.

ROSS, A. A., MARK, H., and LAWSON, R. D. (1956). *Phys. Rev.* **102**, 1613.

ROTENBERG, M., BIVIAS, R., METROPOLIS, M., and WOOTEN, J. K. (1959). *The 3-j and 6-j symbols.* Technology Press, M.I.T., Cambridge, Mass.

RUDDICK, P. and WHITE, P. H. (1964). *J. Nucl. Energy* **18**, 561.

SACHS, R. G. (1953). *Nuclear theory*, p. 241. Adison-Wesley, Cambridge, Mass.

SAILOR, V. L. (1953). *Phys. Rev.* **91**, 53.

— (1956). *Proc. int. conf. on peaceful uses atom. energy, Geneva,* 1955, Vol. 4, p. 199. United Nations, New York.

— Brunhart, G., Passell, L., Reynolds, C. A., Schermer, R. I., and Shore, F. J. (1966). *Bull. Am. phys. Soc.* **11,** 29.

— Landon, H. H., and Foote, H. L. (1954). *Phys. Rev.* **93,** 1292.

Sano, M. and Yamasaki, S. (1963). *Prog. theor. Phys., Osaka* **29,** 397.

Saplakoglu, A., Bollinger, L. M., and Coté, R. E. (1958). *Phys. Rev.* **109,** 1258.

Sauter, G. D. and Bowman, C. D. (1965). *Phys. Rev. Lett.* **15,** 761.

Schermer, R. I. (1963). *Phys. Rev.* **130,** 1907.

Schiff, L. I. (1949). *Quantum mechanics.* McGraw-Hill, New York.

Schrödinger, E. (1948). *Statistical thermodynamics.* Cambridge University Press.

Scott, J. M. C. (1954). *Phil. Mag.* **45,** 1322.

Seeger, P. A., Hemmendinger, A., and Diven, B. C. (1967). *Nucl. Phys.* **A96,** 605.

Seidl, F. G. P., Hughes, D. J., Palevsky, H., Levin, J. S., Kato, W. Y., and Sjostrand, N. G. (1954). *Phys. Rev.* **95,** 476.

Selove, W. (1952). *Rev. scient. Instrum.* **23,** 350.

Seth, K. K., Hughes, D. J., Zimmerman, R. L., and Garth, R. C. (1958). *Phys. Rev.* **110,** 692.

Shakin, C. (1963). *Ann. Phys.* **1,** 373.

de-Shalit, A. (1961). *Phys. Rev.* **122,** 1530.

Shapiro, F. L. (1966). *Nuclear structure study with neutrons* (Ed. M. Nève de Mevergnies, P. Van Assche, and J. Vervier), p. 223. North Holland, Amsterdam.

Sheer, C. and Moore, J. (1955). *Phys. Rev.* **98,** 565.

Sher, R., Tasson, S., Weinstock, E. V., and Hellston, A. (1961). *Nucl. Sci. Engng.* **11,** 369.

Shore, F. J. and Sailor, V. L. (1958). *Phys. Rev.* **112,** 191.

Siegert, A. F. J. (1939). *Phys. Rev.* **56,** 750.

Simpson, F. B. (1966). *Proc. conf. on neutron cross-section technology, Washington,* p. 67. *U.S.A.E.C. Report No. CONF*-660303.

— Burgus, W. H., Evans, J. E., and Kirby, H. W. (1962). *Nucl. Sci. Engng.* **12,** 243.

— and Fluharty, R. G. (1957*a*). *Phys. Rev.* **105,** 616.

— — (1957*b*). *Bull. Am. phys. Soc.* Ser. II **2,** 42.

— and Moore, M. S. (1961). *Phys. Rev.* **123,** 559.

Simpson, O. D., Fluharty, R. G., and Simpson, F. B. (1956). *Phys. Rev.* **103,** 971.

Singh, P. P. (1964). Chalk River Nuclear Laboratories Preprint.

Slaughter, J. C., Harvey, J. A., Block, R. C., and Jenkins, T. (1958). *Bull. Am. phys. Soc.* Ser. II, **3,** 364.

— — — (1961). *Oak Ridge National Laboratory Report No. ORNL*-3085, p. 42.

Smith, M. S., Smith, R. R., Joki, E. G., and Evans, J. E. (1957). *Phys. Rev.* **107,** 525.

Specht, H. J., Fraser, J. S., and Milton, J. C. D. (1966). *Phys. Rev. Lett.* **17,** 1187.

Starfelt, N. (1964). *Nucl. Phys.* **53,** 397.

Stehn, J. R., Goldberg, M. D., Wiener-Chasman, R., Mughabghab, S. F., Magurno, B. A., and May, V. M. (1964, 1965, 1966). *Brookhaven National Laboratory Report No. BNL* 325, 2nd edn., Suppl. 2, Vols. I, II, III.

Stein, W. E., Smith, R. K., and Grund, J. A. (1966). *Proc. conf. on neutron cross-section technology, Washington. U.S.A.E.C. Report CONF*-660303, p. 623.

Stelson, P. H. and Preston, W. M. (1952). *Phys. Rev.* **88,** 1354.

STOLOVY, A. (1959). *Phys. Rev.* **118,** 211.
— (1964). *Phys. Rev.* **134,** B68.
— and HARVEY, J. A. (1957). *Phys. Rev.* **108,** 333.
STRUTINSKY, V. M. (1956). *J. atom. Energy* **4,** 150.
— (1964). *Comptes rendus du congrès international de physique nucléaire, Paris,* 1964, Vol. 2, p. 1140. Editions du Centre National de la Researche Scientifique, Paris.
— (1967). *Nucl. Phys.* A**95,** 420.
— GROSHEV, L. V., and AKIMOVA, M. K. (1960). *Nucl. Phys.* **16,** 657.
STUBBINS, W. F., BOWMAN, C. D., AUCHAMPAUGH, G. F., and COOPS, M. S. (1967). *Phys. Rev.* **154,** 1111.
SUGIE, A. (1959). *Prog. theor. Phys., Osaka* **21,** 681.
— (1960). *Phys. Rev. Lett.* **4,** 286.
TEICHMANN, T. (1950). *Phys. Rev.* **77,** 506.
— and WIGNER, E. P. (1952). *Phys. Rev.* **87,** 123.
THOMAS, L. H. (1926). *Nature, Lond.* **117,** 514.
THOMAS, R. G. (1955). *Phys. Rev.* **97,** 224.
THOMAS, T. D., GIBSON, W. M., and SAFFORD, G. J. (1965). *Proc. symp. on physics and chemistry of fission, Salzburg,* Vol. 1, p. 467. I.A.E.A., Vienna
TOLLER, A. L. and NEWSON, H. W. (1955). *Phys. Rev.* **99,** 1625.
ULLAH, N. (1966). Int. conf. on nuclear physics, Gatlinburg, Tennessee.
URBANEC, J., VRZAL, J., and LIPTAK, J. (1965). *Proc. int. conf. on study of nuclear structure with neutrons, Antwerp,* 1965. Contributed paper no. 97.
USACHEV, L. N., PAULINCHUK, V. A., and RABOTNOV, N. S. (1964). *Atomn. Energ.* **17,** 479.
UTTLEY, C. A. (1965). *Comptes rendus du congrès international de physique nucléaire, Paris,* 1964, Vol. 2, p. 700. Editions du Centre National de la Recherche Scientifique, Paris.
—and LYNN, J. E. (1967). To be published.
— NEWSTEAD, C. M., and DIMENT, K. M. (1966). I.A.E.A. conf. on microscopic neutron cross-section data, Paris. Paper No. CN-23/36.
VANDENBOSCH, R. (1967). *Nucl. Phys.* A**101,** 460.
VLADIMIRSKY, V. V., ILYINA, I. L., PANOV, A. A., RADKEVICH, I. A., and SOKOLOVSKII, V. V. (1957). *Proc. int. conf. on neutron interactions with the nucleus, New York,* p. 52. *United States Atomic Energy Commission Report No. TID*-7547.
VOGT, E. (1958). *Phys. Rev.* **112,** 203.
— (1959). *Nuclear reactions* (Eds. P. M. ENDT and M. DEMEUR), Vol. 1, p. 215. North-Holland, Amsterdam.
— (1960). *Phys. Rev.* **118,** 724.
— (1962). *Rev. mod. Phys.* **34,** 723.
VORONTNIKOV, P. E., DUBROVINA, S. M., OSTROSHCHENKO, G. A., and SHIGIN, V. A. (1966). *Soviet J. nucl. Phys.* **3,** 479.
WAGNER, R., GOOD, W. M., and PAYA, D. (1965). *Proc. int. conf. on study of nuclear structure with neutrons, Antwerp,* 1965. Contributed Paper No. 99.
WANG NAI-YANG, ILIESCU, N., KARZHAVINA, E. N., KIM HI-SAN, POPOV, A. B., PIKELNER, L. B., STADINKOV, T., SHARAPOV, E. I., and YAZINTSKY, YU. S. (1964). *Dubna preprint P*-1564.
— KARZHAVINA, E. N., POPOV, A. B., YAZVITSKII, YU. S., and YAO-CHI-CHUANG (1966). *Soviet J. nucl. Phys.* **3,** 48.
— VIZI, I., EFIMOV, V. N., KARZHAVINA, E. N., KIM HI SAN, POPOV, A. B., PIKELNER, L. B., PRZYTULA, M. I., STADNIKOV, T., CHEN LIN YANG, SHARAPOV, E. I., SHELONTSEV, I. I., SHIRICKOVA, N. YU., and YAZVITSKY, YU. S. (1963). *Dubna preprint P*-1313.

WASSON, O. A., BHAT, M. R., CHRIEN, R. E., LONE, M. A., and BEER, M. (1966). *Phys. Rev. Lett.* **17**, 1220.

— and DRAPER, J. E. (1963). *Phys. Lett.* **6**, 350.

— — (1965). *Nucl. Phys.* **73**, 499.

WATERS, J. R. (1960). *Phys. Rev.* **120**, 2090.

— EVANS, J. E., KINSEY, B. B., and WILLIAMS, G. H. (1959). *Nucl. Phys.* **12**, 563.

WATSON, G. N. (1944). *Theory of Bessel functions*, 2nd edn., p. 77. Cambridge University Press.

WEIGMAN, H. and SCHMID, H. (1967). Private communication and paper to be published in *J. nucl. Energy*, Part C.

WEISSKOPF, V. F. (1956). *Physica* **22**, 952.

— and EWING, D. F. (1940). *Phys. Rev.* **57**, 472.

WEIZSACKER, C. F. (1935). *Z. Phys.* **96**, 431.

WHEELER, J. A. (1956). *Physica* **22**, 1103.

— (1963). *Fast neutron physics* (Eds. J. L. FOWLER and J. B. MARION), Vol. 2, p. 2051. Interscience, New York.

WHITE, P. H., HODGKINSON, J. G., and WALL, G. J. (1965). Physics and chemistry of fission, *Proc. I.A.E.A. Symp., Salzburg*, 1965, p. 219. I.A.E.A., Vienna.

WIBLIN, E. R. (1956). *Proc. int. conf. peaceful uses atom. energy*, Vol. 4, p. 35. United Nations, New York.

WIGNER, E. P. (1937). *Phys. Rev.* **51**, 106.

— (1938). *Trans. Faraday Soc.* **34**, 29.

— (1951). *Ann. Math.* **53**, 36.

— (1956). *Proc. conf. on neutron physics by time-of-flight, Gatlinburg*, 1956, p. 59. *Oak Ridge National Laboratory Report No. ORNL*-2309.

— (1959). *Group theory* (translated by J. J. GRIFFIN). Academic Press, New York.

— and BREIT, G. (1936). *Phys. Rev.* **49**, 519.

— and EISENBUD, L. (1947). *Phys. Rev.* **71**, 29.

WILETS, L. (1959). *Phys. Rev.* **116**, 372.

— (1964). *Theories of nuclear fission*. Clarendon Press, Oxford.

— and CHASE, D. (1956). *Phys. Rev.* **103**, 1296.

WILKINSON, D. H. (1956). *Physica* **23**, 1039.

WILKS, S. S. (1943). *Mathematical statistics*, Chap. XI. Princeton University Press, Princeton.

WOODS, R. E. (1956). *Phys. Rev.* **104**, 1425.

WOODS, R. D. and SAXON, D. S. (1954). *Phys. Rev.* **95**, 577.

YEATER, M. L., HOCKENBURY, R. W., and FULLWOOD, R. R. (1961). *Nucl. Sci. Engng.* **9**, 105.

ZIMMERMAN, R. L. (1957). *Bull. Am. phys. Soc.* II, **2**, 42.

AUTHOR INDEX

SUBJECT INDEX